Ethics and Agriculture

ETHICS AND AGRICULTURE

An Anthology on Current Issues in World Context

Edited by
CHARLES V. BLATZ

University of Idaho Press
Moscow, Idaho

University of Idaho Press, Moscow, Idaho 83843
 Published 1991
Printed in the United States of America
95 94 93 92 5 4 3 2

Permission to reprint the following is hereby gratefully acknowledged: the Humanities and Culture Program of the University of Florida, Gainesville, for William Aiken, "The Goals of Agriculture, " from *Agriculture, Change, and Human Values*, ed. R. Haynes and R. Lanier (Gainesville: 1982); the Maynard Hutchins Center for the Study of Democratic Institutions for Samuel Edwards, "Farming's Rewards at Risk," *The Center Magazine* (September 1980):20-31; Sierra Club Books and the author for Wendell Berry, "The Unsettling of America," from *The Unsettling of America: Culture and Agriculture* (San Francisco: Sierra Club Books, 1978); Michigan State University Press for Philip T. Shepard, "Moral Conflict in Agriculture: Conquest or Moral Coevolution?" from *Sustainable Agriculture and Integrated Farming Systems: 1984 Conference Proceedings* (East Lansing: Michigan State University Press, 1985); Charles V. Blatz, "Ethical Issues in Private and Public Ranch Land Management," *Agriculture and Human Values* 1(1984):3-15; Cornelia Butler Flora, "Women and Agriculture," *Agriculture and Human Values* 2(1985):5-10; Christina H. Gladwin, "Values and Goals of Florida Farm Women: Do They Help the Family Farm Survive?" *Agriculture and Human Values* 2(1985):40-47; Vernon W. Ruttan, "Moral Responsibility in Agricultural Research," *Southern Journal of Economics* (July 1983); Rowman and Littlefield Publishers, Inc. for Patrick Madden, "Values, Economics, and Agricultural Research," from K.A. Dahlberg, ed., *New Directions for Agriculture and Agricultural Research* (Savage, Maryland: Rowman and Allanheld Publishers, 1986); Oxford University Press and the Aldo Leopold Shack Foundation for excerpts from Aldo Leopold, "The Land Ethic," *A Sand County Almanac with Essays on Conservation from Round River* (New York: Oxford University Press, 1966); Island Press for Charles E. Little, "Beyond the Mongongo Tree: Conservation Tillage and the Environmental Trade-off," from *Green Fields Forever: The Conservation Tillage Revolution in America* (Washington, D.C.: Island Press, DATE); Charles V. Blatz, "Why (Most) Humans Are More Important Than Other Animals," *Between the Species: A Journal of Ethics* 1, no. 4(1985); North Point Press and the author for Wes Jackson, "New Roots for American Agriculture," from *Altars of Unhewn Stone* (San Francisco: North Point Press, 1987); the Department of Philosophy of Bowling Green State University and the author for William Aiken, "Using Food as a Weapon," from T. Attig, D. Callen, and R.G. Frey, eds., *Social Policy and Conflict Resolution*, Bowling Green Studies in Applied Philosophy, 6(1984):49-58; the Center for Philosophy and Public Policy and the author for Jerome Segal, "Basic Needs, Income, and Development," *Report from the Center for Philosophy and Public Policy* 5, no. 4 (College Park, Maryland: University of Maryland, 1985); Susan D. Russell and Robert A. Zerwekh, "Social Justice and Moral Responsibility: Agribusiness in the Philippines," *Asian Affairs: An American Review* 13, no. 4 (1986n87):22–40; Yujiro Hayami and Vernon W. Ruttan, "The Green Revolution: Inducement and Distribution," *The Pakistan Development Review* 23(Spring 1984):37-63.

Library of Congress Cataloging in Publication Data will be found at the end of this book.

Contents

Acknowledgments

THERE ARE MANY DEBTS I have incurred in putting together this anthology. One deserving mention right at first is to Norm Bowie of the Center for Values at the University of Delaware who a few years ago began a collection of papers on ethics and agribusiness. Articles by Dana Flint, William Aiken (on the Food Weapon), Paul Thompson (on the Food Weapon), and, Susan D. Russell and Robert A. Zerwekh had their origins in that collection. I gratefully acknowledge the opportunity to consider and include these.

The agribusiness papers went through many hands before being suggested to me by Stan Dundon of the Department of Philosophy of California Polytechnic State University at San Luis Obispo. Stan also gave me extensive comments, advice, and other assistance in connection with those papers. In addition, his support and encouragement was instrumental in this project coming to fruition.

Another whose work has been tremendously important to this collection also deserves recognition as one of the original supporters of systematic work in agricultural ethics. This is Richard P. Haynes of the Department of Philosophy of the University of Florida at Gainesville. Richard is an editor of both the journal *Agriculture and Human Values*, and *Agriculture, Change and Human Values*, the two-volume proceedings of an important conference initiating concerted work in the field. (Both the first few years of the journal and the conference were funded in part by the W. K. Kellogg Foundation.) Most of the papers included here have been published elsewhere or draw heavily on papers published before. Several of these first appeared in the two publications just mentioned.

John Kavanah of the Department of Philosophy at Michigan State University, East Lansing, is also one of those who worked with the Bowie conference papers and supplied me with one item from that collection. That paper is among those here.

Katherine George of the Department of Philosophy at the University of Idaho has provided invaluable editorial assistance, stimulus, and encouragement. James Heaney, director of the University of Idaho

Press has also been a tremendous source of assistance and support. His commitment to works on agriculture is laudable in these present times of great challenge for farms, ranches, and the people who make their way on them.

Numerous others have offered greatly appreciated comments and encouragement. Notable among these is James Campbell of the Department of Philosophy of the University of Toledo. Included in this group should also be some of the students in my previous courses in agricultural ethics. Others, campus colleagues in the College of Agriculture at the University of Wyoming, have worked with me in that course and made suggestions for this collection.

The University of Wyoming, College of Arts and Sciences generously supported my work on the anthology by granting me the freedom of a summer faculty development award and a sabbatical leave. Colleagues and supervisors at the University of Illinois, Champaign-Urbana and the University of Toledo are also owed a debt of gratitude.

The collection's contributors have shown great patience with what has turned out to be the hurry-up-and-wait mode of constructing this anthology. They also have been generous in their willingness to share both thoughts and words.

Never far from my mind during the entire long process of this and related work, my family has given much to the project. I hope their world comes to be better for those gifts. In the love behind that hope, I dedicate the book to my children and the children of others, children everywhere, both on and off the land.

General Introduction

AGRICULTURE IS CHANGING AROUND THE WORLD. The most dramatic of these changes threaten the very ability of humanity to produce the food needed to sustain itself. Yes, we are producing more on less land with less human effort, but some of our methods deteriorate the resources to such an extent that the productive lives of many important agricultural areas can be numbered, not in centuries, but in decades.

Some would say that this is just one manifestation of agricultural policies that have gone bad and need immediate, thorough revision through social and political reform. Others urge that such threats are just inevitable manifestations of economic forces pressing inexorably on the malleable structure and practice of agricultural production. As events take us closer to the breaking point, economics, unfettered by social and political reform, will reshape agriculture in favor of humankind's longer-term well-being.

In between these views is a wide range of stands on what is right and wrong about agricultural production and rural community life. Depending upon which of these outlooks you take, depending upon what values you base your assessments upon, beliefs about the proper aims of agriculture, about who should benefit from agriculture, about how it should be practiced, and about how it should develop as a source of food, fiber, and human opportunity will differ significantly.

This book is a collection of writings that surveys some of those differences. It presents some of the conflicting views taken on ethical issues in agricultural production and rural community life.

The book's first division offers a number of papers defending different descriptions of the proper aims of agriculture. These varying viewpoints will be recognizable in the articles that follow in the next three divisions and address the more specific questions about the proper practitioners and beneficiaries of agriculture, as well as its proper conduct and development. In addition, a number of different ethical theories will be recognized within these views of agriculture's aims. Many are stated and discussed in several of the papers.

No attempt has been made, however, to have every ethical position (or even every view of the appropriate aims of agriculture) detailed for every issue. In fact, although all of the issues raised have first- and third-world, north and south, current and developmental dimensions, not all of these are covered for every issue discussed. Instead, this collection is an attempt to bring together statements of the most prevalent views on specific questions about agricultural production and rural community life worldwide. My hope is that the collection will not just systematize present discussion, but also will stimulate further research. If it does, its appearance will have informed and improved discussions and policy decisions bearing on agriculture. In doing so, it will have provided a much needed service.

The Aims of Agriculture

Right now agricultural policy discussions proceed from a plurality of (often unstated) perspectives on agriculture's appropriate aims. Some, for example, consider agriculture to be a form of business whose laws are those of supply and demand, and in which we are not our brother's (or sister's) keeper. We can imagine those who hold such a view saying, "Profit is the aim and the reward for good execution." " Those who do not profit from the land should lose it." "If producers are bad speculators or are inefficient, and they do not make it in the marketplace, that is unfortunate." "If the smaller producers are not favored by legislation and market practices, well, those are the breaks." "It is just one of those things; we cannot afford to waste time in a lament over the passing of the small family farm." "If someone cannot pay the price for food and fiber, I'm sorry, but business is business." "If the pursuit of maximum profit is hard on land, water, animals, and rural communities, that is a shame, but we must remember that efficiency at getting the most return on the investment is the bottom line, the most important thing."[1]

Others agree agriculture is a business but believe that agricultural policy should protect the would-be consumer, at least to the extent that high-quality food is available to everyone.[2] Others in this camp are even willing to see legislation passed to ensure that small operators, as well as the land, water, and animals of agriculture, are protected from sacrifice on the altar of efficient profit taking.[3] Agriculture is for the profitable production of high-quality food and fiber, but this should be neither at the expense of a just treatment of all producers nor through an exploitative, uncaring treatment of consumers or resources.[4]

Still others go so far as to value, above and beyond profit, a certain way of life, or a certain respect for agriculture's families, animals, and resources.[5] For these commentators, agriculture is to be praised or blamed depending on how well it serves such ends as Jefferson's agrarian ideal of a democracy built on the strong and independent backs of yeoman farmers and their families, or a treatment of the resources that produces good harvests while giving sustainable yields, and perhaps even regenerating the land and water available to agriculture.

These various views of the proper aim of agriculture loom large in discussions of who should practice and benefit from agriculture, how it should proceed, and what its development should accomplish. The details of those discussions are reserved for the introductions and articles in each of the subsequent sections. Still, we will take some time to get an overview of what fuels the fires of talk about ethical issues in agricultural production and rural community life.

The Practitioners of Agriculture

Consider the puzzles raised by asking, Who are agriculture's proper practitioners and beneficiaries? The question includes several issues: What should be the proprietary structure of agriculture and, in particular, who should be agricultural producers? On what lands (public *or* private) and with whose capital should producers produce? Where and how should these producers live and what should be the size, sociology, and amenities of rural communities? What roles will women play in an ethically defensible scheme of agricultural production—will they work on the farm or off, or both, and what should be their expectation of just rewards for doing so? Finally, what contribution will be made to agriculture by an ethically defensible research establishment? Should it benefit the most highly capitalized operators or traditional family farm units? Will research be conducted by industry, by land grant colleges, or by private foundations? A quick look at some statistics makes clear just what has given such urgency to these questions, especially in the United States.

The United States Department of Agriculture (USDA) considers a farm operator to be anyone who has sold, in a given year, at least $1,000 of food and fiber products (before expenses).[6] According to this gross sales figure, then, there were about 2.4 million U.S. farms in 1982.[7] Looked at another way, U.S. farm population in 1980 was a little shy of 2 percent of the country's total population.[8] This is down from one-third of the population in 1910, one-quarter of the population in 1935, a little better than one-tenth in 1955, and one-twentieth in 1967;

2 percent, down from 33 percent, in almost 75 years.[9] And yet even that does not tell us what a quantitatively small contribution to agricultural production most people make.

In fact, in 1983 only 12 percent of the production units were stocking about two-thirds of the farm products on our shelves.[10] Estimates vary but generally agree that one U.S. farmer is able to provide food for fifty to sixty other people. Further, in the U.S. at least, we are enjoying increased yields from smaller areas of good land. For example, in 1981, about 2000 acres of the best farmland were being lost *per day* to the expansion of our cities.[11] And, in the U.S., producers are accomplishing more with less effort. A *Congressional Quarterly* study explains it this way: "Improvements in machinery, fertilizers, pesticides, and plant varieties increased per acre yields and reduced labor needs. In the early 1900s it took 106 hours of labor and seven acres to produce 100 bushels of wheat. By the 1980s it took only nine hours of labor and three acres. Similar advances have been made with other crops."[12]

Some of this more-for-less, "high-tech" magic has also been exported. In fact, because of new domesticated or cultivated plant varieties—cultivars combined with irrigation and chemical inputs of fertilizers and pesticides, crop yields per acre in many of the third world nations are up. In some cases, this has gone along with, or been just subsequent to, a move to mechanize agriculture in those lands, and so has been accompanied by a reduction in worker hours per hectare yield.[13] In other areas, the so-called green revolution has increased the work to be done and so has provided a source of needed jobs.[14]

These technological successes have not been entirely unproblematic, however. In the first place, the dramatically fewer people apparently involved in U.S. food production is misleading. Read the label on the next bag of potato chips or the next jar of peanut butter you buy. In today's world of name-brand food and fiber products, when the food, for example, is often shipped 1300 miles or more before being consumed, all after a great deal of processing, testing, regulating, and expensive packaging, instead of being harvested and sold locally, it turns out that there are many hidden people directly involved in food production and distribution. The addition of those whose efforts produce the tools of the trade, the tractors, pesticides, fertilizers, and so on, as well as the raw materials for them, and those who are involved in the research and retail of food and fiber products, will dramatically boost the numbers of people involved in agriculture today. Fewer people on the land, yes, consolidation of the plant and animal production supplying our markets, yes, but hardly a clear reduction in work force devoted to producing food and fiber in the U.S.[15]

A partial image of the current situation is gained by picturing the pendulum swing between 1910 and 1982, from nonpurchased to purchased inputs necessary to produce our crops.[16] In moving to high-tech agricultural production based on purchased inputs such as machinery and chemicals, by what some have called the "industrialization" of U.S. agriculture, we have not reduced the absolute numbers of people contributing to agricultural production. Instead, we have moved people off the farm and ranch to manufacturing centers, changing their lives as well as the character of food and fiber production.

The world has turned around many times during this transition. There is no single way in which people have been forced to leave the land. Most recently in the United States, however, the cycle has run as follows. Smaller family producers have been unable to afford the high technology of modern agricultural production without loans secured by rising real estate values. These rising land values were based on bright prospects for rising farm exports. When the high technology succeeded, and foreign competition stiffened, production surpluses lowered land values. Many operators faced foreclosure, eviction, and a move to another life. Many went off to manufacturing centers in search of jobs, sometimes working on high-tech agricultural production inputs.

In this century, of course, agricultural production has all along been undergoing consolidation into fewer and fewer hands. Rising populations, war, depression and falling food prices, as well as drought and the Dust Bowl of the thirties, all took their toll, calling for more food from fewer people. In order to keep up or increase production, these fewer producers sought assistance from industrial inputs. Labor was replaced by machinery and chemicals. And, the numbers of non-farm workers in agriculture burgeoned.

Another face of this shift of people off the land is seen in figures for energy consumed to produce, process, distribute, and prepare foods for consumption. According to one source, ". . . the total energy cost is about 9.8 calories of energy per calorie of food consumed in the U.S."[17] This ratio is about ten times more energy consumptive than in ". . . rural populations of developing nations. . . . "[18] That will change, however, to the extent that the United States exports its high-tech food production and consumption systems.

True, there are fewer people on the land in some areas of the world, but that does not necessarily reflect a situation of more food with fewer producers. Still, what if it did? Is productive efficiency as measured by output per worker on the land desirable in itself, or perhaps because of its consequences?

Such efficiency would be desirable, *if* working the land were just toil, and workers of the land were no more than human machines. Contrary to this view, however, even considering the most grueling aspects of agricultural production, many have urged that the producer is a resource steward and nurturer of other people. In these roles, the farmer or rancher is engaged in a process of profound social importance, work that is valuable in and of itself, as well as for the usefulness of its products.

We are hesitant to recognize nobility anywhere, these days. But some can see it in certain forms of the agrarian life. Is it clearly best, then, to celebrate the very production of more by fewer on the land? Work seems like many other things, not just what we would make of it, but also what we would make of ourselves through it. So perhaps its reduction is not always a good thing. Maybe the "more product for less labor" thinking of high-tech agriculture too readily discounts the value of a life on and with the land.[19]

This is not all, however. The reduction in U.S. farm population from 33 percent to less than 2 percent of the country's total population has occurred along with two important changes that are troublesome to many critics.

First, there has been a massive realignment of political associations. The U.S. has moved away from Jefferson's neoclassical hope for a participatory democracy based on political power widely distributed among those who are relatively self-sufficient. Part of Jefferson's idea might have been that (like one classical Greek ideal) the good life is found through an integration of work and other interests.[20] With such an integration, the significant aspects of a person's various pursuits are mutually reinforcing, work and play become so interwoven as to lose their separate character, and the harmony of these integrated interests is conducive to both peace of mind and concerted action, no matter what we are doing. Agrarian self-sufficiency might have struck Jefferson as requiring such an integrated life, while also ensuring that the self-sufficient can get along without depending on others who might expect political support in return. If that is right, if the agrarian life does require integration and self-sufficiency, it is easy to see why Jefferson favored it as the social framework of a people free and independent.[21]

By contrast, the move off the U.S. farm seems to have taken us toward a situation in which specialized divisions of labor create complex interdependencies and a restricting compartmentalization of both efforts and satisfactions. Some wonder if one price of this compartmentalization has been reduced political independence, seen in a greater reliance upon institutionalized channels of power, such as labor organizations or political action groups. And, they wonder if it has cost the happiness that comes from an integrated life. Has this division of labor turned into conflicting dependencies? Have individual interests and identities been fractured and scattered in the consumption of others' products and services? Have the peace and autonomy of self-sufficiency been traded for dependence on the decisions of others and the treadmill of dissatisfaction built into keeping up with the latest product advances?

If so, are these acceptable trades? Some critics have said that these are the trade-offs and that they are not acceptable! If they are right, would a return to small-family agriculture be possible for many, or revitalizing for any, today?[22] If these trade-offs are as suggested, does that justify even sustaining what family agriculture is left today?

Further, to what extent are those same trade-offs facing people in other lands? To what extent does third world development assistance play into the hands of these trades by transferring our agricultural technology to others? Do these transfers displace people from the land, sending them to join a swell of city immigrants, most of whom lack work? Or, for example, does high-tech agricultural production promise higher yields for local and export markets, providing a better diet in the third world and a balance of trade favoring the creation of better urban or rural work? And more generally, do the advantages of such transfers outweigh the disadvantages to the people affected by them?[23]

These are all issues tied to what we might speak of as the political side of recent changes in the structure of agriculture. Other worries arise in connection with the economic side of the changes.

Average disposable U.S. farm income has increased sevenfold since 1946—a figure that sounds pretty attractive until two things are recognized.[24] First, the buying power of the average farm income was very recently at the level of the depression before World War II. Second, wealth and income are becoming increasingly concentrated in the hands of a relatively few producers.

Let us consider these points in turn, beginning with that of the relative buying power of today's farm earnings. The standard measure of this return is expressed as a percentage of *parity*, where 100 percent equals the income that would give farmers the same buying power they enjoyed in 1910-1914, when they presumably had a fair return for their labor. During the depression, particularly in 1932, the parity figure was 58 percent; that is, farmers' income was giving them a little better than half the buying power they had had just before the First World War ended. But if you compare the 61 percent parity of 1981 to the depression year figure of 58 percent, you will see that things were better in 1981 by only three percentage points. In the final month of

1981, the parity figure was actually one percentage point below (57%) the depression figure.[25] So much for the increase in returns since 1946.

Further, in 1982, those with gross farm product sales of $40,000 to $99,000 averaged a net income of only $5,539 from those products. Producers with sales of $100,000-$199,000 netted $19,786. Those having $200,000 to $499,000 in gross receipts netted about $53,500 in income. But the twenty-five thousand (25,000!) farmers with gross sales above the $500,000 figure netted on average $571,097.[26] These figures give a new meaning to the fact that only 12 percent of our farmers are accounting for over two-thirds of our farm products. The top 1 percent of all farmers, as measured by sales, are those netting over $570,000. The next 3 percent are those netting around $53,500 on average. The bulk of the 12 percent of farmers who produce two-thirds of the food would seem to be the 7 percent who net around $19,800, on average. Thus most of our farmers (88%) are deriving a very low income from their work on the land. And most of the biggest producers are deriving what now would be considered only a very modest if not meager income for fully employed people (around $20,000). At the same time, a very small percentage of our producers are doing very well indeed. The income increases since 1946 are not only eaten up by loss of buying power, they are largely going to a very small portion of those on the land.

The consolidation of U.S. agricultural production into fewer and fewer hands has been accompanied by a dramatic consolidation of wealth into even fewer hands. Agriculture has followed the same economic trend that seems to be present elsewhere across the U.S.

This raises many concerns. Consider only one, however. Note that the greater the amount of land and the more agricultural income that are concentrated in the hands of a few, the greater also is the concentration of power—power over the selection of food products to offer, over the way the resources are treated, perhaps even over the future of those in agriculture.[27] These concentrations of power are questioned by some because of the increase of foods whose cost is high or whose overall nutritional value is low, agricultural practices that are taking a devastating toll on production resources, and agricultural subsidies that continue to be very costly while primarily benefiting the largest producers.

Looking beyond our borders, through the eyes of some observers, the transfer of high-tech agriculture to the third world has also served to concentrate wealth and power, sometimes in the hands of local producers, sometimes in the hands of transnational corporations. In either case, the concerns have been the same. Crops for local consumption might be priced out of reach of some indigenous consumers or even displaced in favor of crops for export. The third world country would be producing more, and some of its people eating less. Is this happening? Would it be acceptable, if it were?[28]

The questions do not stop here, however. In the U.S. version of the "more-products-for-less-labor" bargain, rural communities are languishing for want of citizens and want of economic diversity, or so it is claimed. Rural health and educational services are seriously challenged, according to some. Thus those who remain in farming areas now have fewer amenities available to them in their own communities.[29]

Further, in the face of relatively stable product prices and rising operating costs, whether in the form of loan interest, fuel, machinery, fertilizer, or other inputs, many, if not most, small- to medium-scale family farms are sustained by one or more of the adult members' holding down a job off the farm. The toll exacted by this arrangement can be very high, especially for those farm women whose obligations off the farm site are added not only to the duties of running the farm household and perhaps the family vegetable garden, but also to the consuming task of nurturing small children. For many of those left on the land, just getting along has become two or three full-time jobs. Does this situation put an unacceptable burden on rural women?[30] Are rural women, like their husbands, just so many investors of time and fortune taking their chances in the marketplace, or do they even enjoy an equitable financial, legal, and social status with their spouses?

Internationally, questions of equitable treatment of farm women also arise. Women in many cultures traditionally have gardened for the family, and are expected to continue that while also working for wages. And they sometimes seem not to enjoy the economic fruits of their wage labor, often despite taking a leading part in many family financial transactions. At the same time, tradition often prevents women, but not their husbands, from growing cash crops for sale, even if they provide more or less of the labor. The USAID *Blueprint for Development* speaks as though it would regard these practices as unacceptable when it says the following: "We also will continue to increase the attention given both in our own projects and in host country policies, to the major role of women as farm producers. Female access to and control over key productive resources must be planned for in projects."[31]

And what of the research establishment that generated the technology tooling these challenges in today's agriculture? The University of California at Davis developed a mechanical tomato harvester and a new strain of tomato tough enough to be gathered by the machine. For its efforts, it was made the object of a suit brought on behalf of idled agricultural workers. For many, here is the symbol of the clash between public and private agricultural research aimed at production efficiency through high technology, and the producers who are replaced in the field by machines or other inputs like pesticides, or who cannot compete because they cannot afford to put such labor-saving technology on their own land quickly enough. Similar problems are a real danger in the work of international agricultural research institutions. In one sense, their largest constituency is the peasant agriculturalists of developing or underdeveloped countries, and yet, the greatest efforts of these research agencies could be turned to the benefit of highly capitalized producers who are funded by the very financial institutions funding the research agency.

Who should benefit from agricultural research, and, then, what directions should this research be taking? Should food and fiber production research conducted with the public's money, or at publicly funded educational institutions such as land-grant colleges, be subject to regulation by legislation? What is the acceptable balance between the need for agriculturally related basic research, the public interest tied to applied research, and the private interest tied to that applied work? How should this balance be determined and then struck, both here and abroad? How is that balance to be struck in the face of genetic and other biotechnological developments? What legal problems does this new research bring with it? And what are the legal and moral dimensions of using animals in agricultural research?[32]

Every one of these questions about agricultural producers, communities, women, and research has arisen, in its present form, directly out of the social, political, and economic changes that have come along with the abundant yields in modern agricultural production. This is not a blanket indictment of those changes, however. Rather it is to point out that they challenge us to reflect on the ethical dimensions of what we are about. The same is true with respect to many aspects of recent and current agricultural production practice.

The Conduct of Agriculture

As though people in the United States do not have the lessons of the Dust Bowl, of recent and continuing desertification in Africa, or even the lessons suggested by the biblical references to the land of milk and honey, many U.S. farmers find the only way to meet operational costs is to plant a single unrotated crop of some high-yielding variety, using irrigation, fertilizers, and pesticides to harvest the most from the least.

Recently some have turned to rotating crops, using conservation tillage, barely disturbing the soil by planting among the remnants of the previous season's crops, and relying only on fertilizers and pesticides to give the new crop a start.[33] Generally, however, high-input monocrop agriculture has been the rule in the U.S., and the predominant working method has been heavy (high-horsepowered) traction tillage using various forms of the moldboard plow to cut and twist open the earth.

Use of heavy machinery breaks down the crumb structure of the soil, that "bag-of-micro-marbles" texture of good soil that allows it to absorb and store water while accommodating new root growth. Compacted soil, less able to hold water and less adhesive, is more prone to wind and water erosion, and we have seen the results.

Erosion in many areas of the U.S. and elsewhere is at intolerable levels, exceeding those of the depression Dust Bowl days. Irrigation compounds the problem in corn and wheat production on the Great Plains. There, the soil washes and blows away faster than it can be replenished, at rates above those set as tolerable by the Soil Conservation Service of the U.S government.[34] Many, alarmed by estimates of only enough topsoil to last for about 65 more years of corn growing in Iowa, or for 100 more years of agricultural abundance in the U.S., urge legislative reforms to curb the mining of the soil. Others see terrible dangers in the desertification of large areas of Africa by ever-growing numbers of people who kill resource-protective plant life in searching for fuel and grazing for the flocks and herds that constitute possessions so important to their social status. Even many outside agriculture express grave concern over the resource degradation because of the cutting of tropical rain forests for the sale of hardwoods and other fiber products. While swidden, or "slash and burn" agriculture, formerly practiced widely in these forests, was not incompatible with a ten-year (or longer) regeneration of the area used, the commercial cutting and removal of forest materials produces damage lasting far longer and ranging far more widely than that of the swiddens.[35] Some even fear global ecological imbalances or shortages of oxygen because of the loss of rain forest areas. Was the hot, dry U.S. summer of 1988 perhaps a demonstration of such an imbalance?

Producing more from less has not only taken its toll on the soil, but the cost in water also has been severe. The Ogallala aquifer is the well for much of the Great Plains. It extends from the southern portion of South Dakota to the bottom of the Texas Panhandle. At its widest, it stretches from eastern Wyoming three-fourths of the way across Nebraska. Yet for all its size, demands on its reserves have been so great that it is expected to serve us for only another forty years.[36] Just which resource, soil or water, will run out first in the Great Plains granary is an interesting question. The smart money seems to be on water. Even if the water supply were not in danger, drawing it from greater depths requires more energy for the pumps that raise it, increasing producer operating costs and concentrating mineral salts in the water, thereby reducing the soil's productivity. The problem of saline content in irrigation water is even worse in areas of southern California and northern Mexico where large fruit and vegetable crops require the life-giving fluid.[37]

Furthermore, water, like land, is precious to those outside agriculture. As a result, even if the quality of irrigation water were all that might be hoped for, the supply itself would be uncertain because of competition from other demands. This competition can only become stiffer in the U.S. as urban populations grow in the southwest and along the west coast. In fact, at a recent western governor's conference, Governor Lamm of Colorado spoke for many in celebrating the conference resolution which said that water in this arid part of the country should go to the highest bidder. Water to the highest bidder, and yet few would disagree that agriculture, the largest user of western U.S. water, is the least well-equipped to pay for it!

Just as we have seen millions of acres of prime farmland gobbled up by urban growth, we no doubt can look forward to further reduction of agriculture's productive capacities through urban water consumption. Is that acceptable?[38]

The green revolution—the development and introduction of high-yielding cultivars—apparently has brought with it another water related problem in third world countries. Many of the wonders of the revolution depend upon closely regulated growing conditions for the plants through irrigation, fertilizers, and pesticides. This has made the revolution hard to embrace for those who lack the technical sophistication needed to take up its methods.

A more intractable problem is found in the danger that often only the largest producers, the very ones who are best-off financially and and who generally favored by creditors, might have the capital or borrowing power to afford the needed irrigation systems and chemical inputs. Without social reforms providing special assistance to smaller producers in underdeveloped countries, then, the green revolution might succeed in driving these producers down or out, instead of assisting them as was originally intended.[39]

Even when affordable, the chemical inputs of high-tech agriculture seem to be mixed blessings. Without proper planning, as in a system of integrated pest management, or IPM, fertilizers and pesticides might be applied in ways and at times such that their full benefit cannot be derived by the crop. They can wash off or flush through the soil and into streams or lakes to the detriment of waterways. Sometimes they even poison the water supplies of the very producers who have used them. Often the farmer applies them without using proper safety precautions. Sometimes, it is argued, we cannot even determine what appropriate safety precautions are, since it is difficult to reliably establish safe levels of exposure for those who apply the materials and consume the treated products. Part of the trouble, of course, is that "safe levels" is a value-laden term that is properly applied only at the conclusion of an ethical judgment.[40]

Always, the use of pesticides and fertilizers makes agricultural production more costly than it otherwise would be. This exacerbates the financial problems for the small- to medium-scale producer in this and other countries, if input cost is to be absorbed by the producers. Yet if these costs are to be absorbed by the consumers, the price of the goods may be beyond the reach of those who most need them, unless food prices are going to be maintained at an artificially low level by the governments involved. Finally, many point out that we are facing diminishing returns with a number of pesticides, since the target may quickly become immune, or the effect may be diluted by soil microorganisms feeding on the chemicals.[41]

Crop resources are being depleted, degraded, or dealt with in ways that are beyond the financial means of many would-be producers. This is not to say that degradation of resources is the inevitable by-product of high-tech agricultural production. But, if it is not, what are the alternatives and the social costs of implementing them? What justification could be given for the status quo, and for alternative techniques more conducive to sustained high yields and regeneration of crop resources?[42] If we must choose between current levels of productivity, sustained yields and regenerating crop resources, how should we choose and how should we implement these choices? These are just some of the ethical issues raised in current discussions of how agricultural practices bear on crop resources.

Questions just as complex and urgent arise in the face of some treatment of agricultural animals, and in the recognition of two important trade-offs involved in much of present-day agricultural practice.

The welfare of agricultural animals raised for slaughter has often been measured by their "performance," that is, roughly, how rapidly they can be brought to a (maximally profitable) marketable condition on a diet that is economical for the producer. By this test, certain treatment of animals has been justified in spite of the fact that many consider it inhumane. Usually, such questionable treatment of animals has been part of what is called "intensively," as opposed to "extensively," raising animals for market. Intensive animal production can be characterized as the producer's attempt to control the environment of animals to the greatest extent possible, ensuring high performance. Such control may mean, for example, putting several laying hens together into one cage whose slanted wire bottom makes mechanical egg collection easy and facilitates cleaning, while its overall size allows the chickens only enough room to partially flex their wings, but not to move about. Some veal calves are kept in darkened pens with enough freedom of movement to lie down, but not enough to turn around. Sometimes physical contact with other calves is prevented; this is the way the animals stay until they are taken to be slaughtered. Brood sows are often confined in a narrow, barred pen where they are available to suckling piglets, but prevented from rolling over and possibly crushing them. For best performance, intensively raised animals often require continuing subtherapeutic levels of antibiotics as well as other drugs. Often they have been rendered harmless to their neighbors (chickens may be debeaked or cattle bound for the close quarters of trucks dehorned) or made less vulnerable to the attacks of their neighbors (swine detailed).[43]

These and other practices have come under sharp criticism by those protesting that they violate the animals' rights. These criticisms claim that an animal's welfare is not justifiably measured by its "performance." Rather, its welfare depends upon its ability to live a life free of unnecessarily imposed pain, or else a life somehow characteristic of how members of its species would live without human intervention for food and fiber production.[44] Other critics are more moderate on some points, basically urging that there is much needless and, even from the producer's standpoint, counterproductive harm done to animals because of confusion or inconsistencies in research or rearing regimens. Perhaps, these moderates suggest, raising animals for slaughter is justifiable in some circumstances, which would most likely be found on a small family farm that practices extensive rearing. Intensive rearing conditions, however, or so-called factory farming of animals, as well as many practices engaged in within more extensive settings, do not pass muster.

Is veganism, according to which no human ingestion of animal products is justifiable, the defensible course of action? If so, what is to become of present day stock and brood animals? Is some lesser degree of vegetarianism called for? Where, then, is much of the human population to find affordable sources of essential complete proteins? Does it matter, to the questions whether and how to raise animals for slaughter, that human welfare could be affected? What is the measure and weight of animal rights, if such there be?[45]

The technological revolution in agriculture has not only allowed us to produce more crops with less labor, it also has provided new diets, drugs, and environments affording the opportunity to raise more animals with less labor. But to what extent is the use of this technology justified and why? These are some of the ethical issues in the treatment of agricultural animals.

Resting behind many of the practices in intensive animal rearing and high-tech crop production is the use of energy. We noted above that, in some agriculture today, far more energy is expended in producing, processing, distributing, and preparing food than is gained from it. Perhaps this is not so surprising, but in a time when the days of fossil fuels can be numbered, and these fuels are as yet irreplaceable, many have wondered whether highly energy-consumptive agricultural production practices are defensible.[46] Greater reliance on animal power, organic fertilizers, and more localized patterns of food processing and distribution would significantly cut fossil fuel consumption. Is this something we should strive toward? What is an ethically defensible balance between mechanization of agricultural production and the consumption of scarce resources?

Further, just as high productivity in high-tech food and fiber production has required a trade-off with energy consumption, so too has it brought a loss of genetic diversity in our most widely grown field crops. High-performing hybrid plants are developed for their great yield. Their wide adoption reflects the disappearance from use of other, often more locally adapted, varieties of plants. Contrary to popular belief, the breeding process has produced cultivars that are often more resistant to certain diseases or environmental deprivations than the more locally adapted plant strains were. Still ". . . experiments have shown that [while] new hybrids and varieties out yield the old ones under old-style farming conditions, as well as under severe heat and drought or with insufficient nitrogen fertilizer, it is also true that the yield advantage of new varieties over old is usually greatest when yield potentials are greatest, that is, with ample fertilizer and water, favorable weather, and in absence (apparently) of pest problems."[47] Thus, to the extent that diseases and environmental conditions unfavorable to the plant can be artificially compensated for, all will be fine with the new cultivars. The temptation, then, will be to uniformly use these new hybrids and varieties, controlling problems with chemical inputs. But if a disease cannot be controlled or the environmental conditions not properly regulated, then fields devoted to the hybrid in question are vulnerable. The more extensive the use of a vulnerable cultivar, the greater the danger of its widespread destruction. And, if much of our seed stock is just a clutch of eggs in that one vulnerable genetic basket, then not only present harvests, but also future crops are vulnerable. That kind of weakness was attacked in the Irish potato famine, when Ireland's staple crop and seed stock was destroyed, ultimately depriving and displacing millions of people.

Only if we can come back, after the danger has passed, with healthy seeds of the attacked cultivars or with seeds of a cultivar without the vulnerability of our failed crop, will we be able to avoid such a famine. What can we do in the present age of declining use of genetically diverse food plants? How dangerous is the present situation? And, looking both at present and possible precautions, what ought we to do? Is it enough to preserve under special storage conditions a wide variety of seed stocks? Do we need biogeographical islands, or so-called gene parks, that, some have suggested, could serve as natural preserves and breeding grounds of genetic diversity in flora and fauna? Should those in affluent industrialized countries contribute to tropic-preservation endowments such as that now being run by the Belize government with the assistance of the Belize and Massachusetts Audubon Societies?[48] Is the disappearance of genetic diversity even a problem that industrialized plant breeders and biotechnology researchers should be concerned with?

There are also political issues to worry about here. As breeders use the germ plasm from plants in third world countries to develop new cultivars commercially, do the countries of origin retain an economic interest in the final product? What is the equitable way to share and develop the world's stock of genetic diversity?[49] These are some of the ethical issues we might investigate in light of the impact on genetic diversity of current agricultural practices and biotechnological research.

The Development of Agriculture

There is no question that as we look ahead for ways to feed the world's people without "killing the goose that lays the golden egg," we shall look to the science of genetics for assistance. In fact, some suggest that through genetics we may find a way to radically change the nature of agriculture, moving away from a pattern of planting and harvesting annuals to a pattern of nurturing and harvesting perennials. This is one reason for the excitement over the recent discovery of *Zea diploperennis,* a perennial cross-breeding relative of our annual corn.[50] Maybe one day we will eat corn from a perennial plant, and then the loss of topsoil to fossil-fueled traction tillage will be a thing of the past.[51]

Once again, however, questions concerning agricultural change abound. Agriculture based on perennials suggests a kind of final merging of humankind's hunting and gathering mode of existence with its planting and harvesting. Is this a viable possibility? What will be its costs? What would be the ethically optimal structure for ownership and management of such an agriculture? Could it be a form of family agriculture? Should it be? What would be a defensible way to develop and distribute such a system of food production, and of doing so without unjustifiably burning our bridges behind us? Here we have an incredible possibility for the sustained well-being of humankind. What is the best, and the right, way to try to realize it?

Part of the problem in seeing our way clear to agriculture based on perennial cropping lies in the fact that today's high-tech agriculture is structured, in its control and use of resources, so as to generate profit for the *larger* producers and agribusiness concerns. The claims and entitlement that presumably deserve respect are held by individuals and corporate entities that might well oppose moving away from the inputs and products of annual cropping. How, in an ethically defensible way, might that transition be made—or might it be made defensibly only as dictated by economic advantage to the currently powerful producers and input suppliers?

The same sort of problem arises in considering the current prospects for the world's feeding itself. Here, however, we must ask to what extent it is justifiable for the practitioners and suppliers of high-tech agriculture to influence, for profit, the supply of world food. Should world agriculture be regulated primarily, not by the international market in food and fiber, but by the needs or potential of the world's citizens? If the latter, what is the basis for this imperative? What takes such precedence over the pursuit of individual wealth that it provides the standard against which to measure alternative systems of food and fiber production? Is food a public good to which all (or all up to a certain number, the carrying capacity of our sustainable agricultural resources, for example) have legitimate and overriding claim? Or is agriculture an arena of private opportunity open only to those in a position to take advantage of it for profit?[52]

Further, assuming we have more than enough food to meet our own internal obligations, what then are our obligations for food distribution to other countries? Indeed, do countries with food surpluses have an obligation to extend aid in the face of food shortages elsewhere? What is a food surplus? And, with or without surpluses, is it permissible for one country, deliberately and for its own ends, to withhold food from another in need? Can food be an effective weapon and, if so, ought we always, or only sometimes, to refrain from using it?[53]

One reason it might be incumbent upon one country to provide another with food, is that it is necessary for the people of the recipient nation, and everyone (or at least the advantaged) has an obligation to assist others in need.

Really? Is this argument cogent? What is the nature of development? Is it properly a matter of care of a people's basic needs, or does it go beyond that to a realization of the autonomy, the cultural advancement, or the technological sophistication of those people?[54] And, whatever human development is, why is it that we owe it to others to assist them in their development? To what extent are we our international brother's and sister's keeper?

If political, demographic, social, or physical conditions in another country present problems that that country can address itself, and if providing assistance would call for sacrifices on our part, to what extent is the obligation theirs, and to what extent is it ours? What is meant by saying that a country "can" change its own destiny and serve the development of its own people if, for example, the current political or economic regime hinders that development? What is meant by saying a country can affect the development of its own people, if the main obstacle is population size, religious beliefs, or some other condition of the people themselves? Where do we draw the ethical line between aiding in the development of a people in our own or another country and being paternalistic or imperialistic?

Furthermore, what are the appropriate and ethically desirable channels through which to funnel aid to other people's development? Could these be business ventures carried on in one country by entrepreneurs from another country? For example, can foreign-owned-or-contracted plantation agriculture serve as an ethically defensible way to provide international aid?[55] Or should development be fueled by economic ventures carried out by an underdeveloped country that imports technology from another country—with or without that other country's financial assistance?[56] For example, has the export of agricultural technology through the green revolution been a boon to development and thus ethically defensible, or has it not? Does the answer depend upon the country, the technology, and the political and social conditions of the developing country in question?[57] Horror stories abound to the effect that the introduction of green revolution technology has benefited only (or most significantly) the wealthiest producers of food and fiber, thereby further polarizing the economy and perpetuating what many argue is an unjust division of power and opportunity in the developing country. To what extent is this true and to what extent, if it is true, does it depend upon conditions that might be changed by ethically defensible actions within or outside the developing country? If, ethically, we are our brother's and sister's developers, does this mean that we should not withhold what they need to develop or hamper their development initiatives, or does it mean we have a positive obligation somehow to intervene with the intention of encouraging, if not ensuring, their development? Or are "we" just "their" competitors in the world market and, as such, should we withhold food or other assistance?[58] What is the ethically defensible direction in which to develop agricultural production and research when these are considered as means or opportunities for human development in our own or other countries?

Ethics and Agriculture

Not all of the questions just surveyed are addressed, let alone given an arguably plausible answer, in this collection of readings. But many are, and these answers reflect not only varying visions of agriculture's appropriate guiding aims, but also the standpoints of opposing ethical codes. This introduction would be incomplete without a brief and ele mentary survey of some of these conflicting codes.

Since high-tech agriculture, the impetus of so many of the above questions, is often assessed in economic terms, as a business venture, three very different ethical codes might seem right in place in discussions of agricultural ethics.

Ethical Egoism

According to the first, which is called ethical egoism, each person is to maximize his or her own welfare.[59] On this consequentialist type of view what is right is what produces good results, and *the* right action is that one open to the agent, (or else, that one called for by the policy or rule) which gives the best results.[60] Furthermore, egoism claims that the only thing that is good is the agent's welfare, and so all we need in order to figure out what the ethic intends as right is the identity of "the agent" whose interests are to be served.

At this point ethical egoism could go in one of two directions, either choosing some particular individual as the agent whose interest is the standard of all right action, or letting everyone serve as one such standard, thereby providing as many reference points for determining right conduct as there are individuals who might act. According to the first view, what is right, for example in the development, distribution, and use of pesticides, would always be whatever act or policy best serves the interest of some certain single individual. On the second view, the right act or policy of pesticide use would be what best served the interests of a particular industrialist, or farmer, or salesperson, or consumer, depending upon just who among those affected by the act or policy provided the perspective or reference point for the particular decision.

It often seems as though those who would consider agriculture a business governed by the laws of the marketplace want others to believe that egoism, construed in one of these two ways, is the ethical bottom line. If this is so, however, personal and policy decisions for agricultural production have been put on a troubled basis.

Ethical egoism, no matter whether it singles out a certain individual as supplying the standard, or whether it lets anyone and everyone, one at a time, play this role, is indefensibly biased.[61] As philosophers put it, the ethic begs the question against the worth of certain people's aims. In either of its forms, egoism rules out the ethical worth of the aims of all others, in favor of those of some one individual. And it does so without any good reason.

After all, how might we justify the particular ethical myopia that is egoism? What reason could be given to show that right actions or policies serve the interest of a particular individual? Questions of what is really right are settled by ethical standards. What ethical standard will support egoism? One is the egoistic standard itself, but egoists cannot show the correctness of their view merely by reasserting it. That would be question begging. On the other hand, what else could they appeal to—some standard according to which *something other* than egoism is correct, altruism, for example? And if not a standard of either of these sorts, then what, a claim that is not a standard of right action, a statement that says nothing about what is justified or unjustified conduct? How could such a claim be thought to support an egoistic ethic?

It seems ethical egoism founders in the tempest of its own bias. For no good reason, it ignores the importance, and then the rights, of some people.

Rights Approaches

Perhaps, then, we should focus on those very rights that egoism seems to ignore? After all, individuals have rights in that they have legitimate claims, or else entitlement, in the face of which it is at least unjustifiable for others to interfere with the rightsholder doing, possessing, using or consuming whatever is the object of the right.[62] For example, my right to use certain pesticides would entail the (perhaps overridable) unjustifiability of anyone interfering with my purchasing and applying these substances.

Beyond this negative side, however, some rights entitle the holder to the positive assistance of others. Thus, for example, many agricultural producers expect local experiment stations and extension agents to advise them on the best methods of pesticide application and irrigation. They expect this advice even if following it is detrimental to others. Those producers, neighbors or consumers who have rights of their own at stake in the use of pesticides by others can pursue the matter further, perhaps through a court of law. Or, if there are no conflicting rights, then the producer's right to positive assistance with pest control might be the final word.

The uniform unjustifiability of interfering with the rights holder and the occasional obligation to aid the rights holder are offered as a basis for agricultural policy and decisions. What could be simpler?

Therein lies the problem. Making ethical assessments according to people's rights as just explained is far too simple, on two counts. In the first place, while it is granted that people (even profit-oriented agricultural producers!) have rights, the basic question is who has a right to what? Should we say that each of us has an overriding right to whatever she or he chooses? If so, then there is no useful ethical guidance to be found in talking about rights. What each of us should do is stay out of the way of everyone else, in every matter that might bear on their rightful choices. Given our limited knowledge about the choices of others, the conscientious thing to do would be nothing, lest we interfere with another's legitimate claims or entitlement. Clearly this is a silly view. But what is the alternative for those who appeal to rights to support assessments of agriculture?

If a rights ethic is to be more discriminatory, it will have to decide between conflicting individuals, establishing exactly which one has any right or an overriding right to pursue his or her aims. It will need to identify the fabric of law or those independent moral principles in light of which a person has a legitimate claim or real entitlement to something. Those laws or principles, then, will support the assessment that, for example, it is not wrong to interfere with a farmer who unnecessarily follows resource-degrading practices. It will be those *other* ethical guidelines that justify the assertion that the operator has, or lacks, the right to make use of those practices. Thus the lesson here is cautionary.

Despite all I have said, there is nothing wrong with urging that agricultural production is a business and that its conduct is to be assessed in terms of the rights of its producers, distributors, and consumers. Indeed, it is an improvement over egoism, for it avoids a biased discounting of the importance of all individuals other than the agent. At the same time, saying this will not take us very much beyond those biases, until the basis and relative weights of existing rights are made clear by more particular ethical standards of law or morality. To remedy the oversimplified appeal to producer or consumer rights, then, we must get at the guidelines that tell us whose aims count and for how much. Also, we must recognize the conflicts emerging from these guidelines and decide how to defensibly resolve them. There is no short way with the ethical issues in agriculture. We need fully articulated and well worked out ethical principles with which to assess agricultural conduct and development.[63]

Utilitarianism

One ethical position might seem to fill the bill here. It takes us beyond vague talk about rights to a positive ethical code, and it is an ethic often brought into assessments when agriculture is considered as a business. I have in mind the view called "utilitarianism," an ethic which, like egoism, is consequentialist in that right actions or policy serve to produce good consequences. Unlike the egoist, though, the utilitarian must consider the good of all affected by an action or policy when checking its correctness.

Right action consists in maximizing utility or welfare for all those affected.[64] Utility has been said to be a number of things, such as monetary gain, happiness, pleasure, absence of pain; or more generally, satisfaction of individual aims, interests, or preferences. With that much said, it should be clear why utilitarianism is appealing in light of the failings of naive or oversimplified rights approaches. This view does provide a perspective on how to settle conflicts between individuals. No individual is ever more important than another, and individuals are less important than the social goal of a maximum amount of utility.[65] Therefore, we are to resolve individual differences or conflicts by trying to achieve the most happiness, satisfaction, or, in general, utility, through each of our acts or policies.

If the suggestion is made that social welfare be measured by the greatest profit possible, then it is not hard to see why utilitarianism naturally appeals to those in business, including those who consider agriculture a business. Utilitarianism does not single out any particular individual's satisfactions to favor. It is not egoistic. It does not, however, prohibit anyone from accumulating vast surpluses of wealth or otherwise securing far more satisfactions than any other, *if* in the bargain, the greatest welfare for all affected is achieved. In some economically detailed versions of utilitarianism (though this is by no means necessary to utilitarianism), this takes the form of stating that the ethical goal of action or policy is "Pareto optimality," a situation in which no one's position can be made better without hurting that of another.[66] Clearly, Pareto optimality or other expressions of the utilitarian goal are compatible with situations in which there are large disparities in the distribution of goods. (Indeed, one possibility that some classical and neoclassical utilitarians suggest is that the best social arrangement is one in which people are left responsible for their own welfare.[67] This policy of every person for him- or herself as the best way to look out for everyone's welfare is sometimes said to be characteristic of the thinking that guides business.)

At the same time, utilitarian views do not simply ignore the importance of all people or creatures capable of participating in the overall good. It does call for maximizing the welfare of all affected by a given action or policy, and when utilitarianism is set down in a free market economy, this maximum social welfare is supposedly a natural outcome. Thus in classical pictures of free market dealings, the supply of goods will supposedly be kept at a level that balances the interests of consumers *and* producers. This balance will make the goods as affordable as possible, while allowing the producer to take as high a profit as possible.[68] Further, the goods offered for sale will be of the kind and quality demanded by the consuming public. Even ecological responsibility will be called for if resource-conserving technology is available for the goods consumers want and at a cost producers can afford. Thus, utilitarianism's concern for the welfare of all affected supposedly will be served in a classical free-market economy, the very economy in which entrepreneurs have much to gain.

Perhaps in such an ideal situation (it is far from real in any of its elements), not all will benefit equally, but as the most well-off prosper and seek to enlarge upon their own prosperity they will require the services or purchases of others not so advantaged. Supposedly, then, the conditions of well-being will tend to ripple outward from the concentrations of wealth among the most well-off, or as it is more often put, welfare will tend to trickle down from the most to the less well-off, moving perhaps toward a state of Pareto optimality and perhaps, coincidentally, toward the utilitarian ideal of the best outcome for all affected.

Utilitarianism's concern for all affected, combined with its allowance for individual accumulations of wealth, also make it appealing to those who see agricultural production as a business enterprise with a social obligation because of the critical nature of its main product, food.[69] Surely, some might think, since food is essential to human welfare we cannot be callous enough to condone its production for profit, if this runs counter to supplying nourishment for those who need it. Guiding the business of agriculture by a utilitarian ethic might well avoid this intolerable result.

Utilitarianism also could be sensitive to the welfare of animals in the food production system, and even to the ecological integrity of agricultural environments. It all depends on two things: First, how do we define the utilitarian goal; for example, is it the good of any sentient creature or just of human beings? Second, what social and biological circumstances are necessary to reach the utilitarian goal; does a maximum of pleasure or satisfaction depend, for example, upon clean air and water?

If social welfare is understood in terms of pleasure and the absence of pain, and no limits are imposed on which species' pleasure and pain count, then the sentience of livestock, including cattle, sheep, poultry, and brood sows, will give them rights by requiring that their welfare be figured into the utility calculation. Perhaps when their welfare is taken into account, livestock will not end up as food for humans, but then again, perhaps they will.

Further, if ecological integrity is necessary to creatures whose welfare counts ethically, if, for example, agricultural production depends on minimizing erosion or maximizing biological pest control, and this involves preserving habitat for certain birds and "friendly" insects, then derivatively, even some of the concerns that environmentalists have about high-tech food and fiber production will be met by conducting the business of agriculture in a utilitarian way.

Finally, it should be emphasized that utilitarianism is not restricted by the condition that agricultural production be viewed primarily as a business. It might be equally appealing to those who see agriculture as an area of human activity properly devoted to serving the nutritional needs of humans or of all sentient creatures.[70] It could be embraced by those who see welfare, not as a matter of profit making, but of cultural style, and who favor a certain agrarian way of life.[71]

The point is that while the ethic is perhaps appealing as the bottom line to those whose planning period is the next fiscal year and whose tool for making daily decisions is some form of cost/benefit analysis, utilitarianism might be equally appealing to those whose planning period is as extensive as the sustainable carrying capacity of our soil and water and whose tool for daily decision making considers risks and benefits of a nonmonetary sort. There is no single form of utilitarianism; crucially important details of the ethic's dictates vary with the understanding of the good and with the length of time over which good and bad consequences are to be considered. In some forms it might be appealing to those who view agriculture as a business, in others not. Still, it has been extremely influential in the assessment of agricultural production and rural community life. It is an ethic that will be much in evidence in the readings to follow. For this reason we not only need to know some of the forms the ethic can take, but also some of the weaknesses it has in any form.

Consider again the question of what is the good. If utility is said to be something specific like felt pleasure, then we must ask why that and not other specifications of the good? Why should an individual's aims count only to the extent that pleasure is at stake? A survey of the different aims of producers and of the aims supposedly proper to agriculture should make clear that there are many candidates for what is worthwhile to pursue; there seems to be no nonarbitrary way to select only aims with certain objects as worthwhile any more than (in egoism, for example) there is a nonarbitrary way to select only certain people as having aims that are worthwhile.

Also, if utility is said to be something specific like pleasure, how do we measure it? Considering the differences in values between those who take pleasure in profit and those who take pleasure in regenerative stewardship of agricultural resources, how would we proceed to measure the relative pleasure due to an act or policy bearing, for example, on erosion rates? Suppose, however, that utility is something general like satisfaction of individual aims or interests.[72] This seems an improvement over other forms of utilitarianism in which only aims with certain objects are considered worthwhile. Still, this view is biased.

Why, after all, should we favor only satisfactions or success? If the operator of a small-to medium-scale family farm sought to live on and from the land, but because of the economic facts of prices, government subsidies and tax laws, lending institution policies, publicly funded research, and advertising this operator was unable to make a go of it, is that person's aim any the less important in itself or relative to the aims of the largest, most economically successful producers? Surely, the process of pursuing aims or goals is every bit as ethically important as the utilitarian product of satisfied aims.[73] Put another way, the aim of freely living a certain way, of striving for a goal (even when it is unlikely this will be achieved), could plausibly seem as good or ethically important as the aim of reaching some end or satisfying a desire for some product separable from an action. Indeed, there seems to be no nonarbitrary way to favor a product ethic, like utilitarianism, over a process ethic that finds right action in the process of living out various aims. It seems that we must seriously question utilitarianism's product orientation.

Finally, remember that utilitarianism apparently has no built-in need to be fair in its ethical decisions, no matter whether these are decisions of individual actions or large social policies.[74] As we saw, one reason utilitarianism might appeal to those who seek to see agriculture as a business venture is that it does not require opposition to concentrating wealth in the hands of a few most successful competitors, as long as such concentration is part of a distribution of wealth that accompanies either a greatest total or per capita welfare that is open to the agents. The individual plans of the various producers and consumers of agricultural products do not matter except as ingredients in the general welfare, that faceless social goal.

Some allege that the flourishing of high-tech agriculture means people in the United States prosper and enjoy highly diversified diets, while many in some third world countries unfairly languish on the low wages of easily replaceable plantation laborers. Utilitarianism, however, would not necessarily oppose this arrangement. Others allege that irrigation water assured by legislation to small-family agriculturalists in the U.S. is unfairly diverted to the largest producers through the very channels put in place to aid the smaller operator.[75] Utilitarianism, however, would not necessarily oppose this either.

Utilitarianism seems to take us beyond vague talk about individual rights. But to many, it lacks the regard for individual aspirations captured by the idea of rights and is also too tolerant of unfairness.

Social Justice Approaches

Thus, what we might hope for in assessing agriculture is an ethic that gives people what is fair, and what they deserve. If agricultural policy and production decisions were formed with an eye to fairness for all concerned, with an eye to the socially just action, then all would be well.

Maybe. But then the problem becomes, what is fair? Or, what is an acceptable test of what people deserve? Some have answered that all should be treated equally. But people are not identical. They have different opportunities and talents, work more or less, hard, accomplish more or less, and contribute more or less to society. Yes, people should be treated the same, insofar as they *are* the same ethically. But who is the same in ethically important ways? When it comes to fairness and just deserts, what matters ethically about people? Here, as in the case of sorting out rights claims, we need the guidance of further ethical principles. Unfortunately, there is no shortage of candidates.

Aristotle, for example, said that merit is decisive; the more virtuous people should get more and the most virtuous should get the most.[76] This, however, only pushes the problem back, because now we need an ethical test of virtue. Also, not everyone has the same opportunity to be virtuous. Why penalize those who don't have a good shot at being the best?

Others say that people should be given only what they need and should contribute all they can. This socialist or Marxist ideal is also troubled. First, how do you decide what people need? That in itself, is a further ethical question requiring another ethical principle. Second, why should people contribute all they can? Is it not right that people be able to keep much of what they earn or produce? Distributive justice should not preclude commutative justice. Third, why should people have to contribute to others, if the others are not working up to their capacity? How do you ensure that people do work that hard? What does it mean to say that everyone should contribute all he or she can? What if I cannot meet my full potential through no fault of my own? Would I have failed to contribute as I should?

More in the spirit of western industrial countries, an alternative suggestion has been that people deserve only what they earn in a free marketplace. The problem is that the market place is not now free and open in the economist's sense. Not everyone can get the education they need, borrow money to buy land and equipment, or even find good land to work as food and fiber producers. Indeed, not everyone has equal opportunity to gain the wherewithal to consume the products of agriculture. What do people deserve as a result of their efforts when they do not even have the opportunity to expend their efforts effectively? To say that I, a would-be agriculturalist, deserve what I can earn in a free marketplace is beside the real point, a statement irrelevant to the question of what the fair treatment of producers and consumers of agricultural products is in today's world. Furthermore, this view does not even tell us how we can fairly allocate opportunities to earn. Fairness does not dictate that these opportunities go to the highest bidder!

John Rawls, a contemporary philosopher at Harvard, suggested a two-part test of justice that recognizes the tie of fairness to opportunity. First, each individual is to be allowed as much liberty of action as is consistent with an equal amount for everyone else, and second, no one will use up the scarce opportunities in society without those who are shut out being compensated in a way they would agree to.[77] Surely, if we have the same liberty for our pursuits and if we have either the opportunities we need for our pursuits or else acceptable compensation, then we have been dealt with fairly. As we noted above, no one can claim a right to anything and everything, but according to the principles of justice Rawls offers, we will have certain rights. These are, first, a right to our own diverse pursuits, and second, a right to the primary goods; that is "... general all-purpose means normally necessary for developing and exercising" our: *(a)* power to live reasonably with others according to common precepts of justice and *(b)* our power to develop and pursue our own plans and aims. (These "all-purpose means" include: "... freedom of thought and liberty of conscience,..." "... freedom of movement and free choice of occupation...," "... powers and prerogatives of office and positions of responsibility...," "... income and wealth...," and access to "[t]he social bases of self-respect.... " More than these rights we cannot justifiably claim. At least not from the standpoint Rawls takes up; namely, the perspective of member of a democratic society.[78]

As a member of a democratic society, each of us is somehow both free and equal, ready, on the one hand, to operate as someone engaged in rational pursuit of his or her own goals, but, on the other hand, also ready to live reasonably in fair cooperation with others in the society. The two basic principles of justice are intended to guide us in ways that will bring to fruition these potentials.[79] They are just the guidance we need to realize our ideal nature as persons in a democratic state, and as such, then what could be fairer than to determine our rights by reference to them?

The claim to fairness is perhaps made clearer by Rawls' argument that his principles of justice (and so the rights they afford us) would be chosen by the very people they are to govern. Rawls asks us to imagine people deciding what principles to take up as the basic guides in designing and operating institutions for justly distributing the primary goods important to individual pursuits. These individuals would be in the position of constructing the basic rules and standards of justice, the very foundations of reasons for or against an action, procedure, or policy. Those in this position will have no other principles or standards of justice to guide them. Their task is to originate or to found such norms in their work of constructing the basic principles. However, they will not be utterly without guidance. Their task, after all, is one constrained by concerns related to the pursuit of rational goals. In other words, the principles they are after are supposed to serve as a means to some of the ends of those who are constructing the norms. If we find what those ends are and what principles will take people to them, we will have found the principles we are after. Thus we are to imagine the choosers of these basic rules as having certain beliefs as well as certain general aims and preferences. When these beliefs and aims inform the choice (assuming requisite clarity and knowledge of the world), they will sufficiently determine the construction so that one particular set of principles is the outcome, and that set of principles will be completely functional or appropriate for its purpose. It will guide the formation of institutions and policies, so that those justifiable according to the principles will properly serve the pursuits of those with the psychology of the constructors.

Just how we define the beliefs, aims, and preferences of these constructors is known as "the choice problem." For Rawls, this problem is solved by attention to the ideal concept of a member of a democracy. The beliefs and aims of such a citizen will be served by justifiable principles.

Such a person rationally pursues his or her own goals or plans while being reasonable in cooperating with others who are doing the same. In order to ensure that the choice problem allows for the pluralism and reasonableness of a diverse collection of such citizens of a democracy, the constructors are assumed to be rational goal pursuers who know that they are autonomous members of a democracy, but who are ignorant of just what their plans are and of the social, economic, and other advantages they enjoy with respect to those plans. They have some clear idea of what is most generally needed as means to their ends. They appreciate and want some reasonable share of the primary goods of life, but they are ignorant of their own particular aspirations and chances. The principles they would agree upon in this, the "original position" and from behind this "veil of ignorance," will be the proper principles of justice according to Rawls. They will be fair in their assignments of freedom and the opportunities they generate because they will be just what reasonable but rational agents in a democratic society *would agree to themselves* (when their choice was informed by general knowledge about human pursuits, and their rationality was constrained by ignorance calculated to ensure their reasonableness with each other).

The resulting principles will reflect the freedom that every such constructor would assign to members of a democratic society, including the freedoms to ". . . make claims on the designs of social institutions in the name of their highest-order interests and final ends, when these ends lie within certain limits," and the freedom to ". . . stand apart from conceptions of the good and to survey and assess their various final ends." Also, the principles will reflect the nonegoistic character of the reasonableness tempering their rationality. ". . . [T]he parties are mutually disinterested, that is, they aim to secure the interest of their moral personality and to try to guarantee the objective social conditions that enable them rationally to assess their final ends and to do their part in cooperating with other fair social arrangements to produce the all-purpose means to achieve them."[80] What could be fairer than to have your opportunities and freedom limited only by principles you have agreed to as a means to your personal vision of the good, a vision limited only by the kind of being you are as a citizen of a democratic society? Couldn't these principles be the basic norms we seek to guide us in agricultural policy and practice?

Certainly Rawls's view avoids the pitfalls of egoism, whose operation inevitably involves begging the question on behalf of the interests of some particular agent. Here all members of a certain sort of democratic society are given a role to play in making the norms by which they as well as others will be regulated. The rules are the same for all persons ideally understood as citizens of a certain sort of democratic state. And, every person is given standing as one whose plans and related claims on society will be accorded underived ethical significance.

In addition, this view certainly is an improvement over naive rights positions, for it articulates two basic (and other derivative) principles of justice. These, in turn, specify numerous rights of the individuals in the society. This view, unlike a naive rights position, tells us rather clearly what rights we have and why.

Finally, this view is not faceless as is utilitarianism. Individuals and their aims are not ethically secondary to a project of maximum social welfare. Rather, in the theory's favoring of autonomy, constrained by reasonableness in cooperating with others, it gives individuals standing as such and yet, like utilitarianism, Rawls's theory of justice offers a way of resolving conflicts between people without just assuming some individuals or their aims are more important than others.

Is Rawls's approach what we need, namely, an ethic that gives people what is fair and what they deserve, a way to make agricultural policy and production decisions that are socially just? The detail in which I have spelled out the position should help us to answer this question. In the end, it seems that Rawls's view, while better than some, is still problematic.

In fact, one line of objection immediately comes to the fore. Why, the objection runs, should we take an approach to ethics that would *construct* foundational norms and thereby *make up* what is justifiable or not, as opposed to one that suits the statement of such standards to what is really justifiable? Why should we construct principles of justice on the basis of a democratic ideal and then assess all of agriculture by these norms? Agricultural production and rural community life are not tied to membership in a democratic society. Indeed, their history is far longer *outside* of such a society than inside it. Why should the ideal of a member of a democracy orchestrate what goes on in the agricultural arena? If there is no right way to found an ethic to regulate agriculture, then why not select one that is not based on the democratic ideal? Does Rawls not beg the question as much and as unacceptably as the egoist?

There are two accusations we must keep straight here, even though they are intimately related. Let me separate these while showing that Rawls need be embarrassed by only one of them.

The first problem is whether ethical standards are constructions as Rawls would have it or whether they are simply records of some ethical reality found independently of human choice or decision.[81] On this point Rawls has much to say, of course. Here I want to tease out only one *possible* thread of the argument and, without representing it as Rawls's (*let alone the whole*) story, offer it as sufficient for present purposes of showing the plausibility of constructivist ethics in general and of Rawls's constructivism in particular.

This thread is made of two strands: First, (as Rawls seems to think), at the foundations of ethics we cannot justify as true or correct any candidates for basic standards. As we noted above, the basic standards are themselves the beginning points of ethical justification.[82] This does not mean that we can give no justification of our act of selecting certain norms instead of others. Rather, as David Hume first clearly reminded us, it means that there are no norms or standards from which we can deduce the principles that lie at the foundations of ethics. And (Hume might remind us here as he did in discussing the principle of induction), we cannot derive such principles by inductive generalizations from individual assessments of just and unjust acts. We could first spot instances of just or unjust acts only with the assistance of foundational or derivative principles of ethics. These principles must guide, not result from inductive generalizations. Thus we cannot proceed deductively or inductively to show that basic ethical principles are correct, that, for example, individual acts or all acts of certain types *are* just or unjust. Support of basic norms must proceed in some other way. Perhaps, as Rawls says, it must proceed in the direction of showing principles reasonable to accept as the construction of an apt means for our ends, rather than true or correct as an account of how things are, independently of our ends and our choices of means to them.[83] As Rawls puts it:

> Apart from the procedure of constructing the principles of justice, there are no moral facts. Whether certain facts are to be recognized as reasons of right and justice, or how much they are to count, can be ascertained only from within the constructive procedure, that is, from the understanding of rational agents of construction when suitably represented as free and equal moral persons.[84]

And, elsewhere:

> . . . [I]t seems better to say that in constructivism first principles are reasonable (or unreasonable) than that they are true (or false)—better still, that they are most reasonable for those who conceive of their person as it is represented in the procedures of construction.[85]

Perhaps a selection of basic norms at least can be defended as the rational thing to do. Perhaps, then, justifying basic norms is (or is at least) identifying standards functional for our normative ends. What would these normative ends amount to? Well, they certainly involve being able to separate objectionable from acceptable types and instances of action. And, for Rawls, they certainly include suiting basic norms to our most completely considered views about what is just and unjust. As Rawls says:

> The real test is to discover and formulate the deeper bases of agreement which one hopes are embedded in common sense, or even to originate and fashion starting points for common understanding by expressing in a new form the convictions found in the historical tradition by connecting them with a wide range of people's considered convictions: those which stand up to critical reflection.[86]

Thus, constructivism seems unavoidable. And, if a construction is to serve our ends, it seems to Rawls that it must reflect our considered views about what is justifiable and not. If we change those views, the constructed principles could change. But as long as our views are in equilibrium, what Rawls calls "wide reflective equilibrium," the principles will stay the same.[87] Now, if the "we" whose stable considered convictions are being reflected are citizens of a democracy, if they are people imagined as free and equal, the constructed principles and the point of view generating them will end up tolerating differences while affirming individual worth.

> Because its principles are to serve as a shared view among citizens with opposing religions, philosophical and moral convictions, as well as diverse conceptions of the good, this point of view [and the resulting principles need] to be appropriately impartial among those differences.[88]

Thus Rawls's answer to those who would object to his constructivism seems to be that there is no alternative at the foundations of ethics. At best we can show foundational norms to be appropriate means to our ends; we cannot show them to be correct or incorrect. And *that* much seems right.[89]

However, that still leaves the second objection mentioned above, the claim that in suiting the construction to a certain democratic ideal of the person, Rawls has begged the question. In looking for an ethic to help us with the vexing problems of agriculture, we cannot just assume the perspective of a limited political framework such as democracy as defined in the U.S. With this second criticism, I think we must agree.

There is some uncertainty about whether Rawls intends his democratically tied construction to hold for all people everywhere.[90] Indeed, some believe that *something like* Rawls's ideal of the autonomous person is defensible as the guide for all ethical constructions no matter who the constructors.[91] But this much is certainly clear. Rawls cannot legitimately claim to have an unbiased ethical view in a constructivism suited specifically to the Western, let alone American version of the democratic tradition. To that extent, Rawls's construction would not be the fair ethic we are looking for to guide us in agricultural policy and practice.

What would be fairer? Surely not an ethic that abandons the notion of constructivism. The problem with Rawls's view is not clearly a problem of its constructivism. Rather, it is, so to speak, a problem in the strength of the construction his view condones. Rawls's principles of justice are presented only with a claim of being appropirate for those in a certain democratic tradition. The "we" whose stable convictions are to be reflected in the constructed principles is too narrowly defined. In effect this builds certain substantive ethical claims into the very procedures of the construction. That process can take us only to certain principles because of the substantive constraints found in its conception of who is doing the constructing. A certain standardized ideal notion of the person is assumed in the choice problem, posing a dilemma for Rawls.[92]

The assumption makes the resulting principles hold good only for those in a certain restricted group—the group where the standardized ideal fits. This severely restricts the interest of the ethic, suggests a strong form of relativism of principles, and leaves us without a single ethic with which to approach ethical issues in agriculture. Alternatively, Rawls's view begs the question by imposing upon everyone everywhere that standardized notion of whose aims count and why they count in the construction. This imposition ignores all of the beliefs, aims, and preferences that do not match up with those of the ideal democratic citizen. In order to avoid this dilemma, we need a constructivist ethic that is more neutral to different individuals' cultural, economic, and sociopolitical traditions and circumstances. Such an ethic cannot avoid Rawls's problems by idealizing or standardizing further the ideal person whose views and ends the constructed principles serve. That would only relocate the problem in another framework, different from U.S. democracy. Instead, the acceptable construction will diminish the standardization or liberalize the ideal of the constructor's beliefs, aims, and preferences. It will rely less upon any standardized view of the constructor (less on any context-free answer to the choice problem), and leave all but the most general features of the solution to the choice problem up to what real individuals believe and prefer in the contexts and circumstances of the choices they actually face as they see and reflect upon their situation. We need, it seems, a constructivist ethic that is more contextualist in its answer to the choice problem.

The same point can be reached by another route criticizing Rawls's principles of justice. The first principle calls for as much liberty of action as is consistent with an equal amount for everyone. The second calls for equal resources and opportunities in society, and for acceptable compensation for those who don't fare very well in the allocation. The surface issues are varied here, but not the basic problem.

With respect to equal extensive liberties, what is to count as equal when you have people going in different directions with different life projects? How much of an agribusiness executive's liberty should be limited for that of a company employee, consumer of the company's product, or a distant and nonconsuming peasant farm wife? How do we weigh one person's liberties against those of another when people often do not care to pursue the same goods, in the same ways, at the same time?

"Equal liberties" seems a notion that can be put into practice only in a highly contextual manner. Thus in applying his first principle, Rawls seems to face the dilemma just set out in connection with the choice problem. The same is true of applying the second principle, dealing with acceptable compensation.

What compensation is there for missing out on your first choice of final ends? You want to be a farmer, more than anything else. You want to continue the multiple-generation tradition of farming your family's land. However, your banker and competing neighbors have other ideas. How should you or they be compensated if not all of you can win? How should society be restructured to serve all the conflicting aims and interests to whatever extent possible? What would compensate those who lose out in that restructuring, if, for example, farming by diversified corporate holding companies or food processors, as opposed to private individuals, were to become more prevalent than it already is?

It seems, after all, that the question has no answer. There is no compensation for setting aside your life plan. You can bargain for some goods or opportunities in lieu of being able to pursue your plan and we could call that compensation. But missing out on aims or preferences has no price if much of one's identity is invested in them (as would be true of losing out on one's life plans or most important goals). To receive what you would accept as compensation for a different life, you would have to be a different person. There is no compensating *you,* with your original strongest preferences for missing out on striving toward those preferences. Acceptable compensation seems to be determined in part by the contexts of the identity-determining pursuits of individuals and so could not be identified and imposed independently of those contexts. But then compensation for missing out on a developed and identity determining-life plan could only be specified against the background of another identity and life plan. This is what lies at the bottom of the wrong done by public tax and price supports that take people off the land and offer them either a job elsewhere or welfare payments so that they can survive, trading their life as farmers or ranchers for a life as an urban worker or state supported consumer.

Reinforcing the general point about the context in which compensation is specified is the notion that acceptable compensation will depend upon the individual's willingness to sacrifice and be accommodating. Not only is this something that will vary with such things as age, economic status, and education of the individual, but it is also something that varies with what, as we say, the individual makes of the compensation offered—a matter we will not learn about until after one pattern of compensation has been offered, accepted tentatively, and tried. The point here (as above) is that just what is (or could be) acceptable compensation for the loss of opportunities is a highly contextual matter and seems to have no standard characteristics for even the ideal member of the Western industrialized democratic state. Here, as with the previous point, the need for a strongly contextualist approach seems clear if we are to avoid the dilemma posed by Rawls's theory, that is, if we are to avoid restricting the scope of his (or our) ethical principles in a way that makes them relativistic, and to avoid begging the question by forcing everyone into the same mold so that our constructed principles apply to all regardless of their situation.

We want a constructivist ethic strengthened by a healthy contextualism. That is, we want the details of the constructed norms and standards to vary with and depend upon the contextually variable beliefs, aims, and preferences of those to be governed by them. The basic principles of the ethic, if they are to be universal, must leave the details of the ethically justifiable courses of action up to individuals in context.

The basic norms must give only the most general constraints upon the contextually determined details of what is just or right, unjust or wrong. The ethic must not be faceless, like utilitarianism, so it would seem to require that basic principles be dedicated to autonomy. But at the same time, the ethic cannot be a radically contextualistic constructionism leaving up to every individual at any moment the determination of what is acceptable or not. It must not mimic or exceed ethical egoism's incommensurability across agents. What might such an ethic look like?

The IGP Approach

One answer to this question is given in a view I call "the individual goal pursuit (IGP) approach." According to this pluralistic process ethic, justifiable action consists in people pursuing those goals they have chosen freely or autonomously, that is, after reviewing their options and recognizing the risks and prices of their choices, making the decision free of social or biologically determining factors. Further, when people's aims conflict, what we always should do is favor that line of action that will allow for a maximum of the individual (conflicting) goal pursuits affected. The proper way to decide who should be working the land, anywhere, is to examine the conflicting aims that people have, and see whose presence on the land will facilitate the pursuit of as many as these aims as possible, now and into the future.[93] If the land's carrying capacity is higher when it is managed by labor-intensive regenerative practices within a small family farm and ranch proprietary structure, that is, if these practices would nourish a greater number of people over an indefinite period, in a way most compatible with the pursuit of their aims, then small family farms and ranches should be supported. If the resource's carrying capacity would be greater when the land is managed by corporate holding companies with vast vertically integrated food production and processing interests, then this is the structure the IGP ethic would endorse.

If the proprietary structure of agriculture most conducive to embracing the greatest possible number of individual goal pursuits is a Jeffersonian agrarian society, then, once again, the small family farm and ranch would win out. The proprietary structure of agriculture that is ethically preferable on this view would be that system of ownership (stewardship, politics and economics) which on balance will do the most to facilitate the greatest possible pursuit of freely chosen aims. The same would be true for deciding who should work and manage public lands.

This also would be the approach taken by the IGP ethic to deciding the appropriate role of agriculture as a tool and aid in development. Here, once again, the ethical bottom line would be that anyone's aims or goals are as good as anyone else's. There is nothing in the aims themselves, in who they belong to and what their object is, that determines their relative worth. Respecting this in resolving conflicts where, because of limited resources and opportunities, some must defer to others, we would try to facilitate as many of the conflicting aim pursuits as an action or policy would affect.[94]

In a conflict then, the IGP will generally favor those aims that are both harmonious with the pursuits of others (thereby serving to maximize the pursuits of a number of different people), and with other aims of the individual (so that in seeking to lead an integrated life, single agents consume as little as possible the opportunities and resources they might need for other pursuits). Sometimes, however, and particularly at the extremities of available opportunities and resources, the IGP ethic might not favor the person with a set of well-integrated pursuits that are maximally in agreement or minimally competitive with those of another.

If agricultural resources are abused until their carrying capacity for autonomous agents is drastically reduced, then we seem confronted with a hard choice between two options. If the resources can support only fewer people, we must dramatically reduce the numbers dependent upon them. (This could lead, as Garrett Hardin suggested, to letting those die who cannot feed themselves and who are exacerbating their problem by a high birth rate unmatched by their death rate.) Or, if the resources are hopelessly spoiled and can only get worse, the best thing we could do is orchestrate the last decades of all in such a way that they constitute a final burst of light from the star of autonomous goal pursuits. (This is a variation on a theme often recently associated with the name of James Watt, former United States secretary of the interior.) Neither of these scenarios is for the kind or faint of heart, and it is far from clear that the sort of person who would fare best in either, at the hands of the IGP ethic, is one with a well-integrated set of goals harmonious with those of others.

Still, in general, while we enjoy the options to better our agricultural resources and to go our own ways while interfering minimally in the lives of others, the integrated lives of harmonious free agents is what the IGP ethic will call for. To this extent it is akin to another view represented below that is broadly pluralistic and sees the main ethical problem as one of resolving conflicts in ways thwarting the aims of as few as possible, while preferences coevolve toward greater and greater harmony.[95]

The IGP view, like the rights approach, takes each individual's aims or goals seriously. Its concerns are unlike the utilitarian goal of a faceless social product of maximum utility, no matter who in particular benefits. On the IGP view, even in conflicts, even in the most extreme circumstances, it is particular individual plans that we try to accommodate. Like utilitarianism and unlike the rights approach, however, the IGP view has a way to settle conflicts.

Also, this view does not arbitrarily favor just one population's aims or aims with only a certain object, such as felt pleasure. In this way it avoids the bias we have found in some versions of the rights approach, the utilitarian ethic, and Rawls's social justice approach.

Further, this view can be set up so as to reflect real individual differences as it resolves conflicts. The fact is that actions and policies hurt or help people to different degrees, sometimes changing their entire lives, sometimes only costing them an easily afforded extra amount of money for some product or effort for some pursuit. For example, a recent survey by a Harris poll suggested that some consumers are ready to pay more in order to keep family farmers on the land. "More than 60 percent of the respondents . . . indicated that they . . . would even be willing to pay 5 percent more for their food to demonstrate that support."[96] We can imagine that the cost of 5 percent on their food bill is insignificant in comparison to the cost in aim pursuits of those agriculturalists whose lives were disrupted as they left the farm and went to another place, another job, a new, less-integrated way of living.

The pure rights approach has no way to measure such differences. Utilitarianism can measure relative costs, but how these are spread around legitimately is a question that theory does not answer. Pleasure or satisfaction being the same in the end, it would not matter, for example, who is on the land, even if there is a greater toll on the aim pursuits of family agriculturalists than there would be on consumers and stockholders if decisions went the other way. This, I suggest, would not be considered fair by many. The IGP approach avoids this unfairness by being process, not product, oriented. It would recognize the depth of impact on people who have to change most of the aim pursuits making up their way of life. And it would urge against forcing such changes instead of the relatively more shallow changes of food prices or business pursuits.

Some will object, however, that the calculations called for on the IGP approach are every bit as complex and vexed as those needed to put any form of utilitarianism into effect. In order to apply the IGP we should have to design something like an "aim tree" for all those affected by an action or policy, showing for each person the interrelationships between his or her aims that might be affected by the decision, and thereby making clear the breadth and depth of the decision's impact. Having done that for each of the people involved, we should have to reckon the total effect on aim pursuits of the various options before us for all affected. Surely this is not easily done.

What do we do, for example, upon encountering people who, like most of us, have not defined their aims well, let alone thought out the causal relationships and relative importance of their aims? Here is where we need to remember that the IGP ethic under consideration is strongly constructivistic and highly contextualistic. People must be left alone to speak with each other in order to try their various beliefs and aims, and the right must be allowed to emerge from the multiple individual aim adjustments and mutually negotiated accommodations made in the lived context of ethical choice and assessment. The problem of prior calculation of the details of what is just simply should not arise outside of context. And when it is raised in context, it is worked out in the practice of individuals constructing what is right and just within the constraints of the basic norms.

One of these constraints must be a regard for future generations, however. And, just as it might be objected that the IGP ethic is unwieldy with respect to present aims and preferences, it might be objected that it is paralyzed in the face of the unknown aims and preferences of those in unborn generations.

How are we to speak for unborn generations or those otherwise beyond the reach of our investigative process when deciding about an act or a policy? Short of favoring aims with certain objects over those with others, it seems we could only choose to minimize opportunity costs for all affected. To do this, of course, would involve asking some to forego or postpone definite goal pursuits in favor of leaving unknown others the opportunity to pursue unnamed goals, in some undated future, perhaps in other areas of the world. There are intriguing problems here, which must be left for another time. Such a sacrifice of present realities for future potentialities is not now favored by economic, nor, it seems, by all pertinent legal, considerations and decisions. But still we must address the issues of the rights of future generations with respect to agricultural resources and the fruits of these resources. Indeed, it seems we must even address the related problem of population policy.[97]

Further, it might be objected that in generally favoring well-integrated lives harmonious with those of others, this approach favors a kind of standardization of approved pursuits and in so doing stultifies creativity and autonomy. Does this not support the argument of those who see in the consolidation of agricultural production an opportunity for personal growth in people who have to leave the land for the city?[98]

Even so, if we are to facilitate autonomy, we must stand ready to tolerate tradition and a preference for tradition.[99] If, in an autonomous life, the chips fall on the side of tradition, within the basic constraints of a strongly constructivist ethical theory, then that should be acceptable.

Perhaps it will be claimed that the IGP approach is biased against nonhuman animals or the environment when it elevates pursuits of human aims to the ethically privileged place. Why not an ethic of eco-humanism, as one philosopher calls it? On this view, human pursuits are to be facilitated because they are important in their own right, but, only under the constraint of maximally maintaining ecological integrity. Ecological integrity is also important (even if less so) in itself.[100] Certainly, there is more to say on just what or who has ethical standing. Some of the dimensions of the problem, specifically with respect to animals, are addressed below.[101] Still other issues, some of those associated with the standing of plants and places, are raised below as well.[102]

Finally, what of those humans who are not concerned to live autonomously, who are held in place by the intractable weight of hunger and other basic needs? Is the IGP approach not biased against those individuals? Why favor autonomous living when so many require the basic necessities, literally before they can think long or well about some limited set of aims, let alone a life plan? Why should agricultural production not be a means in the U.S. and in developing nations to serve the basic needs of people affected by agricultural policy? Why is that not the most ethically important aim for the present and future of agriculture and rural community life?

This set of issues is also raised below, especially in the context of the definition of development.[103] Of course, the questions are not put to rest there. In the end, the IGP approach would urge that a concern for autonomy does not overlook, but rather brings with it a concern for, basic needs. After all, starvation, ignorance, ill health, lack of access to income, lack of freedom of information and movement are all limits on or impediments to autonomy.[104] Still, all this cannot be settled here.

The Aims of this Book

Although I hope to have shown some reason to believe the IGP ethic is an improvement over the others sketched, this is not the place to take up questions about the detailed implications of any of these views. Proponents of these various codes would be happy to defend them in great detail. However, such a defense belongs in an ethics text or an exclusively philosophical discussion. Just as many suggestions have been made about the appropriate aims of agriculture, so, too, have many suggestions been made about the prescriptions of the proper ethic to use in deciding what the aims, beneficiaries, conduct, and development of agriculture should be. Having recognized this contentious diversity in the abstract, we are now better able to appreciate it in the life-and-death debates on the issues themselves. It is to those debates that we now turn.

The section introductions try to point out how various perspectives on ethics and agriculture might be at work in the readings. Some of the readings present essential background information derived from empirical studies or firsthand experience, while others offer or discuss answers to the ethical questions themselves. Thus contributors are from a number a fields, including agricultural economics, economics, literature, law, geography, anthropology, sociology, theology, health care, business, government, botany, animal science, political science, ecology, producer advocacy, home economics, and philosophy.

In this spirit of an informed multidisciplinary exploration of the issues, the collection is intended for those teaching courses bearing on agricultural or international policy, agricultural ethics, philosophy and technology, environmental ethics, rural sociology and planning, economic issues of the food and fiber system, resource management, agricultural research policy, American studies, and the anthropology, geography, and development of peoples in third world countries. It is also intended for use by legislators, political action committees; and producer, consumer, environmental, or industry advocacy groups, indeed, for use by anyone who faces the difficult task of deciding and implementing today policies bearing on the agricultural production and rural community life of tomorrow. Finally, it is intended for the interested general reader who will find in the issues discussed what many specialists have already found, namely, a set of puzzles, conflicts, hopes, and fears that affect no less than the material and spiritual well-being of the entirety of humankind, today and tomorrow. Perhaps there are no more globally important issues than those discussed in the articles that follow. Because of that, perhaps there are no other issues where we, all of us, should put so much hope and effort into a rational resolution of our problems and differences.

Notes

1. See below, Samuel Edwards, "Farming's Rewards at Risk;" and Herb Metzger, "Livestock Industry Views and Concerns," in James H. Smits, ed., *Privatizing the Public*

Lands: Issues Involved in Transferring Federal Lands to Private Owners (Washington, D.C.: Public Lands Council, 1983), pp. 41-46.

2. See below, Luther Tweeten, "Food for People and Profit: Ethics and Capitalism," and also below, Harold Breimyer's reply, "Food for People and Profit: An Alternative Interpretation."

3. See below, Breimyer, "Food for People and Profit: An Alternative Interpretation;" and Arthur H. Smith and William E. Martin, "Socioeconomic Behavior of Cattle Ranchers, with Implications for Rural Community Development in the West," Arizona Agricultural Experiment Station Journal Article no. 1897, *American Journal of Agricultural Economics* 54, no. 2 (May 1972):217-25.

4. See below, William H. Aiken, Jr, "The Goals of Agriculture."

5. See below, S. J. Dundon, "Sources of First Principles for an Agricultural Ethic;" and Wendell Berry, "The Unsettling of America."

6. *1984 Fact Book of U.S. Agriculture* (United States Department of Agriculture, Miscellaneous Publication no. 1063), p. 82; and *1987 Fact Book of U.S. Agriculture* (revised no. 1063), p. 106.

7. *1984 Fact Book*, just cited, p. 22. Comparable information not given for 1987.

8. *1984 Fact Book*, just cited, p. 82.

9. Nancy A. Blanpied, ed., *Farm Policy: The Politics of Soil, Surpluses, and Subsidies* (Washington, D.C.: Congressional Quarterly Inc., 1984), pp. 7 and 127.

10. *Farm Policy: The Politics of Soil*, just cited, p. 159.

11. Wes Jackson, *New Roots for American Agriculture* (San Francisco: Friends of the Earth; and, Salina, Kansas: The Land Institute, 1980), p. 24.

12. *Farm Policy: The Politics of Soil*, cited in note 9, p. 7.

13. See Albert Krebs, "Corporate Accountability: Who Eats and Why?" in manuscript, and below, Susan D. Russell and Robert A. Zerwekh, "Social Justice and Moral Responsibility: Ethical Reflections on Agribusiness in the Philippines."

14. See below, Yujiro Hayami and Vernon Ruttan, "Green Revolution Controversies: A Retrospective Assessment." Perhaps it is fair to say that the results are not yet in on the biotechnological revolution. See, for example, Harold H. Lee and Frederick E. Tank, "The Socioeconomic Impact of Agricultural Biotechnology on Less Developed Countries," World Employment Programme Research, Working Paper 199 (Geneva: International Labor Organization, 1989) ; and Jeffrey Burkhardt, "Biotechnology, Ethics and The Structure of Agriculture," below.

15. See below, Michael Perelman, "Energy and Agricultural Production."

16. *1984 Fact Book of U.S. Agriculture,* cited in note 6, pp. 9-10; and pp. 11-13 for the years 1920-1984 in the 1987 revision.

17. Amory B. Lovins, L. Hunter Lovins, and Marty Bender, "Energy and Agriculture," in Wes Jackson, Wendell Berry, and Bruce Colman, eds., *Meeting the Expectations of the Land: Essays in Sustainable Agriculture and Stewardship* (San Francisco: North Point Press, 1984), pp. 68-69.

18. Ibid.

19. See, for example, below, Wendell Berry, "The Unsettling of America."

20. I have in mind the images of the good life (life with a just soul) described in, for example, Plato's *Republic*.

21. For further attention to agrarian visions, see below, James Montmarquet, "Philosophy and Agrarianism."

22. See, for example, William C. Norris, "Responding to the Challenges of Small-Scale Agriculture," no. 18 in Control Data Corporation's Booklets on Technology (Minneapolis, Minnesota: Control Data Corporation, 1981); and below, Wendell Berry, "The Unsettling of America."

23. See, for example, the articles below in the section "Agriculture in Development."

24. *1984 Fact Book*, cited in note 6, pp. 96-97. Total gross income for farmers increased almost sixfold from 1946 to 1985 according to the *1987 Fact Book*. What neither of these figures shows, of course, is the distribution of these increases. That is one of the points taken up below.

25. *Farm Policy: The Politics of Soil*, cited in note 6, pp. 6 and 152. In 1985 adjusted percentage of parity was 55%, three points *below* the 1932 figure. See p. 121 of the *1987 Fact Book*.

26. *1984 Fact Book*, cited in note 6, p. 22.

27. Consider, for example, the most recent omnibus farm bill, whose target prices and new conservation reserve program seem to favor the largest producers the most.

28. See, for example, below, the sections on "Obstacles to Food for the World," and "Agriculture in Development."

29. See, e.g. below, Sam Cordes, "Questions of Equity in Health Care and Other Amenities of the Countryside," and Mary Gore Forrester, "Some Considerations of Justice in Rural Health Care Delivery."

30. See below, Cornelia Butler Flora, "Women and Agriculture;" and Christina H. Gladwin, "Values and Goals of Florida Farm Women: Do They Help The Family Farm Survive?"

31. "Blueprint for Development," *The Strategic Plan of the Agency for International Development* (Washington, D.C.: Bureau for Program and Policy Coordination, Agency for International Development, June 1985), p. 36.

32. See below, the section on "Agricultural Research."

33. See below, Charles Little, "Beyond the Mongongo Tree: Conservation Tillage and the Environmental Tradeoff."

34. See, for example, Jackson, "New Roots for American Agriculture," cited in note 11, ch. 2; and Michael Perelman, *Farming for Profit in a Hungry World: Capital and the Crisis in Agriculture* (Totowa, New Jersey: Allenheld, Osmun & Co. Publishers, Inc., 1977), pt. 2.

35. Robin Clarke and Geoffrey Hindley, *The Challenge of the Primitives* (New York: McGraw-Hill Book Company, 1975), ch. 2. Also see below, Hugh H. Iltis, "Tropical Deforestation and Biological Diversity: The Erosion of a Global Resource."

36. Donald Worster, "Thinking Like a River," in *Meeting the Expectations of the Land*, cited in note 17, p. 61.

37. See, for example, below, Helen M. Ingram, Lawrence A. Scaff, and Leslie Silko, "Replacing Confusion with Equity: Alternatives for Water Policy in the Colorado River Basin." Also see below, Donald Scherer, "Towards an Upstream-downstream Morality for Our Upstream-downstream World."

38. See, for example, Alvin M. Josephy, Jr., "The Time is Now," in E. Richard Hart, ed., *The Future of Agriculture in the Rocky Mountains* (Salt Lake City: Westwater Press, Inc., 1980), pp. 19-26; and below, Terry L. Anderson and Donald R. Leal, "Going with the Flow: Expanding the Water Markets."

39. See below, Hayami and Ruttan, "Green Revolution Controversies."

40. See below, Kristin Shrader-Frechette, "Pesticide Policy and Ethics;" and Sara Ebenreck, "Pest Control for a Whole Earth."

41. On the problem of diminishing returns, see Jackson, *New Roots for American Agriculture*, cited in note 11; and "Pesticide Policy and Ethics," just cited.

42. See, for example, *Regenerative Farming Systems*, Workshop Proceedings (Emmanus, Pennsylvania: The Rodale Institute, 1985)

43. See, for example, Ruth Harrison, "On Factory Farming," in Stanley and Roslind Godlovich and J. Harris, eds., *Animals, Men, and Morals* (New York: Taplinger Publishing Co., Grove Press, 1972), pp.12-24.

44. See, for example, Bernie Rollin, "Social Ethics, Animal Rights and Agriculture," below; and Susan Isen, "Beyond Abolition: Ethical Exchanges with Animals in Agriculture," *Between the Species*, vol. 1, no. 4 (Fall, 1985). Also see below, Stanley E. Curtis, "The Welfare of Agricultural Animals."

45. See below, Dana Flint, "Factory Farming and the Interests of Animals;" and Charlie Blatz, "Why (Most) Humans are More Important than Other Animals."

46. See below, Perelman, "Energy and Agricultural Production;" and, Lovins, Lovins; and Bender, "Energy and Agriculture," cited in note 17.

47. See Donald Duvick, "Plant Breeding: Past Achievements and Expectations for the Future," *Economic Botany* 4, no. 3(1986):289-97.

48. See Peter Tonge, "Endow Now, Enjoy Later," *Christian Science Monitor*, Tuesday, May 30, 1989, p. 13; and also below, Iltis, "Tropical Deforestation."

49. See, for example, Donald Duvick, "North American Grain Production: Biotechnology Research and the Private Sector," in C. Ford Runge, ed., *The Future of the North American Granary: Politics, Economics, and Resource Constraints in North American Agriculture* (Ames, Iowa: Iowa State University Press, 1986). Also see below, Donald N. Duvick, "Genetic Diversity and Plant Breeding."

50. See, for example, Hugh H. Iltis, "Tropical Forests: What Will Be Their Fate?" in *Environment* 25, no. 10(1983); and below, "Tropical Deforestation and Biological Diversity."

51. On the matter of perennial cropping, see below, Jackson, "New Roots for American Agriculture."

52. See for example, below, Eugene B. Shultz et al., "New Strategies for Bioresource Development in the Third World;" and Kent Mathewson, "Plantations and Dependencies: Notes on the 'Moral Geography' of Global Stimulant Production."

53. See Robbin Johnson, "The Soviet Grain Embargo: What Can It Tell Us About Future U.S. Grain Policy," in manuscript; and below, William H. Aiken, "Ethical Problems with the Food Weapon;" and Paul Thompson, "Of Cabbages and Kings."

54. See below, Jerome Segal, "What is Development;" and Charlie Blatz, "Risk Taker's Stewardship, Agriculture and the Aims of Development."

55. See below, Kurt Mathewson, "Stimulants, Plantations and Dependencies: A Partial Aetiology of Capitalism's Global Fixes."

56. See below, Russell and Zerwekh, "Social Justice and Moral Responsibility;" and Rachel McCleary, "Justice as a Kind of Proportionate."

57. See below, Hayami and Ruttan, "Green Revolution Controversies."

58. See below, Earl D. Kellogg, "Agricultural Development in Developing Countries and Changes in U.S. Agricultural Exports."

59. See, for example, William K. Frankena, *Ethics* (Englewood Cliffs, New Jersey: Prentice-Hall, Inc., 1973), pp. 17-23.

60. There are two forms of procedures that have been recognized as rational means of deciding what is or is not ethically justified. In the first, or *act decision procedures*, the attempt is made to apply our standard(s) directly to the options before us, checking to see which one meets, or best meets, that standard(s). Thus an egoist using an act decision procedure, at a choice point calling for a recommitment to or a change from present direction of action would examine his or her options at that point with an eye to which will maximize his or her self interest. The alternative is *a rule decision procedure* that examines types of action, not specific opportunities for action of various types. The ethic's basic standard(s) is then applied to all actions *of a ;given type* (considered by themselves or as opposed to all actions of another certain type) with an eye to determining whether or not, over the long run, acting in the way in question will pass or best meet the ethic's basic standard. Thus an egoist using a rule decision procedure would ask, for example, of telling the truth or not telling the truth, which is the type of action such that, over the long run, performing as many actions of that kind as possible will maximize his or her self interest. Rule decision makers recognize that a rule can pass muster even though not every action conforming to the rule will. Also, they allow that some times (just when varies with the theorist) rules need to be reassessed and might be changed. Taking into account these last two points and seeking to keep the exposition brief, when it is appropriate to allow for both act and rule decision procedures in applying an ethic, I shall speak in terms of "the right act or policy" according to that ethic. Suffice it also to note that this brief account of decision procedures only scratches the surface.

61. See, for example, the debates in David P. Gauthier, ed., *Morality and Self-interest* (Englewood Cliffs, New Jersey: Prentice-Hall, Inc., 1970)

62. See, for example, H. J. McCloskey, "Rights," *The Philosophical Quarterly* 15, no. 59(1965):115-127; Joel Feinberg, "The Nature and Value of Rights," *Journal of Value Inquiry* 4, no. 4(Winter, 1970):243-57; A. I. Melden, *Rights and Persons* (Berkeley: University of California Press, 1977); and Henry Shue, *Basic Rights: Subsistence, Affluence, and U.S. Foreign Policy* (Princeton, New Jersey: Princeton University Press, 1980).

63. See, for example, Shue, *Basic Rights*, just cited. Also, in discussing below the position of John Rawls, we shall return to an account of the basis and extent of rights.

64. See, for example, Jeremy Bentham, *An Introduction to the Principles of Morals and Legislation*; and John Stuart Mill, *Utilitarianism*.

65. There are, of course, many varieties of so-called positive and negative utilitarianism calling for something other than a simple maximization of utility. See, for example, Amartya Sen and Bernard Williams, eds., *Utilitarianism and Beyond* (Cambridge, New York: Cambridge University Press, 1982).

66. See, for example, below, Tweeten, "Food for People and Profit."

67. John Stuart Mill talks this way to some extent in *Utilitarianism*. For some discussion of the optimal utilitarian social arrangements, see, for example, Michael D. Bayles, ed., *Contemporary Utilitarianism* (Garden City, New York: Anchor Books, 1968); and John Stuart Mill, *On Liberty*.

68. See Adam Smith, *The Wealth of Nations*.

69. See below, Tweeten, "Food for People and Profit."

70. Compare Tweeten, "Food for People and Profit," and Breimyer, "Food for

People and Profit: An Alternative Interpretation," below, with Peter Singer, *Animal Liberation: A New Ethics for our Treatment of Animals* (New York: The New York Review of Books, distributed by Random House, 1975). Also see Dundon, "Sources of First Principles."

71. See, for example, below, Berry, "The Unsettling of America;" James Montmarquet, "Philosophy and Agrarianism;" and Richard P. Haynes, "Science, Technology and the Farm Crisis."

72. See, John Harsanyi, "Morality and the Theory of Rational Behavior," in Amartya Sen and Bernard Williams, *Utilitarianism and Beyond*, cited in note 65.

73. See for example, below, Charlie Blatz, "Risk Taker's Stewardship."

74. This is a typical criticism. See, for example, William K. Frankena, *Ethics*, cited in note 59.

75. See, for example, below Helen Ingram et al., "Replacing Confusion with Equity: Alternatives for Water Policy in the Colorado River Basin."

76. See Aristotle's discussion in the *Nichomachean Ethics* and compare the present discussion (up to the discussion of Rawls) with Frankena's discussion in *Ethics*, cited in note 59.

77. John Rawls, *A Theory of Justice* (Cambridge: The Belknap Press of Harvard University Press, 1971), pp. 60 and 302.

78. See John Rawls, "Rational and Full Autonomy," in *Kantian Constructivism in Moral Theory: The Dewey Lectures 1980*, *The Journal of Philosophy* 77, no. 9(September, 1980):525-26, 518.

79. *Ibid.*, pp. 518-19, 530-31; and John Rawls, "Construction and Objectivity," in *Kantian Constructivism* cited in note 78, pp. 564-70.

80. John Rawls, "Representation of Freedom and Equality," in *Kantian Constructivism* cited in note 78, pp. 543, 547.

81. See, for example, the excellent article by David O. Brink, "Rawlsian Constructivism in Moral Theory," *Canadian Journal of Philosophy* 17, no. 1(March, 1987):76.

82. See below on the IGP approach and the articles by Blatz in this volume.

83. See Brink, "Rawlsian Constructivism in Moral Theory," cited in note 81, passim.

84. Rawls, "Rational and Full Autonomy," cited in note 78, p. 519.

85. Rawls, "Construction and Objectivity," cited in note 79, p. 569.

86. Rawls, "Rational and Full Autonomy," cited in note 79, p. 518.

87. *Ibid.*, p. 534.

88. Rawls, "Representation of Freedom and Equality," cited in note 80, pp. 542-43.

89. See the following section of this introduction and the articles in this volume by Blatz.

90. See Brink, "Rawlsian Constructivism in Moral Theory," cited in note 81, p. 81, note 6.

91. See below, Blatz, "Why (Most) Humans Are More Important than Other Animals," and "Risk Taker's Stewardship."

92. For more on universality of norms (discussed in the context of international development), see Onora O'Neill, *Faces of Hunger: An Essay on Poverty, Justice and Development* (London: Allen & Unwin [Publishers] Ltd., 1986); and Charlie Blatz, "Ecology, Ethics and Agriculture," in manuscript.

93. See, for example, the stewardship allocation proposal made below in Charlie

Blatz, "Ethical Issues in Private And Public Ranch Land Management and Ownership."

94. See below, Blatz, "Risk Taker's Stewardship," for an articulation of principles along these lines.

95. See below, Philip T. Shepard, "Moral Conflict in Agriculture: Conquest or Moral Coevolution."

96. See Richard Hart's "Introduction" to *The Future of Agriculture in the Rocky Mountains*, cited in note 39, p. 9.

97. See below, Hugh H. Iltis, "Tropical Deforestation."

98. Suggested, for example, by Luther Tweeten, "The Economics of Small Farms," *Science* 219(March 1983):1039; and below, Vernon W. Ruttan, "Moral Responsibility in Agricultural Research."

99. See Peter L. Berger, *Pyramids of Sacrifice: Political Ethics and Social Change* (New York: Basic Books, Inc., Publishers, 1974).

100. See William Aiken, "Ethical Issues in Agriculture," in Tom Regan, ed., *Earthbound: New Introductory Essays in Environmental Ethics* (New York: Random House, 1984), pp. 247-88, 272.

101. See, for example, below, Blatz, "Why (Most) Humans are More Important than Other Animals."

102. See, for example, below, Aldo Leopold, "From 'The Land Ethic'."

103. See, for example, below, Richard P. Haynes, "Food and Justice: The Real Issues;" and Jerome Segal, "Basic Needs, Income and Development."

104. See, for example, O'Neill, *Faces of Hunger* cited in note 92; and Charlie Blatz, "Agricultura, Desarrollo y Autonomia," trans. Julio Baera, in *La Revista de Filosofia de la Universidad de Costa Rica* 27, no. 66(1989):339-48.

I.
Agriculture's Aims

The Goals of Agriculture

GOALS, AS WILLIAM AIKEN POINTS OUT, can serve both as alluring destinations and compass needles in our travels along the crop rows and fence lines of agricultural policy and practice. Aiken's identification of five predominant aims of agriculture can serve as an orientation for much of the rest of our discussion. Four of the five goals indicated (profitable production, sustainable production, environmentally safe production, and the satisfaction of human needs) would seem to fit most naturally with a consequentialist ethic. According to such a guide, what makes an action right or wrong, justifiable or not, lies in its consequences. The fifth goal, production that is compatible with a just social order, suggests a deontological or nonconsequentialist ethic as our guide in assessing agricultural policy and practice. Such a view would find what is right or wrong not in good or bad consequences, but in the very nature of the acts under assessment. It is in this way that we often speak of injustice as wrong in itself, or as an intrinsically unethical mistreatment of someone—as opposed to the injustice being wrong by virtue of its consequences. An injustice, whether or not it is all for the best in the end, is wrong. Agriculture, assessed in terms of a just social order, would amount to what is fair and right in itself in the production of food and fiber.

Aiken analyzes each of these goals in general terms, pointing out not only what they do involve, but also what they don't; making clear not only ways in which they might cohere, but also ways in which they might conflict. In the end, which goals are the most important in conflicts is a substantive issue of values. The solution to this problem calls for a careful and open discussion. That discussion is the objective of this book.

Stan Dundon is less concerned to stimulate and orient discussion on agricultural policy and practice than to suggest that a certain set of agricultural goals already enjoys general acceptance among a large segment of farmers, both in the United States and indeed around the globe. Dundon's suggestion goes so far as to claim that this consensus could serve as the basis of a generally defensible ethic that mixes concern for human and environmental welfare with a respect for individual human life and aspiration. The goals he speaks of are identified by a number of characteristically democratic (Christian) religious groups. These goals—adequate "healthy and sustainable food supplies [produced] by means which respect the rights and dignity of all participants"—are similar to some of these Aiken discusses (page 66). A concern for profit is not an important part of the consensus that Dundon reports, however. Instead, that agreement centers on the importance of sustainable family agriculture and respect for life and work on small-to-medium-scale family farms. Land is divinely trusted to us for sustenance and occupation. The need to protect the resource and respect the dignity of human labor follows from this premise and guides much of the rest of the discussion. Dundon finally explores the religious consensus concerning the deleterious effects on small-scale family farm life and work insofar as these effects are attributable to changes in farming's proprietary structure in U.S. agriculture.

While Dundon calls for philosophical exploration of the consensus he reports, one of the article's chief merits is as a presentation of views on proper agricultural production and rural community life that are based on religion. If nothing else, the paper presents the beginnings of one possible religious agricultural ethic.

In stark contrast to the egalitarianism of the views Dundon reports are the values espoused by Samuel Edwards. In "Farming's Rewards at Risk," Edwards is concerned to remind us of the threats to the hard- (and hardly ever) won monetary rewards of farming. Edwards makes clear that at every turn, from government policy, to the cost of supplies, to the difficulties of cost accounting, farmers in the U.S. today are in danger of losing their livelihood and their capital investment, the farm itself. The goal that is most prominent here is the profitably of the individual farm. The ethic at work may be ethical egoism according to which what is right is whatever best serves the interests of the agent—in this case the individual farmer.

Presumably, we have a right to pursue our own interests, and the best way in which to do that is to maximize individual profit. If, in the bargain, farm size grows larger and farm operation is made more complex by the introduction of externally controlled variables like foreign markets and chemical inputs, well, then that is part of the price we have to pay in the pursuit of our own just deserts and the rewards of our personal efforts.

Luther Tweeten in his discussion "Food for People and Profit" wishes to go beyond the individual-agent-centered ethic that Edwards seems to assume. Tweeten wishes to balance the ethical concern for basic human needs that Dundon discusses with the pursuit of individual profit that motivates Edwards's farmers. An ethical scale capable of measuring out proper portions of both sorts of consequences in the conduct of agriculture is, according to Tweeten, utilitarianism. As Tweeten sees it, utilitarianism brings with it a concern for a situation of social welfare in which no one can be made better off without someone being made worse off, and in which everyone has at least his or her basic needs seen to.

Free market economics will perhaps see to the concerns of individual profit. But it is not clear that it will see to the concerns of just distribution of the means to meet basic human needs. The latter might be addressed only through government intervention. Thus the bulk of Tweeten's discussion concerns the balance between the public and private sectors that will achieve the utilitarian goal of food for people and profit. In general, Tweeten believes that the utilitarian goals will be properly seen to with a minimum of government intervention and regulation.

Harold Breimyer does not share that faith and in fact despairs of individuals serving the public good through competitive participation in the market. That would be simply heroic. Individual interests are typically selfish and thus run counter to highly competitive production and sale of food, which keeps prices low. Breimyer discusses the problems that may ensue unless the government is ready to intervene to ensure the kind of competition that will reduce dependence on further government action. He also points out that individuals must have the wherewithal to buy food and the knowledge to buy intelligently. With both of these needs, the government can help. However, in the end, it seems that only a wise and public spirited administration attentive to the details of the food marketing system might make a competitive food market serve the goals of both food for people and for profit. If so, perhaps the utilitarian marriage of public and private sectors will not be as harmonious as Tweeten suggests. Indeed, perhaps the selfish actions of individuals will prove inconsistent with the alleged (blind) public-spiritedness of any actual workings of the food production and distribution system. As long as profit is the motivation of individual agents, will exploitation of individuals and the environment by food producers and processors be the result?

Wendell Berry seems to express that pessimistic view in his essay, "The Unsettling of America." On his view, the great watershed in agricultural resource use and management divides the nurturers from the exploiters. The nurturers are the small-to-medium-scale family farmers carrying on the agrarian dream of self-sufficiency and respect for the land who regard it as an entrusted source of sustainable food and fiber supplies. The exploiters, on the other hand, are interested first and foremost in short-term profit through the application of ecologically insensitive or extractive technology and production strategies. Berry, in his comparison of these two groups, strongly suggests that the pursuit of profit from the land, instead of a living on the land, will lead to the destruction of the resource, and thus of the very food we need for survival; our sacred role as stewards of the land, and thus of our essential nature as ethical beings; and the beauty of an integrated life lived in the very processes of sustaining those here now, and nurturing those who are to come.

For Berry, our task is to stop trying to force our living from the land, and instead accommodate both our numbers and aspirations to its sustainable limits. Here there can be no compromise with the exploitive attitudes of the past. The problem is not one of moderating our previous excesses,but of reforming ourselves so that we find our autonomy in trusteeship of the productive resource. Richard Haynes does not go quite so far.

In his discussion "Science, Technology and the Farm Crisis" Haynes sees the agricultural crisis as stemming from some of the same practices, institutions, and strategies as does Berry. We have sought to reduce labor while producing more, a challenge of efficiency suited to the pursuit of profit. Now we run the risk of destroying the productive resource itself.

Haynes examines the paradigm of production and research that has led to the industrialization of agriculture. He contrasts it with the agrarian ideal centered on contextualistic and ecologically sensitive or accommodating stewardship of the land. Haynes rejects two arguments for the agrarian perspective, arguments based, first, on the quality of life claimed exclusively for small-scale family farmers, and, second, on the dangers of industrialization for our food self-sufficiency. More promising seems to be the argument that the caring farmer, unlike the industrial farmer, will protect the resource to make it a reliable source of food and fiber. Haynes closes his discussion with an exploration of how research goals might be redirected away from the farm crisis and toward the promise of the caring farmer. If Haynes is right, the reforms he suggests can bring together profit and sustainability, social concern and respect for individual aspiration, both on and off the farm.

Agriculture can thus pursue conflicting goals through conflicting strategies. With these goals come concerns for individual interest, social welfare, social justice, and individual autonomy, each of which suggest an ethic. These ethics will take both secular and sacred forms. Not every one of these goals and ethics will easily harmonize with the others. They have diverse strengths and weaknesses, as we shall see.

Thus the question arises how can these many voices for policy and practice blend into a chorus?

Philip T. Shepard suggests an answer in his essay "Moral Conflict in Agriculture: Conquest or Co-evolution?" Perhaps, Shepard claims, resolving ethical or moral differences about agriculture is not a matter of sorting things out to the final truth, but of constructing, through an evolutionary process, a more harmonious and mutually accepted moral viewpoint from which to make our assessments. The aim is not to reach unanimity, but rather tolerant, functional, and mutually respectful plurality. The aim is to hear and enjoy a chorus, not a solo. Perhaps that is the best we can hope for as we proceed through a more detailed audition of each of these varied goals and ethical standards of agriculture.

The Goals of Agriculture[1]

William Aiken

THERE WAS A TIME, at least in our cultural memory, if not in actual history, when agriculture was heralded as the backbone of society. Unfailingly, this foundational structure supported the cultural overlay of flesh and sustained us through our social life. We tend to nostalgically look back to the time when most of us lived on farms and this backbone was as strong and rigid as Thomas Jefferson hoped it would be. But today most of us are huddled into megacities and if we think about agriculture at all, it is to groan and complain. Our backbone is increasingly giving us backache. Social criticism has often become intense, and agriculture and related industries are being blamed for all sorts of things. There are fierce battles raging with charges and countercharges, clashes of values, and occasionally some mud-slinging and name-calling. In the midst of all this chaos, it is easy to get lost among the zealous rhetoric of reformers, the deceptive propaganda of marketeers, and the ever-present minutiae of economic charts. Although we may generally be able to figure out what our opponents in these debates are talking about, it is not always clear exactly where they are coming from. Or to put it another way, the assumptions which underlie people's beliefs are often concealed, even from themselves.

One such type of assumption in the debates on agriculture has to do with the goals or objectives of agricultural activity. Since agriculture is a form of purposive activity, it aims at some result or end. How one sees the goal one is aiming at shapes the way one engages in the activity. So a goal acts as a determinant of one's manner of acting. It also serves as a standard or norm to determine success. Though it is common to have more than one objective when engaged in an activity, it is important to see what these may be and how they are related to each other. In this essay I will attempt to isolate the various goals or objectives which those engaged in agriculture do, or in some cases should, strive for. Many of the debates surrounding agricultural practices result, I suggest, from differences between opposing parties in the number of these objectives adopted, the way in which they are interpreted, and the way they are seen to dictate practices.

Profitable Production

It is probably a truism to say that this goal is the overriding objective for most people in the agricultural industry. The battles which surround this goal concern farm size and overproduction. Big farms tend to yield higher profits. If the only goal of agriculture is to be profitable, then the conclusion seems to be that big is better. And all the grousing of family farmers is merely the sour grapes of a non-competitive cottage industry which is being eliminated by corporate farming. Critics of the trend toward bigness may be able to fault megafarms on efficiency criteria but when it comes to productivity, they excel. As production is increased, profitability is threatened by the specter of overproduction, which drives down prices and can drive out many smaller operators. If prices are not controlled by regulation or subsidies, then new markets must be created to insure continued profitability. This can be done either by reductive processing or by discovering new export markets. Continuously creating new markets to absorb surpluses to insure profitability will produce an even greater demand for higher output and an increasingly taxing extraction of agricultural resources. Eventually these resources will no longer be profitable to "mine." However, if maximal profit is the sole goal you are pursuing, then this fact is merely one of the realities of business. When the mine plays out, you simply move on and invest your assets elsewhere. Ghost towns are an unfortunate by-product of extractive industries pursuing maximal profitability. I would think that any owner-operator would shudder at this vision of the land made sterile by quick-buck farming; and this leads to the second goal of agriculture.

Sustainable Production

If sustainable production is seen as a goal of agricultural activity, then "success" is measured not by total output (with maximal income) for only a short time, but by the average output over an indefinitely long period of time. The trick is to find that balance of maximal output compatible with the sustainability of the resource. Or, as all trout fishermen know, you don't overwork your favorite stream—it takes a while to grow a lunker.

Except perhaps for some imprudent profit-maximizing interests, this goal should be acceptable to most of those involved in agricultural activity. There is little controversy over whether we ought to have sustainable agriculture. The controversy arises over interpretation of what this means and how to achieve it: whether chemically or organically. Organic farmers see this goal as requiring such things as crop rotation and fallowing to insure that the organic content and health of the soil is regenerated. The ideal is to obtain maximal yield that is compatible with the carrying capacity of the resources, but not to overstep the regenerative powers of that resource. But this is not what everyone means by "sustainable" production. There are those who see sustainability to be a matter of system management skills supplemented by the ever-new products of agriculture research. Sustainability will be insured by scientific innovation and careful management to insure efficiency. Exhausted resources can be replaced by substitutes. Whether current levels of production can continue to be sustained in this manner depends very much on our faith in scientific innovation. It also depends upon the length of time we are considering. It is difficult to imagine what another hundred years of non-regenerative agriculture will do to our topsoils.

Environmentally Safe Production

Some of the most ardent criticism of contemporary agriculture has its origins in a concern for the natural environment. Farming requires the transformation of a natural habitat and this is likely to affect it adversely. The goal of environmentally safe production requires a broad consideration of the total impact which agriculture has on environmental quality and health including water, air, soil, plant, and animal life. Unlike the goal of sustainable production, which is restricted to agriculture, this goal requires us to examine the effects of farming beyond the borders of the farm itself.

Three controversies arise with regard to this goal. The first is over economic feasibility, the second over the standard used to determine "safety," and the third over the question of "safe for whom?" If you assume that current levels and methods of production must be maintained, one could make a case that achieving this environmental goal is just not economically feasible. Viewed from the perspective of the individual farmer this goal is somewhat external to his operation. Naturally there is a disincentive for the individual to include this goal since it will no doubt be costly to him to conform his practices and this would make him less competitive. So this goal would be most effectively adopted if imposed by external regulation which would distribute the burden of compliance upon all equally.

Suppose that this goal were to be adopted as an important goal of agriculture, the crucial question would be, what do you mean by "safe"? What are the standards to determine safety and are these standards reasonable given the other realities of modern farming? To simply say that we seek to minimize the negative impact of farming practices upon the environment so as to delay or at least not accelerate its deterioration does not tell us how to go about this. The creation of appropriate standards which simultaneously encourage current methods and volume of production and environmental safety is not an easy task. It may be necessary in order to promote the goal of environmental safety, to take positive measures to restore the "health" of overused or abused areas. Such measures would probably set constraints upon farming methods but may be necessary to insure that future generations will inherit an environment that is inhabitable and productive. Of course, not everyone agrees that we have responsibilities to future generations. Nor would everyone allow that there is value in preserving wild species and natural ecosystems. To the extent that the biotic community is seen as having value independent of human use, then attempting to achieve the goal of environmentally safe agriculture may entail a drastic reformation of current practices and methods. The controversies surrounding this goal are far from being resolved.

Satisfaction of Human Needs

Our discussions of the first three goals have concentrated upon the "production" end and have, by and large, adopted the perspective of the producers who can comfortably embrace these three goals (though differences on priority may arise). In turning to the goal of satisfying human needs, we must shift the focus away from the perspective of the producer to that of the society at large. From this broader perspective the purpose of agriculture is to supply people with food and fiber which they need to live. This is the overall "purpose" of agriculture and is, from a social perspective, the primary objective. We want a sufficient amount of food to meet human needs which is of an appropriate quality (nutritionally adequate and safe).

Does agriculture in the United States meet this goal of satisfying human needs? There are numerous debates surrounding quality. At the heart of these debates over quality is an assumption about consumer "satisfaction." The overriding assumption of the industry is that "wants" and "needs" are indistinguishable. Though token homage is paid to the fact that people have a biological need for food, the standard thinking goes on to see consumers' "subjective preferences" (as reflected in market transactions) as the way these human needs are to be understood. Many of the debates which surround the issue of quality take place within this preference framework. Attacks upon agribusiness and especially food processors are often on the grounds that there is not adequate competition or that there is monopolistic control which is discouraging variety or that not enough information is given on labels to allow for rational informed choice of products. These criticisms are a call for more free choice for consumers.

But the problem here is not only one of rational self-interest in choosing how we meet our biological needs. There is also a matter of taste. People often prefer what in fact does not meet their biological needs over something which does meet their needs. To just assume that preferences will account for needs is to assume that our preferences are controlled by rational choice. More frequently, they are a product of our social and cultural conditioning. To even suggest that preference in consumer behavior is an indication of a completely rational choice concerning the fulfillment of needs seems naive. But, of course. no one really believes this as is testified by the advertising budget of any major food firm. Food industry advertising excels in molding tastes and shaping consumer preferences.

To understand the intensity of some attacks on the food industry, it is necessary to see that this whole preference-free choice framework is being challenged. It is not just free market versus monopoly: it is rather the feeling of being coerced, controlled by and manipulated by agribusiness with all of its effective tools of persuasive marketing. Critics try to expose these techniques to make people aware of the manipulation of their tastes and preferences. Though these exposes are designed to help us become truly rationally informed and thus to be cautious in our choices, they cannot ultimately change our tastes. A created preference is still a preference. There must be other ways to insure that agroindustry is in fact oriented toward meeting the nutritional needs of people. Eventually we are going to have to face this question since failing to fulfill this predominant goal of agriculture is a serious indictment upon any civilization.

Compatible with a Just Social Order

At first glance, the idea that agriculture must be compatible with a just social order seems very foreign to farming; what has farming to do with justice? To see how this can be seen as a goal of agriculture, consider the antebellum plantation system which was made possible on an efficient scale by slave labor. If the system of production required slave labor to function then it was incompatible with a just social order. So too, if the colonial system applied in much of Africa and Latin America required appropriation of land which in turn made it impossible for local peoples to meet their food needs, then this system is incompatible with a just social order. Of course, arguments surrounding this objective hinge upon our understanding of a "just" social order. In historical cases there is less dispute over what is and is not just. We seem to see injustice most clearly in retrospect, especially when it does not involve us.

Historically, it seems, every era has its "justice" questions, though they may not be clearly identified or settled until later. I suggest that the overriding issue of "justice" in our era is the question of centralization versus decentralization. The trend in agriculture toward bigness, corporate control, monoculture, intensive technology, and expanded markets is countered by a call for decentralization, local control, and diversity. This call is made by those who despair the loss of the family farm, those who call for adaptation to local environments, those who want a competitive free market system, those who want self-reliant democratic socialistic communities, those who call attention to the needs of rural peoples, those who despair the social effects of displacement on urban centers, those who want more healthful food, and those who seek more autonomy and control over their lives. What unites all of these diverse critics is the feeling that the trend toward centralization in the food industry is in some sense unjust and should thus be constrained. But systems seem to be all-engrossing; it is difficult to be partially involved. If you are going to survive you must, it appears, adapt or radically change the system. We are adapting, though with protest. But should we adapt? Is this emerging system just? We could say that it is merely the march of progress as we enter into a new age in the art of reaping food from the good earth's bounty; an age dominated by technology, high finance, professional management and vertical integration. Though our new age will ultimately be judged in retrospect by later generations, it seems reasonable to debate the justice of this trend now. There is no question that the trend toward centralization is profitable (for some), but that will not justify it if it indeed is creating injustices. It would seem that the defenders of this trend should address the charges of injustice more directly. Merely repeating its profitability will not rebut the charges.

Which Goal Has Priority?

In examining these goals of agriculture, my primary purpose has been to help to identify assumptions underlying disputes. But inevitably questions about the interrelation of these goals come up. Are they compatible or inherently conflictual? If they are compatible, does the pursuit of more than one simultaneously require modifying our anticipation of the level of success attainable in any single one? And perhaps most importantly, which goal or goals ought to be given priority in our decisions, actions, policies, and institutional arrangements? Though analyzing the compatibility of these objectives is perhaps best left to the experts, the setting of priorities involves making value judgements whose outcomes affect the entire community. Policy decisions which shape the nature and future of an enterprise as vital to our national well-being as agriculture is should be informed by the views and choices of the society at large. They cannot be left entirely to the experts. What is needed is an open dialogue on the priorities of American agriculture. Is production and equitable distribution of safe and nutritious food to meet human need both now and in the future going to be the central focus of American agriculture? Or is the goal of profitability going to dictate the direction of American agriculture to the total exclusion of the other goals? It is time for open debate on these questions in the public forum.

Notes

1. This is a condensation of a longer essay by the same title which appeared in Richard Haynes and Ray Lanier, eds., *Agriculture, Change and Human Values* (Gainesville, Fla.: Humanities and Agriculture Program, University of Florida, 1982), pp. 29–54.

Sources of First Principles for an Agricultural Ethic

Stanislaus J. Dundon

THE PURPOSE OF THIS STUDY is to make explicit a set of dynamic first principles for an applied ethics in agriculture, a set whose ability to underpin ethical discussions is based on its content and on the consensus it can win for itself. Ideally such a set would form at once the professional ethics of the agricultural community and the highest standard by which the broader public judges food and agriculture issues. However, most would agree that we are not now in the ideal state. The consensus these principles represent must be of our society but for it as well; a guide as much or more than a description.

Thus we are after a set of principles whose members are: dynamic in the culture, appropriately critical, consensual enough to elevate and integrate the judgments of the whole society, and transcultural with respect to the external impacts of our agricultural practice and policy.

One source has the potential to deliver such a consensus. This is the Judeo-Christian ethics in the area of food, farming, land use, the dignity of work, the rights of laborers, and transcultural equity. This ethic is present in nearly every culture, race, and economic system. The consensus-gathering power of the ethic will be explored further below. But, it can be noted here that the social ethics of most large American Protestant churches are developed democratically. In every case, the documents I consulted were developed by commissions with broad representation, both in profession, class, and locale. The documents are then subjected to democratic amendment and adoption at national synods or conferences by elected representatives. In most cases farmers and farming interests formed the majority of the study commissions.

I want to look at eight documents that have arisen from such a process. These are

1. "Care for the Earth: Theology and Practice," in *Occasional*

Papers(27-36), adopted at the 1982 general synod of the Reformed Church in America.

2. *The Family Farm,* adopted by the United States Catholic Conference, 1979.

3. *The Land,* statements of the American Lutheran Church, adopted at General Councils of the church from 1978 to 1982.

4. *Listening to People*, a series of eight pamphlets on agricultural topics derived from consultations with largely rural groups from 1977 to 1982. [These pamphlets are not official statements of the Lutheran Church in America, which sponsored the consultations and published the pamphlets.]

5. *Rural America: Life and Issues*, a pronouncement of the 12th General Synod of the United Church of Christ, 1979.

6. *Strangers and Guests, Toward Community in the Heartland,* a midwestern regional Catholic bishops' statement on land issues, 1980.

7. *This Land: Ours for a Season*, a report of the Study Committee on the Church and Agriculture, published by the General Board of the Church of the Brethren, 1974.

8. *Who Will Farm*, adopted by the General Assembly of the United Presbyterian Church, 1976, with exception of some reservation on the descriptive material in the first, background, paper on the family farm.[1]

There is a surprising degree of consistency among the eight documents. The consistency is so strong that a sequential review of each would be repetitive. Nevertheless, each differs slightly in tone, in the severity of critique of the current practices, in the scriptural quotations cited, and in the values listed. What I propose to do is list all the distinct principles I find. First, I will isolate general principles of land ownership and use. Second, I will group more specific principles of agricultural practice by their apparent relationship to the four goals of agriculture: providing adequate, healthy, and sustainable food supplies by means which respect the rights and dignity of all participants. In the fourth area, the rights and dignity of participants, I will include as well values that the documents seem to see as especially at stake in agricultural enterprises. This will involve looking further at farm life, farm work, farm families and communities, and farm labor.

Land Ownership and its Beneficiaries

All the documents implicitly and many explicitly state that private ownership is conditioned by its impact on the common good. The reason given is that agricultural resources are God's gift to all humans. *Strangers and Guests* states that there is a social mortgage on the land, that civil title is limited for values including recreational and aesthetic.[2] Private property is a value because of the good it confers on the many, not because of the advantages it gives a few.[3] *This Land* somewhat more tentatively states: "We heard increasingly that land use is a social privilege and not alone a right gained by economic power."[4] But in the context the point is to promote the broadest participation in land ownership, not to attack it. In addition, the context is to prevent non-family corporate ownership from increasing.

Also beginning from the responsibility to be stewards of God's earth, *Who Will Farm* affirms responsibility to the poor, concluding that economic efficiency in farming is not an end in itself but must serve the needs of the people.[5] The general principle that *economic efficiency is a means to social efficiency and subordinate to it* is echoed in many of the documents. The pertinent scriptural passage is a call for deliberately inefficient harvesting techniques so that something will be left for the poor.[6]

Before applying this principle of social efficiency to the issue of structural shift in American agriculture (toward huge farms under corporate control), *The Family Farm* states: "... [T]he excellence of a society depends upon the extent to which it fosters justice and serves the common good. Even if one could demonstrate that some absolute economic gain could be realized from further concentration in the agricultural sector, that gain would not be worth the price paid in social terms."[7]

In *Farmland*, from the *Listening to People* series, we read: "The Old Testament principles of justice and social order show God's clear intention that the values of people and society are to be based on the quality of human life rather than economic factors." Also, under *Ownership* it states: "As stewards we are responsible to use land to the best advantage of all God's children, and not [solely? the text has "society"] for personal gain."[8]

It is striking that these statements of the general subservience of private ownership to public ends are always in the context of the most strongly stated justifications for the benefits of private ownership. They are intended to underpin policy recommendations for extending private ownership or some ownership of the means of production through cooperatives. The ideal seems to be ownership in the hands of the largest possible number of persons consonant with other human needs. While large corporate interests and other large landholders will find direct criticism of their role in agriculture here, there is no evidence of any special preference for socialistic systems.

Adequacy of Food Supply and Sustainability of Production

The documents see two threats to an adequate food supply: global inadequacy due to absolute loss of sufficient agricultural resources, and localized inadequacy due to political and economic causes of poverty. The causes of both are the same, and usually include preemption of the best land for nonagricultural purpose, excess consumption by wealthier populations, and reduction of land available for food production for the local population. This last is traced to the so called "Global Supermarket" phenomenon, and is referred to in "Care for the Earth."[9] The principle is: *Excess consumption by one group at the cost of another group is unjust.* A similar condemnation of hunger caused by the pursuit of cheaper agricultural production by multinational corporations is implied in *Listening to People.*[10] And it is stated positively in "Care for the Earth": The earth's resources should "be shared justly with all people."[11] The article refers to the economic power of America, which would allow it to outbid the poor of other countries for the product of their lands after we have wasted our soils in the pursuit of short-term profits or have covered them with airports and parking lots.

Each of the documents states the obligation of stewardship roughly as: *The land is ours to care for, the fruit is intended for all humans equitably.* There is a strong dependence on revealed religious truth in the verb "is intended." Philosophers will have to debate the rational status of this principle of equity when applied globally; an application we read in *Who Will Farm*: *"Safeguarding the capacity of our country to produce food in a way oriented to serve human need to the maximum extent is a global concern"*.[12] But this cannot be read as an endorsement of the thesis that America should be a global breadbasket. In fact, significant permanent and vulnerable dependency on outside food sources is treated as a disvalue for any group. Land and labor policies are usually advocated precisely to diminish that kind of dependency. In this context there is also a new motive for simplicity of lifestyle: not to purify the soul, but to avoid consuming the bread of the poor. Also in *Strangers and Guests*, we read as a principle aimed at adequacy: "*Land ownership should be as widely distributed as feasible to meet the needs of the local and national communities and of the human family as a whole.*" And Pope Leo XIII is cited as calling for laws which will maximize the number of persons who own land.[13]

As another aspect of stewardship with the end of adequate and sustainable food supplies, *Strangers and Guests* asserts a negative principle: *"The control of seeds, because it implies also the control of food production and indeed of life itself, should not be appropriated to itself by any company or nation."*[14]

Healthy Food, Healthy Environment

Relatively less attention is given to principles affecting the values of growing and marketing of nutritious and safe foods. In *Who Will Farm*, one argument supporting the family farm reveals fears that the larger, more industrialized, farming operations have to rely on toxic chemicals that may become health hazards to consumers.[15] Environmental pollution and sustainability are more often the issues raised in the context of dependence on agricultural chemicals. Several documents call for research and changes aimed at reducing chemical dependence, mentioning explicitly the advantages of modern organic methods, and integrated (largely biological) pest management.[16]

Another number of the *Listening to People* series, *The Politics of Food*, explicitly condemns the loss of nutrition in food due to the pursuit of profit and efficiency by food processors. It also condemns the "circle of poison" phenomenon, whereby dangerous chemicals prohibited in one country (Canada) are shipped abroad for use by other farmers. The danger to health of consumers and the economic disadvantage to Canadian farmers are contextual justification for this condemnation. No special religious doctrine is appealed to here beyond the usual stewardship principles.

In a sweeping condemnation of all environmental pollution including that due to agriculture, "The Care of the Earth" applies the notion of sin (pursuit of quick profits, injustice, self-indulgence) as the cause of the "brokenness" of both the person and the environment. This is a philosophically difficult notion, but the theological use of it is practical: The religious response to encountering this sin in ourselves is to allow the resurrection to renew ourselves and the environment, healing all of creation by our own action and political advocacy.[17]

Sustainability, Ownership, and Economics

One of the interesting differences between these documents and nonreligious writings explicitly aimed at preserving agricultural resources is the people-orientation of the religious documents. There is an awareness that personal greed can cause farmers to be careless with their land. But in general there is an assumption that the family-owned-and-operated farm will only fail to be oriented toward sustainability practices through economic pressures to the contrary. The realism of *Listening to People, Farm and Food Issues* is disheartening: ". . . [A]s much as farmers may want to practice good resource conservation, they cannot, will not, and should not be expected to unless their operation is assured the cost of production. . . . And how can they be expected to refrain from pressing for maximum production regardless of the consequences to the land and water?" [This is not intended as a doctrinal teaching but simply a statement of predictable human behavior.]

In spite of this realism, there is a kind of confidence that the owner-operator has the motivation to practice good stewardship, and that sustainability is the value, more than any other, that supports a variety of principles defending the family-owned-and-operated farm. Thus in *The Family Farm* we read: ". . . [T]he owner-operator has incentives to preserve the health of the land that the renter cannot be expected to share."[18] Similar pessimism about the likelihood of sustainability-oriented stewardship in corporations is found in almost all the documents. Thus also in *Who Will Farm*, we read:

> The family farm system has built into it a relationship of personal stewardship of resources and commitment to preserve the long-range capacity for food production;. If farming becomes increasingly industrialized, thus further removing direct owner-operator responsibility and substituting short-term managerial responsibility, the commitment to future productivity of the land may be weakened.[19]

There is an awareness that "the simple life" has sustainability implications and that farmers are as subject to temptations toward greedy lifestyles as anyone else.[20] Nevertheless the closeness of the family to its farm and the remoteness of the corporation causes most of the documents to add sustainability as a value that can be promoted by supporting the family farm. The family farm is usually defined without income-level criteria, but with such criteria as permanent residential and intergenerational identification of a family or partnership of families with the land. The size of the family farm enables the family to do most of the labor itself, except at peak seasons. The principle that *the family farm is to be promoted to the extent consistent with other important values* is clearly based on the notion that scriptural exhortations on the obligation to practice stewardship should not be inserted into an economic environment in which natural family love, self-love, and love for one's descendants war against the obligation.

This means that philosophic moralists asserting a rational obligation to sustainable stewardship, based on equity considerations for future generations, must demand a policy in which that concern for the future does not require the sacrifice of basic human loves within the present generation, e.g., of the farm family's love for itself and its dependents. The religious principles build on natural loves and do not rely on heroism for a policy of sustainability.

Of course, the religious documents have many more values tied up in the family farm, some of which we will deal with below. Many of these values may also be susceptible to insertion into purely philosophic principles.

If this embrace of the value of the family farm on rational grounds is possible, then acceptance of the principle that "*the future must provide opportunities for tenants [farmers] to become owners*" should be straightforward.[21]

With Means that Protect the Rights and Dignity of All Participants

These documents were composed at a time of farm family and farmworker crisis and unrest. Hence it is not surprising that the rights of farmers and farmworkers form the main focus of the statements which are concerned not with the production goals but with the impacts which current agricultural economics, technology, research, and government policies are having on rural residents and laborers. The impacts are noted as deriving principally from the shift in farm ownership (proprietary structure) and as principally affecting the values of farm family life and its work, rural communities, and farmworkers.

Farm Life, its Virtues and Proprietary Structure

The documents speak of the experience of a family working together as a unit, about the identification with the land and seasons, the independence of work, of the special sharing in a rural community, about economic democracy and its loss, about the creativity, challenge and risk of farming. "The farm is essentially a communal enterprise, providing a solid foundation for family life. While strong families thrive in all settings—urban, suburban and rural—the farm environment encourages the development of patience, self-reliance, a simplicity of outlook and the particular bond that comes when father and mother and children join in earning their common bread."[22]

The values noted in this quotation are threatened by the loss of the family farm through change of farm structure. Many utilitarian arguments are offered in the documents to justify efforts to preserve these values, including such things as sustainability, market competition, and genuine (not tax-based or purely pecuniary) resource efficiency. But this quotation makes clear that the retention of the family farm is based on the absolute values of the quality of life lived by farm families and in rural communities. These values are worth policy attention even without the further defense based on utility.

Value of Farm Work and Proprietary Structure

In addressing the question of the ethical imperative to preserve any given form of employment in the rural area, not just farming, *Rural America: Life and Issues* draws from scripture and the teaching of Martin Luther the notion that all useful labor, and not just religious work, is a God-given vocation. It complains that increasing size of operations and mechanization are producing a sense of helplessness and alienation, especially in the enterprises now springing up in rural sections of America. The decisions affecting the work available in rural areas where there is rarely a chance to find alternative work opportunities *must be accountable to the criteria of human justice and enhancement of human community, not just the criteria of minimal labor costs and maximal profits.*[23]

Farm Families, Good Communities and Proprietary Structure

Thus, while there is no favoring of socialism in these documents, there is also a clear denial of the appropriateness of any laissez faire abandonment to a realm of "externalities" of any of the social or communal consequences of economic activity. The authors apply this principle to the family farm (which they have defended on sustainability and efficiency grounds) and state that, *in order to stabilize the economic and social quality of rural life, commercial family farms should be protected and preserved as the dominant pattern in the USA.* In harmony with the communal responsibility noted above, it is interesting that this document aims not at the quality of the life of the farm family itself for itself, but the quality that the prevalence of such families gives to the rural community. Thus "*the family farm is a crucial ingredient in the rich quality of rural life. [And therefore] public and private policies should support the family farm.*"[24]

In this context, with respect to impact on both family farms and farmworkers, several documents imply the principle: *If technological development, especially mechanization, is good, its developers and promoters must be responsible for the impacts it has on humans.* And this is urgent because neglect of positive assumption of responsibility leads to harm. Thus in *This Land: Ours for a Season* we read: "But, if left unguided, it [capital intensive agriculture] leaves in its path the degradation of people with hideous social and political results."[25] This growth in the scale of economic and social institutions is also opposed in "Care of the Earth," which sees it as a loss of "the values of economic democracy."[26] In *Rural America*, rural residents are called to resist further centralization of political, economic, and social institutions. There is an implied principle that *local leadership, community responsibility, and institutions with real power to influence events should be sought.* And the very means used to establish these changes are to be as local as possible, according to the "principle of subsidiarity" stated in *The Family Farm*: *In order to preserve citizen liberties, action to promote social justice should be taken at the lowest practical level within a society.*[27] One general implication is clearly that increasing moral distance between an agent and his or her effects leads to deterioration and hence should be resisted. For example, in *The Land* opposition to investor ownership of farmland is based on the conviction it "brings about the indifference and neglect of community well-being generally characteristic of absentee ownership. . . ."[28]

What seems to exist here is a rather sensitive balance, of the sort we saw in advocating limits on private property in the very context of seeking its widespread enjoyment, a defense of family farms and of smaller economic and political enterprises so that individuals and communities will not become powerless. Yet this pursuit of autonomy is not an end in itself, but is meant to preserve the possibility of genuine community.

In view of the powerful forces that threaten these values almost all the documents advocate community in action to resist the loss of power. Comparing farmers in the sale of farm products to workers in the sale of their labor, *The Family Farm* states: "In the absence of power that only determined collective action can provide, neither group has much control over its economic life." And the report quotes Pope John XXIII, who in writing on the need for communal action by farmers stated: ". . . [I]t is unquestionably true that the solitary voice speaks, as they say, to the winds."[29]

The Dignity of Farm Labor

Finally, under the heading of "respecting the dignity of all the participants," these documents reveal the moral courage we noted above as needed for truly elevating principles. In general, the communities supporting the development of the documents consist largely of members of the farmer and farm-labor employer classes, although farm labor is represented. Nevertheless, equity to workers is clearly defended. Support for farmworker unionization is explicit and is based both on equity considerations and on the fact that we eat the food in whose production they have labored.[30] It is recommended that farm workers receive the same minimum wage and unemployment protection as industrial workers and that their right to collective bargaining be guaranteed.[31] There is a general recognition that charity is not adequate when basic justice is missing.

Philosophic Utility of the Principles

It is hard to read this material without being struck by the beauty of the ideals it proposes. Yet our ultimate concern should be to go as far as reason can go in seeking a solid defense of the human values at stake in agriculture.

The principles articulated in the documents we have studied seem to have a real potential for providing that defense. For example, consider the equity principles: *All humans should have secure access to their own food production or to the means to purchase food.* This is defensible by the religious underpinnings of the documents we have studied. But also it seems acceptable from the secular standpoint sensitive to our biological needs and to a claim of our human right to productive labor and the dignity and independence that labor provides.

Similarly, consider the defense of ecological integrity and the condemnation of pollution and needlessly intrusive forms of pest control that we see in these documents. Surely reason can demonstrate the irrationality of destroying or damaging the essential ecological relationships of animate nature. And if so, this concern, acceptable both to the religious communities we reviewed and to secular reason, should be widely acceptable as a reforming ethic for agricultural policy.

Other examples can be found in the principles dealing with the structure of agriculture and its sustainable production of healthful food. Indeed, in the case of all the principles we have articulated above, we have ethical guides with genuine therapeutic potential because of their content and the consensus they enjoy in both religious and secular systems of thought.

Philosophers, economists, and other thinkers who contribute to the foundations of policy should examine these same principles for their constructive potential. If they discover the acceptability I predict, they will also have the comfort of knowing that they do not have to supply the moral energy to bring large numbers of affected parties to implement the principles nor face unnecessary danger of resistance from deeply held value systems.

Notes

1. Since the authors of the eight church documents used in this chapter are not identified by name, citations will be made by the institution that authorized them.

2. Midwestern Regional Catholic Bishops, *Strangers and Guests, Toward Community in the Heartland* (Sioux Falls, South Dakota: Heartland Project, 1980), p. 14.

3. *Ibid.*, p. 15.

4. Church of the Brethren General Board, *This Land: Ours for a Season* (Elgin, Ill.: Church of the Brethren General Board, 1974), p. 25.

5. General Assembly of the United Presbyterian Church, *Who Will Farm* (New York: General Assembly of the United Presbyterian Church, 1978), p. 4.

6. *Leviticus* 19: 9-10.

7. United States Catholic Conference, *The Family Farm* (Washington D.C.: United States Catholic Conference, 1979),p. 11.

8. Division for Mission in North America, Lutheran Church in America, *Listening to People; Farmland* (New York: Lutheran Church in America, 1982). *Farmland* is one of eight unpaginated pamphlets in the *Listening to People* series. Each pamphlet is so brief that it is not difficult to locate any of the citations used here. The title of the individual pamphlet, included with the series title, will suffice.

9. General Synod, Reformed Church in America, "Care for the Earth: Theology and Practice," *Occasional Papers*, Autumn 1982, p. 36.

10. Lutheran Church in America, *Listening to People; Food, Nutrition and Youth.*

11. General Synod, Reformed Church in America, "Care for the Earth," p. 36.

12. General Assembly of the United Presbyterian Church, *Who Will Farm*, p. 4.

13. Midwestern Regional Catholic Bishops, *Strangers and Guests*,p. 15.

14. *Ibid.*, p. 36.

15. General Assembly of the United Presbyterian Church, *Who Will Farm*, p. 20.

16. United States Catholic Conference, *The Family Farm* p. 12, and Lutheran Church in America, *Listening to People; The Land: Does it Have a Future?*

17. General Synod, Reformed Church in America, "Care for the Earth," p. 31.

18. United States Catholic Conference, *The Family Farm* p. 12.

19. General Assembly of the United Presbyterian Church, *Who Will Farm*, p. 20.

20. Church of the Brethren General Board, *This Land: Ours for a Season*, p. 3.

21. United States Catholic Conference, *The Family Farm* p. 6.

22. *Ibid.*, p. 4.

23. General Synod of the United Church of Christ, *Rural America: Life and Issues* (New York: United Church of Christ, 1979), unpaginated.

24. *Ibid.*

25. Church of the Brethren General Board, *This Land: Ours for a Season*, p. 24 and p. 10. Also Midwestern Regional Catholic Bishops, *Strangers and Guests*, p. 10.

26. General Synod, Reformed Church in America, "Care for the Earth," p. 28.

27. United States Catholic Conference, *The Family Farm* p. 22.

28. The American Lutheran Church, *The Land* (Minneapolis: Augsburg Publishing House, 1982), p. 16.

29. United States Catholic Conference, *The Family Farm* p.12.

30. General Synod, Reformed Church in America, "Care for the Earth," p. 31.

31. *Ibid.*, p. 37

Bibliography

The American Lutheran Church. *The Land.* Minneapolis: Augsburg Publishing House, 1982.

Church of the Brethren General Board. *This Land: Ours for a Season*. Elgin, Ill.:Church of the Brethren General Board, 1974

Division for Mission in North America, Lutheran Church in America. *Listening to People*. New York: Lutheran Church in America, 1982.

General Assembly of the United Presbyterian Church. *Who Will Farm*. New York: General Assembly of the United Presbyterian Church, 1978.

General Synod of the United Church of Christ. *Rural America: Life and Issues*. New York: United Church of Christ, 1979.

General Synod, Reformed Church in America. "Care for the Earth: Theology and Practice," *Occasional Papers*, Autumn 1982.

Midwestern Regional Catholic Bishops. *Strangers and Guests, Toward Community in the Heartland.* Sioux Falls, South Dakota: Heartland Project, 1980.

United States Catholic Conference. *The Family Farm* Washington D.C.: United States Catholic Conference, 1979.

Farming's Rewards at Risk[1]

Samuel Edwards

My credentials in agriculture are not academic; they are practical. I am one of the fourth generation of a century-old family farming operation. Prior to our recent merger into a larger farming organization, we farmed over 2500 acres, most of them in Southern California. We also have soybean and corn land in Illinois, and have raised multiple crops on our properties in Northern California. I have been the chief financial officer of these operations. About twenty-five years ago, we had approximately four thousand acres. Members of the third generation felt that they could no longer hold that size operation together. They began to sell some of the land. That was a travesty, I think, because we sold some valuable farmlands the potential of which had not been appreciated.

Three factors made the family sell, and these are faced by all small farmers today: first, inability to cope with the burgeoning complexities of farming; second, management problems and difficulty in finding manager successors as older generations faded; and third, inability to cope with the tremendous financial fluctuations and complexities of farming, including the newer techniques of capitalization and operating on borrowed money.

In considering the decline of the family farm, it is important, first of all, to define a farmer. In a jocular vein, a farmer has been described as a man who is outstanding in his field. Actually, American farmers are outstanding in their field. They can grow more, grow better, and grow in tougher circumstances than anyone else, anywhere, at any time.

It is important also to remember that a farmer is a businessman. Altruism and philosophy play a small part in the thinking of the average farmer. He operates his farm and his ranch to make a profit. Since he rarely succeeds, he is driven always to do better and better, and financial concerns become paramount.

Perhaps the most dramatic change in agriculture today is the trend toward fewer and larger farms. In recent years, the average farm size, the investment requirements for farms, and farm income all have increased tremendously.

The California Institute for Rural Studies published a survey of the size of farms in California, called GETTING BIGGER. It reported that 3.7 per cent of California farms operated three-fifths of the state's cropland. The 211 largest California farm operators averaged 11,500 acres, or eighteen square miles, apiece. These 211 largest operators in California operated one-fifth of the land, and yet they constituted only one-third of one per cent of the farms.

By the late 1970s in the United States overall, fifty thousand farms—or less than two per cent of the total—accounted for more than one-third of farm sales. The largest quarter in size of farms in the country accounts for eighty- five per cent of the sales.

Also, the number of farms in the United States is decreasing. It reached a maximum in 1930, when there were approximately seven million farms. By 1950, the number had dropped to 5.6 million. In 1975, there were only 2.7 million farms. More recent census polls suggest that both the number of farms and, surprisingly, the number of the smallest farms, are increasing. (Here problems of defining what actually constitutes a "farm" confuse the issue.) Anyway, it is the middle-sized farms that are disappearing.

Although the small farm seems to be having trouble, the owner-operated farm does not. The latter still predominates. The feeling in America that small farms ought to play a role in our society is strong. However, the word "small" may be more philosophical than descriptive. The U.S. Department of Agriculture had a conference devoted to this question: What is the small farm? The participants left at sword's point after a day of debate.

Larger farm operations tend to be family-owned, and many of the largest farm operations, particularly in California, are family-owned. Of those 211 largest farms in California that I mentioned earlier, only twelve per cent of the land farmed was controlled by non-farm interests.

Many factors affecting the scale of operation are irrefutable. There definitely is an economy of scale. Larger farms tend to operate more effectively and more cheaply than small ones. Unit costs are lower for the large operator. Volume discount buying has a statistical and a practical advantage. The technology available to the large operator increases productivity and decreases the cost per operating unit. Innovations in farming, as in most scientific endeavors, have been dramatic. Tractors, mechanical harvesters, herbicides, pesticides, improvement in varieties and strains that are planted, more efficient and greater use of water—all these have tended to increase farm size. Commodity pricing tends to favor the large farmer, and he tends to receive higher prices for his product.

In changing markets—and ours is a world of ever more greatly changing markets—the need to diversify grows. The large operator can diversify more quickly and more easily. He is more adaptable to the changing environment.

Today, the margin between a farmer's costs and the prices at which he sells his product has so narrowed that his operation must be larger in order to make an adequate profit. Larger operations benefit from cost accounting procedures, investment credits, and tax credits.

Larger operations can hire better managers, and better managers promote the development of a larger operation, which can then acquire better managers, who promote larger operations, and so on.

It is easier for larger operations to borrow money. They are usually able to obtain lower interest rates. It also is much easier for larger operations to tolerate the incapacity of some of their key operators and managers. On the smaller family farm, when the owner-operator breaks his leg, his farm is out of luck for a while. The larger operation has greater depth.

Farming is a risky business. Those who are not farmers do not understand this living with risk and loss. Every farmer has loss years; every farmer knows that in certain years he will make no money, that he may even lose money. In most businesses that is catastrophic, but in farming that is the way it is. It is accepted.

A number of things contribute to making farming risky. The farmer's greatest effort is directed against crop failure. If a farmer has good production, he still may lose money in a given year, but at least he obtains the satisfaction of producing a crop. The farmer first of all wants to grow his crops. Contributing to crop failure, he faces many potential disasters: freezes, floods, droughts, pests and even volcanoes.

Market failure and export market collapses also are ever- present difficulties. American farmers have become dependent on the export market, which often takes our finest produce. That dependence is affected by politics. The Japanese become angry when we raise tariffs on their cars, and so they refuse to buy our lemons. Then the entire American citrus industry howls.

The U.S. government has made some misjudgments in regard to agricultural policy, and those have increased the farmer's risk. In 1973, there was a fiasco in corn exporting. The prices of corn and grain skyrocketed, and some land in the Midwest tripled in value, only to fall precipitously later in time of overproduction and surplus. Farmers who bought land at those high prices could not meet their loan payments when corn prices dropped. The 1979-80 embargo on grain to Russia disrupted markets considerably. These governmental decisions are all beyond the control of the farmer, and yet they affect financial returns for his crops.

There are other problems. Oversupply immediately is equated with low prices. In the citrus industry, it has been said that four percent overproduction will halve the return to the grower. Boycotts, strikes, and other labor actions at the time of harvest render the farmer helpless, because he has only days—sometimes hours—to remove his crop from the field. If he is not able to harvest his crop, or take it to the processor, he is finished. That is his one shot in the year. Distrust and hostility between growers and farm labor are great. I question whether growers and workers will ever mature sufficiently to work out a reasonable relationship.

Financial problems abound. Interest rates have been too high. Most farmers operate on borrowed money, but loans are not always available. Sometimes credit is constricted. At other times, a farmer's financial losses may exceed the borrowing capacity of his farm, and then his hand is dealt out. In times of falling farm land values, land equity valuation falls below loans outstanding, ending the farmer's credit.

These problems, combined with increasing costs, heighten the risk of farming for the small operator. As it costs more and more each year to grow the crop, the operator has to put at risk more and more of his net worth. In a major loss year he may be extended too far to recover. That is the end of his operation. Unlike those in industry, the farmer cannot price his products to reflect his increased costs. He has to take what he is offered for them. That is true for large and small farmers alike.

Farmers perceive the environment in which they operate—the institutional setting of agriculture—quite differently from the rest of the populace. For the farmers it is a hostile environment. Bureaucratic entanglements are extraordinarily difficult for an independent man of the land. They seem to be complex, bewildering, inconsistent, and oppressive. He finds the increased paperwork and office work onerous.

Water matters are paramount. A senior economist of a large agricultural lending bank in California, has stated that assurance of an adequate clean water supply is the major problem agriculture has to solve. Until agriculture solves that problem, he has said, all other problems remain secondary. Water availability, restrictions, reporting requirements, taxes, all the bureaucratic entanglements associated with water use, are multiplying in complexity and number.

Many farmers feel that new bureaucratic regulations on the use of pesticides and chemicals in California will preclude using the old methods of pest management. Agricultural burning, environmental impact reports, the Environmental Protection Agency, and pollution regulations present difficulties for the farmer. The labor contracting regulations and the Agricultural Labor Relations Board cause difficulties. Regulations by the Occupational Safety and Health Administration regarding safety requirements, workmen's compensation, vehicular regulations, and an endless stream of other forms make office work a major part of all farming operations now. Obviously, the large operator who has a business office can cope with these better than the small operator who does not.

Consumerism is a problem for the farmer. Consumers are intensely concerned with the farmer's use of pesticides and fertilizers, and with weed control, water pollution, and other environmental pollution issues. Consumers want perfect fruit, but they do not want any chemicals sprayed on the fruit. Environmental contamination is a big issue. That is ironic, because the farm is surrounded by the town, its best land having been taken out of production and used for houses and shopping centers. Then the people who move into these houses begin harassing the farmer for contaminating the environment.

Land use restrictions lock the farmer into farming his land. He cannot sell it for other uses. Of course, that is the result of a community's desire to keep some of its land in agriculture. However, other lands that are not in farming can be manipulated as the owners wish.

Farmers have little political clout. They make up only five per cent of the population, while everyone is a consumer.

Lending institutions have fluctuating commitments to agriculture. The Federal Land Bank and the Production Credit Association have helped significantly, but in times of tight credit, severe restrictions are placed on farming operations.

In spite of relief which is afforded now to the widows and families of farm owners, the payment of estate taxes is a major reason why farms are sold. The farmer tends to be land-poor. When he dies, his assets amount essentially to the land that he holds. The land is valuable, but it is not a liquid asset.

The Internal Revenue Service depreciation allowance is inadequate. Technology continues to cost more. Inflation makes replacement cost much higher than the original cost. Yet the depreciation allowance permits deduction of only the original cost of the item. Therefore, more and more capital items must be paid for by the farmer with after-tax dollars. And while there is a tendency to replace labor with capital, and men with machines, that is very expensive. The land itself, the farmer's most expensive tool, cannot be depreciated.

The farmer has a low return on capital. The return on investment capital for the average of the 211 largest operators in California mentioned above was sixteen per cent. But the reason it is that high is that these operators came into agriculture when land was cheap compared to what it costs today. Book value of their land is low. The usual return on capital in agriculture in today's land market is 3.5 to four percent.

The major return to the farmer is the appreciation in value of his land through time. The deflating farm crisis of the 1980s, following the rapid appreciation of farm land values in the 1970s, has disrupted this trend somewhat.

Farm land value appreciation is "paper profit" until the land is sold. Still, the value of farmland holdings supports the quip that a farmer is a man who loses money every year, yet lives well, educates his children, and dies the wealthiest man in the community.

Modern farming is not only risky, but also complicated. To survive, the farmer must cope with a wide range of bewildering complexities—some of them already mentioned—with skill and understanding.

Budgeting is critically important, for both operations and capital development. Accounting and money management skills are beyond many farmers. Projecting capital needs requires expert cost accounting; that is a sophisticated skill and one which must be achieved by the successful farm operator.

A keen understanding of the time value of money is crucial, especially times of rising inflation. Knowing how to use money as a tool—an expertise required in any business—is also required in contemporary agriculture.

Accounting and tax planning become more complex, and this is particularly troublesome as the dollar value of both the costs and the returns to the farmer increase. The graduated income tax becomes more of a problem as dollar amounts increase.

Computer technology has now reached agriculture. The farmer who can analyze his production records, financial projections, production timing, payroll, and employee records has an advantage over the one who cannot. Still, computer technology is quite foreign to most farmers.

The modern farmer must diversify his crops. The "always grow the same crop" philosophy is no longer viable. Today's operators must shift their crops prudently, often on short notice. Government land use restrictions limit the owner's option for sale and other use, so he must be innovative in his agricultural use of the land. Most large-farm operators lease a third more land than they own; but most of them also lease land to others.

The smaller the farm, of course, the more the farmer and his family can provide the farm labor. Years ago when farms were smaller, the farmer and his family worked harder during hard times, and that made up the difference. Today, working harder does not make up the difference. The cost/revenue squeeze continues, because the farmer has trouble passing along his increased costs. As costs rise, his returns may not, as the farmer must take what is offered for his crops. Economists contend—and I dispute this with them, although they are persuasive with their graphs—that farm prices over extended spans of time tended to keep up with inflation. But at any given time the farmer may be lagging in what he receives for his crops. He takes little consolation in the fact that prices may eventually catch up. He looks at the present.

Oil and energy costs at times have risen faster than inflation as a whole. Agriculture is energy-intensive. The cost of fuel, pesticides, fertilizer, chemicals, electric power, and the development of water (which involves electricity) has increased faster than inflation generally.

Supply and demand for water—particularly in California—is a matter of great concern. Four-fifths of the water developed for use in California goes to agriculture. Every year, agriculture demands and uses more and more water. As other sectors of the community demand their share of more water, agriculture is going to have to squeeze down its demands, because all the easy water development has now been achieved. All of us are thinking about who should pay the tremendous costs of new water development.

Civil liability is another concern of the farmer. Malpractice insurance, as it is called in medicine, may be needed in every industry, including agriculture. Accidents on the farmer's property, environmental pollution, contamination—all these are liabilities for the farmer, as they are for industry. Insurance is harder to obtain, and much more expensive than in the past.

Continuing education is a necessity in agriculture. How does one develop an ongoing expertise in the new technologies as they emerge? The University of California and the land-grant colleges have been very helpful in many different areas. For example, they have been instrumental in developing harvesting mechanisms for various crops, have developed improved crop strains, and many other helps. The schools' help to the farmer extends across a broad range of problems—including those peculiar to the small farmer.

In addition, the university provides an interface with the centers of political power where bureaucratic entanglements often originate. Frequently, it is the university that can convince legislators that some of the regulations impinging on farmers are not in the public interest.

Although the small farmer faces all the difficulties I have been listing, the reasons why he holds on and continues to farm are many and powerful. Tradition and family ties are important. Farm families love the land and they love to farm. That strength should not be underestimated. Farmers will hang on the the bitter end.

Also, there is a little bit of the farmer in all of us. When I was at sea in the Navy, the sea captains talked for hours about how they were going to retire to their little farms someday.

Inertia, too, is a factor, as in all businesses. The farmer either does not want to have to decide what else to do, or he does not think he can do anything else. So he stays in farming.

The capital appreciation of farmland makes farming attractive. The farmer's accountant says "Your farm is really valuable! Look at what you're worth now." So he goes on with his negative income statements and watches his balance sheet look better and better.

Capital gains taxes discourage sale of a farm. Taxation of capital gains as regular income may discourage sale even more. The farmer comes in at a low base and the land appreciates, but Uncle Sam collects some of the gain if he sells, and that may dissuade him from selling.

A farmer may lease out his farm, thereby retaining ownership, and move into town to another job. Or, he may lease out the farm and continue to work on it on a sharecrop basis. In that way he can spread the risk; in loss years the loss will not be all his.

There is considerable help for the small farmer. Public sentiment favors the small farmer. We all feel sorry for him. We talk about the small farmer the way we talk about motherhood and the flag.

Government loans are helpful. The Federal Land Bank and the Production Credit Association provide money for almost all farmers who can qualify in almost any sense. The farm credit system is severely distressed at this time but remains an important assistance to farmers. Subsidies, price supports, and other government support programs are numerous. Bankers tend to favor small farmers, offering favorable loan rates and treating farmers leniently in hard times. Estate tax relief has been afforded, although it is still a long way from solving the problem of having to sell the family farm to pay the estate taxes.

State and county officials realize that property taxes can be unfair to the farmer. Most counties now levy property taxes according to the profit of the farm rather than to the higher use value of the land. So, in times of financial reverses, the farmer does not have to pay a high property tax.

Now, what about the future? I have pointed out some unpleasant aspects of farming, but, as are all farmers, I am optimistic. We are going through dramatic transformations in organization. Management will continue to have to adjust to these transformations. The so-called normal times, such as the 1950s and 1960s, which we look back upon as a glorious era, will not be seen again. The successful operator will have to continue to adapt to change quickly, if he is to succeed. Those who cannot adapt will have to leave.

Agriculture will remain a major industry in the United States and California. Other nations will continue to look to the United States for food and fiber, and exports will become even more important than at present. Farming operations will continue to be profitable for the large, efficient operators. Farmland will continue to be a good investment, and its appreciation is assured.

Small farms will give way to large farms, as the consolidation process continues. Prime agricultural land will continue to be diverted to non-agricultural "higher use," but productivity will continue to increase, and make up some of this difference.

Finally, governmental constraints and encumbrances will also increase; we will just have to cope with them.

Notes

1. This is from an article and discussion which originally appeared in *The Center Magazine* (a publication of The Robert Maynard Hutchins Center for the Study of Democratic Institutions), September/October 1980, pp. 20-31. Reprinted with the kind permission of the author and *The Center Magazine.*

FOOD FOR PEOPLE AND PROFIT
Ethics and Capitalism[1]

LUTHER TWEETEN

CRITICS HAVE CHARACTERIZED THE FOOD SYSTEM as being made up of soulless corporations which reap obscene profits while providing unfair returns to family farmers and exploiting workers. Describing our food supply system Robbins[2] states "shot through it is with waste and inequities and laced through it is with deception and outright fraud." Critics of the system say food should be for people and not for profit.

These charges of immorality must be answered on grounds of moral philosophy and not just of economics. That is the purpose of this paper. Few, if any, critics are saying that people supplying food are immoral. Rather, the food system is on trial. That system includes input supply, farm and marketing firms, and industries, along with the public sector that serves the system. A food system out of step with the moral philosophy of the nation will not survive. But is it out of step?

In the following pages, I first briefly review a norm of moral philosophy used to judge performance of the food system. The remainder of the report examines two systems, the market sector and the public sector, for their ethical promise and performance in serving people.

Moral Philosophy

To judge morality, a norm is essential. I contend that the appropriate norm to use in judging the food system is utilitarianism, perhaps the most widely shared ethical system in America. Utilitarianism holds that judgments of right or wrong ought to be based on what is variously termed well-being, satisfaction, quality of life, welfare, avoidance of pain, pursuit of happiness, or the greatest good for the greatest numbers of people.

As a norm of food system performance, utilitarianism raises several questions.

1. Whose utility should be increased? Utility applies to "society," but who or what is society? The answer is critical because utility can be increased for one individual, interest group, or nation at the expense of others. Does "society" include foreigners and illegal aliens, unborn generations, and animals? The last is not a frivolous addition as evidenced by the emerging animal rights movement. The issue of whom to include is not resolved here but I proceed on the assumption that society includes all Americans. Later I will turn to the issue of balancing interests of individuals with those of society.

2. Can utility be measured? If utilitarianism is to be used to judge whether actions are right or wrong, then satisfactions must be measurable. Measurement need not be precisely quantitative, however. In general, individuals are presumed to be rational in determining and acting upon what gives them pleasure or pain. A more troublesome issue is whether one individual or group can measure the utility of another individual or group. Elected officials repeatedly must make such judgments. Implicitly, so does the market price system. Psychologists and sociologists have devised sophisticated attitudinal scales to measure well-being but the predictive power of such scales is limited. Although useful comparisons can be made among groups of individuals, the conclusion is that utility can be measured only imperfectly.

3. Is utilitarianism inconsistent with our humanist and Judeo-Christian heritage and national civil codes? Religious and civil laws providing moral imperatives to judge right or wrong would seem to conflict with the utilitarian philosophy that acts are not intrinsically moral or immoral but must be judged according to their consequences for the well-being of people.

Our nation's laws, formulated under the presumption that they enhanced well-being (avoided dissatisfaction), have often been changed when they became inconsistent with the perceived welfare of society. Examples are changes in laws to end slavery and discrimination against females and minorities.

Some regard the laws from Mount Sinai against lying, stealing, and killing as absolute moral imperatives, but most Americans sanction just wars, white lies, or stealing a loaf of bread to save the life of a starving child—presumably because such actions promote a greater good or prevent a greater evil. Jesus stressed that the Old Testament law of the Ten Commandments could be fulfilled only through obedience to the higher law. "Love they [sic] neighbor." Because concern for one's "neighbor" extended to more than just the person next door (as taught in the parable of the Good Samaritan), it seems clear that Christian moral law is not inconsistent with utilitarianism.

There is almost universal agreement that above all else the food system must serve the needs of people. The major participants in the American food system, producers and consumers alike, probably accept in principle this utilitarian ethical philosophy.

The issue is not food for people versus profit but public sector versus private sector. I shall contend that the private sector is generally more efficient than the public sector in converting resources into output. Government takeover of production and marketing activities now performed by the food-for-profit sector would not serve the public interest. I also content that laissez-faire is inappropriate; an activist government is essential to preserve competition, provide essentials for those with inadequate resources, improve technology through basic science, and perform other functions the market cannot do well.

The controversy in ethical systems is not so much over this dominant philosophy as over the best means of serving utilitarianism. Some system must determine what, when, where, and how to produce and distribute food. Billions of decisions must be made each year. Without a coordinating framework, decision makers acting individually could not promote the general welfare. By pursuing self-interests, individuals would bring greater harm to society than benefit to themselves. Accordingly, society established institutions to coordinate food production activity and to balance competing interests for the benefit of society. Two major institutions perform this role, the *market system* and the *public system*. The "public system" here broadly refers to all nonmarket allocating institutions including family and government. It also includes individuals or groups acting for others and chosen by tradition, election, or appointment.

Theory and performance help to appraise how well each system serves utilitarian ends. We shall note that in theory either the public or the market system can be consistent with utilitarian ethical philosophy. Another test is how well the assumptions are satisfied for each system to work. The most important test of all, however, is how well each system performs.

The Market System

Adam Smith, who held an academic chair in moral philosophy, early showed that under certain conditions the market price system would maximize utility. Each person "intends only his own gain, but he is in this . . . led by an invisible hand to promote an end which was no part of his intention." I show[3] that under strict assumptions the allocations of what economists call "perfect competition" maximize utility of society. It is critical to note that this optimal allocation of resources and products is the same for a barter, socialist, capitalist, or any other economic system. Before critically examining assumptions and performance, let us briefly review some outcomes of profit-seeking behavior within this ideal competitive framework.

Profit and the competitive market price system are not ends in themselves but means to serve the needs of people. Under competitive markets, price is a measure of utility value per unit of a resource or product. Because the search for profit causes firms to allocate resources and products to highest value uses, profit-seeking provides allocations consistent with utilitarian moral precepts.

To see why a market serves utilitarian objectives by responding to needs of people, consider the case of hard tomatoes, a popular topic in the critical press. If consumers are dissatisfied with hard tomatoes, they can vote with their dollars for tasty, thin-skinned tomatoes and depend on a profit-seeking capitalist to supply them. If this capitalist's profit rate is "obscene," they can count on other self-serving producers to enter the market with tasty tomatoes. The increased supply of tomatoes will reduce profit rates.

Profit is for people because it provides incentives for firms to supply food that meets people's wants. Profit is also for people because it either is invested to produce more or is distributed to the persons who own the firm. Profit is for people because it compensates the investor for risk and for consumption sacrificed while his or her capital is used to produce output for others.

But to make more profit don't private firms in a competitive market economy exploit their workers, paying them less than they contribute to the firm? Most workers have skills that can be used by more than one firm. A firm initially paying less than what workers contribute to output will lose profits as these workers are bid away to other firms. Similar reasoning applies to race and sex discriminations. If women and blacks are paid less than they contribute to output value, firms increase profit by hiring them. If people value information on safe and nutritious foods, it will pay a profit-making firm to draw customers by advertising food benefits.

Critics contend the market system wastes fossil fuel, spends too much on transportation, and provides too little regional self-sufficiency. But if firms seek profit and if energy is properly priced, firms can be depended upon to conserve energy and provide appropriate regional self-sufficiency.

Those who favor reliance on the market often hold several value judgments. They hold that people are basically self-serving and require an extensive check and balance system if individuals are to act in the public interest. They hold that each individual is owed *commutative justice* as the value of his/her contribution to society. They hold that the best way to achieve a just society is to rely on the market price mechanism, with each producer freely allocating resources in search of profit and each consumer freely allocating resources to satisfy his/her needs. They hold to the enterprise creed that each individual (or immediate family) ought to be primarily responsible for his/her economic security and that a prime function of the government is to ensure a healthy climate for exercise of business enterprise and consumer sovereignty. They hold that the system of property rights is fair and equitable. They hold that "that government is best that governs least."

These values notwithstanding, more solid grounds must exist to choose an economic system. Critical choices depend on conditions required for the market price system to work and how in fact it does work. The market price system brings outcomes in the public interest if (1) resources are equitably distributed, (2) costs of good and services to firms and individuals coincide with costs to society, (3) there are enough buyers and sellers to provide effective competition, and (4) firms act to increase profits. How well are these conditions met?

Evidence of the Profit Motive

Subjective and objective information suggests that firms do act to increase profits. On the subjective level, firm decision makers say they do. On the objective level, economists have found that firms act as if they seek profits. Indeed, because profit is essential to survive in the market system, it is difficult to believe that firms could behave otherwise. Firms also pursue growth, security, and other goals. But profit must be a key objective if firms are to serve utilitarian ends in a market economy.

Equitable Distribution of Resources

Even if firms act to increase profits, the market price system will not serve society well if resources are inequitably distributed. *Distributive justice* refers to fairness in access to economic opportunity, in sharing of economic outcomes, and in making rules of the economic game.

The issue of optimal distributive justice in a utilitarian framework need not be solely a value judgment. Marginal products and marginal utilities required to calculate appropriate transfers have been measured crudely. Results indicate that maintaining incentives and fostering well-being in society require a somewhat uneven distribution of income rather than equal income for each person.

Economists call the outcome of a well-functioning market a "Pareto Optimum," defined as an allocation of resources and products where one individual cannot be made better off without making someone else worse off. Efficiency is at a maximum with this optimum if we naively assume everyone receives the same satisfaction from another dollar of goods or services. Commutative justice is also served because each worker is paid what he/she contributes to society.

The problem is that this outcome depends on the initial distribution of resources. If one person begins with few human and material resources, that person may starve while others are sated with food under *Pareto Optimum* efficiency. Thus commutative justice is served by the market price system but distributive justice is not. Utility could be increased by transferring income or resources from the sated person to the starving person.

The public intervenes in the market in numerous ways to provide distributive justice. Examples are food stamps, public education, social security, and public assistance. Redistribution of income requires taxing some producers' output, a violation of commutative justice. Distortion of incentives reduces national dollar output. To be consistent with utilitarianism, such reallocation is justified only if the utility gained by transfer recipients outweighs the utility lost by others.

Cost (Benefits) to Firms Coincide with Costs (Benefits) to Society

For the profit-motivated market to serve society well, prices must signal private firms to act in the public interest. If incremental costs or benefits to firms differ from those to society, the market price system will not bring desired allocations. Prices and markets do not even exist for many goods and services. For example, individuals and families allocate human emotions without benefit of markets or property rights.

The lack of markets to allocate air and water causes problems. Individuals and firms paying no charge to dump wastes in the air pollute the atmosphere to the detriment of society. Soil erosion may occur because the farm operator is unaware of the problem, does not care, or is concerned with immediate output only. Losses are incurred by other farmers "downstream," by future operators of the eroded farm, and by consumers. A related example is the cost to consumers who are unaware of chemical pesticide residues or harmful microorganisms in purchased food. When benefits of safe, nutritious foods are not perceived by consumers, they will pay no premium for such foods. Thus firms will lack incentives to supply them.

Benefits to society exceed benefits to private firms engaged in basic agricultural research. Because an improved wheat variety can easily be propagated by one farmer without the knowledge of the seed developer and sold to other farmers, the firm that develops the new variety is unable to appropriate enough benefits to cover research and development costs. Consequently, if research is left to the private sector it will be underfunded. Risks also dampen incentive for private firms to develop new varieties. A public research facility operating on a large scale can average out these risks. It can continue to produce new technologies which, on the average, provide a high rate of return, but which a private firm will forego because it cannot chance bankruptcy producing technologies that are mostly losers. Only rarely does a big winner compensate for the many losers in basic research.

Public education and incentive programs improve the efficiency of the private market by aligning private and social costs (benefits). The government has intervened in markets to establish food grades and standards, information systems, health and safety requirements, and labeling regulations. The federal government provides soil conservation cost-sharing, technical assistance, and educational programs to supplement the market. Taxes on tobacco and alcohol consumption help bring costs to individuals who use these products into line with the cost which society bears as a result of their use.

Competition in the Marketplace

The price system ideally provides people options to enter the marketplace without arbitrary constraint, trading goods and services only if a transaction benefits both buyer and seller. But all parties do not enter the marketplace with equal bargaining power. A sole buyer may exercise bargaining power to absorb the gains from trade with many unorganized sellers. Or a single seller may exercise bargaining power to absorb the benefits from trade with many unorganized buyers. Concentration of economic power can lead to high prices, reduced output, and benefit to the few at the expense of the public at large. Do such concentration and associated costs characterize U.S. farm and food industries?

Farm production is increasingly concentrated on fewer farms. In 1981, the 298,000 farms with sales of $100,000 or more accounted for 12 percent of all farms and for two-thirds of all farm output (sales). By the year 2000, only 50,000 large farms will account for two-thirds of all sales if current trends continue. However, farm production in the foreseeable future is in no danger of being concentrated in so few firms that monopoly pricing and profit will be a problem.

A number of studies indicate that market concentration does not significantly influence profit rates until eight firms control 65-80 percent or four firms account for 50-65 percent of the output of an industry. No major farm commodities are characterized by such degrees of industry concentration. The most concentrated major component of agriculture is broiler production and processing. An estimated 97 percent of all broilers are produced under vertical coordination—90 percent under production contracts and 7 percent directly by integrated broiler processing firms. In 1975, 30 percent of broilers were processed by the 8 largest firms and 50 percent by the 11 largest firms. Through production contracts with growers or company owned growing operations, these firms could effectively control broiler production for their processing facilities. Despite this high degree of concentration, or because of it, broiler production efficiency has increased more rapidly than beef and pork production efficiency. Cost savings have been reflected quite fully in wholesale broiler prices. From 1955 to 1970, for example, the wholesale price per pound of broilers fell from 42 cents to 25 cents while the cost of production fell from 36 cents to 27 cents per pound.

Concentration of economic activity in the hands of a few dominant firms is more prevalent in the farm input supply and product marketing sectors of agriculture. Turning first to inputs, the large numbers of private and cooperative firms provide workable competition in the feed, fertilizer, and credit industries supplying farmers. The farm machinery industry is highly concentrated in a few private firms, but competition among these firms is intense and innovation is rapid. Industry profit rates have not been high on the average and some firms are on the brink of bankruptcy. If the demand and price situation warrants, foreign manufacturers are positioned to enter the machinery industry and provide effective competition.

Market power is of greatest concern in the food marketing industry which performs wholesaling, processing, transportation, storage, and retailing functions from the farm gate to the consumer. With few exceptions, profit rates of marketing firms have been no higher than those of other industries. Because profit rates indicate monopoly power inadequately (equity values of firms with monopoly power tend to be bid up by investors until profit rates are comparable to those of firms in other industries), economists use other approaches to estimate the costs of monopoly.

Parker and Connor[4] estimated that "consumer loss due to monopoly in the U.S. food-manufacturing industries in 1975 was at least $10 billion, but possibly as high as $15 billion." At 6-8 percent of the value of shipments, this is the highest relative loss estimated for any major food marketing industry. The Parker-Connor estimates have been disputed—other economists measuring the same phenomenon derived estimates only 3 to 6 percent as great as those from Parker and Connor. In 1982 Gisser[5] found a statistically positive and highly significant association between food manufacturing concentration and productivity, a relationship which economists had found earlier for the entire U.S. industrial sector and had accounted for by economies of large size. Benefits accruing to consumers from increased productivity were omitted by Parker and Connor, but according to Gisser they were sufficient to offset their estimates of welfare losses from monopoly.

Even if the Parker-Connor results are taken as fact, they do not necessarily constitute a case for a major restructuring of the industry into many small private firms or into cooperative or public firms. The inefficiencies of alternatives could exceed those of the current market structure. Nonetheless, the situation needs to be monitored. Antitrust and other laws to maintain competition and stop unfair business practices must be applied when warranted.

The conclusions from these studies, as well as from a large number of other studies of food marketing industries, is that efficiency losses from market power in food industries are of modest proportions.

Overall Food System Performance

The American food system, relying primarily on the market price system but supplemented by public intervention to correct for market inadequacies, has compiled an impressive record. Americans receive a high quantity, quality, and variety of food at lower real cost in terms of income than do consumers in any other country.

From 1920 to 1981, farmers increased output 140 percent with approximately a constant volume of total production inputs. They accomplished this feat on fewer harvested acres in 1981 than in 1920. In the absence of productivity gains, million of acres of fragile lands subject to soil erosion would have been cropped. Progress in soil conservation also is notable because farmers are rapidly adopting reduced-tillage techniques that protect soil to increase their profits.

In the final analysis, the case for the market system rises or falls on the issues of whether competitive markets (1) reward labor and other factors of production according to their contributions, (2) direct output to markets of highest returns, and (3) move apace toward equal (equilibrium) rates of return on resources. The empirical evidence in support of each of these issues is compelling. May calculations for 1960, 1965, 1970, and 1981 indicate that production resources on adequate-size farms have earned returns at least comparable to returns on resources in the nonfarm sector. (My cost-return results for 1981 are reported elsewhere.[6]) Other rates of return are reported in *A Time to Choose* by the U.S. Department of Agriculture.[7]

The impressive performance of agriculture is in no small part the result of a highly successful synergism between the private sector and public agricultural research and extension—one of the few public sector performances that is truly exemplary. But even here the record is flawed by too little public investment. For a more complete treatment see Ruttan[8] and the paper by Bobby Eddleman in this series. Public sector research and extension constitute only 1 percent of the nation's farm resources, hence private sector decisions dominate economic performance.

The level and distribution of returns among land, labor, and capital have behaved about as predicted by economic theory. As resources and products moved to highest value uses the structure of the farming economy changed massively, which resulted in utility gains to society, especially to low income consumers who spend a high proportion of their income for food. I have documented[9] that those who left farming also improved their circumstances.

After lagging sharply for decades, income per person in farming gradually improved to parity with non-farmers' income per person by the late 1970s. With net farm income unusually low in 1981 (the second lowest in real terms since the early 1930s), farm income per capita from all sources still averaged nearly 90 percent that of nonfarmers! The incidence of farm poverty has dropped from about 50 percent as recently as 1960 to approximately 14 percent today, about the same incidence as nonfarm poverty. Many of the once massive family income differences among farm size classes and geographic regions have been eliminated. The major reason is rural industrial development induced by market incentives. This development created jobs, giving farm families—especially those on small farms—off-farm income to supplement their adequate farm incomes.

The Public Sector System

Americans widely favor at least some regulation, taxes, and subsidies by the government in order to align private incentives with social ones, to avert restraint of trade, and to provide for those who are incapable of providing for themselves. Central to the food for profit or people controversy is the question of whether the public sector should undertake the basic production-marketing activities now performed by the private sector for profit. To examine that issue and appraise overall performance of the public sector, this section draws heavily on international experience.

Public sector food systems range from cooperative farms such as the Israeli kibbutz (where residents make decisions more or less democratically and sell to the private market) to the centrally planned and administered agricultures of communist countries. The key feature of such systems is that principal decisions regarding what, when, how, and where to produce and distribute are guided by individual or collective judgments rather than by the market price system.

Those who advocate public allocation of food system resources and output frequently hold the belief that people are basically good, although they are corrupted by institutions. They hold that the good society must provide a just wage for labor, a just interest rate on financial capital, and a just rent for physical capital. They hold that people have a right to food, a right to a clean environment, and a right to a fair return on investment. They hold that a just society requires production from each according to his/her ability and allocates to each consumer according to his/her needs. They hold that, above all, society owes distributive justice to each individual.

In theory, informed managers committed to utilitarian ethical philosophy and operating a public sector food system could allocate resources and products to maximize utility of society. For public sector allocations to bring outcomes in the public interest, those making allocative decisions must (1) desire to serve the public interest, (2) recognize preferences, and (3) have the administrative and analytical capabilities to serve the public interest.

Do Individuals Serve Self or Society?

Great thinkers have long debated whether man is basically selfish or altruistic. The issue is not resolved here, but worldwide experience is compelling: impersonal man cannot be depended on to act in the best interest of others. Nonmarket allocation seems to work only in groups with strong affective bonds such as families or small communes. Large groups have succeeded only if they have been bonded and motivated by strong religious or political ideology.

Recognizing Preferences

Public decision makers, however well intentioned, cannot serve society without knowing people's wants. Decision makers rely on various institutional systems to gauge the preferences of those they serve. In a democratic society, the voting process is used to reveal preferences and maintain accountability. The one person-one vote system may seem intuitively fairer than "dollar voting" in the market system. But democratic systems are notoriously clumsy, costly, and subject to manipulation by special interests. Representative systems, as opposed to "town hall" democratic systems, give rise to fragmented jurisdiction—politicians find it difficult to resist programs for supporters paid for by others. Benefits of public programs are frequently concentrated among the few while costs are widely distributed. In the political arena, millions of indifferent losers are no match for a few determined gainers, even when aggregate utility losses far exceed gains.

Those successful in forming power collectives aggrandize themselves at the expense of the unorganized. A responsive public sector is likely to serve multiple objectives, each supported by narrow constituencies with no recognition of the cost to society of serving self. In contrast, a well-functioning private market serves society by pursuit of the singular profit objective. An effective, efficient check and balance system cannot be built into large democratic systems; no invisible hand guides government decision makers to serve the public interest.

Administrative and Analytical Capabilities

Even if the political process accurately signaled the highest and best uses of resources and products of the food system and if all public decision makers were well intentioned, the administrative decision processes would require so many resources that society's welfare would be sharply reduced. Faced with more decisions than can be made, bureaucratic systems simplify administration. Because each producer and consumer has unique wants and needs, simple rules will not do—for example, that each individual should receive the same food.

Even the most complex econometric models of the U.S. food economy predict economic outcomes very imperfectly. Highly trained and experienced analysts frequently err in projecting implications of proposed public policy. The analyst needs to foresee impacts on the general welfare which result from complex policy options working through millions of producers and consumers but he cannot do so. Given the formidable obstacles to competent planning, it is not surprising that public sector political-administrative processes frequently produce outcomes opposite to those intended.

Public Sector Performance

Centrally planned and administered food systems have performed better in distributing food than in producing it. Food presumably produced for people and not for profit has been lacking in quality, variety, and often in quantity. Consumers pay a high percent of their income for food and often spend hours waiting in line for it.

As food production systems the centrally planned economies have failed dramatically, with the Soviet Union the most obvious example. Chronic food deficits in socialist economies contrast sharply with chronic food surpluses in the U.S. Producers paid according to their needs, rather than according to their abilities or contributions, receive inadequate incentives to produce. The ideology of self-sacrifice for the good of society seems not to endure long after the revolution. Producers contribute less than what they are able to produce, consumers take more than they need. Altruism fades in the absence of adequate checks and balances, the pursuit of self-interest emerges in the form of waste, mismanagement, and corruption. Centrally planned production systems seem to work only by introducing economic incentives (profits)—with notable recent examples of modest success in Hungary and the People's Republic of China. Western countries have similar experiences with socialism—state-owned firms operate efficiently and compete in international markets only if they are allowed the freedom to operate like profit-seeking private firms. Where exact operational management and worker dedication are essential, as in planting and harvesting crops on time or in overseeing sow farrowing at midnight, no substitute has been found for the market system where the owner-operator has a direct stake in the outcome.

Undertaking food production and marketing may not be viable options for the public sector in this country. How well has the public sector performed its more traditional role in market economies, the role of providing distributive justice, stabilization, and correction for market distortions? Here attention is focused on a range of public activities influencing the food system directly and indirectly.

Stabilization

Performance of government monetary-fiscal policies to dampen business cycles while promoting growth without inflation has been disappointing. Monetary and fiscal policies have been erratic and sometimes at cross purposes, adding instability and uncertainty to the economy. I have elsewhere[10] examined in some detail the debilitating impact of periodic inflation, high real interest rates, and other products of failed monetary-fiscal stabilization policies on the farming sector.

Distributive Justice

Public efforts to force private firms to pay a "just" wage and to promote organized labor have caused unemployment for disadvantaged workers, reduced output, and interfered with the ability of U.S. firms to compete with international firms (notable recent examples are the steel and auto industries). Regulation forcing low interest rates on savings has reduced savings, investment, and economic progress. Approximately three-fourths of the nation's massive transfer payments go to the nonpoor. (This estimate originates with data published by Robert Lampman, extended to include farm commodity programs and updated.[11]) Public assistance payments encourage family disintegration. The working, intact-family poor found disproportionately in rural areas are often not eligible for payments.

Correction of Market Distortions

Government programs to control soil erosion and other environmental problems have not been well-targeted or cost-effective. In the food sector and in sectors influencing the food sector, government has been responsive to special interest groups such as labor and trade associations. The results have been tariff and other international trade barriers, unnecessary licensing requirements for entry into trades and professions, along with featherbedding and other arbitrary rules that restrain productivity gains. Government agencies to regulate economic activity have often become the tools of the regulated. The elimination of many banking and trucking regulations gives the promise of large benefits to society.

Shortcomings of government attempts to regulate are not confined to the United States. Olson[12] provides an absorbing historical exposition of how failure of government to block labor and trade association activities in restraint of trade caused an institutional sclerosis which stagnated economies the world over. One needs only to observe evidence from centrally planned countries to realize that capitalists have no monopoly on the suborning of public officials.

Although government intervention may actually rarely be needed to correct farm price distortions, it is, in fact, commonplace. Such intervention frequently is made not to align private incentives with social incentives, but to distort private actions that initially were in line with social incentives. Schultz and others[13] have documented research which reveals a pattern of governments in developing countries artificially holding down farm prices, thereby causing hardship to producers and reducing output. On the other hand, developed countries frequently hold farm prices artificially high. In the case of the European Community, domestic farm commodity price supports generate excess production which is exported at considerable cost to European taxpayers and chagrin to American farmers. The distorted price incentives are not an attempt to correct for private market failures but rather the result of successful public lobbying by the urban elite in developing countries and a few powerful producer organizations in developed countries.

Many criticisms of markets, when analyzed in depth, turn out to be criticisms of government actions which encouraged or forced markets to work poorly. Perhaps "leftover" tasks assigned to government are more difficult to perform than are the tasks performed by the market sector. But an increasing body of economic analysis and world experience reveals that government failure to perform what is expected of it is far more pervasive than is market failure.

Summary and Conclusions

The American food system is a mixture of a public sector guided largely by political-administrative processes and a private sector guided largely by the price system and profit motive. The private market dominates, however, and in recent years the entire system has been severely criticized for producing food for the profit of corporations rather than for the needs of people. Judging whether the food system is for people or for profit requires evaluation of ethical standards as well as the performance of the food system in serving these standards.

The limitations of the market must be recognized. It will not serve the needs of those who enter the market with no resources: it will not serve where social needs have no market or where private price incentives fall short of social incentives. Acting alone, it will concentrate economic activity temporarily (business and commodity cycles) and interpersonally (case poverty). If the market is evaluated only in regard to what it can be expected to do, its performance has been exemplary in directing resources and products to highest value uses, and hence, in serving utilitarian ends. It is quite robust in providing utilitarian outcomes even when the number of domestic firms is not large—especially if international trade channels are kept open.

The public sector supplements the market sector to correct incentives and to promote stability and distributive justice. As government efforts have been extended, weaknesses of public allocation have surfaced. Public decision makers and administrators often do not act in the public interest. Worldwide experience gives no evidence that a check and balance or incentive system can be designed to ensure that they do. Analytical systems cannot be devised to enable these decision makers to foresee consequences of complex and far-reaching policies with sufficient clarity for even well-intentioned, wise, responsive public officials to act in the public interest.

Public involvement is essential for environmental protection, poverty alleviation, and national economic stabilization, but in the light of history, one cannot predict that such intervention will be well done. Outstanding examples of effective and efficient public sector performance occur but they are not the pattern. The optimal food system consistent with utilitarian moral philosophy utilizes the market system to the extent possible and confines the public sector to functions the private sector cannot perform. The widespread evidence of government failure suggests caution in extending the public sector into activities now performed by the private sector—the costs of government intervention may be greater than those of the market failure which it was intended to correct.

Impersonal markets alienate many by unceremoniously releasing workers from employment or by pricing consumers out of the market without regard for personal consequences. American farmers have long viewed banks, railroads, and grain exchanges as diabolical and sinister. Alienation and resulting populist and protest movements arise in part because producers do not understand or trust an impersonal market system operating with an invisible hand. Alienation is not confined to market economies, as illustrated by the widespread social unrest in Soviet satellite countries and by the high rates of alcoholism and the heavy-handed measures required to squelch dissent in the Soviet Union itself.

In the past, the promise of socialistic economic organization was frequently contrasted with the reality of the market price system, with the latter often coming out the loser. The market system looks much better when it is compared with the reality of the performance of centrally-planned economies and of public sector performance in the U.S. While in theory each system can be consistent with the utilitarian ethic, in reality the market system performs much more efficiently and it is being injected into food systems in centrally planned economies. At the same time, a pure market system does not alone serve utilitarian needs of society. A mixed public-private food system is optimal. The search for proper proportions of the two systems will perennially create conflict, in part because of the inherent tension between distributive and commutative justice.

Notes

1. This paper is number 5 in the 1983 *Farm and Food System in Transition* series published by the Cooperative Extension Service, Michigan State University, East Lansing, Michigan, 1983.

2. William Robbins, *The American Food Scandal* (New York: William Morrow and Company, Inc., 1973).

3. Luther Tweeten, *Foundation of Farm Policy* (Lincoln: University of Nebraska Press, 1979).

4. Russell Parker and John M. Connor, "Estimates of Consumer Loss Due to Monopoly in the U.S. Food-Manufacturing Industries." *American Journal of Agricultural Economics* 61(1979): 626-39.

5. Micha Gisser, "Welfare Implications of Oligopoly in U.S. Food Manufacturing," *American Journal of Agricultural Economics* 64(1982): 616-24.

6. Luther Tweeten, *Excess Farm Capacity: Permanent or Transitory?* Proceedings, National Agricultural Policy symposium, March 28, 1983. (Columbia, Missouri: University of Missouri, in press).

7. U.S. Department of Agriculture, *A Time to Choose*, 1981, p. 51.

8. Vernon Ruttan, *Bureaucratic Productivity: The Case of Agricultural Research* (St. Paul: Economic Development Center, University of Minnesota, 1982).

9. Luther Tweeten, "The Economies of Small Farms," *Science* 219(March 4, 1983): 1037-41.

10. Luther Tweeten, "Impact of Federal Fiscal-Monetary Policy on Farm Structure," *Southern Journal of Agricultural Economics* 3(July 1983): 61-68.

11. Luther Tweeten and George Brinkman, *Micropolitan Development* (Ames, Iowa: Iowa State University Press, 1976), p. 165.

12. Mancur Olson, *The Rise and Decline of Nations* (New Haven: Yale University Press, 1982).

13. T. W. Schultz, et al., *Distortions of Agricultural Incentives* (Bloomington, Indiana: Indiana University Press, 1978).

Food for People and Profit:
An Alternative Interpretation[1]

Harold F. Breimyer

The suggestion that America's system can work without anyone having good motives—without public-spiritedness—gives people an easy conscience about pursuing private interests through public policies.

George F. Will

Present-day society [is] 'rent-seeking,' everyone out for incomes in excess of what can be earned in a competitive market.

Anne Kreuger

The most absolute contradiction in the universe must be that the individual human being seeks a private existence in a public world.

Harold F. Breimyer

ALMOST 20 YEARS AGO the National Commission on Food Marketing summarized the findings of its study of the food marketing system in these terms:

> The American food industry . . . represents one of the outstanding achievements of the American economy. [It] has developed under a system in which individual business firms have made virtually all operating and investment decisions within general limits established by public policy. . . . The role of Government has been to provide certain services and to establish rules to assure that the competitive system operates in the interest of the public and of the industry itself.
>
> Our studies have convinced us of the vitality of the food industry. . . . [However,] we are of the view . . . that a truly competitive environment, appropriate services to consumers, and equity for producers can be more fully assured by certain modifications of existing statutes, regulatory activities, and governmental services. . . .[2]

As the quotation indicates, the Commission gave the food industry a high mark. It also noted exceptions and opportunities for improvement.

In academic terms, the Commission assigned a grade of about B+.

That overall judgment is still valid today. The food marketing system performs technological marvels. How well it meets welfare criteria for all its members—producers, consumers, and marketers themselves—is less certain.

Most disputes about the system revolve around that question, not technical performance. The question takes on more force in the 1980s than it did in the 1960s. Most of the recommendations made by the Food Commission were not acted on, and the criteria for a competitive marketing system are not met as well today as they were then.

Faith in Competition

The Food Commission was indeed dedicated to the principle of competition. The food industry that the Commission endorsed with reservations is "a product of a competitive economic system." Such a system, the Commission was quick to note, "requires competitors." That is to say, "it works best when the number of competitors is sufficiently large so that they impose mutual restraints on each other, with the result that their collective activities are guided along paths consistent with the public interest."

This axiom is the purest check and balance concept. The Commission stressed numbers first. It wanted many firms battling to serve farmers, consumers, and each other. In its text it also called for information, grading, and other traditional supporting services. The Commission did not inquire further into the meaning and significance of a competitive system for marketing the food products of agriculture. It did not emphasize how very demanding are the terms of a competitive system, or how hard—even guilefully—the participants in the sytem will try to manipulate it to their individual benefit.

The Heroics of Competition

The idea that individual producers—and individual consumers too—can interact competitively in a manner to drive and guide the economy to meet the objectives we set for it is heroic. It is almost other-worldly. The idea is heroic first of all because competition marshalls not the nobler instincts of human beings but their selfish aggressions, yet it does so for primarily social rather than private purpose. Its object is not to enable the successful few to exploit all others, but to let all citizens contribute to social output and share in its consumption.

It follows that competition is heroic because it succeeds socially only as it partially fails privately. It achieves social goals by means of individual frustration. Competitors try to outcompete their rivals, that is, to eliminate them. The system works only insofar as they fail to do so. Economic competition, unlike the law of the jungle, succeeds not primarily by elimination of rivals but through reciprocal checkmating. This is indeed heroic!

Economic competition is like a game of marbles. In the game, the object is for each player to win the others' marbles. But if one player wins all of them, the game ends. Competition in the economy continues only insofar as no competitor wins all the economic marbles. Quite literally, whenever too many economic marbles get into too few hands, it becomes necessary to introduce either social (governmental) control, or programs to redistribute wealth and income.

Yet another moral follows. Big firms or powerful labor unions or cartel-like market groups may say, "We are justified in making extraordinary returns because the system is supposed to work that way." Wrong. A truly competitive system works in exactly the opposite way. In it the great benefits are social, not private.

The Object of Economic Competition

Competition is a process. It has form and substance but it does not itself establish objectives. The National Commission on Food Marketing endorsed the virtues of competition as a process and said a lot about how to improve its functioning, but did not say why it was good in the first place, or what common objectives are held for it.

Both economic writings and the mores of our nation say much about what we seek in our economic system, and therefore also in marketing the food products of our agriculture. As the title to this paper tells us, we want "food for people." For the reasons just named, we introduce "food for profit"—included in the title not as a companion goal nor even as an alternate one, for it cannot be either. It is subordinate, instrumental. Profit enters into the system not as a goal for it but as an integral part of the competitive instrument.

At this point we get into one of the touchiest and most misunderstood principles in the economics of competition. Profit is morally ambiguous. What really counts is *pursuit* of profit, not its realization. A modest rate of profit arising from its motivating role is not merely acceptable, but essential. Yet anything more than that is dirty, antisocial, and a threat to continuation of the competitive system itself.

What is meant by food for people, as our wish for the food system? In simplest terms, what we want is to utilize our resources for producing and distributing food in a manner that balances twin goals of meeting at least the minimum needs of human beings, and rewarding participants proportionately to their contribution.

These are two goals, not one. Often, only the second is named, and it frequently is couched in terms of marginal return for marginal contribution. To address only the second goal is wrong. We must always recognize both.

The most obvious example of meeting basic needs for food irrespective of economic contribution is that of individuals who are unable to earn enough income to buy the food they need. They may be unable to do so because of physical handicaps, or because the economy is in recession and does not offer opportunities for employment. So it is that we provide for orphans, the aged, the infirm, the emotionally unstable. We soften the consequences of industrial unemployment, by means of unemployment insurance, Food Stamps, and other grants that make it possible for individuals to have food even though lacking the wherewithal to buy it.

We do not confine our humanitarian considerateness to our national boundaries. We give a modest amount of food to poor people of other nations, or sell it to them at a concessionary price.

Enhancing the Capacity to Produce and to Buy

The second of the twin goals is fundamental. Its simple phrasing can hide its signficance. Making it possible for individuals to earn food via their own economic contribution is a grand principle. But how can it be realized? In particular, how can people develop the capacity, and be assured the opportunity, to earn an income that will enable them to buy food for a good diet? This is a powerful question, and therefore gives rise to major public issues.

In our high-technology world, individuals are not natively equipped to be productive. They must be trained, educated. And the door of opportunity must be open, allowing them to use their talents. It's a tall order!

It is worth noting that competition is not only a process, but pretty much a process of the moment. It does not project well in time, backward or forward. It deals better with events in the here-and-now, than with futurity.

Yet education is futuristic. To develop the capacity of individuals to produce, and thereby to be able to consume, requires action outside the competitive sphere. It calls for social—public—action.

Competition falls short too of bringing about the development of physical resources that have long term benefits. Hydroelectric facilities are a familiar example. In food production, conservation of the soil resource is equally illustrative. Some conserving practices yield contemporary returns to the farmer who performs them and the competitive system can be relied on to bring them about. But others require installations that are more in the interest of future generations than of the farmer of today. We can get them only if we invest socially—via government.

Another feature of projects to develop physical resources is that their benefits often cannot be channeled solely to the sponsors but instead become social property. This is a second reason for using public funds for hydroelectric development, and for highways, public health services (as spraying for mosquitoes), and agricultural experiment stations.

This is the principle of externalities. Competition, being a private process, works well only to reconcile costs and benefits that are internal in nature. It does not bring spending for public benefit—positive externalities. It can also lead, if unrestrained, to action for private benefit but social injury—negative externalities.

The Burden of Information

A competitive food system imposes yet another requirement for its effective operation. It is the requirement of information.

Knowledge is the necessary companion of high technology. As our food system is now one of complex techniques and many highly processed food products—indeed, some fabricated ones—it will work well only if accurate information about it is disseminated widely. Information ranges from market news to product labeling to providing data about opportunities for investment and employment.

Informational services are engaged in both privately and by agencies of federal and state governments. A public role is essential, and it definitely must counteract damaging misinformation that may be put out privately.

Institutional Complexities

Still another consideration enters into the attractive principle that participants in our economy shall earn their food by means of rewards they get for their own economic performance.

It is that everyone who works (or manages, or invests) must therefore be paid off accurately in line with his contribution, and further that the products that are produced (food in this case) must be priced in line with cost of their production.

In other words, the principle carries a heavy institutional obligation. It is the obligation of accurate pricing of services contributed, and of product produced and sold. It permits no anti-competitive practices that distort the pricing process.

This condition is met most readily in an economy of small entrepreneurs selling their products in open markets. A soybean farmer who gets 30 bushels of beans per acre can live better than one whose harvests average 20 bushels. A cobbler who makes one pair of shoes in a day can buy more beefsteak than one who requires a day and a half.

Only a small part of the economy of today works that way. Instead, it is highly institutionalized. Many wage rates are negotiated in collective bargaining. Prices of most industrial products, including processed foods, are arrived at not in open auction but "administratively"—that is, by administrative decision in a corporate business. This is not to suggest that the many ways wages and prices are determined nowadays are suspect, or that they always violate the principle of reward commensurate with performance. But they could fall short of what is desired.

The institutional organization of the food marketing system is not neutral; it affects the performance of the system. Also, its complexity adds to difficulty in making accurate judgments about it.

Moreover, most processed food products are now turned out by firms that produce a large number of products by using large, costly capital installations. In other words, they are highly capitalized industrial firms. To say that products shall be priced equal to the cost of inputs used in their production is an empty phrase, because so much of the cost structure spreads over many products, or over an indeterminate number (of units) of a given product. Theoretical economists have tried to resolve the puzzle by inventing a formula for equating costs and returns "at the margin." But the marginal cost of producing an automobile, a cotton shirt, or a one-pound can of luncheon meat depends on whether it is the thousandth unit to come off the production line and be sold, or the ten-thousandth.

Moreover, as was observed above, every person and firm in the system tries to avoid having his services priced at the margin. We may teach in our economics classes that marginal-product pricing characterizes the marketing system for farm products. It would be more accurate to say that marginal pricing is carried on wherever it cannot be avoided.

Where, and how often, textbook-competitive pricing "at the margin" is engaged in is a question of empirical fact, to be determined only by observation. The principle being explained here is that persons and firms behave competitively only insofar as the competitive make-up of the system forces them to do so.

To repeat, these reminders of flaws and complexities in the system for marketing farm products are not to be interpreted as general disapproval of the existing system. They do warn against making easy judgments about whether our food system effectively and efficiently produces food for people.

Not Generalized, but Particularized, Judgments

This essay addresses the principles—the ethics—of our food system and is not itself an evaluation of the system now in operation. Question naturally arises, though, about how well our system of today conforms to the idealized criteria that have been established for it.

No all-inclusive, sweeping judgment will be offered. If one were necessary, it would be about the same as what the National Commission on Food Marketing said nearly 20 years ago. The system accomplishes wonders. It also has its faults, failures, imperfections.

So where does that leave us?

It leaves us first with the stern instruction that adverbs of general approval or disapproval of the marketing system as a whole are next to useless. No person or firm markets a composite of all foods. All marketing is of a particular commodity done by a single marketer at a given time and place. The appropriate question is how well that selected transaction is carried out.

A naval experience provides an analogy. Years ago a flag officer, confronted with an obvious miscarriage of justice at the expense of his own coxswain, blindly refused to intervene on grounds that "the Naval system of justice is the best in the world." No room for error in his pontification or cause for expression of concern.

Perhaps our markets are among the world's best. But if a Tennessee cattle feeder must accept below-market prices for his cattle owing to quiet collusion among local buyers, if a food processing industry is so oligopolistic as to overprice its product, if a small food firm is frozen out by a big competitor's sales below cost, the deficiency in each case is genuine and harmful irrespective of the praise that may be sung—perhaps with good cause—about the system as a whole.

It is possible that we expect too much of our marketing system. Even as the system becomes more complex, as noted above, and therefore harder to evaluate, we lift higher our expectations for it. Environmental concerns are an obvious example of a sensitivity that is now sharp. In earlier years it amounted to little more than making sure milk bottles were scalded before being filled. In a good resume of concepts and techniques in studying market performance, Marion and Handy write that not only are performance parameters now hard to estimate accurately, but performance has become "multidimensional."[3]

Probably everyone feels fairly comfortable about judging the quality of markets to the farm, where crops or livestock are sold in open trading and many buyers compete to buy a standard product. Marketing of that kind is textbook-traditional; it is understood well, and any flaws are readily observed.

But the largest part of the food marketing system is of a different makeup. At later stages firms are fewer, product is differentiated, and price is arrived at not in open auction but "administratively." This part of the marketing system is sometimes called merchandising-oriented. In technical economic terms, competition is imperfect. It is harder to judge performance of merchandising-oriented marketing than of traditional markets near the farm.

Eternal Vigilance to Monitor the System

Finally, the marketing system for food will be a system of food for people only if its performance is monitored to make sure it functions in that way.

The monitoring is necessarily done by government. The role of government is essentially to provide supporting services and set rules. Most of the services are of long standing and not generally in dispute. They have been catalogued often, most recently in a report, *Federal Marketing Programs in Agriculture: Issues and Options*.[4] The repertory is familiar: market information, grading and standardization, promotion, research, provision for group action (as farmer marketing cooperatives), and trade practice regulation including protection of safety in foods.

The strongest instrument of government is anti-trust regulation. It can forestall or correct the most blatant violations of the many-firm competition that the Food Commission regarded as integral to our food marketing system. Unless government does that, there can be no hope for a truly competitive food marketing system that achieves the idealized goal of food for people. If participants in marketing are allowed to act noncompetitively without restraint, either the goals will not be met, or a governmentally regulated system will eventually prove necessary.

Yet from a different point of view, the basic issue, in the final sense, is not one of private vs. public confrontation. Instead, we find here the ultimate contradiction: the wisest and most effective action taken by government to keep the food marketing system efficiently competitive will in fact reduce the governmental presence.

To put it differently, a competitive food marketing system can effectively do just about everything except provide for its own preservation. Only a public involvement will establish the terms of competition and institutional structure to enable the system to be essentially private yet act to provide food for people—and thereby earn its own continuity. A system that performs well is self sustaining without need for further public action.

Let it be said once more. To expect a marketing system driven by pursuit of private profit to provide food for people is nothing less than heroic. It is heroic because the participants individually seek other goals. They strive not merely for a normal or necessary profit but for more than that. As Anne Kreuger observes in an opening quotation, they are rent-seekers. They seek rent in any advantage they can get. Whether they are able to do so, collecting excess profit, or instead are mutually checkmated and act in the common interest, depends on the wisdom of the public action taken to keep the system competitive. It depends on whether a public concern is exercised responsibly. And the more responsibly that concern is exercised, the more private the system can be.

All of which testifies to the wisdom George Will expressed in an opening quotation. For the economic system to work someone must have good motives, public-spiritedness. In our democracy, that "someone" must somehow manifest the nobler instincts of all our citizens.

Notes

1. This paper is number 6 in the *Farm and Food System in Transition* series published by the Cooperative Extension Service Michigan State University, East Lansing, Michigan, 1983.

2. National Commission on Food Marketing, *Food from Farmer to Consumer* (Washington, D.C.: U.S. Government Printing Office, 1966), p. 105.

3. Bruce W. Marion and Charles R. Handy, *Market Performance: Concepts and Measures*, U.S. Department of Agriculture, Economic Research Service, Agricultural Economic Report no. 244, 1973.

4. Walter J. Armbruster, Dennis R. Henderson, and Ronald D. Knutson, *Federal Marketing Programs in Agriculture: Issues and Options* (Danville, Illinois: Interstate Printers, 1983).

The Unsettling of America[1]

Wendell Berry

One of the peculiarities of the white race's presence in America is how little intention has been applied to it. As a people, wherever we have been, we have never really intended to be. The continent is said to have been discovered by an Italian who was on his way to India. The earliest explorers were looking for gold, which was, after an early streak of luck in Mexico, always somewhere farther on. Conquests and foundings were incidental to this search—which did not, and could not, end until the continent was finally laid open in an orgy of gold-seeking in the middle of the last century. Once the unknown of geography was mapped, the industrial marketplace became the new frontier, and we continued, with largely the same motives and with increasing haste and anxiety, to displace ourselves—no longer with unity of direction, like a migrant flock, but more like the refugees from a broken ant hill. In our own time we have invaded foreign lands and the moon with the high-toned patriotism of the conquistadors, and with the same mixture of fantasy and avarice.

That is too simply put. It is substantially true, however, as a description of the dominant tendency in American history. The temptation, once that has been said, is to ascend altogether into rhetoric and inveigh equally against all our forebears and all present holders of office. To be just, however, it is necessary to remember that there has been another tendency: the tendency to stay put, to say, "No farther. This is the place." So far, this has been the weaker tendency, less glamorous, certainly less successful. It is also the older of these tendencies, having been the dominant one among the Indians.

The Indians did, of course, experience movements of population, but in general their relation to place was based upon old usage and association, upon inherited memory, tradition, veneration. The land was their homeland. The first and greatest American revolution, which has never been suspended, was the coming of people who did *not* look upon the land as a homeland. But there were always those among the newcomers who saw that they had come to a good place and who saw its domestic possibilities. Very early, for instance, there were men who wished to establish agricultural settlements rather than quest for gold or exploit the Indian trade. Later, we know that every advance of the frontier left behind families and communities who intended to remain and prosper where they were.

But we know also that these intentions have been almost systematically overthrown. Generation after generation, those who intended to remain and prosper where they were have been dispossessed and driven out, or subverted and exploited where they were, by those who were carrying out some version of the search for El Dorado. Time after time, in place after place, these conquerors have fragmented and demolished traditional communities, the beginnings of domestic cultures. They have always said that what they destroyed was outdated, provincial, and contemptible. And with alarming frequency they have been believed and trusted by their victims, especially when their victims were other white people.

If there is any law that has been consistently operative in American history, it is that the members of any *established* people or group or community sooner or later become "redskins"—that is, they become the designated victims of an utterly ruthless, officially sanctioned and subsidized exploitation. The colonists who drove off the Indians came to be intolerably exploited by their imperial governments. And that alien imperialism was thrown off only to be succeeded by a domestic version of the same thing; the class of independent small farmers who fought the war of independence has been exploited by, and recruited into, the industrial society until by now it is almost extinct. Today, the most numerous heirs of the farmers of Lexington and Concord are the little groups scattered all over the country whose names begin with "Save": Save Our Land, Save the Valley, Save Our Mountains, Save Our Streams, Save Our Farmland. As so often before, these are *designated* victims—people without official sanction, often without official friends, who are struggling to preserve their places, their values, and their lives as they know them and prefer to live them against the agencies of their own government which are using their own tax moneys against them.

The only escape from this destiny of victimization has been to "succeed"—that is, to "make it" into the class of exploiters, and then to remain so specialized and so "mobile" as to be unconscious of the effects of one's life or livelihood. This escape is, of course, illusory, for one man's producer is another's consumer, and even the richest and most mobile will soon find it hard to escape the noxious effluents and fumes of their various public services.

Let me emphasize that I am not talking about an evil that is merely contemporary or "modern," but one that is as old in America as the white man's presence here. It is an intention that was *organized* here almost from the start. "The New World," Bernard DeVoto wrote in *The Course of Empire*, "was a constantly expanding market. . . . Its value in gold was enormous but it had still greater value in that it expanded and integrated the industrial systems of Europe."

And he continues: "The first belt-knife given by a European to an Indian was a portent as great as the cloud that mushroomed over Hiroshima. . . . Instantly the man of 6000 B.C. was bound fast to a way of life that had developed seven and a half millennia beyond his own. He began to live better and he began to die."

The principal European trade goods were tools, cloth, weapons, ornaments, novelties, and alcohol. The sudden availability of these things produced a revolution that "affected every aspect of Indian life. The struggle for existence . . . became easier. Immemorial handicrafts grew obsolescent, then obsolete. Methods of hunting were transformed. So were methods—and the purposes—of war. As war became deadlier in purpose and armament a surplus of women developed, so that marriage customs changed and polygamy became common. The increased usefulness of women in the preparation of pelts worked to the same end. . . . Standards of wealth, prestige, and honor changed. The Indians acquired commercial values and developed business cults. They became more mobile. . . . "

> "In the sum it was cataclysmic. A culture was forced to change much faster than change could be adjusted to. All corruptions of culture produce breakdowns of morale, of communal integrity, and of personality, and this force was as strong as any other in the white man's subjugation of the red man."

I have quoted these sentences from DeVoto because, the obvious differences aside, he is so clearly describing a revolution that did not stop with the subjugation of the Indians, but went on to impose substantially the same catastrophe upon the small farms and the farm communities, upon the shops of small local tradesmen of all sorts, upon the workshops of independent craftsmen, and upon the households of citizens. It is a revolution that is still going on. The economy is still substantially that of the fur trade, still based on the same general kinds of commercial items: technology, weapons, ornaments, novelties, and drugs. The one great difference is that by now the revolution has deprived the mass of consumers of any independent access to the staples of life: clothing, shelter, food, even water. Air remains the only necessity that the average user can still get for himself, and the revolution has imposed a heavy tax on that by way of pollution. Commercial conquest is far more thorough and final than military defeat. The Indian became a redskin, not by loss in battle, but by accepting a dependence on traders that made *necessities* of industrial goods. This is not merely history. It is a parable.

DeVoto makes it clear that the imperial powers, having made themselves willing to impose this exploitive industrial economy upon the Indians, could not then keep it from contaminating their own best intentions: "More than four-fifths of the wealth of New France was furs, the rest was fish, and it had no agricultural wealth. One trouble was that whereas the crown's imperial policy required it to develop the country's agriculture, the crown's economy required the colony's furs, an adverse interest." And La Salle's dream of developing Louisiana (agriculturally and otherwise) was frustrated because "The interest of the court in Louisiana colonization was to secure a bridgehead for an attack on the silver mines of northern Mexico. . . . "

One cannot help but see the similarity between this foreign colonialism and the domestic colonialism that, by policy, converts productive farm, forest, and grazing lands into strip mines. Now, as then, we see the abstract values of an industrial economy preying upon the native productivity of land and people. The fur trade was only the first establishment on this continent of a mentality whose triumph is its catastrophe.

My purposes in beginning with this survey of history are (1) to show how deeply rooted in our past is the mentality of exploitation; (2) to show how fundamentally revolutionary it is; and (3) to show how crucial to our history—hence, to our own minds—is the question of how we will relate to our land. This question, now that the corporate revolution has so determinedly invaded the farmland, returns us to our oldest crisis.

We can understand a great deal of our history—from Cortés' destruction of Tenochtitlán in 1521 to the bulldozer attack on the coalfields four-and-a-half centuries later—by thinking of ourselves as divided into conquerors and victims. In order to understand our own time and predicament and the work that is to be done, we would do well to shift the terms and say that we are divided between exploitation and nurture. The first set of terms is too simple for the purpose because, in any given situation, it proposes to divide people into two mutually exclusive groups; it becomes complicated only when we are dealing with situations in succession—as when a colonist who persecuted the Indians then resisted persecution by the crown. The terms exploitation and nurture, on the other hand, describe a division not only between persons but also within persons. We are all to some extent the products of an exploitive society, and it would be foolish and self-defeating to pretend that we do not bear its stamp.

Let me outline as briefly as I can what seem to me the characteristics of these opposite kinds of mind. I conceive a strip-miner to be a model exploiter, and as a model nurturer I take the old-fashioned idea or ideal of a farmer. The exploiter is a specialist, an expert; the nurturer is not. The standard of the exploiter is efficiency; the standard of the nurturer is care. The exploiter's goal is money, profit; the nurturer's goal is health—his land's health, his own, his family's, his community's, his country's. Whereas the exploiter asks of a piece of land only how much and how quickly it can be made to produce, the nurturer asks a question that is much more complex and difficult: What is its carrying capacity: (That is: How much can be taken from it without diminishing it? What can it produce *dependably* for an indefinite time?) The exploiter wishes to earn as much as possible by as little work as possible; the nurturer expects, certainly, to have a decent living from his work, but his characteristic wish is to work *as well* as possible. The competence of the exploiter is in organization; that of the nurturer is in order—a human order, that is, that accommodates itself both to other order and to mystery. The exploiter typically serves an institution or organization; the nurturer serves land, household, community, place. The exploiter thinks in terms of numbers, quantities, "hard facts"; the nurturer in terms of character, condition, quality, kind.

It seems likely that all the "movements" of recent years have been representing various claims that nurture has to make against exploitation. The women's movement, for example, when its energies are most accurately placed, is arguing the cause of nurture; other times it is arguing the right of women to be exploiters—which men have no *right* to be. The exploiter is clearly the prototype of the "masculine" man—the wheeler-dealer whose "practical" goals require the sacrifice of flesh, feeling, and principle. The nurturer, on the other hand, has always passed with ease across the boundaries of the so-called sexual roles. Of necessity and without apology, the preserver of seed, the planter, becomes midwife and nurse. Breeder is always metamorphosing into brooder and back again. Over and over again, spring after spring, the questing mind, idealist and visionary, must pass through the planting to become nurturer of the real. The farmer, sometimes known as a husbandman, is by definition half mother; the only question is how good a mother he or she is. And the land itself is not mother or father only, but both. Depending on the crop and season, it is at one time receiver of seed, bearer and nurturer of young; at another, raiser of seed-stalk, bearer and shedder of seed. And in response to these changes, the farmer crosses back and forth from one zone of spousehood to another, first as planter and then as gatherer. Farmer and land are thus involved in a sort of dance in which the partners are always at opposite sexual poles, and the lead keeps changing: the farmer, as seed-bearer, causes growth; the land, as seed-bearer, causes the harvest.

The exploitive always involves the abuse or the perversion of nurture and ultimately its destruction. Thus, we saw how far the exploitive revolution had penetrated the official character when our recent secretary of agriculture remarked that "Food is a weapon." This was given a fearful symmetry indeed when, in discussing the possible use of nuclear weapons, a secretary of defense spoke of "palatable" levels of devastation. Consider the associations that have since ancient times clustered around the idea of food—associations of mutual care, generosity, neighborliness, festivity, communal joy, religious ceremony—and you will see that these two secretaries represent a cultural catastrophe. The concerns of farming and those of war, once thought to be diametrically opposed, have become identical. Here we have an example of men who have been made vicious, not presumably by nature or circumstances, but by their *values*.

Food is *not* a weapon. To use it as such—to foster a mentality willing to use it as such—is to prepare, in the human character and community, the destruction of the sources of food. The first casualties of the exploitive revolution are character and community. When those fundamental integrities are devalued and broken, then perhaps it is inevitable that food will be looked upon as a weapon, just as it is inevitable that the earth will be looked upon as fuel and people as numbers or machines. But character and community—that is, culture in the broadest, richest sense—constitute, just as much as nature, the source of food. Neither nature nor people alone can produce human sustenance, but only the two together, culturally wedded. The poet Edwin Muir said it unforgettably:

Men are made of what is made,
The meat, the drink, the life, the corn,
Laid up by them, in them reborn.
And self-begotten cycles close
About our way; indigenous art
And simple spells make unafraid

The haunted labyrinths of the heart
And with our wild succession braid
The resurrection of the rose.

To think of food as a weapon, or of a weapon as food, may give an illusory security and wealth to a few, but it strikes directly at the life of all.

The concept of food-as-weapon is not surprisingly the doctrine of a Department of Agriculture that is being used as an instrument of foreign political and economic speculation. This militarizing of food is the greatest threat so far raised against the farmland and the farm communities of this country. If present attitudes continue, we may expect government policies that will encourage the destruction, by overuse, of farmland. This, of course, has already begun. To answer the official call for more production—evidently to be used to bait or bribe foreign countries—farmers are plowing their waterways and permanent pastures; lands that ought to remain in grass are being planted in row crops. Contour plowing, crop rotation, and other conservation measures seem to have gone out of favor or fashion in official circles and are practiced less and less on the farm. This exclusive emphasis on production will accelerate the mechanization and chemicalization of farming, increase the price of land, increase overhead and operating costs, and thereby further diminish the farm population. Thus the tendency, if not the intention, of Mr. Butz's confusion of farming and war, is to complete the deliverance of American agriculture into the hands of corporations.

The cost of this corporate totalitarianism in energy, land, and social disruption will be enormous. It will lead to the exhaustion of farmland and farm culture. Husbandry will become an extractive industry; because maintenance will entirely give way to production, and fertility of the soil will become a limited, unrenewable resource like coal or oil.

This may not happen. It *need* not happen. But it is necessary to recognize that it *can* happen. That it can happen is made evident not only by the words of such men as Mr. Butz, but more clearly by the large-scale industrial destruction of farmland already in progress. If it does happen, we are familiar enough with the nature of American salesmanship to know that it will be done in the name of the starving millions, in the name of liberty, justice, democracy, and brotherhood, and to free the world from communism. We must,I think, be prepared to see, and to stand by, the truth: that the land should not be destroyed for *any* reason, not even for any apparently good reason. We must be prepared to say that enough food, year after year, is possible only for a limited number of people, and that this possibility can be preserved only by the steadfast, knowledgeable *care* of those people. Such "crash programs" as apparently have been contemplated by the Department of Agriculture in recent years will, in the long run, cause more starvation than they can remedy.

Meanwhile, the dust clouds rise again over Texas and Oklahoma. "Snirt" is falling in Kansas. Snow drifts in Iowa and the Dakotas are black with blown soil. The fields lose their humus and porosity, become less retentive of water, depend more on pesticides, herbicides, chemical fertilizers. Bigger tractors become necessary because the compacted soils are harder to work—and their greater weight further compacts the soil. More and bigger machines, more chemical and methodological shortcuts are needed because of the shortage of manpower on the farm—and the problems of overcrowding and unemployment increase in the cities. It is estimated that it now costs (by erosion) two bushels of Iowa topsoil to grow one bushel of corn. It is variously estimated that from five to twelve calories of fossil fuel energy are required to produce one calorie of hybrid corn energy. An official of the National Farmers Union says that "a farmer who earns $10,000 to $12,000 a year typically leaves an estate valued at about $320,000"—which means that when that farm is financed again, either by a purchaser or by an heir (to pay the inheritance taxes), it simply cannot support its new owner and pay for itself. And the *Progressive Farmers* predicts the disappearance of 200,000 to 400,000 farms each year during the next twenty years if the present trend continues.

The first principle of the exploitive mind is to divide and conquer. And surely there has never been a people more ominously and painfully divided than we are—both against each other and within ourselves. Once the revolution of exploitation is under way, statesmanship and craftsmanship are gradually replaced by salesmanship. Its stock in trade in politics is to sell despotism and avarice as freedom and democracy. In business it sells sham and frustration as luxury and satisfaction. The "constantly expanding market" first opened in the New World by the fur traders is still expanding—no longer so much by expansions of territory or population, but by the calculated outdating, outmoding, and degradation of goods and by the hysterical self-dissatisfaction of consumers that is indigenous to an exploitive economy.

This gluttonous enterprise of ugliness, waste, and fraud thrives in the disastrous breach it has helped to make between our bodies and our souls. As a people, we have lost sight of the profound communion—even the union—of the inner with the outer life. Confucius said: "If a man have not order within him / He can not spread order about him. . . . " Surrounded as we are by evidence of the disorders of our souls and our world, we feel the strong truth in those words as well as the possibility of healing that is in them. We see the likelihood that our surroundings, from our clothes to our countryside, are the products of our inward life—our spirit, our vision—as much as they are products of nature and work. If this is true, then we cannot live as we do and be as we would like to be. There is nothing more absurd, to give an example that is only apparently trivial, than the millions who wish to live in luxury and idlenesss and yet be slender and good-looking. We have millions, too, whose livelihoods, amusements, and comforts are all destructive, who nevertheless wish to live in a healthy environment; they want to run their recreational engines in clean, fresh air. There is now, in fact, no "benefit" that is not associated with disaster. That is because power can be disposed morally or harmlessly only by thoroughly unified characters and communities.

What caused these divisions? There are no doubt many causes, complex both in themselves and in their interaction. But pertinent to all of them, I think, is our attitude toward work. The growth of the exploiters' revolution on this continent has been accompanied by the growth of the idea that work is beneath human dignity, particularly any form of hand work. We have made it our overriding ambition to escape work, and as a consequence have debased work until it is only fit to escape from. We have debased the products of work and have been, in turn, debased by them. Out of this contempt for work arose the idea of a nigger: at first some person, and later some thing, to be used to relieve us of the burden of work. If we began by making niggers of people, we have ended by making a nigger of the world. We have taken the irreplaceable energies and materials of the world and turned them into jimcrack "labor-saving devices." We have made of the rivers and oceans and winds niggers to carry away our refuse, which we think we are too good to dispose of decently ourselves. And in doing this to the world that is our common heritage and bond, we have returned to making niggers of people: we have become each other's niggers.

But is work something that we have a right to escape? And can we escape it with impunity? We are probably the first entire people ever to think so. All the ancient wisdom that has come down to us counsels otherwise. It tells us that work is necessary to us, as much a part of our condition as mortality; that good work is our salvation and our joy; that shoddy or dishonest or self-serving work is our curse and our doom. We have tried to escape the sweat and sorrow promised in Genesis—only to find that, in order to do so, we must foreswear love and excellence, health and joy.

Thus we can see growing out of our history a condition that is physically dangerous, morally repugnant, ugly. Contrary to the blandishments of the salesmen, it is not particularly comfortable or happy. It is not even affluent in any meaningful sense, because its abundance is dependent on sources that are rapidly exhausted by its methods. To see these things is to come up against the question: Then what *is* desirable?

One possibility is just to tag along with the fantasists in government and industry who would have us believe that we can pursue our ideals of affluence, comfort, mobility, and leisure indefinitely. This curious faith is predicated on the notion that we will soon develop unlimited new sources of energy: domestic oil fields, shale oil, gasified coal, nuclear power, solar energy, and so on. This is fantastical because the basic cause of the energy crisis is not scarcity; it is moral ignorance and weakness of character. We don't know *how* to use energy, or what to use it *for*. And we cannot restrain ourselves. Our time is characterized as much by the abuse and waste of human energy as it is by the abuse and waste of fossil fuel energy. Nuclear power, if we are to believe its advocates, is presumably going to be well used by the same mentality that has egregiously devalued and misapplied man- and womanpower. If we had an unlimited supply of solar or wind power, we would use that destructively, too, for the same reasons.

Perhaps all of those sources of energy are going to be developed. Perhaps all of them can sooner or later be developed without threatening our survival. But not all of them together can guarantee our survival, and they cannot define what is desirable. We will not find those answers in Washington, D.C., or in the laboratories of oil companies. In order to find them, we will have to look closer to ourselves.

I believe that the answers are to be found in our history: in its until now subordinate tendency of settlement, of domestic permanence. This was the ambition of thousands of immigrants; it is formulated eloquently in some of the letters of Thomas Jefferson; it was the dream of the freed slaves; it was written into law in the Homestead Act of 1862. There are few of us whose families have not at some time been moved to see its vision and to attempt to enact its possibility. I am talking about the idea that as many as possible should share in the ownership of the land and thus be bound to it by economic interest, by the investment of love and work, by family loyalty, by memory and tradition. How much land this should be is a question, and the answer will vary with geography. The Homestead Act said 160 acres. The freedmen of the 1860s hoped for forty. We know that, particularly in other countries, families have lived decently on far fewer acres than that.

The old idea is still full of promise. It is potent with healing and with health. It has the power to turn each person away from the big-time promising and planning of the government, to confront in himself, in the immediacy of his own circumstances and whereabouts, the question of what methods and ways are best. It proposes an economy of necessities rather than an economy based upon anxiety, fantasy, luxury, and idle wishing. It proposes the independent, free-standing citizenry that Jefferson thought to be the surest safeguard of democratic liberty. And perhaps most important of all, it proposes an agriculture based upon intensive work, local energies, care, and long-living communities—that is, to state the matter from a consumer's point of view: a dependable, long-term food supply.

This is a possibility that is obviously imperiled—by antipathy in high places, by adverse public fashions and attitudes, by the deterioration of our present farm communities and traditions, by the flawed education and the inexperience of our young people. Yet it alone can promise us the continuity of attention and devotion without which the human life of the earth is impossible.

Sixty years ago, in another time of crisis, Thomas Hardy wrote these stanzas:

Only a man harrowing clods
    In a slow silent walk
With an old horse that stumbles and nods
    Half asleep as they stalk.

Only thin smoke without flame
    From the heaps of couch-grass;
Yet this will go onward the same
    Though Dynasties pass.

Today most of our people are so conditioned that they do not wish to harrow clods either with an old horse or with a new tractor. Yet Hardy's vision has come to be more urgently true than ever. The great difference these sixty years have made is that, though we feel that this work *must* go onward, we are not so certain that it will. But the care of the earth is our most ancient and most worthy and, after all, our most pleasing responsibility. To cherish what remains of it, and to foster its renewal, is our only legitimate hope.

Notes

1. This paper appears in Wendell Berry, *The Unsettling of America: Culture and Agriculture* (published by Avon Books, New York, in cooperation with Sierra Club Books, San Francisco, 1978. Copyright 1977 by Wendell Berry.) Reprinted by permission of the author and Sierra Club Books.

Science, Technology, and the Farm Crisis

Richard P. Haynes

THE FARM POPULATION IN THE U.S. TODAY is less than three million, one tenth of what it was seventy years ago. And there are only a third as many farms. The owner-operated full-time family farm has been the hardest hit. Many have left farming unwillingly because of economic difficulties. This "farm crisis" is really part of a long-term trend that is the result of national policy to improve farming in the U.S.

It is debateable whether the benefits of this policy have been fairly distributed. The good results are an abundant and low-cost food supply, higher incomes for successful farmers, and more on-farm consumption of off-farm products, hence, more off-farm jobs. The bad results are devastated rural communities, urban ghettos, and dislocated farmers.

This trend is not unique to the United States. Is it, on balance, socially desirable? There are two camps—"industrializers" and "agrarianizers."[1] In what follows, I consider part of the debate between those who would industrialize agricultural production and those who support the agrarian ideal of more traditional small-scale family farming (and ranching). I take up the agrarianizers' side of the debate second, coming to it from a criticism of the industrializers' side. The place to begin then, is with a look at the dominant paradigm of the industrializers.

Industrializers

This paradigm functions by collecting and linking various research goals. Some of these goals dominate agricultural research. Others are merely myths used to justify policy, even though the resulting policies have "unintended consequences" and so fail to promote the research goals in question.[2]

The industrializers' paradigm does more than set the research agenda, however. In addition, it defines what are considered to be problems and the range of acceptable or orthodox solutions in agricultural production and marketing. It thus drives the research and development agenda in agriculture, and drives out alternatives.[3]

The agrarianizers would have us set aside this paradigm in favor of preserving a farm structure which included smaller-scale production units in far greater numbers than they exist in today. Two arguments are commonly given to support the agrarianizers position. I will consider these briefly and add a third. The first two arguments turn respectively on the points that the quality of life in rural communities is significantly better if the economy of that community is based on owner-operated farms, and that the U.S. may lose food self-sufficiency if the industrializing trend results in production moving to third world countries. The third argument turns on a profound problem of the industrializers' paradigm; namely, that the industrializers' approach to agricultural research, production, and marketing is not sustainable. It is destroying our national production resources in the name of efficiency. If this challenge succeeds, then public sector agricultural research has a responsibility to make radical changes in its research agenda. That agenda will need to be changed in what might well be an agrarian direction. In closing I indicate what some of these changes could look like.

Research Goals and Agricultural Development

The Industrializers' Paradigm

The agricultural subgovernment in the U.S. commands a significant amount of resources and purports to serve a number of different sectors.[4] In general, agriculture wants to ensure the conditions for the profitable operation of farming enterprises by seeking stable domestic markets and prices, while expanding foreign markets. But within this framework, different constituencies vary about how their individual goals can be served by research.

Progressive farmers generally want technologies that increase yields and can be controlled by the operator. Labor-intensive technologies are usually rejected unless a cheap and controllable labor market is available. Consumers want a cheap, wholesome, and convenient food supply, and, indirectly, export goods to balance foreign payments. Agricultural industries and their employees want markets for inputs and cheap raw material to which they can add value for the market.

These various and potentially competing goals are integrated by a philosophy which determines the methods by which the goals are to be realized, including the type of technology that will be developed and employed and the criterion for evaluating it. Generally, technologies are developed that are commercially exploitable and that increase the efficiency of production. The criterion for efficiency is primarily an economic one—the ratio of the value of goods produced to the cost of inputs used to produce them. One technology is more efficient than another if that ratio is higher. When employed as a criterion for research and technology development carried out by researchers fragmented by disciplines, efficiency tends to translate into the development of technologies that increase yields per unit of space employed.

This type of efficiency does not always produce desirable results. Those that use it must be able to control costs and market prices, which usually only very large producers can do. So the benefits are not equally distributed among small and large producers. Further, these technologies often have unnoticed negative impacts that are felt outside of the production system, but the costs of those impacts are not included in the evaluation of the technology's economic efficiency. These externalized costs ("externalities") are often not seen because of the failure to allocate adequate resources to impact monitoring. Consider the following examples of specific externalities.

—Capital-intensive intervention technologies are generally designed to import relatively uniform conditions into productive systems. This results in ignoring resources that are unique to local ecosystem production sites in favor of resources that are brought into the system. Imported resource utilization may be inefficient if measured in terms of energy trade-offs.

—Some of the resources of ecosystems are assumed to be constant backgrounds, when in fact intervention technologies may deplete these background resources. For example, good soil structure and biota may be lost through the use of heavy traction equipment compacting the soil, chemical inputs, or through erosion.

—Ecosystem stability may also be lost as a result of monocropping practices or pest-control practices. Natural plant predator and pest predator balances may be lost through interventions that seek to control pests through extermination. The resulting development of new pesticide-resistant varieties may exclude the crop from the system, unless new intervention technologies are developed to control for a new generation of pests. Polyculture production systems often avoid these problems, but most technologies are designed for monocropping systems.

—Many practices also threaten waterways and off-production

sites through soil transportation, drinking water supplies by pesticide runoffs, and water table levels by excessive drawdown from deep aquifer irrigation.

—Another of the major drawbacks to current agricultural practices is the loss of genetic diversity. The tendency to concentrate on a limited number of selected varieties is gradually reducing the number of varieties used in crop production. The continued availability of these varieties has a number of advantages. They represent agricultural resources that can be produced on-site, and which can utilize more efficiently other on-site resources, thus reducing dependency on purchased inputs. Varieties compatible with a diversity of growing conditions are valuable resources to ensure against production system instability.

—Genetic diversity is also valued for the role that a large gene pool can play in engineering new plant varieties that are more compatible with intervention technologies, e.g. resistance to herbicides. These technologies are often attended with special problems: The new variety can be patented and its access controlled commercially, a new technology may be required when herbicide resistant weeds develop, and the technology for preserving seed varieties is itself selective, resulting in gene pool decline.

What about the negative social impacts of research attuned to the industrializers' paradigm? By social impacts I mean the impacts on social structures rather than the direct impact on individuals. Are there valuable social resources that are being threatened by our industrializing policies, such as the loss of full-time, owner-operated farms?

There is dispute about whether farmers should be counted as a valuable resource. The question of the value of the full-time, owner operated farm is controversial and laden with sentiment. I will consider briefly three arguments for preserving the full-time, owner-operated farm. The third argument will use the criticisms of the dominant paradigm given above as support for a special version of the agrarianizers' position.

The Quality of Rural Living Argument for Agrarianism

It has been argued that there is an important connection between the quality of rural life and the viability of owner-operated farms; hence, the farm crisis is a general rural crisis. Classical postwar studies tried to establish that the quality of life in rural communities surrounded by independent farmers is superior to life in rural communities where farming operations are linked to larger industries.[5] However valid these studies may be, they do not consider comparisons between agriculturally based rural communities and rural communities dependent upon a nonagriculturally based economy. Studies have shown that alternative economic bases can be supplied through industrialization and the rise of cottage industries and services.[6] Thus the argument is inconclusive.

The Food Self-Reliance Argument for Agrarianism

Some fear that the trends in ownership concentration and the vertical integration of producers and processors and input manufacturers will gradually shift agricultural production outside of the U.S. Lower labor costs in third world countries will favor this trend. If that shift is made after the demise of most of our producers, the U.S. will lose its food self-reliance and be vulnerable to interruptions of supply or increased food costs. Such a loss would be especially difficult to repair if we have lost a basic resource—knowledgeable producers who are willing to produce at a relatively low income because they have their way of life, and because they can cut some of their consumption costs by producing goods for themselves. While this argument has some plausibility, its critics point out that current trends do not point to a total elimination of U.S. food producers and production efforts. Thus the fear is unwarranted.[7]

The Caring Farmer–Sustainable Food Supply Argument

The third argument turns on the unsustainability of current industrialized agriculture. It focuses on the resource-conserving producer, the caring farmer. The reasoning begins with the claim that farms operated by full-time resident owners have a greater potential for resource conservation than absentee owners, if several conditions are met: The resident owner-operator has a commitment to a long-term relationship to the farm; derives considerable satisfaction not merely from independence, but from participating in the "healthy" functioning of a productive ecosystem; and has the means for keeping the unit economically viable.

The caring farmer cares about the health of the farm ecosystem, and practices that care as a way of life. By farming and living in a manner that preserves the resources unique to the production site, the caring farmer reduces both input costs, and off-farm negative impacts. From the point of view of conserving national resources, a caring resident operator is more likely to be able to observe and understand the production ecosystem needs and to know how to integrate them with the household needs.

This type of farming and its advantages have been described by a number of writers.[8] But to what degree does this, perhaps imagined, class of caring farmers coincide with the class of farm operators that are disappearing and the agrarian tradition that they allegedly represent?

While there is much that is mythical about the role of the agrarian tradition in the United States, there is also much of substance to this tradition, especially the role that experience plays in learning, the type of knowledge it acquires, and the manner in which it transmits this knowledge. Site-specific knowledge transmitted on-site in the context of a strong identification with that site may be essential for a success as a caring farmer. People who grow up on farms not only know things that others have to learn from those who grow up on farms, but they have a different way of identifying with that knowledge. Who will train the future farmers when all the educators grow up in the city? Thus, full-time owner-operators may be the best human resource for staffing a changed conception of good farming.

New Research Goals and the Farm Crisis Response

I have argued that the adoption of the technologies developed under the paradigm that has dominated agricultural research in the U.S. has had serious negative consequences in depleting national productive resources. This is largely because the criterion for evaluating technologies is a very narrow conception of economic efficiency. This conception allows for the externalization of the negative impacts we identified above. I have also argued that agricultural production should be carried out by farmers who care about these negative impacts and are in a position to produce accordingly. This argument becomes an argument for agrarianism if the full-time owner operator is the best candidate for becoming a caring farmer, given a change in the priorities accorded to the various goals of the agricultural policy. What implications would a change in priorities have for a shift in research goals, and how likely is such a shift to occur?

Alternative research agendas dedicated to preserving an agrarian tradition of caring farmers have been articulated by a number of writers. Some institutions, mostly private, have developed research programs supporting them. But these concerns have penetrated the agricultural subgovernment only peripherally. The potential is there for greater penetration.

The factors favoring greater penetration are public sentiment that supports the "family farm," increased public concern about environmental impacts, and a serious shrinking of the number of traditional clientele served directly by the agricultural subgovernment. These factors have not been integrated into a new policy. For example, responses to the farm crisis from the subgovernment have been of three sorts: assistance to soften the blow to affected families and to facilitate the transition to a different type of employment, management counseling to increase operator business skills, and examination of alternative agricultural commodity production options. None of these responses specifically addresses the problem of helping the caring farmer. The potential is there, however, for a longer-range policy of research and development that integrates the goals of family farmers, environmentalists, and agricultural profit seekers.

—The demand for more environmental-impact-monitoring information could be integrated with support for the family farm by efforts to support the caring farmer model. In this way, impact-monitoring could become the responsibility of the caring family farmer and so be integrated with agricultural production rather than remaining merely a regulatory responsibility of someone outside of production.

—Research on economic survival strategies can be better integrated with environmental policies by stressing the development of outlets for products that are identified in the marketplace by specific features related to their particular production site.[9] Wyoming range-fed "lean" beef, Vermont sharp cheddar cheeses, and Washington State apples are three different sorts of products with marketed production-site identities. The possibilities for even more localized market-identity appeal are clear.

—Research on farms as systems, if carried out to include the ecosystem, can help integrate what are now conflicting environmental and entrepreneurial goals.

—In the same way, general research to reduce input costs should complement research on increasing the variety of outputs, including methods of integrating the farming system with community and bioregional needs. The caring farmer could draw income from a variety of economic sources, including the maintenance of wildlife corridors to help preserve threatened species; the lease of hunting, picnic and camping rights; retreats and educational projects; and on-site research and monitoring grant or contract funded projects.

—There is also a need to develop small-scale farming technologies that can be used in connection with crops grown in (annual or perennial) polyculture.

While research may facilitate changes in the farm structure by providing the kind of information that can make caring farming more economically viable, the public must support these changes with a more realistic understanding of the social and environmental costs of various farming practices, and they must make changes in social policy that reward good farming practices. These rewards can be given directly through subsidies restricted to need, or indirectly by paying caring farmers for other services, and valuing their products more highly in their food-buying habits. Such support can help to bring together sustainable uses of agricultural production resources and the profitable production of food and fiber. It can help to ameliorate the terms of agricultural commerce and minimize the conflicts caused by the present dominant paradigm of agricultural product research and development. It can help make our food production activities socially regenerative.

Notes

1. In using these labels, I am borrowing from an article by Richard S. Kirkendall, "Up to Now: A History of American Agriculture from Jefferson to Revolution to Crisis," *Agriculture and Human Values* 4, no. 1 (Winter, 1987):4–26. Agrarianizers normally appeal to Jefferson's visions for America, a democracy based on the independent family farmer. Justin Morrill may be considered to be one of the chief spokesmen for the industrializers. Morrill wanted manufacturing to be the chief base for the American economy. Oddly, one of his reasons for opposing the Jeffersonian vision was his criticism of the inefficiencies of the American farmer, based on the fact that they so often depleted their soil base and then moved on westward. The caring farmer vision that I introduce later in this paper does not really fit into either paradigm. It is, in fact, more consistent with indigenous agricultural practices, which were replaced by the agrarianizers as they took control of Indian lands.

2. Don F. Hadwiger, "Evaluating Agricultural Policy," in R. Haynes and R. Lanier, eds., *Agriculture, Change, and Human Values* (Gainesville, Fla.: Humanities and Agriculture Program, University of Florida, 1984).

3. The existence of the industrializers' paradigm and its historical role in accelerating industrializing trends have been discussed in a number of studies. See, for example, Kenneth A. Dahlberg, "Towards a Typology for Evaluating Conventional and Alternative Agricultural Systems and Research Strategies," paper presented at Sixth International Scientific Conference, IFOAM, Santa Cruz, Calif. August, 1986; Charles E. Rosenberg, *No Other Gods: Science and American Thought* (Baltimore: Johns Hopkins Press, 1976); Margaret W. Rossiter, *The Emergence of Agricultural Sciences: Justus Liebig and the Americans, 1840-1880* (New Haven and London: Yale University Press, 1975); David D. Danbom, *The Resisted Revolution* (Ames, Iowa: Iowa State University Press, 1979); Jane Knowles, "Science and Farm Woman's Work: The Agrarian Origins of Home Economics Extension," *Agriculture and Human Values* 2, no. 1 (Winter, 1985); Lawrence Busch and William B. Lacy, *Science, Agriculture and the Politics of Research* (Boulder: Westview Press, 1983); Frederick H. Buttel, "The Land-grant System: A

Sociological Perspective on Value Conflicts and Ethical Issues," *Agriculture and Human Values*, 3, no. 2 (Spring, 1985); John Perkins, *Insects Experts and the Insecticide Crisis* (New York: Plenum Books, 1982); and Stanislaus J. Dundon, "Hidden Obstacles to Creativity in Agricultural Science," in R. Haynes and R. Lanier, *Agriculture, Change, and Human Values*.

4. See, for example. USDA/CRIS, *Manual of Classifications of Agricultural and Forestry Research* (Washington, D.C.: USDA/CRIS, 1970. Rev. III, 1978).

5. Walter Goldschmidt, *As You Sow, Three Studies in the Social Consequences of Agribusiness* (Totawa, N.J.: Allanheld, Osmun, 1978). Part I was published in 1947.

6. See, for example, William L. Flinn, "Communities and Their Relationships to Agrarian Values, " in Don F. Hadwiger and Peter G. Brown, eds. *Rural Policy Problems: Changing Dimensions* (Lexington: Heath and Co., 1982).

7. See, for example, Francis Moore Lappe and Joseph Collins, *Food First* (New York: Ballantine Books, 1978), esp. Chapter 34.

8. See, for example, the papers in Wes Jackson, Wendell Berry, and Bruce Coleman, *Meeting the Expectations of the Land* (San Francisco: Northpoint Press, 1984).

9. For a description of "ecodevelopment" in relationship to coffee production and marketing in Mexico, and the obstacles to eco-marketing produced by the standardizing effects of the internationalization of capital, see Theodore Downing, "Ecodevelopment: An Alternative Future," *International Affairs* 37, no. 2 (Summer, 1978); and Theodore Downing, "The Internationalization of Capital," *International Affairs*, 41, no. 3 (Fall, 1982).

Moral Conflict in Agriculture

Conquest or Moral Coevolution?[1]

Philip T. Shepard

PEOPLE REACT TO FOOD AND FARMING controversy in ways shaped by background images, borrowings from common culture, especially from science and politics. But as long as crucial assumptions remain in the background, unobserved and unexamined, all of us are prone to exacerbating our conflicts, to talking past one another, to begging critical questions, and to further polarizing opinions and feelings. To meet the moral challenges posed by controversy, then, we must bring into the foreground much of what has been background and re-examine many of those habits of thought and disciplinary norms that have been taken for granted as part of the "normal" course of political and academic discussion.

Facts and Values

Agricultural scientists, among others, have taken for granted a distinction between facts and values. Facts are seen as irrevocable descriptions of the actual state of the world, the objective and ultimate touchstones of science, independent of opinion and preference. Values, however, are subjective; they are the mud in the water that stops us from seeing clearly to the bottom of things. To resolve our disagreements, then, we must clear away the value questions that muddy up our attempts to get at the facts and use them rationally to solve our problems. Support for this view comes from norms of academic and scientific specialization that divide problems into categories of available expertise. To make good use of experts in problem solving, we are enjoined to distinguish the job of the scientist from those of ethicists and policy-makers.

Unfortunately, the problems agriculture faces don't always conform to a neat dichotomy of facts and values. Some questions about persistent pesticides, for example, are "trans-scientific"—they can be raised in strictly scientific terms, but they cannot be answered without importing extra-scientific assumptions that are laden with values.[2] At very low doses what will be the response to exposure in a large sample of humans? Because of ethical constraints on experimenting with human subjects, data available on the dose-response relationship for various persistent pesticides are drawn largely from animal experiments. To get a measurable response, practical limits on the sample size that can be studied force the experimenter to use doses much higher than are likely to be encountered by humans.

Two basic problems arise as a result. First, how to extrapolate known dose-response data from animals to humans at comparable dose levels. Second, how to determine the effects of very low doses. In the absence of an ethically and technically feasible way of getting direct and unambiguous data, known data must be extrapolated to the low end of the dose-response curve. Accordingly, decisions on acceptable exposure levels will depend on judgments of both the likelihood and the seriousness of the hazards involved. So trans-scientific questions are neither strictly factual nor strictly value questions. To answer them soundly, facts and values must be integrated into one framework in which neither constituent is more basic than the other.

Ignoring trans-scientific questions will not make them go away. Nor will suspending judgment avoid bearing responsibility. The use of persistent pesticides eliminates in effect the difference between disbelief and suspension of belief in harmful consequences of low-level exposure. Both fail to guard against hazards.

The situation is like that of an official contemplating whether or not to issue a storm warning on the basis of weather bureau reports of tornado conditions nearby. If the warning is not given and a tornado strikes, intellectual abstention on the issue of imminent danger will have had the same consequence as outright disbelief.

When the issue is thus sufficiently pressing and vital, as has often seemed to be the case with persistent pesticides, the decision maker's hand is forced and the rationally defensible options shrink to belief or disbelief; suspending belief becomes tantamount to shirking responsibility.

In the case of persistent pesticides, as in many others, scientists share a collective responsibility to accurately and impartially inform the public of the results of relevant scientific investigations. Since there are trans-scientific questions involved, however, the scientist who rigidly segregates facts and values will not be able to meet this responsibility. To show the relevance of scientific knowledge to the controversy over persistent pesticides, dose-response data must be related to value laden questions, such as the seriousness of the possible hazards and the appropriateness of various decision rules.[3] If scientists refuse to do so, then the collective responsibility they share will go begging.

Images of Moral Conflict

Reticence to confront normative questions is by no means peculiar to agricultural scientists. Many others as well are put off by images of moral conflict. First, by images of competition—a "zero sum" game—in which someone must lose and, usually, lose big. Second, by images of groundlessness—though the battle be joined, there is no ground to stand on and fight; differences of opinion as to what is right or good, desirable or valuable, cannot be "put to the test" but like matters of taste are seen as free-floating, idiosyncratic, and irrational.

Winners and Losers

Thinking of moral conflict as competition, we look for winners and losers. Eventually some people must prevail in a moral dispute, and when they do the losers become the "bad guys." Thus no one can afford to approve of their opponents or admit their own mistakes, let alone defeat. With the personal stakes so high, attitudes become polarized and commitments hardened, risk and vulnerability are avoided, and we become more and more defensive, less and less able to cope with human differences, less open to others and less able to work toward resolution.

In our defensiveness, we see the issues in categorical terms. Pesticides, for example, are defended as wholly positive—with them we can feed the world, without them we will starve; or attacked as wholly negative—to use them is to poison the environment and ultimately ourselves. Thus we sacrifice both accurate scrutiny of facts and clear understanding of values. With rational recourse blocked, the games of "black and white," "us and them," "find the culprit," and "pin the blame" become self-perpetuating.

If the foregoing depiction seems uncomfortably close to much of the conduct of recent agricultural controversy, then we should ask where we have gone wrong and how we may forestall and counteract the polarization and defensiveness engendered. It doesn't help to look to new technology to remove the sources of conflict, on the grounds that technology is above morality and politics. This response ignores whether new technologies have been implicated in the issues raised and begs the question of the value-neutrality of science and technology.[4]

Instead of avoidance, we need to explore the prospects of coping directly with moral conflict in agriculture. We can begin by trying to see an outcome without winners and losers. If we can, then we may be able to adopt a different image of moral conflict.

Moral Coevolution

In nature, species coevolve. Each depends on contact or interchange with the others to complete the cycling of material and energy on which all depend. New adaptations in one species, thus, induce complementary adaptations in others. Only rarely and over considerable time do species disappear altogether.

Something similar occurs between moral viewpoints within a political culture. The themes championed in one view derive meaning, in part, from the contrast with other views. While contact between views can reinforce identity and solidarity, it also provides the opportunity and impetus to strengthen the views by articulating specific, detailed positions and supporting arguments. But the survival of a view does not depend on any one specific position, any more than the survival of a species depends on any one of its members. If one position fails, others can be put forward by reinterpreting core themes.

Revision is usually feasible because the value themes at the core of a viewpoint are less determinate than positions addressed to a specific situation or issue.[5] The theme of productivity in conventional agricultural outlooks, for example, can be interpreted in terms of yield per acre or net return for the whole farm. It can be read on the narrow basis of farm produce, or, more broadly, as including farm-based services (recreation, education) or even external costs such as from field runoff water. Similarly, themes like sustainablity, love of the land, and community have a range of workable interpretations within each of several viewpoints.

In the evolution of moral viewpoints, survival is not very solid assurance of exclusive moral correctness, and dominance reflects only a temporary advantage over competitors. To be sure, there is struggle and confrontation as well as interdependence and cooperation, but competition is not eliminated. Some less favored views will come back with more favorable interpretations of their core values. Success is always relative to the objections and preferences of other views—objections that can be overcome both directly by argument and persuasion, and indirectly by revisions that render the view less objectionable.

There is, then, an alternative image of moral conflict in which many viable outlooks evolve in complementary ways, i.e. they coevolve. Many viewpoints survive the selective pressure of moral confrontation; many can attain prominence simultaneously. Indeed, it could be argued that a healthy political culture requires such a diversity of moral views and that all members confront moral conflicts in that common environment, i.e. as lay persons, not as experts.

Pluralism vs. Relativism

If a pluralist image of moral conflict is available, then why not use it? The usual answer equates pluralism with relativism: if more than one viewpoint can be morally correct, then how can there be a difference between right and wrong? Moral pluralism, by rejecting moral absolutism, seems to lead to moral relativism.

The ethical dilemma between absolutism and relativism is reinforced by modern scientific culture, particularly the assumption that meaningful questions have one and only one correct answer. The principal vehicle for this assumption is the concept of truth as correspondence: a claim is correct if and only if it corresponds to an actual state of affairs in the world. If what we say matches the way the world is, then it is true, otherwise not. Thus it is assumed not only that there is some way the world really is, but also that there is only one way the world is. To avoid the dilemma, then, we must countenance many incommensurate truths. Instead of one way the world is, there are many ways the world is. The way we believe the world to be is as much a matter of construction as of discovery, of making as of finding, of the taken as of the given.[6]

To use the pluralist image of coevolution coherently, we must change the way we think about truth, especially factual truth. Suspect are both the strategy of breaking disagreements down to minimal, independent components and the insistence that meaningful differences are verifiable by observation and experiment. Clues to an alternative come from recent value theory.

Some humanists and social scientists have seen values as relational and interdependent. In practice, the meaning of value assertions depends on both the values favored and those disfavored. What is implied by a single value assumption depends on what other values are, or are not, held in context, albeit often implicitly. Human values are systemic. The unit that has determinate meaning, or is fully meaningful, is not an isolated value but a system of values operating in a concrete context.[7]

Holistic value theory has important implications for relating both actual and value considerations in one framework. Instead of seeing facts as the sole basis for empirical knowledge, consider the systemic interdependence of facts and values: values preselect and shape facts, facts clarify and refine values. Facts and values depend on each other.

The theory that facts and values are interdependent draws support not only from value theory, but also from the history, sociology and philosophy of science. Much recent work has sharpened awareness of how major shifts in scientific outlook are accompanied by fundamental shifts in cultural values.[8] Moreover, the failure of positivism to successfully demarcate science from non-science suggests that metaphysics and deep scientific theory are areas where facts and values interact the most intensively in shaping our ways of being in and seeing the world.

Common Ground

To cope better with moral conflict in agriculture, we need to understand better what shapes conflicting outlooks, how in different ways facts and values are co-constructed and co-discovered from experience and a common cultural heritage. But where in this confusing melange of differences can we find enough common ground to allow us to talk and work together even in the face of disagreement on fundamentals? How can we benefit from our differences rather than succumb to them?

The problem will be more tractable if we resolve to mend the split between reason and feeling in our thinking about moral judgment. Some of our feelings have moral significance, which is embodied in the judgments we make from reading them in context.[9] For example, when someone's manner elicits loving feelings from us, we may, depending on our reading of the context, conclude that she is a lovable person. The judgment is supported by our having had loving feelings toward the person in an appropriate context. In this way, moral judgments involve reason and feeling operating with facts and values.

We can work with moral differences, then, by comparing judgments with situated feelings and examining both the contexts and the readings that lead us to disagree. Affective meaning and cognitive meaning are equally important. The same frameworks of facts and values that shape our ways of being in and seeing the world also shape the ways we interpret our situated feelings in moral judgment.

To help reduce polarization and defensiveness in agricultural controversy, scholarly work is needed to identify and map the elements that shape participating moral perspectives. Persistent metaphors can be traced in the different ways we speak and act: images of nature, human nature, social order, effective and responsible action, science, and research, among others. Thus we can hope, through a limited though large set of comparisons and contrasts, to effectively delimit the commonalities and differences in prevalent moral outlooks.[10]

Conclusion

In contrast with the deductive stance of ethical theorists, the coevolutionary view depicts the morally responsible person as proceeding from practice to practice by way of feeling and reflection. Both the immediate and the ultimate moral prospect include many moral viewpoints that compete with and complement each other within political culture.

In this pluralistic perspective, moral responsibility has a humble aspect. Rather than judging others, we are hard pressed to respond ourselves with moral sensitivity and in good conscience, with respect for other views and the complexity of concrete situations. We find satisfaction in better ways of coping with conflict. Far from expecting to eliminate conflict, the coevolutionary view is suspicious of such a prospect. For it sees the persistence of some level of moral conflict as a necessary and valuable part of the human condition—the part that stimulates the full development of our humanity.

Notes

1. Revised and condensed by the author from a paper of the same title in T.C. Edens, et al., eds., Sustainable Agriculture and Integrated Farming Systems: 1984 Conference Proceedings (East Lansing, MI: Michigan State University Press, 1985), pp. 244–55; also reprinted in Agriculture and Human Values 1 (Fall 1984): 17–25.
2. A. Weinberg, "Science and Trans-science," Minerva 10 (1972): 209–222.
3. Gary A. Malinas, "Pesticides and Policies," Journal of Applied Philosophy 1 (1984): 123–31.
4. See David Dickson, The Politics of Alternative Technology (New York: Universe Books, 1974), and B. Fey, Social Theory and Political Practice (London, England: George Allen and Unwin Ltd., 1975).
5. On the distinction between core and application see Denis Goulet, The Cruel Choice: A New Concept in the Theory of Development (New York: Atheneum, 1971), who credits Georges Allo as source, pp. 345–46.
6. See Nelson Goodman, "The Way the World Is," Review of Metaphysics 14 (1960): 48–56; and Ways of World Making (Cambridge, Mass.: Hackett, 1978).
7. See Clifford Geertz, "Ideology as a Cultural System," in David E. Apter, ed., Ideology and Discontent (London, England: The Free Press of Glencoe, 1964), Stuart Hampshire, Morality and Conflict (Oxford: Basil Blackwell, 1983), and Sidney M. Wilhelm, "A Reformulation of Social Action Theory," American Journal of Economics and Sociology (1967): 23–31.
8. For example, Thomas S. Kuhn, The Structure of Scientific Revolutions, 2nd ed. (Chicago: The University of Chicago Press, 1970); Steven Shapin, "History of Science

and Its Sociological Reconstructions," History of Science 20 (1982): 157–211; and Steven Toulmin, Foresight and Understanding (New York: Harper and Row, 1961).

9. Two recent proponents of this view are George C. Kerner, "Passions and the Cognitive Foundations of Ethics," Philosophy and Phenomenological Research 31, (1970): 177–92; and R.C. Solomon, The Passions (Garden City, N.Y.: Doubleday, 1977).

10. Philip T. Shepard and Christopher Hamlin, "How Not to Presume: Toward a Descriptive Theory of Ideology in Science and Technology Controversy," Science, Technology, and Human Values 12, no. 2 (Spring 1987): 19–28.

II.
Agriculture's Practitioners

II.A.
The Structure of Agriculture:
Who Will Be On The Land?

NOTHING MAKES A GREATER DIFFERENCE to what is grown and how it is grown than who is on the land, and who controls it. The articles in Part II.A take up questions of proprietary structure, of who should own and manage the resources that we use to produce food and fiber. Most of the answers fall on the side of individual ownership and management; however, many views are represented. Also, virtually all of the discussions are concerned with the United States. (Part IV.B and C take up some of the international issues of proprietary structure.)

In Part I, some of the articles argued that perhaps only the caring small-scale family farmer, who knows the resource intimately and seeks a sustainable yield, can be expected to be ready and able to protect the future of our food production. Ingolf Vogeler in "The Structure of U.S. Agriculture: Agribusiness or Family Farms" agrees. But he also sees a history of taxes, federal farm programs, and land-grant college research that has left fewer and fewer of those caring farmers on the land.

The choice is between maximizing short-term profit and meeting human needs in the short *and* long term without overburdening those who will follow us. Put another way, the choice is between individual productivity and a costly social welfare and justice system. Or again, from the perspective of Vogeler's class-sensitive analysis, the choice is between capitalism, based on inequality, and democracy, based on equality; between a political economy of capitalists or one of labor. In the end, Vogeler's analysis urges us away from an agrarian capitalism toward an agrarian democracy.

Kristin Shrader-Frechette's article "Property and Procedural Justice: The Plight of the Small Farmer" concerns social justice in the food production system. In this, as in her account of the size-bias in certain U.S. federal and regional policies, she agrees with Vogeler. But she argues from considerations of procedural justice, rather than the socialist perspective of class struggle. A denial of proper procedural justice, not capitalist oppression, puts small producers off the land.

Discussing farmers in Appalachia and California, Shrader-Frechette urges limiting property rights, not to achieve a certain ethically preferred end-state, but to maintain a free market and other dimensions of procedural justice in the agricultural sector. She suggests a general argument for the limitation of property rights, a principle that looms large in each of the remaining articles in this section.

Charles Blatz in his paper "Ethical Issues in Private and Public Ranch Land Management" first explores reasons for limiting rights to the personal use of private property, and the pursuit of the public good on public land. Arguing for norms upholding the ultimate ethical rule of individual autonomy and a maximum of (harmonious) individual pursuits, Blatz outlines a procedure for allocating federal rangelands to individuals through long-term leases. These would be awarded on the basis of individual (or group) use plans incorporating in the ethical principles just mentioned.

The government's role in this scheme would be threefold. It would review proposed use plans and award the leases, oversee compliance with the authorized plan, and enforce the provisions of approved plans. The government should be able to facilitate a system of rangelands management that will be eco-accommodating while maximizing individual autonomous pursuits on federal lands. Thus, federal rangelands policy should be informed by an ethic of autonomy, favor individual producers intimately familiar with the resource, and still retain public ownership of the resource. Blatz concludes with a critical review of some of the arguments for privatizing federal lands.

Many of those in favor of selling public agricultural lands to private owners would object to Blatz's conclusions on the grounds that the federal government should not assist (they would say "subsidize") agricultural producers through low-cost long-term leases of grazing lands. James Montmarquet in his paper "Philosophy and Agrarianism" takes a historical look at the broader question of whether society should assist agriculture at all. Considering agrarianism as any view that supports such assistance, Montmarquet investigates the historical philosophical basis for agrarianism.

A case can be made from Aristotle's beliefs that government should nurture virtue, and that the virtues of democratic citizens will be found among small farmers. Similarly, in Locke and Jefferson, Montmarquet points out, a natural rights tradition can be found that will defend individual rights to both what is produced and the opportunity to produce. Radical agrarians of the eighteenth and nineteenth centuries go further, tending toward an opposition of individual ownership of land toward "a universal right to [use] land" and to retain the product of that use. The origin of the tendency away from private ownership seems to be biblical, its roots nourished by the same soil as the modern-day consensus Dundon spoke of in Part I.

Montmarquet offers his own revised basis for agrarianism. He suggests moving beyond traditional utilitarian ethics to the spirit of the Aristotelian and natural law traditions. We must come to value activity that realizes human potential. Reminding us of what Berry urges above in "The Unsettling of America," Montmarquet goes further to find in all productive activity—including agricultural—the very essence of human nature. This theme is explored in connection with the passing of small family farms, which he sees as a loss of human productivity.

Although Montmarquet sees agrarianism as feasible for today, he describes how it might be brought about. John Hart, in his essay "Jubilee and New Jubilee—Values and Visions for the Land," offers a radical suggestion for agrarian reform. Beginning with a critique of what he characterizes as greed-driven market distribution of agricultural resources, Hart reviews the biblical concept of a Jubilee year in which debts are forgiven and land redistributed. Finding the basis of pertinent ethical principles in revealed scripture, Hart urges that the land is entrusted to people to be shared in equally for the common good. Putting this belief into practice through steeply progressive taxes, among other measures, will lead to a redistribution of land to small-scale family farmers and to cooperative farming enterprises. Hart shows concern specifically for the regeneration and protection of agricultural resources, the fair restructuring of agricultural debt, the economic empowerment of unlanded agricultural workers, and a redistribution of the land that benefits everyone through individual or communal land control and management.

Thus, in these papers we see several approaches to the question of who should be on and in control of the land. All have argued for small-scale individual or cooperative proprietary arrangements, contrary to current ownership and management trends. Socialist egalitarianism, concerns of procedural justice, principles of autonomy, the pursuit of essential or characteristic human excellence, and biblical principles all serve as ethical bases for deciding who should be on the land. The primary alternative discussed is a proprietary structure determined by the market constrained as it is today in the United States. In Part II.B, we move from proprietary structure to the infrastructure of contemporary agriculture in the United States.

The Structure of U. S. Agriculture
Agribusiness or Family Farms?

Ingolf Vogeler

THE ECONOMIC AND POLITICAL FRAMEWORKS in which U.S. farmers operate profoundly affects their lives. These frameworks have been created on the basis of ethical decisions, yet when altered they can create fundamentally different (better?) ways of farming for the remaining farmers and for the urban society as a whole.

By the middle of the nineteenth century two competing agrarian ideals already existed in the U.S.: the family-farm ideal of self-sufficiency, and the profit-maximizing ideal, which was later called agribusiness. Each ideal (in reality most farmers represent a mixture of both) was and is based on very different ideological and ethical notions. Understanding these underlying concepts leads to a truly comprehensive and effective grasp of U.S. agriculture.

Ideally, family farmers own the farmland, buildings, machinery, and livestock, perform the farm work, provide the working capital, and make the day-to-day and long-term decisions. Family-farm production units are necessarily limited to a size that can be worked and managed by the farm families themselves. For production of any particular crop or animal, the larger the acreage and the greater the reliance on hired labor, the less likely that the operation will be a family farm. Family farms, being owner operated, also require a close geographical association between household residence and farm operation, although the location of the farm and family residence need not be identical. The business of agribusiness is short-term profit maximization. For this profit to be socially acceptable (since it is usually acquired under noncompetitive market conditions and exploitative labor conditions), agribusiness relies heavily on the competing ideals of the family farm and large-scale efficiency, using whichever one is most expedient to justify and disguise its exploitation of farmers and consumers.

The agribusiness model has traditionally been considered undesirable, whereas the family farm ideal has been valued since the eighteenth century. Even in the face of the growing importance of agribusiness, writers, academics, and politicians have exalted the virtues of family farming because it has been thought to be essential for the social well-being of the nation and the production of adequate supplies of food and fiber. The family farm ideal continues to be popular for it is deeply embedded in the dominant cultural values of rugged individualism, independence, self-sufficiency, opportunity, success through hard work, competition, and efficiency—all hallmarks of characteristically American cultural norms.

The genuine goal of farm families and the espoused goal of federal farm programs—to keep family farmers in agriculture—is not being achieved. Each year the number of farmers decreases and the remaining ones continue to face economic uncertainty. Since 1920, the farm population has declined by almost 60 million. Only 2.3 million farms remain, down from a peak of nearly 7 million in the 1930s. In 1985 one-third of the 679,000 family-sized commercial farms, with sales between $50,000 and $500,000, faced critical financial uncertainty. In other words, 31 percent of all U.S. farms had debts equaling 40 percent and more of assets.[1] Regardless of how hard family farmers work and how efficient they become, they are not treated equally with large-scale producers. Unequal treatment of one group, family farmers, in a society allegedly dedicated to justice and equality, has created a crisis.

Agricultural policy must come to grips with the contradictions between the family farm and the agribusiness ideal. Will U.S. agriculture be organized to achieve short-term profit maximization for large-scale producers or to provide employment and food for human needs in the short and long term without disproportionately burdening a few groups with the costs (environmental, social, and economic) of such production? To effectively answer these questions, we must examine the historical land-based policies and farm programs of the U.S. government and the nature of the private agricultural market economy.

The Historical Demise of Family Farming

Federal Land-Granting Policies

Before the U.S. government could distribute its vast land holdings (the public domain) in the interior, it had to devise an easy and quick method of surveying the land. The township and range land survey system, established by the Ordinance of 1785, was revolutionary in its intent and potential: equal blocks of land were divided to provide equal access to the land. In the early stages of national development, land was the critical form of wealth for new and old immigrants alike. With a widely held egalitarian land base, the democratic institutions of the new nation were to be guaranteed—economic democracy was to sustain political democracy. This revolutionary ideal inspired people around the world to come to the U.S. or to copy its ideas elsewhere.

The Ordinance of 1785 stipulated that one-half of the townships were to be sold as a whole and the other half in sections of 640 acres. This land was sold through auctions which, although they appeared to be fair, enabled wealthy buyers to outbid and buy more land than low-income immigrants because no acreage limitations were placed on land purchases. Two hundred and twenty million acres were sold for cash and credit. Pressure from settlers and some progressive members of Congress gradually reduced the parcel size to 320 acres in 1800, 160 acres in 1805, and finally 80 acres in 1820. Even though an 80-acre farm could be acquired for $100 cash, a tract of 640 acres went for about $400 cash. Thus, a parcel of land eight times as large cost only four times as much—an advantage for already wealthy land buyers. The Preemption Acts (1830-1891) recognized that the poor had not benefited from the cash sales system and hence allowed settlers to occupy unsurveyed public land, work it, and produce enough wealth to pay the $1.25 per acre after fourteen months of residence on the land. But many ways were used to circumvent these pro-settler acts.

In territories that were bought by and annexed to the U.S., large French and Spanish private land claims existed. Congress and the Supreme Court took the position "that the right of private property in land in the acquired territories should not be affected by the change in sovereignty regardless of treaty stipulation."[2] A total of 34.6 million acres of private claims were consequently honored and thus excluded from the public domain and the reach of ordinary settlers. In California, Spanish estates, or *latifundias*, were "protected" from the Preemption Acts even though valuable valley land was held by only 813 claimants, 87 of whom had obtained their grants during the last six months of Mexican rule.[3]

Some Spanish land grants were subdivided before the end of the Mexican period, especially in northern California, where population pressures allowed huge profits to be made from the sale of undeveloped lands. Instead of small farms of 100 or 200 acres, bonanza farms of 500 to 5,000 acres were created, particularly in the Sacramento Valley. Among the California estates that continue to exist today are the Kern County Land Company with 389,000 acres, the Tejon Ranch with 79,000 acres, now owned by Standard Oil Company of California, the Irvine Ranch with 110,000 acres, Rancho California, owned by Aetna Life Insurance and Kaiser, with 97,000 acres, and the Newhall Ranch with 43,000 acres.

The entrance requirements for California and Utah statehood clearly indicate what political rights were being protected by the U.S. government. Although the U.S. Constitution guarantees civil rights, capital accumulation—profits acquired through land acquisition in the California example—reigned supreme. The Bill of Rights and Constitution protects freedom of religion and the separation of church and state, respectively. Yet Utah was forced to deny Mormons their religious right to practice polygamy before being allowed to join the Union. California, on the other hand, was allowed to enter the Union without breaking up its large feudal estates, even though these subverted the goals of the Jeffersonian yeoman farmer ideal as well as federal laws such as the Preemption Acts. Thus the U.S. government sided with private property rights for the wealthy, which were not constitutionally protected, and violated constitutionally guaranteed religious freedom for the majority of the population!

School children learn about the best-known land-granting law, the Homestead Act of 1862, because of its egalitarian goals. Citizens or persons intending to become citizens could file claims to parcels of unappropriated public land up to 160 acres. After paying ten dollars and promising that the land was for actual settlement and cultivation, settlers received title after five years of continuous occupancy of their land. Yet major opposition existed to "this wise and popular measure." President Buchanan vetoed a similar bill in 1860 and southerners were vehemently opposed to free land because yeoman farmers required no slaves. The Homestead Act would prevent the spread of slavery and plantation agriculture into the West, a decided disadvantage from the perspective of white plantation owners. Even with the proslavery proponents absent from Congress in 1862 (because of the Civil War), the final opposition by northern capitalists was overcome only when evidence from the General Land Office showed that land had already ceased to be a source of revenue for the government. They had feared that the loss of such revenue would result in taxation of the affluent. In the end, the debates in Congress indicated that despite the sentiments of ordinary settlers, the Homestead Act was enacted only when southern capitalists were absent and northern capitalists were certain their interests would not be harmed.

Another frequently ignored aspect of the Homestead Act is the significance of its date of passage. Most of the agricultural land in the humid East had already been settled by the 1860s, hence most homesteading took place in the western Midwest, semiarid Great Plains, and arid West where 160 acres were inadequate, except in "wet" years, for a family farm. The default of these farms provided cheap land for bonanza wheat farms and huge cattle ranches. Despite the intentions of the act, the physical environment in which it was applied presented one more obstacle to its real success.

Agribusiness: A Profit-Maximizing Model

Conventional wisdom has it that as farms increase in size, farm populations decrease, and small towns die because the inefficient producers are weeded out. This efficiency myth renders efficient family farmers noncompetitive and facilitates farm expansion and increased profits under the disguise of productivity.

Farm size is a critical variable in measuring efficiency. What size, large or small, provides the best and least costly delivery of agricultural products? This question must be answered as it relates to individual farmers, to the agricultural sector in general, and indeed to the society as a whole. In popular and scientific publications, efficiency is usually associated with large-scale farm operations and inefficiency with small-scale farms.

The term "economies of size" refers to the reduced production costs and increased returns that are achieved when farmers expand their operations. Fixed costs, e.g. land, machinery, and buildings, can be spread over more and more units of output, resulting in lower costs per unit. But the economies of size do not increase with unlimited expansion. J. Patrick Madden and Carl J. Partenheimer, who examined seven types of crop farming under fourteen different circumstances in five different states, concluded that "in most of these studies, all the economies of size could be obtained by modern and fully mechanized 1-man or 2-man farms."[4]

Increasing farm size beyond the two-person family farm is not justified on the basis of efficient resource use. Why then do farmers expand beyond the maximum unit of efficiency? In the U.S., conventional wisdom believes that increased profitability is synonymous with greater efficiency. In reality, profits increase with farm size, irrespective of efficiency, which eventually levels off and declines. D. K. Britton and Berkeley Hill provide a simple arithmetical example to show that the two objectives of efficiency and profitability are contradictory.[5] In terms of efficiency, it is better to achieve an output of $12,000 from an input of $10,000 than it is to achieve an output of $23,000 from an input of $20,000. The first example is more efficient since every dollar of input yields $1.20 of output. In the second case, each dollar yields only $1.15. But most farmers would certainly prefer the second situation since it leaves them with a balance of $3,000—a 50 percent improvement on the balance of $2,000 resulting from the first situation. Empirical studies show that as long as large-scale producers can increase their profits, it is in their self-interest to expand, even if this means becoming relatively inefficient. Hence, what is rational and beneficial for those farm operators who can finance such expansion is irrational and wasteful (inefficiency in resource allocations and underutilization of the displaced farm population) for the society as a whole.

Family farmers, in particular, face a further problem in the efficiency-profitability squeeze. In his presidential address to the American Agricultural Economics Association, B. F. Stanton outlined the problem:

> A farm family tries to get the most it can out of the bundle of resources it controls. And it is not net income by itself that matters to a family. Rather, it is some larger combination of things including survival, net income over time, enlarging the bundle of resources [for the next generation] that the family controls, and increased prestige within the local social system.[6]

Family farmers, especially in contrast to large-scale industrial farm operators, are motivated by the desire to achieve the ideals of family farming. These very positive human goals are exploited under present conditions of agrarian capitalism to the detriment of family farmers themselves who achieve efficiency without the profit they have produced.

Two approaches exist to achieve the goal of maximum efficiency under present technological conditions. Proponents of agribusiness argue that if farms get larger they will automatically become more efficient; proponents of family farms argue that by increasing farm intensification, farms will become more efficient. The former approach has the disadvantage of concentrating landownership, wealth, and political power in fewer hands, displacing more farm families, and not increasing efficiency (indeed, in some cases, actually lowering efficiency). The latter approach has the advantage of displacing fewer farm families, sharing rural decision making and wealth widely, and increasing total efficiency and output.

Ideologically most scientists have sided with agribusiness in the use of neoclassical economic models. The selection of their theoretical framework allows them to ignore relevant human factors in the expansion of farm sizes. The concept of efficiency has thus been measured and interpreted in its narrowest form: to achieve short-run, individual gains. The concept itself is valuable, but its application has been distorted and used against, rather than for, family farmers.

Social Justice and Economies of Size

The myth of large-scale efficiency provides a justification for the massive displacement of rural people and for getting the remaining farm families to produce even more food for less income. From 1950 to 1976 the parity ratio (prices received divided by prices paid by farmers) declined by 40 percent. Parity averaged 56 percent from 1982–85, and stood at 50 percent in 1986.[7] The relative increase in net farm incomes for large-scale producers in particular has obscured the absolute increase in exploitation of farmers in general. Efficient producers often receive inadequate income from their work. Instead of rewarding efficiency in production, market forces and federal farm programs and tax laws reward inefficient producers because they are sufficiently large to be profitable. In the United States, profitability is the actual measure of success. Using "efficiency" to stand for "profitability" hides the negative consequences of agribusiness and reduces public criticism of the free market economy.

Technical efficiency, which is a measure of capital, does not address the question of social justice, a measure of labor. For individuals and society as a whole, a slightly "inefficient" agricultural sector, in the technical sense, may achieve higher social justice and thus increase the overall "efficiency" of the national economy—fewer people on welfare in cities, less unemployment, less malnutrition, and less concentration of economic and political power. Both efficiency and social justice can be achieved in U.S. agriculture. By truly rewarding efficiency, family farmers will be strengthened; by discouraging inefficiency, large-scale producers will be reduced. The two goals of efficient allocation of national agricultural resources and survival and prosperity of family farmers are the same. Large-scale farmers, on the other hand, stand in conflict with national economic and democratic goals. From the standpoint of these goals, discussion of large-scale efficiency may be a matter of "finding out the best way of doing something that should not be done at all."[8] Poet Wendell Berry stated the choice this way:

> The standard of the exploiter is efficiency, the standard of the nurturer is care. The exploiter's goal is money, profit; the nurturer's goal is health—his land's health, his own, his family's, his community's, and his country's.[9]

Federal Policies: Production Over People

Tax-Loss Farming

In a market economy the federal government and business view social problems from essentially the same perspective. Federal tax laws, farm programs, and agricultural research inevitably support large-scale producers and strengthen the grip of agribusiness. Tax-loss farming—or how to lose at farming and still make a profit—is one source of federal subsidy to corporations and wealthy urban investors. Rather than work the land—a hazardous business in the best of years—they milk the tax laws. In detail, this practice is complicated, but in principle, it is simple: lose money in farming and write those paper losses off against real nonfarm income.

Since the Revenue Act of 1916, the federal government's tax laws have provided greater advantages to nonfarm investors and large-scale producers than to small-scale family farmers. Most of the special tax legislation has been justified as making life easier for farmers and assisting them with the higher risks of raising crops and livestock. Many income tax rules that make tax-shelter farming possible are not specially designed for farming; farming is simply a convenient way of taking advantage of these laws. But, as in other governmental policies, in practice the benefits of these tax loopholes go largely to those least in need of special assistance. High-income doctors, lawyers, politicians, movie stars, and athletes enjoy winning by losing in agriculture. Tax-shelter farming is a rich person's game. Newspaper advertisements soliciting investors for agricultural schemes specify that no one need apply whose tax bracket is less than 50 percent. So while the rich get richer, family farmers are competitively disadvantaged. Agricultural markets are distorted, the public treasury is avoided, land values are artificially inflated, and consumers are faced with higher taxes and higher food prices.

The effects of tax-loss farming are unfair competition to bona fide farmers, higher land prices, overproduction of certain crops, expansion to larger-than-efficient farm sizes, absentee ownership, and the demise of family farms. Those who accumulate various tax subsidies do not have to rely solely on the land to produce an acceptable return; rather, they combine the income produced from the land with tax subsidies. Thus, subsidies have the effect of driving out those who rely on income from the land. When tax-loss investors pay more for an acre than its projected yield warrants, the price of land is driven up, making entry into farming for young farmers more expensive and usually impossible. Existing farmers, without nonfarm income, are also financially squeezed by these higher land prices. Tax-loss farmers effectively make the working farmers' costs rise to meet theirs.

Tax laws also encourage the wasteful use of natural resources. In the Sandhills of Nebraska, for example, investors are installing center-pivot irrigation systems. Nearly 40 percent of the purchase price of irrigated Sandhills land can be recovered in state and federal tax savings by high-income investors. Irrigated Sandhills farmland is especially amenable to investment credits, depreciation on irrigation equipment, and deductible development expenses because more than half the $800-per-acre value is in the irrigation well and equipment.[10]

Investments in vineyards and tree crops for tax-shelter purposes can result in overproduction. Since these commodities face an inelastic market demand (consumers can consume only so much fresh fruit, for example, regardless of how low the price goes), oversupplies depress prices and have disastrous effects on small producers, who have no outside incomes to tide them over. Because of tax write-off advantages, investors are less concerned about low prices for their commodities.

To the extent that subsidized investments come in big amounts—and the bigger the investments, the bigger the subsidies—tax loopholes encourage large-scale operations. In California the entire grape acreage in 1972 consisted of 400,000 acres, of which 93,000 was planted in the previous three years—with 53,000 acres in 1972 alone. Two partnerships alone were projected to plant 50,000 acres. This spectacular growth is due to tax shelters and to the increased consumption of wine in the United States. Similarly, tax-subsidized investments give large cattle feedlots, which custom-feed under limited partnerships, advantages over family-farm feeding operations.

In summary, tax-loss farming allows corporations and high-income persons to receive preferential treatment from the Internal Revenue Service, solely because of their large incomes. The rich become richer and working farm families are placed at a disadvantage in making a living. Bona fide farmers must compete with investors who are not even farming for profit. Rational decisions for relatively few farm-loss investors create irrational market conditions for large numbers of family farmers: artificially high land prices, lower commodity prices for producers, and more absentee and large-scale producers.

U.S. farm tax policies do help individual family farmers at any given time, but in the long term these policies help large-scale farmers more and thereby reduce the ability of any one family farm to compete successfully. Such tax benefits help create and reinforce inequities in agriculture. Because selective consequences of farm tax loopholes affect who can survive, they work indirectly to aid nonfarm investors, corporations, and large-scale producers in controlling increasing portions of U.S. agriculture. Taxpayers pay for these subsidies to agribusiness in two ways, in higher taxes and in the higher prices of an agribusiness-dominated agriculture. Consequently, farm families and consumers in general are not only financing but also absorbing the social and environmental costs of agribusiness dominance.

Federal Farm Programs

Federal farm programs were designed to benefit family-sized farms, but larger-than-family farms benefit disproportionately. The absurdity of federal commodity programs is in letting the same rules that established the inequality serve as the allocation model for the administration of benefits—namely, farm size and production. The larger the producers are, the higher their total yields are and the more public assistance they have received. Thus, the net impact of public policy from the 1930s to the 1970s was to encourage farm size increase. Whereas farm subsidies have been defended to the nation as a means of preserving the political and social values of small-scale family farming, this kind of farming has actually declined. Don Paarlberg, director of agricultural economics at the U.S. Department of Agriculture in 1972, concluded that farm subsidies have been a "big hoax" over the last thirty years.[11]

The various farm commodity programs have been counterproductive to maintaining family farms for five reasons:

1. Farm price support programs cost taxpayers an average of $5 billion per year from 1968 through 1970, $11.9 billion per year in the early 1980s, and $25.6 in 1986 alone.[12] In 1972, the Joint Economic Committee of Congress pointed out that farm subsidies were inequitable and wasteful, not only because taxpayers had to pay enormous subsidies to wealthy farmers but also because the price supports resulted in an additional $4.5 billion in artificially high food prices. The total bill was $10 billion in one year! The total federal, state, and local cost of public welfare programs for the poor, including Medicaid, was slightly over $10 billion in 1969, no more than federal agricultural welfare for the wealthy.

2. Most subsidies farmers receive depend on the size of their acreage allotment or their production, both of which vary directly with farm size. These payments are vested in farmers not as workers or farm operators but as landowners. Farm operators benefit from commodity programs solely on the basis of their control or ownership of land and productive resources. An ever larger share of income, in the

form of farm subsidies, goes to the relatively fixed and unequally distributed ownership of farmland. Increasing income inequality is based solely on property rights rather than on the labor contribution to agricultural production.

3. Conversely, no money from these programs goes to farm workers, who own nothing but their labor power. In fact, farm programs hurt farm workers by keeping land out of production, thereby reducing the need for labor and increasing unemployment.

4. Government farm subsidies drive up farmland prices. Because of the income floor provided by the subsidies, land prices are bid up to reflect the land's earning potential. The chief beneficiaries have been those who purchased land before subsidies became prevalent, not young farmers or those expanding their acreage. Farmers who have rented land find many farm-program benefits disappearing in higher rental payments to landlords.

5. High and stable commodity prices stimulate production, particularly through a faster acceptance of new techniques and a higher rate of investment than would otherwise have been the case. Larger production is counterproductive to the intent of farm programs—which were based on the proposition that the growth of farm productivity so far outstripped the growth in demand for farm products that price supports and acreage restrictions were required.

In summary, the net results of the farm programs are not surprising: Farm workers are not helped at all, poor farmers are helped slightly, middle-income farmers are helped somewhat, and rich farmers are helped a great deal. Thus farm programs continue a consistent pattern of exploiting family farmers throughout U.S. history.

Class Interests, Congress, and Farm Subsidies

Why does Congress pass farm legislation that consistently favors well-to-do farmers and largely harms modest- and low-income farm families? The answer is not hard to find. It takes money to get elected to Congress; the greater the financial resources one has, the easier it is to be elected (especially since the Supreme Court ruling that the Campaign Reform Acts restrict all donors in the amount they can give, but not the candidates themselves, who may spend an unlimited amount in an attempt to be elected).

People of wealth tend to support government farm policies and programs that reflect their own personal and class interests. Ralph Nader's Citizen Action Group showed that the 1975 Senate had at least twenty-one millionaires but only five senators who shared the material condition of 99 percent of Americans—less than $50,000. Wealth and political ideology are strongly related. Americans for Democratic Action (ADA) found that senators with the lowest assets had the highest liberal voting record (92 percent of all votes cast), while the millionaires had the lowest liberal voting rate (29 percent).[13]

The Land-Grant College System

The total funds for agricultural research and development, public and private, are now approximately $1 billion per year. Between $600 and $750 million of public funds are spent by the land-grant college system each year. Because people in rural America, particularly working farmers, farm workers, and small business people, do not have the private resources and training to do agricultural research, public funding of the land-grant colleges has been justified since its inception. Agribusiness firms such as Safeway, Del Monte, Tenneco, and Ralston Purina are capable of doing their own research and need not be subsidized by taxpayers. Yet instead of focusing on the needs of rural people, the land-grant college system serves the interests of capital and technology—in short, agribusiness.

How does the land-grant college system spend its money? Who makes these decisions? Who benefits? Who gets hurt?

The purpose of the extension service is to disseminate the results of agricultural and rural community research to rural people and to help them solve the problems they face. But as land-grant colleges and experiment stations have a bias toward large-scale producers, extension workers, not unexpectedly, share this same bias. Extension service workers devoted 86 percent of their resources to the wealthiest one-third of America's farmers. On a per capita basis, wealthy farmers received fourteen times as much attention from the extension service as low-income farmers.[14] Out of the 15,000 extension workers, approximately 500 work in the area of rural development, the rest assist to increase production. Generally, the plight of agricultural workers—whether migrants or farm owners—is considered the responsibility of some other agency, such as the Department of Labor or Department of Health and Human Services.

This bias is particularly troublesome because the quality of life in many rural communities is dismal, urgently in need of extension services. In the early 1970s, for example, 46 percent of the nation's poor were located in nonmetropolitan areas; median family income of rural people was 27 percent less than that of urban families; almost 60 percent of the nation's substandard housing was located in rural areas; and rural education attainments lagged far behind that of urban populations. But these pressing rural issues have received little attention from extension workers or from researchers who develop the knowledge disseminated by extension workers.

Who Benefits and Who Pays?

The tax-supported land-grant college system has used its vast financial, research, and extension resources primarily for the benefit of large-scale producers and agribusiness firms. These are the farm operations with the acreage and borrowing power to invest in the new machinery, technologies, and management techniques. At best, land-grant college research benefits are geared to the needs of no more than 35 percent of the country's farmers, those with annual sales in 1974 above $20,000. More realistically, mechanization research is designed to meet the specifications of the largest producers: the 7 percent of all U.S. farms in 1974 with annual sales of $100,000 or more that produced 54 percent of the total value of agricultural sales.

Taxpayers, through the land-grant college system, have given large-scale farmers technology suited to their scale of operation and designed to increase their profits. While mechanization research is not designed to force the majority of American farmers off farms, it has that effect. Farm workers and most farmers are the victims of mechanization, in part because they are not involved in the design of agricultural research for their needs. Severe neglect and discrimination against the rural poor by agricultural researchers and extension workers, and indifference to the impact of change upon small-town people, are thoroughly documented by presidential commissions, the U.S. Civil Rights Commission, congressional committees, and scholarly studies.

The Future: Agrarian Democracy or Agrarian Capitalism?

To understand the source of rural problems we must ask: Are the problems haphazard misfortunes, or are they structurally related to each other in a significant, causal way? Who benefits from our current agricultural system and who pays the price? To solve these problems, we must further ask: Will people be rewarded for merely owning wealth or for working to produce wealth? Will investment decisions be made by a few people to benefit themselves; by a majority of people to benefit a few, or by a majority of people who work and are collectively rewarded for their skills, risks, and labor? Will human material needs, such as food, shelter, and health care, be as basic as civil rights? The answers to these questions will mold future developments in rural America. In agriculture the ideology of laissez-faire economics has been used to mystify the tyranny of economic exploitation, which is no longer accepted by workers in most other sectors of the economy. Farming plays a special lingering role in the perpetuation of the myth that political democracy and capitalism are compatible.

For conservatives, the importance of agribusiness in U.S. agriculture is the inevitable and desirable result of the natural workings of a free market. Those leaving agriculture—family farmers, tenants, migrants, and small-town merchants—are failing through their own "inefficiency." The system is merely "removing unnecessary fat." The treatment of minorities in agriculture is justified by their "laziness" and "racial inferiority."

Liberals recognize the fallacy of the conservative argument. But their reform attempts to pass legislation, for example, setting upper limits on agricultural payments per grower; improving health, education, and shelter for migrants; and providing low-interest loans to farmers have not prevented the demise of family farming and the exploitation of racial minorities in rural areas. Liberals have sympathized with the victims of agribusiness, but their analysis has not recognized the structural relationships of problems under agrarian capitalism. The social and economic problems we face today are inherent and inevitable results of capitalism.

Capitalism is based on inequality, democracy on equality. The U.S. Constitution guarantees life, liberty, and the pursuit of happiness, and under this political democracy individuals are treated equally (one vote per person and equal rights for all). An economy based on labor contributions is also based on equality because each member of that society can contribute labor. But an economy based on capital accumulation for its own sake, as capitalism is, creates a society of economic inequality because access to productive resources (land, factories, money) is not equally available. Under capitalism, "equality of opportunity"—espoused in the land grants of the nineteenth century but not labeled as such until the 1960s—is more concerned with opportunity than with equality. Individuals who fail to achieve equality can then be blamed for not having taken advantage of opportunity. In the United States political rights are nominally guaranteed, but economic rights must be fought for repeatedly. Our current economy makes individual farmers responsible for their own economic survival under impersonal market forces. But exploiting recognition of agrarian capitalism—the system under which U.S. farmers work—compels an analysis of the problems facing family farmers from a different perspective, one that finds the nature of the market economy itself inadequate.

A two-sided or class analysis of U.S. society exposes the relationship between persons with capital (capitalists) and persons with labor (workers). Family farmers, migrants, and other workers earn their income from their labor, while capitalists, including the owners of agribusiness, receive their income because they own the workplaces—land, machines, and buildings—in which workers toil. In its most abstract form the struggle is between labor and capital, between those who produce wealth and those who own and appropriate wealth. Under capitalism the owners of the means of production decide which, how many, and under what conditions employees will labor. Workers respond by demanding control of their workplaces and the decisions of how and for what purpose the value of their labor shall be used. Labor and capital, then, are fundamentally opposed to each other and constitute the oppositional unity of agrarian capitalism. Such a class analysis is both more comprehensive and more powerful than conventional social science analysis.

These rural class relations, however, are more complex than a simple polarization of capital and labor. Large-scale producers such as larger-than-family farmers, industrial farmers, and corporations in farming represent the purest form of agrarian capitalists, the agrarian bourgeoisie; hired farm workers clearly represent labor, or the rural proletariat. But small-scale producers such as family and tenant farmers and sharecroppers are caught somewhere in between, having characteristics of the capitalists and the proletariat; they are the protoproletariat. All three classes have different control over resources, decision making processes, and labor relations.[15] Roger Barta, a rural sociologist, has pointed out that as long as the agrarian structure is dominated by the capitalist market, the inevitable tendency is toward a deeper differentiation or polarization of the rural population and the proletarianization and pauperization of family farmers. The term protoproletariat, "a group clinging to a semantic grey zone,"[16] is especially appropriate for family farmers. Although the myth of the independent, self-determining family farm allows family farmers to identify with the agrarian bourgeoisie, their structural relations tie them economically to the rural proletariat. Their protoproletariat status distinguishes them from landless farm workers yet recognizes their overwhelming similarity to them. With the continuing penetration of capital into the countryside—whether through greater bank control, contract farming, or direct farm production—the remaining family farmers will first become more marginalized and finally be reduced to the ranks of the rural or, more likely, urban proletariat. Since 1920, almost fifty million farm people have experienced this consequence of agribusiness.

The first U.S. revolution resulted in political freedoms; the second will be for economic freedoms. Democracy based on individual political rights is meaningless for people without economic rights. Civil rights have been granted in liberal democracies only when they have not threatened the basic economic system. The next revolution in the U.S. will require the expansion of political democracy to include economic democracy; only then can agrarian capitalism give way to agrarian democracy.

Notes

1. Economic Research Service, U.S. Department of Agriculture, *A Summary Report on the Financial Condition of Family-Size Commercial Farms* (Washington, D.C.: Government Printing Office, 1986), p. 59.
2. Benjamin Horace Hibbard, *A History of the Public Land Policies* (Madison, Wisc.: University of Wisconsin Press, 1965), p. 24.
3. Paul Wallace Gates, ed., *California Ranchers and Farmers, 1846–1862* (Madison, Wisc.: State Historical Society of Wisconsin, 1967), pp. 7–8.
4. Patrick J. Madden and Carl J. Partenheimer, "Evidence of Economies and Diseconomies of Farm Size," in A. Gordon Ball and Earl O. Heady, eds., *Size, Structure and Future of Farms* (Ames, Iowa: Iowa State University Press, 1972), pp. 91–107.
5. D. K. Britton and Berkeley Hill, *Size and Efficiency in Farming* (Lexington, Mass.: Lexington Books, 1975), pp. 9–10.
6. B. F. Stanton, "Perspective on Farm Size," *American Journal of Agricultural Economics* 60, No. 5 (1978): 730–6.
7. Farmer and Rancher Congress, *Strengthening the Spirit of America* (St. Louis, Mo.: Farmer and Rancher Congress, 1986), p. 17.
8. Kenneth Boulding, "In Praise of Inefficiency," *Graduate Women* 73, no. 4 (1979): 29.
9. Wendell Berry, *The Unsettling of America: Culture and Agriculture* (New York: Avon Books, 1977), p. 7.
10. Chuck Hassebrook, "The Lure of Land Speculation," *New Land Review* (Summer 1979): p. 12.
11. George Melloan, "Time to Phase Out Farm Subsidies," *Wall Street Journal*, May 4, 1972, p. 4.
12. Mark Drabenstott, "The Long Road Back for U.S. Agriculture," *Economic Review*, Federal Reserve Bank of Kansas City (December 1986): 40–53.
13. Jim Chapin, "The Rich Are Different . . . ," *Newsletter of the Democratic Left* (November 1976): 3.
14. Lauren Soth, "Tides of National Development," in U.S. Congress, Senate, *Farmworkers in Rural America, 1971-1972*, Hearings before the Subcommittee on Migratory Labor of the Committee on Labor and Public Welfare, 92d Cong., 2d sess., part 4B (Washington, D.C.: Government Printing Office, 1972), p. 2911.
15. For a more complete discussion of these conceptual issues, see Ingolf Vogeler, *The Myth of the Family Farm: Agribusiness Dominance of U.S. Agriculture* (Boulder, Colo.: Westview Press, 1981), pp. 279–94.
16. Roger Barta, "Peasants and Political Power in Mexico: A Theoretical Approach," *Latin American Perspectives* (Summer 1975): 29.

Property and Procedural Justice
The Plight of the Small Farmer

Kristin S. Shrader-Frechette

AFTER THE FEDERAL DEPOSIT INSURANCE CORPORATION (FDIC) was created in 1933, 350 insured banks failed during the depression. Since 1981, the beginning of the recent farm crisis, more than 400 banks have failed, most of them agricultural banks having most of their loans in agricultural credits to small farmers facing foreclosure.

This essay argues that at least part of the reason for the farm and financial crisis is that land has been allowed to serve the private, rather than public, interest. If farmland needs to be preserved, then land-use controls offer one way to secure this public goal. Every public good, however, is bought at a price. Part of the price of land-use controls is a restriction on property rights, a problematic restriction since they are often held more sacrosanct than civil rights. I argue that procedural justice requires, *in particular cases*, that we restrict property rights in natural resources, e.g., California agricultural land. If this argument is correct, then we have a moral imperative to use land-use controls (e.g., taxation, planning, zoning, and acreage limitations) to restructure land ownership and land use in a far more radical way than has ever been accomplished in the past.

California agricultural land presents an important case study for land-use controls because owning even a small piece of it may confer a great deal of economic and political power. California is the largest producer of many specialized crops, and ownership of several hundred acres with rare soil and a specific climate can give one a great amount of power, for example, in setting the price of broccoli, asparagus, or artichokes.

The top twenty-five landowners in California hold at least 58 percent of the state (Fellmeth 1973:9). A recent study of land ownership also revealed that forty-five corporate farms, representing less than one-tenth of one percent of the commercial farms in the state, control approximately 61 percent of all farmland in California (Fellmeth 1973, 12; Hightower 1975). According to a recent survey done by the U.S. Department of Agriculture and the Agricultural Extension Service of the University of California, the larger the number of acres held by an owner, the more likely he or she is to be a nonresident of California (Fellmeth 1973, 12; Strong 1981, 217–33). The same study reveals that this highly concentrated, absentee ownership of land results in more concentrated and effective political and economic power and greater ability to oppose contrary interests than does widely diffused ownership. Only a few large landowners can create a powerful lobby advocating particular legislation, e.g., subsidized water. As the authors of the study put it: "The few, who own more and more of California's land, control their own political and economic destinies; the many are more subject both in economics and politics to the automatic regulation of competition" (Fellmeth 1973, 14–15; Andrews 1979).

Such a situation suggests, therefore, that large and small landowners do not have equal opportunity in the marketplace because of the political and economic effects of large real estate holdings. And if they do not have equal opportunity, then it is questionable whether the demands of procedural justice are met in situations where large absentee landlords and small resident farmers compete in and for the same agricultural and economic markets.[1]

One of the practical reasons why small farmers cannot compete with the large absentee-controlled conglomerate farmers is that they must continually purchase or rent more land, a nearly impossible task because of inflated land costs (Hamilton and Baxter 1977, 91–96; Davidoff and Gold 1979, 79–84). Moreover, because of higher land costs, the smaller farmers receive proportionately smaller returns for their labor. Even farm-income maintenance programs have aggravated, rather than alleviated, this problem, since they have made the relatively richer farmers wealthier, at considerable expense to the public (Fellmeth 1973, 74).

Substantial capital gains, favorable depreciation rates on equipment and machinery, and tax losses written off against nonfarm income are major benefits that return sizeable tax savings to absentee investors and large corporations that engage in farm and nonfarm enterprise. The independent owner-operator of a small farm who earns his living entirely from farming may, of course, make some use of depreciation and capital gains provisions, but he is not likely to have taxable nonfarm income against which to offset farming losses. For this reason, a recent U.S. Secretary of the Treasury argued that current tax policies "create unfair competition for farmers who may be competitors and who do not pay costs and expenses of tax dollars, but who must make an economic profit in order to carry on their farming activities" (Fellmeth 1973, 75–76; see Dangerfield 1975). As a consequence, small farms have decreased dramatically. Since 1954 small farms (under ten acres) have declined by 53 percent, whereas farms between 500 and 999 acres decreased by only 9 percent, and farms larger than 999 acres decreased by only 8 percent. Because the profit margins in farming are so narrow, and because small farmers have been victimized by both intentional and unintentional discrimination, they have a credit squeeze and are unable to accumulate the resources of land and loans that would give them opportunities equal to those of the corporate farmer (Fellmeth 1973, 78, 81; Fritsch 1982, 15–19).

Much the same situation exists in other farm regions of the country, except that the small farmer is often disadvantaged relative to other land interests, e.g., coal corporations. In Appalachia, for example, most of the land is concentrated in the hands of a few absentee corporate holders, causing unequal political and economic opportunity for the small farmer and the subsequent decline of small farms (Griffin 1979, 40).

Recently the Appalachian Regional Commission sponsored a major study of land ownership, one of the most comprehensive ever completed in the U.S. To draw profiles of eighty counties in Alabama, Kentucky, North Carolina, Tennessee, Virginia, and West Virginia, the researchers traveled 75,000 miles and gathered information on more than 20,000 acres. The conclusions of the 1981 study were that most of the region's woes, that is, the decline of the small farmer, the housing shortage, and environmental degradation, were caused by concentrated absentee ownership of most of the land. The researchers discovered that almost all owners of mineral rights pay less than a dollar an acre in property taxes, that three-fourths pay less than twenty-five cents, and that 53 percent of the total land surface in the eighty counties is controlled by only 1 percent of the total population, by absentee individuals and by corporations. Furthermore, they discovered that about three-fourths of the surface acres surveyed are absentee-owned, and four-fifths of the mineral acres are owned by out-of-state or out-of-county owners. Of the top fifty private owners, forty-six are corporations (Egerton 1981, 43; Gaventa and Horton 1981, 25–29, 210–11).

Using more than 100 socioeconomic indicators, the Appalachian land-use researchers drew some startling conclusions. —The greater the concentration of land and mineral resources in the hands of a few, and the greater the absentee ownership, the less the money generated by coal production remains in the counties giving up their resource wealth. —Little land is owned by, or accessible to, local people. For these reasons, many ills plague Appalachia: inadequate local tax revenues and services, lack of economic development and diversified job opportunities, loss of agricultural land, insufficient housing, a lack of locally controlled capital, and a rate of outmigration proportional both to corporate ownership and to concentration of land and mineral wealth in the hands of a few. Both in California and in Appalachia, researchers concluded that land reform or land-use controls were a necessary, although not sufficient, condition for correcting socioeconomic ills and providing equal opportunity to the small farmer (Gaventa and Horton 1981, 210–12; Nader 1975, 144–47; Egerton 1981, 44; Moss 1977, 235–36; Fellmeth 1973, 85; Faux 1975, 187; and Griffin 1976, 1–11).

If one assumes that the researchers just cited are *factually* correct about the causes of unequal opportunity for small farmers, whether in California or in Appalachia, and if one assumes that they are correct about at least one necessary remedy, land-use controls, then there are important grounds for limiting the property rights of California's and Appalachia's corporate absentee landlords. A case could be made that, because most Appalachian and California land is concentrated in the hands of so few, the property rights of these land owners should be limited, so that the land could be distributed equally. Such an argument, however, appeals to a socialistic political philosophy, and hence has little chance of being adopted in the U.S., regardless of its intrinsic merit. The most successful argument is likely to be based on broadly acceptable philosophical considerations. Since virtually everyone admits the legitimacy of principles of procedural justice (see note 1 and Nelson, 1980), one plausible argument is the following:

—Concentrated absentee ownership of Appalachian coal land and California agricultural land leads to concentrated political, legal, and economic power in the hands of the owners.

—Such concentrations of political, legal, and economic power limit the *voluntariness* of land (and other) transactions between the large owners (holders of power) and others, especially small farmers.

—Apart from legitimate reparation or punishment, whatever social institutions limit the voluntariness of transactions limit the "background conditions" necessary for procedural justice, and hence limit procedural justice itself.

—Whatever limits procedural justice should be avoided.

—Concentrated absentee ownership of land ought to be avoided.

Of course the main stumbling blocks in this argument are the first two premises. They are factual (and therefore contingent) propositions whose truth depends on the soundness of a number of related arguments and insights.

One insight is that monopolies tend to reduce the freedom of market transactions. Another is that property generates inequality, and inequality menaces liberty. Land economists, in particular, have explicitly noted how concentrations of rural land in the hands of a few owners leads to monopsony (owners' control of wages), the absence of developable land, the lack of a diversified economy, and the absence of local capital. These factors, in turn, limit the voluntariness of transactions between large land owners and others (Griffin 1976 and 1979, 225–33; see Gaventa and Horton 1981, 2, 28; Samuels 1972, 140–41; Pennock 1980, 269). Because they limit voluntariness, they thereby limit certain "background conditions" (e.g., the existence of a *free*, competitive market) necessary for procedural justice.

When transactions are not voluntary, then presumably they are made under duress, extorted consent, and the like—conditions that limit procedural justice because they limit fairness. For Nozick, Rawls, and virtually all moral thinkers, procedural justice requires fairness, and fairness requires background conditions such as the existence of voluntary transactions. Rights and obligations incurred in justice arise only if the transactions generating them are voluntary (Rawls 1971, 111–13, 342–47; Nozick 1974, 90–93).

Perhaps the main reason for claiming that transactions between large landowners and others in Appalachia might not be voluntary is that the small farmers and landowners often cannot do otherwise than to sell their land to the large absentee landlords and coal companies. A number of philosophers maintain that a person's action cannot be called free or voluntary unless the person could have done otherwise (see Aquinas 1947; Hume 1966; Bradley 1968, 272–83; Campbell 1961, 2, 213 ff.; Ryle 1949, 70; Moore 1963, 126; Gustafson 1964, 493–501; Brady 1972, 98–99; and Sweeney 1977, 196–210). If land concentration, monopsony, and the absence of local capital and developable land mean that small landowners are forced to sell their land, then obviously their selling is not voluntary in the sense that they could have done otherwise. And if the selling is not voluntary, then its ethical defensibility is questionable, for the reasons sketched in the previous paragraph.

But what does it mean to say that the small farmers probably do not sell their land voluntarily? Ryle, Hart, Honore, and others have claimed that an action is not voluntary when it is accomplished under external coercion or duress, or when it is done by mistake, by accident, in the absence of muscular control, under pressure of legal and moral obligation, or even under the pressure of making a choice as the lesser of two evils (Ryle 1949, 75; Foot 1963, 505–15; Hart and Honore 1959, 254–55; Samek 1963, 198–216; Stalley 1980, 448–53; see also Rankin 1960, 361–71; Moore 1963, 131–32; Melden 1956, 523–41; Nowell-Smith 1970, 609–19).

Hart, Nowell-Smith, Austin, and others maintain that concepts like "voluntary" are not definable in terms of necessary and sufficient conditions, but are understandable only in terms of the specific factors that limited voluntariness (Hart 1959–60, 1961, 145; Austin 1961, 8, 1961a, 128; Hughes 1961, 230; Nowell-Smith 1954, 296; Bronaugh 1964; Haksar 1966, 187–222; Whiteley 1966, 223–26). In the case of the small California or Appalachian farmer, factors limiting the voluntariness of land transactions include monopsony, the lack of alternative employment opportunities, and the absence of local capital.

In arguing that the decisions of many small farmers to sell their lands are not voluntary, I am relying in part on moral philosopher Alan Gewirth's analysis of voluntary action. Gewirth argues that non-voluntary or coerced action has at least three characteristics: it is compulsory, undesirable, and the result of threat. As Gewirth points out, a choice is compulsory if it is between undesirable alternatives, none of which one would choose if he were totally free. The choices of many Appalachian landowners are surely compulsory in the sense that they probably do not wish to choose either to lose their small farms or to live on the brink of starvation. Likewise the main options open to them are undesirable. What decisions they make, because of the power of monopsony, the lack of local capital, and the absence of developable land, appear to be made in order to avoid a threat of serious harm. Hence Gewirth would probably say that the choice of such Appalachian landowners probably were "irreducibly involuntary, " like choices between taking a pay cut or being fired, when jobs are scarce (Gewirth 1978, 27–34).

Moreover, as Gewirth notes, just because "the normal or natural or expected course of events" is that many people face just such choices, e.g., between taking a pay cut or being fired, does not mean that their choices are voluntary, just because their incidence is so great. "Surely the forcedness of choice is not removed when these features [of compulsion, undesirability, and threat] are a regular part of someone's life or of the institutional structure of a society." (Gewirth, 1978, p. 34)

Of course, the obvious objection to the claim that a great many choices made in contemporary industrial-agricultural society are forced or not voluntary is that such a claim makes the conditions of morality—voluntariness, for example—irrelevant and unrealistic, since virtually all choices may be alleged to be nonvoluntary. This objection will not hold, however. *First*, a number of choices in contemporary society are not made in the context of serious threats to well-being, at least insofar as they are made by those who are well off and financially secure. *Second*, many of the alternatives people face in making choices are not undesirable. To say that all choices were undesirable, for everyone, would be to presuppose a great exaggeration of human desire. Such exaggerated desires are probably more characteristic of Plato's insatiable tyrant and of Freud's id than they are of many human beings. But if so, then it is plausible to claim that the land transactions of many small Appalachian farmers, and others like them, are probably not voluntary (see Gewirth 1978, 33–34, 256–58; 1982, 28, 114–17, 268–69; Cohen 1979, 179–90; Bell 1978, 65–73; Heslep 1986, 379–91).

Because Appalachia is a rural-agricultural region with little industry, the small farmer has rarely been able to engage in voluntary transactions and to compete fairly with the large landowner, who very likely owns the community bank and the general store and "noncoercively" controls the whole community. Now suppose a mining company owned by a multinational corporation makes a contract with a small farmer to purchase title to his land. Granted, the farmer may not be defrauded; he may "voluntarily" sell his property. Yet consider the following factors: he is chronically impoverished, is perhaps poorly educated, and (in part because of tax laws) faces the impossibility of competing with the large farmer. He has no capital investment for keeping his land and farming or mining it himself, and there are no other (i.e., nonagricultural, nonmining) jobs available. Surely he is not in a equal bargaining position with the large absentee landlord. Surely selling his land is not entirely voluntary, since the background conditions for the exercise of procedural justice have not been met (see Held 1976, 171–72; Sterba 1980; and Ray 1975, 176–80). Justice cannot be met if allegedly voluntary decisions or transactions are coerced or forced. But if so, then there may well be ethical grounds for limiting the property rights of large absentee landlords (like those in California and Appalachia), so that they would be less likely to hold coercive power over typical market transactions.

If there are ethical grounds for limiting the property rights of large absentee landlords, then the obvious issue is what sorts of limitations ought to be pursued. One reasonable position would be to argue for the fewest restrictions necessary to meet the minimum background conditions for procedural justice. I shall not take the time to argue here which limitations are likely to meet these minimum conditions. However, I believe that it is not difficult to show that acreage limitations, as well as certain controls on the *right to use* one's property and specific limitations on the *right to income* from it, would counteract most ill effects of concentrated ownership (see Becker 1980, 190–91; Shrader-Frechette 1988, sec. 5.4; see also Fellmeth 1973, 85; Taylor 1975, 113–17; and Staley 1975, 222–24; Kaufman 1975, 152–53; McClaughry 1975, 154–59; de Neufville 1981, 31–49; Dorner 1972).

Basically, the argument to limit property rights (through acreage limitations, restricted right-to-income, or restricted right-to-use) requires us to accept the premise that we should avoid certain societal institutions insofar as they preclude the "background conditions" (such as a free, competitive market) necessary for procedural justice. The key insight on which this argument rests is fundamentally Rawlsian: "Only against the background of a just basic structure . . . and a just arrangement of economic and social institutions, can one say that the requisite just procedure exists" (Rawls 1971, 87; 1977, 160).

If one accepts this argument for limiting property rights, then one has admitted that, *in some instances*, the operation of the market runs afoul of the Lockean proviso that the condition of others not be worsened by our appropriation and use of property. But if the operation of the market, at least in Appalachia and in California, does run afoul of this proviso, then, on their own terms, even libertarians would be required to accept limitations of the property rights whose exercise is responsible for violation of the Lockean proviso (Locke 1980, V, par. 27; 1984, 138; Becker 1977, 89–94).

In response to this procedurally based argument for land-use controls (or even land reform), a number of objections can be made. An opponent might claim, for example, that the argument rests on socialistic principles,[2] that there is no clear criterion for when social processes are truly voluntary and when the background conditions for procedural justice have been met, and that the argument violates property rights (see Nozick 1974, 238).

Although space limitations prevent my defusing these objections, each of them can be countered quite easily (see Shrader-Frechette 1988, sec. 6). In sum, the first fails because the argument given relies on no end-state principles (see note 1) or socialistic principles, but only on principles of procedural justice accepted by nonsocialists and socialists (Scanlon 1976, 8; Nozick 1974, 181, 342). The second objection can be easily dealt with since it requires only that ethical analysis, rather than some simple algorithm, be used to determine when actions meet criteria for voluntariness. The third objection fails because it begs the question (Nozick 1974, 262, 264).

A more general argument for limiting property rights, especially property rights in natural resources, can be made on two grounds. It is not clear that a person can have full property rights in anything that was not created by his or her labor, and natural resources are not created primarily by human labor (See Locke 1980, V; 1984; Nozick 1974, 174–78; 1984, 146–49; Becker 1977, 43–45). It is not clear that property rights to land and other natural resources can be justified if their implementation involves (or renders highly probable) the exhaustion of a significant resource, e.g., coal, by a subset of the total population. The second argument can be substantiated on the Lockean grounds that one may own or appropriate property only so long as "as much and as good" is left for others (Locke 1980; 1984; Becker 1977, 43–45, 109–10; Nolette and Fritsch 1982, 3). Space prohibits presenting this second argument here, but analysis of it and of objections to it can be found elsewhere (see Shrader-Frechette 1988, sec. 8).

If the preceding analysis, despite its admitted incompleteness, is largely correct, then there are strong grounds for further consideration of the conclusion that in areas such as Appalachia and California that are particularly prone to monopolistic control of land, procedural justice suggests that property rights to finite natural resources ought to be limited. We ought to insure that private property does not harm the public good.

Notes

1. Principles of procedural justice describe fair or correct methods for arriving at any distribution, e.g., of land; pure procedural justice obtains when there is no independent criterion for the right outcome or distribution. Instead there is a correct or fair procedure for insuring a correct or fair outcome; see Nozick 1974, 1984; Rawls 1971:86. End-state principles provide reasons for a particular distribution of goods, whereas principles of procedural justice describe fair or correct *methods* of distribution.

2. I am grateful to Ernie Partridge and Doug Den Uyl for spelling out this objection.

References Cited

Andrews, R., ed. *Land in America*. Toronto: D. C. Heath, 1979.

Aquinas, Thomas. *The Summa Theologica*, First Part of the Second Part, vol. 2. New York: Benzinger Bros., 1947.

Austin, J. L. "A Plea for Excuses." In Morris, 1961.

———. *Philosophical Papers*. Oxford: Clarendon Press, 1961.

Barnes, Peter, ed. *The People's Land.* Emmaus, Pa.: Rodale Press, 1975.

Becker, L. C. *Property Rights: Philosophic Foundations*. Boston: Routledge and Kegan Paul, 1977.

———. "The Moral Basis of Property Rights." In Pennock and Chapman, 1970.

———, and K. Kipnis, eds. *Property*. Englewood Cliffs, N.J.: Prentice-Hall, 1984.

Bell, N. K. "Nozick and Fairness." *Social Theory and Practise* 5, no. 1 (Fall 1978): 65-73.

Bradley, F. H. *Collected Essays*. Freeport: Books for Library Presses, 1968.

Brady, James. "Indifference and Voluntariness." *Analysis* 24, no. 2 (January 1972): 98-99.

Bronaugh, R. "Freedom as the Absence of an Excuse." *Ethics* 74, no. 3 (April 1964): 161–73.

Campbell, C. A. "Self Activity and its Modes." *Contemporary British Philosophy*, Third Series. New York: Macmillan, 1961.

Cohen, Stephen. "Gewirth's Rationalism: Who is a Moral Agent?" *Ethics* 89, no. 2 (January 1974): 179–90.

Dangerfield, J. "Sowing the Till." In Barnes, 1975.

Davidoff, Paul, and N. Gold. "The Supply and Availability of Land for Housing for Low- and Moderate-Income Families." In Listokin, 1979.

de Neufville, J. "Land Use." In de Neufville, 1981.

———, ed. *The Land Use Policy Debate in the United States*. New York: Plenum, 1981.

Dorner, Peter. *Land Reform and Economic Development*. Baltimore: Penguin, 1972.

Egerton, John. "Appalachia's Absentee Landlords. " *The Progressive* 45, no. 6 (June 1981): 42–45.

Faux, G. "The Future of Rural Policy." In Barnes, 1975.

Fellmeth, R. C. *The Politics of Land.* New York: Grossman, 1973.

Foot, P. "Hart and Honore: Causation in the Law." *Philosophical Review* 72, no. 4 (October 1963): 505–15.

Fritsch, A. J. *Green Space*. Lexington, Ky.: Appalachia Science in the Public Interest, 1982.

Gaventa, John, and Bill Horton. *Ownership Patterns and Their Impacts on Appalachian Communities: A Survey of 80 Counties*, Volume 1.

Washington, D.C.: Appalachian Regional Commission, February 1981.

Gewirth, Alan. *Human Rights*. Chicago: University of Chicago Press, 1982.

———. *Reason and Morality*. Chicago: University of Chicago Press, 1978.

Griffin, K. *Land Concentration and Rural Poverty*. New York: Holmes and Meier, 1976.

———. *The Political Economy of Agrarian Change*. London: Macmillan, 1979.

Gustafson, D. F. "Voluntary and Involuntary." *Philosophy and Phenomenological Research* 24, no. 4 (June 1964): 493–501.

Haksar, V. "Responsibility." *The Aristotelian Society*, Suppl. XL (1966): 187–222.

Hamilton, S. W., and D. E. Baxter. "Government Ownership and the Price of Land. " In *Public Property*. Vancouver: Fraser Institute, 1977.

Hart, H. L. A. "Ascription of Responsibility." In Morris, 1961.

———. "Prolegomenon to the Principles of Punishment." *Proceedings of the Aristotelian Society* LX (1959–60).

———, and A. M. Honore. *Causation in the Law*. Oxford: Clarendon Press, 1959.

Held, Virginia. "John Locke on Robert Nozick." *Social Research* 43, no. 1 (Spring 1976): 168–95.

Heslep, R. D. "Gewirth and the Voluntary Agent's Esteem of Purpose." *Philosophy Research Archives* XI (March 1986): 379–91.

Hightower, J. "The Industrialization of Food." In Barnes, 1975.

Hughes, Graham. "Omissions and *Mens Rea*." In Morris, 1961.

Hume, David. *Enquiry Concerning Human Understanding*. Oxford: Clarendon Press, 1966.

Kaufman, P. "The Severance Tax." In Barnes, 1975.

Listokin, David, ed. *Land-Use Controls*. New Brunswick: Rutgers University, 1979.

Locke, John. "Of Property." In Becker and Kipnis, 1984.

———. *Second Treatise of Government*. Edited by C. B. McPherson. Indianapolis: Hackett Publishing, 1980.

McClaughry, John. "Taxes for Land Acquisitions." In Barnes, 1975.

McGinley, "Aristotle's Notion of the Voluntary." *Apeiron* 14, no. 2 (December 1980): 125–33.

Melden, A. I. "Action." *Philosophical Review* 65, no. 4 (October 1956): 523–41.

Moore, G. E. *Ethics*. London: Oxford University Press, 1963.

Morris, H., ed. *Freedom and Responsibility*. Stanford: Stanford University Press, 1961.

Moss, Blaine, Natural Resources Defense Center. *Land Use Controls in the United States*. New York: Dial Press/ James Wade, 1977.

Nader, R. "Property Tax Evasion." In Barnes, 1975.

Nelson, William. "The Very Idea of Pure Procedural Justice." *Ethics* 90, no. 4 (July 1980): 502–11.

Nolette, Mark, and Albert Fritsch. *The Community Land Trust*. Lexington, Ky.: Appalachia Science in the Public Interest, 1982.

Nowell-Smith, P. H. "Comments and Criticism: On Sanctioning Excuses." *Journal of Philosophy* 67, no. 18 (September 1970): 609–19.

———. *Ethics*. Baltimore: Penguin, 1954.

Nozick, Robert. *Anarchy, State, and Utopia*. New York: Basic Books, 1974.

———. "Locke's Theory of Acquisition." In Becker and Kipnis, 1984.

Pennock, J. R. "Thoughts on the Right to Private Property." In Pennock and Chapman, 1980.

———, and J. W. Chapman, eds. *Property*, Nomos XXII. New York: New York University Press, 1980.

Rankin, K. W. "Doer and Doing." *Mind* 69, no. 275 (July 1960): 361–71.

Rashdall, Hastings. "The Philosophical Theory of Property." In Bartlett, 1915.

Rawls, John. *A Theory of Justice*. Cambridge, Mass.: Harvard University Press, 1971.

———. "The Basic Structure as Subject." *American Philosophical Quarterly* 14, no. 2 (April 1977): 159–65.

Ray, V. "They're Destroying our Small Towns." In Barnes, 1975.

Ryle, Gilbert. *The Concept of Mind*. New York: Barnes & Noble, 1949.

Samek, R. A. "The Concepts of Act and Intention and Their Treatment in the Law." *Australasian Journal of Philosophy* 41, no. 2 (August 1963): 198–216.

Samuels, W. "Welfare Economics, Power, and Property." In Wunderlich and Gibson, 1972.

Scanlon, Thomas. "Nozick on Rights, Liberty, and Property." *Philosophy and Public Affairs* 6, no. 1 (Fall 1976): 3–25.

Shrader-Frechette, K. "Agriculture, Ethics, and Restrictions on Property Rights," *Journal of Agricultural Ethics* 1, no. 1 (1988), 21–40.

Staley, O. "The Family Farm Anti-Trust Act." In Barnes, 1975.
Stalley, R. F. "Austin's Account of Action." *Journal of the History of Philosophy* 18, no. 4 (October 1980): 448–53.
Sterba, J. P., ed. *Justice:* Alternative *Political Perspectives*. Belmonst: Wadsworth, 1980.
———. "Neo Libertarianism." In Sterba, 1980.
Strong, A. "Land as a Public Good." In de Neufville, 1981.
Sweeney, J. E. "G. E. Moore and Voluntary Actions." *New Scholasticism* 51, no. 2 (Spring 1977): 196–210.
Taylor, P. S. "The Battle for Acreage Limitations." In Barnes, 1975.
Whiteley, C. "Responsibility." *The Aristotelian Society*, Suppl. XL (1966): 223–34.
Wunderlich, G., and W. Gibson, eds. *Perspectives of Property*. Pennsylvania State University: Institute for Land and Water Resources, 1972.

Ethical Issues in Private and Public Ranch Land Management[1]

Charles V. Blatz

THE ETHICS OF RANCH LAND MANAGEMENT addresses several fundamental questions: How do we identify legitimate goals for the use of potential ranch lands? How do we prioritize those goals and set policy to pursue them with minimal opportunity costs? How do we remain responsive to conditions that might change our priorities? How do we decide who should carry out policies and for what lands? The answer is the same throughout. We should favor the aims of the individual free agent in setting our priorities.

Whose Aims Count and How Much?

What goals are legitimate and how important are they? For private lands, perhaps only individual rights should be respected. Any aim of the owner is worthwhile, but since only the owner's aims count on private land, the owner's preference is the test of relative merit. Assuming efficient opportunity-preserving means are used to pursue private goals, whatever the owner prefers on reflection will be the most important use.[2]

At the same time, it might seem that on public lands with ranching potential, the public's good should be favored. This land belongs to all, at least in the sense that it should serve the good of all. The Taylor Grazing Act of 1934 went a long way toward ensuring that in public ranch land management, individual ranchers would count the most. But those days are past. The Grazing Act has been superceded by the 1964 Classification and Multiple Use Act and the Federal Land Policy and Management Act (FLPMA) of 1976, which made the order of the day multiple use and the officer of the day the federal government. These acts have been reinforced by President Reagan's executive order 12348, which called for public lands inventories leading to the sale of unneeded lands, the proceeds to go toward the national debt. In determining which lands will be retained, competing potential uses will be weighed before decisions are made. In such decisions, presumably no one individual looms larger than another; it is types of uses that are weighed against each other, not individual plans and aims. The prevailing ethical standard seems to be the utilitarian one of producing as much good as possible for as many people as possible. The good is somehow linked to the multiple competing uses championed by ranchers, foresters, mineral developers, recreationalists, and environmental preservationists.

Private rights on private lands, the public good on public lands—no, things are not that simple. Private lands turn out *not* to be completely private in their use. Appeal to the landowner's rights will not properly answer ethical management questions. On the other hand, ethically speaking, public lands should be viewed as private in ways that are overlooked where the public good is favored.

Consider running private lands simply by looking to the rights and preferences of individual landholders. The problems here are clear enough. First, rights to the various uses for private land are often divided. An operator cannot legitimately claim all the water he wants to use. The owner often has no claim on the minerals lying beneath the land's surface. Owners are often required to provide a right-of-way to areas they don't control. Second, ecosystems are open to influence across deeded boundaries. Erosion due to improper range use and damage caused by unfenced animals are examples of harm neighbors may cause one another. The lesson should be clear: Private lands become embroiled in conflicts in the same ways that public lands do. The legitimate uses of particular parcels are often linked across ownership boundaries.

Thus, if on private lands only the rights of the deed holder count, other vested rights will have to be ignored. And to say only that the deed holder's rights in and of themselves count the *most* requires groundless bias or special pleading on behalf of certain landowners against their neighbors and other interested parties, such as mineral developers and energy consumers. How can such favoritism be justified? One person's rights are as important as another's, and any ethical principle favoring certain rights as most important will be biased against holders of the unfavored rights.

Thus, ethical tests of worthwhileness and relative merit of aims must not treat only the aims of selected people as important or as most important. *Any* individual's aims need to be taken into account and treated equally, *if* the management of private lands might adversely affect them. Conversely, however, public land use is private in ethically important ways. Federal managing agencies seeking the public good will not always recognize this.

Utilitarian or social welfare ethics are what I call "product" as opposed to "process" oriented. They ask that we maximize the public good, understood as some desirable end-state. We measure success in numbers of net dollars gained, animal units per month grazed, numbers of board feet harvested, tons of ore extracted, numbers of visitors recorded and so on. The more units of welfare the better, *up to a limit* imposed by the carrying capacity of the resource for the periods of use planned for. If a potential user would not respect those limits, then the user should not be allowed access to the resource, regardless of what market incentives led the user to want to overuse it or what conservative standards of good stewardship led him to underuse. The aims of such a potential user will always lose out to those of the person oriented toward optimal production. An ethic striving to maximize the public good will always discount the aims of the less than optimally productive, treating such aims as less important than the aims of the optimally productive.

But why should such an ethic be accepted? To do so is to engage in a certain form of special pleading. What should be ethically important is the pursuit of goals—that process—not a certain product.

Another problem of special pleading faces utilitarian management of public lands because of its preference for efficiency. Suppose, for example, that it would be less costly to administer public lands if there were fewer graze permit holders. And suppose that in the bargain the administering agencies would be better able to ensure that optimal use was made of the land by allocating it among the largest operators, corporate or individual. Suppose those are the outfits that by virtue of size are able to afford the highest fees while putting the optimal number of animals on the land year after year. Utilitarian management procedures would then favor public land use by these people over even current permit holders. But such an ethic would assign the permits in an inequitable way, overlooking the importance of the disfavored operator's aims.

Finally, this ethic would make public land administration excessively public-oriented by ignoring the *degree of impact* from its policy decisions. Suppose, for example, that we could increase the wealth gained from public land, and with it the number of people who benefit from its development, both in jobs and, ultimately, in lowered cost of living. This could be done by turning over to mineral development lands previously used for grazing, watershed, and recreational purposes. But also imagine that in the bargain it becomes much more difficult for certain ranchers to operate, forcing them to sell out or to supplement their income by working at the mine. We have changed their lives in deeply significant ways, eliminating or seriously curtailing their ability to pursue their aims.

On the other side, the effects on the others are far less significant. The mine workers who aren't from the area would have been mining elsewhere. The lease holders would have developed elsewhere, and the energy consumers would still have run their microwave ovens, though at slightly higher costs per kilowatt hour. We are imagining, then, only a small economic gain for many at the expense of the entire life plan of some—a small economic gain with a total net loss of aims the affected people can pursue.

But this preference would be considered unfair. It is wrong to wipe out the way of life of some just so others can be slightly better off economically. It amounts to favoring a relatively restricted set of goal choices, namely of lower utility bills over the myriad goal choices in a life on a working ranch. Thus, it treats the agriculturalists' aims as less important than those of the mineral developers and their customers. The social-good ethic ends up biased against those who have the most to lose because it ignores the relative impact on the aim pursuits of individuals affected by its policy decisions.[3]

But what is the alternative? We need tests of worthwhileness and relative merit that treat as equally important every aim affected by policy and that do not discount any aim in favor of others. This suggests the following: *The test of worthwhileness of an aim is simply whether or not someone has that aim and whether policy decisions could thwart its pursuit. Each and every aim affected by policy counts.* Further, the test of relative merit assumes that every aim affected by policy counts as much as any other. In an ideal world aims would flourish regardless of their relative merit, but in the real world, aims conflict and must be weighed against one another. However, in the spirit of fairness the policy that will allow for as much pursuit of the conflicting aims as possible, over the long haul, must be favored. Those aims whose pursuit reduces the diversity of competing aim pursuits will be rejected to avoid favoring certain kinds of pursuits or the pursuits of certain individuals. Aims whose pursuit reduces the yield time the resource is capable of sustaining shall also be rejected to avoid bias in favor of present and against future resource users. In short, *we should always seek to employ the resource in favor of allowing as many of the conflicting aim pursuits as we can for as long as we can.*

Public and Private Land Management Responsibilities

But then, who should manage what lands? Just who has responsibilities for *privately* owned resources seems clear, either the owner or an agent of the owner. The obligations of the private manager are to implement policies likely to reach the owner's aims (avowed or projected), taking advantage of available opportunities. The opportunities of the private manager are afforded by technology, operating capital, applicable statutes, general ethical considerations of the sorts explained above, skills of potential employees, and the land itself. Disputes between private managers, if not resolved by the parties themselves, will need to be decided by whoever can settle them in favor of a maximum of competing goal pursuits, generally, the courts. But whoever adjudicates such disputes, the policies on trial will be those of the individual private managers, not those of someone else.

Just who has what responsibilities for *publicly* owned resources is not so clear, however. What is the government's role, and the role of the private manager on public lands? To sort this out, let me ask first what are the ethically justifiable roles for *government agencies at any level*? What, in general, should government managers be authorized or obligated to accomplish?

If public land management should be for the public good, then possibly government managers should identify what that good is and how to achieve it, and then work toward that end. On this view, government managers are agents with goals and aims of their own, pursued by allocating public land resources to private individuals or commercial ventures. They decide what is to be done, when, by whom, for how long, and why. The agency manager, not the private user, in every important sense, controls the project. The guiding light is the maximum profit the land can generate, by the satisfaction of multiple-use demands or other forms of that ethical chameleon, the public good. But this thinking puts the cart before the horse.[4]

No form of government can claim intrinsic legitimacy. If we were to assert this as our special insight or argue it on the basis of self-evident or otherwise unsupported foundations, those who disagree could legitimately accuse us of special pleading.

Alternatively, then, we need to justify our choice of having any government, and then of having a particular one that is an effective means to our ends, the ends, presumably, we are justified in pursuing. Forms of public authority *do not come* justified in and of themselves. They *become* justified insofar as they are good tools for the job at hand, for assisting with the legitimate aim pursuits of the governed. Government is justified instrumentally, not intrinsically. Its proper end is to aid us, the governed, in the pursuit of *our* aims, the realization of *our* plans, the gaining of *our* successes. In doing so, governmental managing agencies will play three important roles.

Land use patterns will have to be determined first by resolving the conflicts between the various potential users. To ensure that their aims are adequately represented, individuals should be required to present and defend a detailed use proposal. This would outline their proposed use over time, the expected impact on the resource yield capacity, and their plans to maintain the resource for sustained yield. Further, and very importantly, the user should state which other aim pursuits are compatible or incompatible with those of the user. Insofar as the conflict-resolving agency is trying to maximize harmonious and competing aim pursuits, plans for innovative, cooperative, and diverse uses can be expected from each applicant. Plans should also specify the extent to which the proposed management would aid in keeping the land in a condition favorable for other demands. This would show how a proposed use would minimally reduce the land's diversity of uses.

Single users could file such proposals for certain parcels. Groups of individuals could file joint single-use proposals for groups of contiguous parcels. Private special use organizations with open membership up to the carrying capacity of an area could file proposals for hunting or fishing privileges that could also include plans for habitat improvement or maintenance at the group's expense.

Always, the user who will hurt others the least but can be hurt the most by other users will be given the greatest freedom where there are several users. For example, the rancher who would use the land for grazing without precluding recreational uses or oil and gas development would be given the most freedom, the others being required not to interfere with the rancher's operations or improvements.

When deciding between use proposals, managers should consider the history of use on the parcel in question. There is good evidence that a history of public land leases running with deeded land increases the value of the deeded land. Use of public land has often led ranchers to make capital improvements to better the land as a ranching resource.[5] Compensation for loss of deeded land value and capital improvement investment when the permit holder loses the land to a nonagricultural use is therefore justified. After all, these are losses of the permit holder's ability to pursue chosen aims. The alternative use plan that maximizes conflicting aim pursuits thus will minimize such losses.

At the same time, the transfer of a use permit from one responsible agricultural user to another would represent no net gain in ranching aim pursuits. Thus, in maximizing aim pursuits, public lands will not be transferred from one responsible agricultural user to another. On the other hand, the transfer of use from an irresponsible user is justified by the increase in agricultural aim pursuits in the long run, again with compensation for the actual (decreased) land and improvement value lost.

In all these ways, the individual aim pursuit approach would enable government managers to equitably settle conflicts over justifiable land use. But the government also has another management role to play.

Government agencies can justifiably serve as overseers conducting periodic reviews of the activities of the individual users. The only legitimate purpose here would be to determine whether the merits of the proposal are merits of actual operation. The only question should always be, was this user correctly the judged steward of the land for maximizing conflicting goal pursuits?[6]

Finally, government managers would have to be empowered to enforce their individual use proposal decisions. However, policy on broader issues like water tables and aquifer drawdown will require broader enforcement authority.

Alternatives for Private Management and Disposition of Public Lands

All this assumes continued governmental ownership of some ranch lands, however. And we cannot merely take it for granted that these lands should not be private.[7] Still, once the various arguments are marshaled they seem to favor government retention of some lands.

The *arguments in favor of transfer* fall into three categories concerned with resource productivity and protection, intangible user benefits, and monetary gains for the user, local tax district, national budget, and taxpayer.

Under resource productivity and protection fall the following claims. If public lands were in private hands, they could be managed in a way most responsive to market opportunities. Also, since the resource would have to benefit the rancher over the years, there would be a monetary incentive to keep the land in condition for optimal sustained yield.

But not all ranchers will suit their style of operation to optimal productivity, and, as we have seen, they shouldn't have to. Further, some ranchers become land speculators, converting grazing lands into croplands for relatively high-priced quick sale. Monetary incentives foster, if anything, good capital stewardship, not good land stewardship. Besides, there is no guarantee in the government plans that the land would end up in the hands of agriculturalists in the first place. And finally, with the use proposal and user management scheme sketched above, individual enterprise could be allowed for, along with resource-protecting oversight.

Second, the argument for privatization may turn to individual user freedom or autonomy and related satisfaction. Transfer would serve freedom and its satisfactions, values cherished as part of our heritage. But again, this assumes that the land will wind up in the hands of agriculturalists. It also assumes that local restrictions like zoning and pollution laws will be less restrictive than federal regulations. Again, the main point is that limits on user freedoms might be due not to public ownership, but to the present attitudes and policies of public managers. The use scheme I have proposed will allow for what is, ethically speaking, the maximum of user freedom. This includes a guarantee of tenure for a presumably extended time during which the use proposal would maximize conflicting aim pursuits.

Third, transfer is said to increase the local tax base, recognize the user's economic interest in the public lands, and cut federal management agency costs and help reduce the federal deficit. All this seems naive. After all, if many public lands in agricultural use were transferred at a rate that would maximally benefit the local tax districts, agricultural uses would not pay those taxes. Further, the government retention scheme I propose could reflect in tenure and rate structure the value users add to the land. Finally, there is no guarantee that transfer will reduce current management costs, rather than shunt present levels of spending in different directions. There is also no guarantee that land transfer fees will be great enough to help the taxpayers or even be used on the national debt.

On the other hand, the management scheme I propose would encourage governmental management at reduced cost as a way to maximize affected aim pursuits. Secure meaningful tenure might allow higher use fees that could go toward the national debt or be returned to the local tax district. Finally, government retention of lands and their low-impact local management by agriculturalists will best preserve the lands' diverse potential, while allowing for the maximal responsiveness needed to resolve conflicts. Whether government retention should be preferred deserves further attention. I do not presume to have settled that or the other questions I have discussed. Perhaps, though, I have provided a useful introduction to the ethics of ranch land management.

Notes

1. A longer version of this paper first appeared in *Agriculture and Human Values* 1, no. 4 (Fall 1894): 3–15. It is reprinted here with permission of the journal and the Agriculture and Human Values Program at the University of Florida, Gainesville.

2. For owners, this would amount to a form of egoism in ethics. See, for example, W. M. Sibley, "The Rational versus the Reasonable," *Philosophical Review* 62 (1953): 554–60. The argument brought here against owner hegemony, namely, that this theory is biased in favor of one of the competing rights holders or landowners, can be generalized and brought against Sibley's view of rational conduct. See my "Incommensurability, Impartiality and Constructions of the Foundations of Ethics," in manuscript.

3. I outline how to determine the depth of impact upon someone's aim pursuits in my paper, "Conflicts Facing Western Agriculture: A Proposal for Their Resolution," in manuscript.

4. See, for example, Robert F. Burford "BLM's Asset Management Program," and Catherine England, "Background of Privatization Issues," in James H. Smits, ed., *Privatizing the Public Lands: Issues Involved in Transferring Federal Lands to Private Owners* (Washington, D.C.: Public Lands Council, 1983) p. 98.

5. Cf. Gary D. Libecap, "Economic Interests of Grazing Permittees," in Smits, just cited, pp. 53–58. While Libecap's analysis and argument for privatization here and elsewhere are interesting, they are incomplete, not considering, for example, the sort of scheme I offer.

6. This question would be within the spirit though not the letter of the Taylor Grazing Act. See, for example, England, cited in note 4, p. 11.

7. See Smits, *Privatizing the Public Land*, in particular, Bruce I. Selfon, "President Reagan's Property Sale Program," pp. 16–17

Philosophy and Agrarianism

James A. Montmarquet

SOCIAL PHILOSOPHY IS CONCERNED with the basic principles, political and moral, governing man in society. As a part of society—and historians link agriculture to the very *origins* of stable, large-scale human societies—agriculture is an important, though too-often neglected, subject for social philosophy. In this essay I will be addressing perhaps the most basic question posed for social philosophy by agriculture, namely: To what extent (if any) and why (if at all) should society adopt policies specifically *favorable* to agriculture? The belief that such policies should be adopted is commonly known as "agrarianism." So my main question can also be put in this way: What basic reasons, grounded in social philosophy, may be given in support of agrarianism?

Aristotle and Classical Thought

The literature and philosophy of ancient Greece and Rome (the "classical" period) was lavish in its praise of the agricultural way of life. No less than Socrates himself, not commonly known for his views on agriculture, is credited by Xenophon with such comments as "not even the blessed can abstain from farming" and that "the best kind of work and the best kind of knowledge is farming, by which human beings supply themselves with necessary things." (*Oeconomicus* of Xenophon, C. Lord, trans.)

Similar sentiments are to be found in Hesiod, Virgil, Cicero, Cato the Elder, and a host of other classical authors.[1] But I am interested here not so much in cataloging these as in this philosophical question: Assume that agriculture *is* an especially virtuous calling. How would it follow that *society* should adopt policies that are especially favorable to agriculture? It is at this point that the philosophy of Aristotle, and Aristotle's philosophical tradition, becomes highly relevant, particularly in three regards:

First, for Aristotle, the proper function of the state (of government) is to realize, as he puts it in the *Politics* (I, 2) "the good for man." The function of government, that is to say, is a specifically *moral* one: it is to perfect us, to realize our highest potentialities as social and rational beings. Aristotle's conception of the state, then, is not at all like the modern idea of government as a kind of neutral arbiter between contending individuals and interests, each with their own private conception of the good. Rather, his ideal state will be committed to the promotion of those qualities—"the virtues"—that all human beings need in order to live well. Hence, if it is true, as we have been supposing, that an agricultural life promotes such virtues, we can say that Aristotle's philosophy—with some qualifications to be noted later—would support a proagrarian policy. Aristotle, that is, would *not* view agriculture simply as one "interest group" to be accommodated politically—which is very much the present view.

Second, a derivative, but still very important, theme in classical thought concerns its view of *property* and property relations. It is significant, especially for a discussion of "family farming," that Aristotle begins his discussion of property with a treatment of its function within the *household*. For it is property held in this connection, and not the general idea of pursuing wealth, that Aristotle regards as contributing to human virtue. W. Mathie nicely summarizes the relevant point:

> Aristotle's claim that wealth has a limit and his attack on the limitless pursuit of wealth are, in the first instance, a subordination of what we call economic activity to the management of the household.[2]

Aristotle is no socialist, no opponent of private property. Rather, like those who defend small family farms today, he thinks that "living well" is more important than the *limitless* pursuit of wealth, and that private property up to a point can serve this end of living well. Beyond this point, as Mathie suggests, Aristotle opposes what later theorists would call "property rights."

Third, another important theme in Aristotle's political philosophy is his association of particular character traits and occupations with particular forms of government (democracy, aristocracy, and monarchy). Here he claims, for example—as Thomas Jefferson would later—that "the best material of democracy is an agricultural population."[3] His idea is that certain forms of government (democracy, for instance) depend on for their existence, and in turn tend to develop in their citizens, certain kinds of character traits (independence, say, in the case of democracy). If we are agreed, then, (as Aristotle was not) that democracy is the best form of government, we will want to support those occupations (like agriculture) that either directly contribute to support for democracy or tend to develop virtues essential to democracy.

All three points, then, converge to give impressive support to agrarianism from Aristotle's perspective. But if we go on to ask, what *sorts* of proagrarian policies would Aristotle's view support, the picture becomes rather more clouded.

Here we can begin by noting that many policies designed today to be favorable to the agricultural sector (e.g., tax credits on the purchase of expensive agricultural equipment, publicly financed agricultural research, and large-scale projects of the sort undertaken by the Army Corps of Engineers) seem to favor not small farming and its associated virtues, but the very limitless acquisition of wealth and productive capacity that Aristotle would have condemned—and that contemporary agrarians do condemn. Also, it is very apparent that most of the central virtues associated with an agricultural life—independence, self-reliance, wise household management, simplicity, industry—by their very nature preclude heavy admixtures of outside assistance. This is not to say, of course, that a basically self-reliant way of life could not from time to time (especially in emergencies) receive outside assistance from government or any other benefactor. But surely there are *limits* operative here. Where, for example, more than half of farm income is derived (as it is today) from one or another type of government assistance program, the justification for these can hardly be that they are to maintain farming as a self-reliant way of life! Moreover, even such a virtue as industriousness is seriously undermined by this state of affairs. Surely an important part of the value of hard work is the sense that one is being rewarded for the *product* of one's labor, as opposed merely to the fact that one is laboring hard.

Modern Political Theory: Locke and Jefferson

We have seen that Aristotle's central concept of virtue provides some justification, though of a limited sort, for an agrarian program of support for agriculture. Let us turn now to the single work of political philosophy that, more than any other, marks a great turning point in Western thought—away from Aristotle and towards more recognizably "modern" ways of viewing man and society. This work is John Locke's *Two Treatises on Government* (ca. 1688).[4]

Like all revolutions, Locke's did not mark a complete break with the past. Locke, for example, inherited from Aristotle (and his followers) the idea that government and its laws must agree with what was called "natural law." Moreover, like Aristotle and Cicero, Locke speaks of natural law as a rule of "man's reason": to follow natural law is to follow those rules that recommend themselves as valid to the rational creatures who we are, and this is the standard against which the actual laws passed by men are to be judged. But if Locke's concept of natural law is traditional, his *use* of this concept is hardly so.

For Aristotle, the starting point for social philosophy is that man is a "social animal" who can only realize his human potential through his relationships to other human beings—within a family and a larger society. The specific provisions, then, of natural law will be rules as to how these social institutions are best operated. For Locke, however, the starting point is radically different. Locke begins by considering what natural laws apply to man in a *pre*-social setting, a "state of nature" in which no organized government or society exists. These rules, in turn, yield a framework of natural *rights* (a concept quite foreign to Aristotle), i.e., rights that would have existed prior to government and that ultimately serve to limit the powers of government.

Among the most important of these rights, and the one most central to my concern here with agriculture, is that of *property*. According to Locke, the original property right each of us has with respect to his own body (par. 27) is extended to objects of our possession when a person "hath mixed his Labour with, and joined it to something [his body] that is his own," thereby removing it "from the common [i.e., unowned] state Nature placed it in . . . " This natural right we have to acquire the fruits of our labor, Locke insists (par. 28–29), is not dependent on the consent of others. Instead, it is limited by other requirements of natural law, namely, that we cannot acquire more than what we could profitably use before it would spoil, and that after we acquire land in this way, there must still be "enough and as good" a quality available for others (par. 31, 33).

From this it should be clear that there is much to please an agrarian—and there was much that *did* please that great agrarian, Thomas Jefferson—in Locke's philosophy. In fact, as Eugene Hargrove has pointed out,[5] it is but a small step from such views of Locke as we have surveyed to that hallmark of American agrarianism, the Homestead Act of 1862, which offered free title to 160 acres of land to anyone who cultivated that land for five consecutive years. Homesteading, however, concerns the quite special case of previously unowned land. Historically, the main problems of agriculture have involved more the tendency of *scarce* lands to be consolidated into relatively few hands, with a resultant large class of landless poor. Jefferson himself, we know, sought to limit this phenomenon by abolishing laws of "entail" (laws that limited inheritance to one or a few offspring in a family). Is there, though, anything in Locke's philosophy to prevent, or argue against, this consolidation of landholdings?

It seems that there is not. As C. B. Macpherson observes,[6] Locke's "astonishing achievement" was to base property right on natural right (and natural law) and then to effectively eliminate all natural law *limits* on property rights. This Locke does, according to Macpherson, through his doctrine (par. 36–37) that once *money* is introduced into society, the two previously mentioned natural law limits cease to apply. Now, with money, goods that would have spoiled may be exchanged for ones that will not; with money, even if acquisition of land by X leaves less *land* for Y, if X would make more productive use of this land than Y and if Y can work elsewhere to buy some of this agricultural produce for his own needs, then the amount of *wealth* still left for Y needn't have declined. So understood, Locke is clearly a defender of the kind of changes in British agriculture that were going on in his own time. Through a process known as "enclosure," rights to lands that had once been farmed in small strips by peasants as part of a village commons were now being asserted by local nobility anxious to consolidate their holdings and increase production. In time, these changes were to considerably increase agricultural production in England, while causing great social dislocation. Surely an agrarian philosophy should do more than endorse such changes, but it is unclear that Locke's philosophy does more than this.

Radical Agrarianism

Arguably, Locke's philosophy constitutes an important advance on Aristotle's in at least one respect: in making *rights* central to political philosophy, Locke's philosophy can speak to the needs of the landless poor, can give voice to their demands for land. In this respect, Aristotle's concern with "virtue" seems, at best, slightly irrelevant; for the needs of these individuals are for property and economic betterment—not virtue *per se*. This promise of Locke's philosophy, however, as we have just seen, is quickly squandered. What I call the "radical agrarians" are interesting here precisely because they go beyond Locke, in insisting on something like a universal right to land, a right that is not alienated by the mere introduction of money into society.

The unifying principle of radical agrarianism is well stated at the beginning of William Ogilvie's "Essay on the Right of Property in Land":

> The earth having been given to mankind in common occupancy, each individual seems to have by nature a right to possess and cultivate an equal share. This right is little different from that which he has to the free use of the open air and running water; though not so indispensably requisite at short intervals for his actual existence, it is not less essential to the welfare and right state of his life through all its progressive stages.[7]

So land, on this view, should be no more open to unlimited private ownership than other natural resources like air and water. Consider now some of its further subtleties and ramifications:

1. Basic to this view is a distinction between rights of *use* and rights of *ownership*. Individuals can possess a right to use, by themselves or in combination with others, a resource without being granted private ownership of it. (The case of water and rights to use water is a perfect illustration.) Radical agrarians are opposed to rights of private ownership of the land—and here they may invoke the biblical phrase, "The Land shall not be sold in perpetuity; for the Land is Mine, saith the Lord" (*Leviticus*)—not private use.

2. Equally basic to this view is the distinction between labor as giving one title to a resource and labor as giving one title to the products and improvements derived from or done to that resource. Here Henry George—the late-nineteenth-century American economic theorist and perhaps the most famous radical agrarian—puts the matter very well:

> If I clear a forest, drain a swamp or fill a morass, all I can just claim is the value given by these exertions. They give me no title to the land itself, no claim other than to my equal share with every other member of the community in the value which is added to it by the growth of the community.[8]

According to the radical agrarian, Locke's philosophy of property goes astray precisely in overlooking this distinction, precisely in supposing that labor can give one a right of ownership of a resource itself.

3. We have discussed Locke's views on how the introduction of money greatly expands each individual's right to acquire land. On this issue, the radical agrarians patently do not agree with Locke. Of the right to own land, Ogilvie writes (p. 9) that it "is a birthright which every citizen still retains." The mere availability of other wealth does not remove this right; it can only be removed by the individual's express wish "after having been in actual possession, or having had a free opportunity of entering into possession of his equal share."

4. What are the practical implications of the radical agrarians' views? Henry George's suggestion, much celebrated and ridiculed in

his own day, was for a single, very heavy ("confiscatory") tax on land *rents*:

> I do not propose either to purchase or to confiscate private property in land. The first would be unjust; the second, needless. Let the individuals who hold it still retain, if they want to, possession of what they are pleased to call *their* land . . . We may safely leave them the shell if we take the kernel. It is not necessary to confiscate land; . . . only rent (p. 343).

George's ideas spawned an important social movement that lasted into the first decade of the twentieth century—but subsequent history, and opinion, have been less favorable to them. Contrary to his expectations, land values as a percentage of national wealth have *declined* sharply this century. If implemented today, his idea for a single tax on rents, it is estimated,[9] could hardly pay for a tenth of the federal budget. As for the idea of a guaranteed minimum in land for each citizen, this, too, is not without its difficulties. If this birthright is to an economically *viable* unit, there would hardly seem to be enough land to go around. But if it is not to such a unit, it is unclear what practical import it could actually have. Most individuals would predictably sell or rent their lots to those who wished to farm, eventuating, one imagines, in something like our present situation. To be sure, there is a laudable goal here: that of achieving the widest possible distribution of landownership, but such a goal may well be more efficiently promoted by less radical-sounding schemes, e.g., by ensuring loan opportunities for those wishing to enter farming or by the government's *not* adopting policies that artificially force up the value of farmland.

Agrarianism Today

We have seen that some support—though more in theory than in practice—is provided for agrarianism by the two great traditions we have surveyed: the "moral virtue" tradition of Aristotle and the "rights" tradition of Locke. (We may here understand the radical agrarians as combining the two: combining Locke's concern with a property right to land with the classical idea that land and farming have special values, which are not reducible to their money equivalents.) What, then, is the status, within a contemporary context, of agrarianism and agrarian ideas?

My own suggestion is that a viable agrarian philosophy is possible today, but only in the context of a new recognition of the value of productive activities *generally*. The philosophies we have examined, I suggest, do take us some of the way towards such an agrarianism—but let me show, briefly, how further advance might be possible.

Economic theory, almost since its inception, has presupposed the value of essentially just one thing: *consumption*. The various activities economics studies—trade and international finance, capital formation, public finance and governmental policy, banking and interest—are deemed valuable to the extent that they contribute to present or future satisfaction of consumers. The contemporary writer, Lester Thurow, speaking of his own profession, puts the matter thusly:

> Economic theory has always treated work—the giving up of leisure time—as an unpleasant disutility that one must be bribed to accept. All enjoyment—utility—is assumed to spring from consumption rather than production. . . . To the economists, man is not a beaver who loves to work but a grasshopper who will work only if privation looms.[10]

Philosophically, the underpinnings of this view are given by a single term: *utilitarianism*. Now utilitarianism involves a combination of two ideas: first, that ultimately what is valuable is pleasant or agreeable states of mind; second, that social arrangments and individual actions should be judged as good or bad strictly to the extent to which they produce such states of mind (and avoid their opposite). Thus, for the utilitarian economist, production is valuable only to the extent to which it leads to agreeable mental states (typically on the part of those who consume what is produced).

There is an alternative to this view, both philosophically and practically. This alternative derives from Aristotle and the natural law tradition we have sketched. This natural law tradition is *teleological*, rather than utilitarian. For the teleologist, the consequences of an act are important, but they in no wise exhaust its moral significance. For the teleologist, moral significance resides in the *nature* of the being who we are, and the extent to which our actions reflect, or *realize*, that human nature. Thus, take the present case of productive activity. The teleologist sees that productive acts are good, in part, because they produce good consequences (e. g., consumer satisfaction), but they are also good as fulfillments of man's innate need and capacity to create sources of future satisfaction. In realizing this need and capacity, agriculture can have a moral significance which, if it is not independent of its consequences for society, is not reducible to them either. And the same would, or could, be true of a steel mill or a university.

This, notice, helps to explain why the average person, who is not schooled in economic theory, views the loss of farmlands, or steel mills, or even universities, as something more than an economic readjustment to changing consumer demands or contingencies of productive efficiency. It also helps to explain, I believe, our willingness—and the willingness of every nation who can afford this—to heavily subsidize basic industries, including agriculture. It may even help to explain our apparent indifference to the fact that such subsidies, even when they are targeted for small producers, have almost always disproportionately benefited larger ones. If the deepest significance of agriculture lies in its being one of man's primary ways of wresting wealth from nature, smallness of operation will not as such be a virtue.

The agrarianism I advocate will mourn the loss of a family farm neither as simply the loss of a commercial enterprise nor as a morally superior "way of life." Unlike Aristotle and the classical tradition, I make no special case either for the moral superiority of agriculture or for the role of government in promoting the morally superior life. (Likewise, unlike the radical agrarians, I make no special case for the unique moral or economic significance of land, and therefore, none for anything like a universal right to land, as opposed to other forms of wealth.) But unlike Locke and the economic tradition which his views on land and money presaged, I see the loss of a farm as not just the failure of a business. Not all means of satisfying consumer demand—and not all consumer demands, for that matter—have equal moral significance. Thus a kind of agrarianism, to my way of thinking, is eminently possible—and necessary—in today's world. This is an agrarianism based not on the fantasy of agriculture as a special occupation, morally more virtuous than others, but on a real description of agricultural productivity and its very human significance.

Notes

1. For further references and discussion, see my paper "Philosophical Foundations for Agrarianism," *Agriculture and Human Values* 2 (1985): 5–14.

2. W. Mathie, "Property in the Political Science of Aristotle" in *Theories of Property: Aristotle to the Present*, Anthony Parel and Thomas Flanagan, eds., (Calgary: Calgary Institute for the Humanities), p. 15.

3. *Politics*, Book VI, ch. 4. It is interesting that Aristotle's reason for this pertains not to the civic-mindedness of farmers, but to their *dis*interest in matters of state. "Being poor, they have no leisure, and therefore do not often attend the assembly," Aristotle remarks.

4. References henceforth, which will be to the second of these treatises, are inserted into the text.

5. Eugene Hargrove, "Anglo-American Land Use Attitudes," *Environmental Ethics* 2 (1980): 121–48.

6. C. B. Macpherson, *The Political Theory of Possessive Individualism* (Oxford: Oxford University Press, 1962).

7. William Olgilvie, *Birthright in Land* (1782; reprint, with notes and a biographical essay by D. C. Macdonald, New York: Augustus Kelley, 1970), p. 7.

8. Henry George, *Progress and Poverty* (1879; reprint, New York: Schalkenberg Foundation, 1955), p. 343. George is criticized on this point by Robert Nozick, *Anarchy, State and Utopia* (New York: Basic Books, 1974), p. 175.

9. See on this point Jacob Oser, *Henry George* (New York: Twayne Publishers, 1974), pp. 54–55.

10. *Dangerous Currents* (New York: Random House, 1983), p. 120.

Jubilee and New Jubilee
Values and Visions for the Land

John Hart

ACROSS RURAL AMERICA TODAY, barn raising is being replaced by barn razing: the lifting up of barns is being supplanted by the leveling down of barns. Celebratory gatherings of families and neighbors pounding hammers have been supplanted by sorrowful groups of spectators jolted by the poundings of the auctioneer's gavel. And each pounding of that gavel seems to drive another nail into the coffin containing the shattered remains of a farm family's dreams.

It is not only the owner-operated family farms that are disappearing. On Main Street, the friendly cafe or barber shop or grocery store is boarded up, and the elementary school playground is empty at recess time. Gone are the morning jokes over coffee, and the children's laughter around the school yard. And the wind blowing through broken windmills seems to ask, "Why?"

The wind blows, too, through forests, where it becomes the voice of trees who lift their leafy arms upward in otherwise silent prayer: blowing through those leaves it becomes the voice of the voiceless, the cry of a creation whose poisoned water, land, and sky threaten the very life they are intended to sustain. The forests, like the farms, are dying: acid rain assaults them from the air above, and chemical wastes from factory and agribusiness attack them from the water below; through their leaves and their roots their life is being taken from them. Again the wind asks, Why?

In the great mining pits across the nation, the voice of the wind is heard only at night. During the day, giant shovels and trucks roar across that land, deafening plants, animals, and people while scarring once-beautiful fields and hills. Their work finished, they move on, bringing "progress" to yet another site, and their owners restore the shattered earth only to the minimum extent required by law. And once again, the wind mournfully asks, Why?

Why, indeed. Why are owner-operated family farms, and the rural banks and businesses that depend on them and support them, vanishing from across rural America in Great Depression numbers? Why are the forests dying? Why are the whales disappearing from the oceans, and why did the buffalo almost vanish from the plains? Why is the federal government trying to force 10,000 Navajos from their lands in Arizona, and why is Peabody Coal Corporation waiting in the wings for them to do so? And why does the artwork of children across the United States increasingly include drawings of mushroom clouds?

Why? Because there is a conflict between people's dreams and profitable nightmares, and a conflict between perceptions of the earth as God's creation and perceptions of the earth as humanity's possession.

Creation in Crisis

The land crisis about which we are concerned today is the inevitable result of capitalism at its best: heightened personal greed and ruthlessness supported by government policies are leading to increased consolidation of the land base of America into fewer and fewer hands. A consequence of this consolidation is that the land is desecrated, people are displaced, and communities are dying. And while this is going on, preparations are underway for the ultimate desecration of the earth: her destruction through a nuclear exchange initiated in order to protect the power of the few to continue their exploitation. When greed is elevated to a virtue, and supported by economic advantage and government policies, Mammon becomes Moloch throughout the land: the god of greed demands human sacrifice. In the process, the God who has created, redeemed, and sanctified the land, a God of justice and compassion, is thrust aside.

Creation is in crisis today. This beautiful earth, full of such bounty for meeting the needs of her children, is being exploited to satisfy the greed of a few. Like the rich farmer in Luke's gospel who wanted to hoard the earth's produce for himself and "eat, drink and be merry" (Lk 12:16–21), the few who control most of the private land in this country wish to proudly celebrate riches garnered at society's expense. They deny their indebtedness to God, to the earth, and to those who labor for them. Their despoliation of God's creation is seen most glaringly in clear-cut forests, in strip mines, in fields planted fencerow to fencerow, in long lines at welfare offices, and, in agricultural areas, in the transformation of farmers from producers of foodstuffs to consumers with food stamps.

The rural crisis does not result from people freely choosing to shift occupations. It is caused by the ideology of greed that permeates the structures of the capitalist economic system, and that is reinforced by the educational and political systems.

In some areas, where black farmers or Native American landowners are trying to hold onto their land base, the ideology of greed is linked to racism. Thus, "heir property" cases are used to deprive blacks of their land, while "allotments" and "termination" are used to violate treaties with, and accelerate injustices against, indigenous peoples.

The Jubilee Year

In 1986, the Catholic bishops of the United States issued an economic pastoral document entitled *Economic Justice for All: Catholic Social Teaching and the U.S. Economy.*[1] In Chapter 2, "The Christian Vision of Economic Life," the bishops note (paragraph 36) that in Old Testament times:

> Every 50th year a jubilee was to be proclaimed as a year of "liberty throughout the land" and property was to be restored to its original owners (Lv 25:8–17, cf. Is 61:1–2; Lk 4:18–19).

There were, actually, four provisions of the Jubilee year: the land was to lie fallow, debts were to be cancelled, Hebrew slaves were to be freed, and the land was to be redistributed.

The biblical context for the promulgation of the Jubilee is the arrival of the Jewish people into a new territory (which would become Israel) after they were liberated from slavery in Egypt. The area in which they were going to settle was very arid: it had little rainfall and few bodies of water to meet the agricultural needs of the people. Thus, a very practical problem emerged: who among the people would have first choice of the best agricultural land? The people decided that the fairest means of land distribution would be by casting lots. This was done by tribes and then by family groupings within tribes, until all those who would work the land had a homestead.

There was a certain flaw in the distribution that resulted, because of its inevitable consequence: those who began with the economic advantage of the best agricultural land would, over time, acquire the lands of their less fortunate neighbors. Eventually, a handful of families would own all of the lands of Israel, and possess great political and economic power over the rest of Israel. That this was not God's intention is evident in another part of Leviticus: when the people arrive in this new region, they are instructed by God:

> The land belongs to me, and to me you are strangers and guests upon the land (Lv 25:23).[2]

God tells the people that there is no ultimate human ownership of land property on the earth, no absolute right to private property in land: God is the ultimate owner of the land. God does allow private ownership in terms of civil laws, but the objective of such ownership must be that the land so owned must meet not only the needs of its owners, but of the broader community as well. God has entrusted a part of his domain to human care, to the community of Israel as a whole. Those who have property in land are, in effect, then mortgaging their holdings from the community as a whole.

Therefore, if the land of Israel were to be consolidated into just a few hands, those few owners might tend to forget the purpose of private ownership, and dominate the rest of their people. And so we read further in Leviticus:

> This fiftieth year you shall make sacred by proclaiming liberty in the land for all its inhabitants. It shall be a jubilee for you, when every one of you shall return to his own property, every one to his own family estate. In this fiftieth year, your year of jubilee, you shall not sow, nor shall you reap the aftergrowth or pick the grapes from the untrimmed vines . . . (Lv 25:10–11).

In this injunction to the people of Israel, three of the Jubilee prescriptions are presented: slaves are to be freed, the land is to be redistributed, and the land is to be rested (see also Lv 25:40–43; 25:13, 23–25, 31–34; and 25:20–22 for reinforcement of these three prescriptions of the Jubilee). The fourth prescription, cancellation of debts, is presented in Deuteronomy 15:1–2 and implied in Leviticus 25:39–40.

The Jubilee year, then, was to be a chance for the poor to begin over: to be freed from slavery, from debts, and from working for others rather than on their own lands.

It is not known how often the biblical Jubilee was practiced. As time went on, those who had acquired large estates in land refused to restore the homesteads to those who now worked for them—or who had been forced from the land entirely and now worked in urban settings. In the eighth century B.C./B.C.E., the prophet Isaiah of Jerusalem proclaims:

Woe to you who join house to house, who connect field with field, till no room remains and you are left to dwell alone in the midst of the land! (Is 5:8)

It is evident that the land is no longer distributed and redistributed among the many, but is being forcibly retained as the private property of a few.

Two centuries later, another prophet writing under the name of Isaiah declares that the Jubilee will be reestablished when God's chosen one comes to the people:

The Spirit of the Lord God is upon me, because the Lord has annointed me; he has sent me to bring glad tidings to the lowly, to heal the brokenhearted, to proclaim liberty to the captives and release to the prisoners, to announce a year of favor from the Lord and a day of vindication by our God, to comfort all who mourn (Is 61:1–2).

Biblical scholars note that the "year of favor from the Lord" is the Jubilee year. Consider, then, that Jesus, in his first sermon in the Gospel of Luke (4:16-21), given in his hometown synagogue of Nazareth, declares after reading those words of Isaiah: "Today this Scripture passage is fulfilled in your hearing" (Lk 4:21). Jesus makes two affirmations with those words: that he is God's annointed one (Messiah), and that it is time for the biblical Jubilee to be observed once again. This, indeed, would be "good news to the poor" (Is 61:1; Lk 4:18): their debts would be cancelled, they would be freed from slavery, and they could return to their ancestral lands.

For the authors of Leviticus and the book of Isaiah, and for Jesus, a value is placed on widespread land distribution. Dispersal of property in .land (and therefore, by extension, of resources in the land) is seen as a means of ensuring the common welfare: people will be better able to earn their own livelihood, political and economic power will be broadly distributed, and society will be periodically reminded of its responsibility for its poorest members. Ultimately, the land belongs to God; historically, it belongs to the community as a whole, and is intended by God, its absolute owner, to meet the needs not only of the relative owners but of the broader community as well. Those who do hold civil titles in land are called to be stewards of the land entrusted to the community by God—and therefore must be concerned not only about the well-being of the neighbor, the other members of the community, but also about the well-being of the earth itself. The Jubilee required that the neighbor's well-being be assisted through cancellation of debts, freedom for Hebrew slaves, and land redistribution; and it required that the earth's well-being be assisted through periodic rest for the land.[3]

A New Jubilee

With the passage of centuries, religious values such as concern for the poor, care for the earth, and community orientation—values embodied in the Jubilee prescriptions—were supplanted by ideologies based on greed, despoliation, and individualism.

What is needed in the United States today, where these selfish attitudes predominate and have become an accepted and promoted aspect of culture, is a New Jubilee, a spiritually based land reform effort that would facilitate dispersed individual and cooperative ownership of the nation's land base, and promote stewardship of that land base by people conscious of their responsibilities as the earth's caretakers.

In the spirit of the Jubilee proclaimed by Jesus, the New Jubilee would attempt to contemporize the basic values of the biblical Jubilee, and thereby offer a new vision for the earth and promote steps toward the concrete social realization of that vision.

The New Jubilee would include:

PERIODIC REST FOR THE LAND, to parallel the Jubilee prescription of letting the land lie fallow: In regenerative agriculture, through cycles and practices that would enable the earth to be replenished and farmers' and ranchers' livelihoods to be maintained; in extractive, non-regenerative industries such as mineral and energy removal, through an earth-respective pace of harvest, and through post-extractive practices that most gently impact the earth and most beneficially allow for her reclamation and recovery; and on public lands such as national forests, parks, seashores, and wilderness areas, in a manner promotive of their pristine beauty and protective of their wildlife.

RESTRUCTURING OF DEBTS encumbering agricultural land, in a manner that would enable owner-operators to retain ownership and practice stewardship, while not endangering the just compensation of those who have extended credit to agriculturalists, as a parallel to the Jubilee requirement that debts be cancelled.

FREEDOM FROM ECONOMIC SLAVERY, to parallel the Jubilee requirement that Hebrew slaves be freed: In agriculture, for migrant farmworkers and tenant farmers, with the objectives of both just compensation for their labor and an opportunity for them to become individual or cooperative owners of agricultural enterprises; and in business and industry, for all working people, that they might receive a just wage for their labor.

COMMUNITY-ORIENTED DISTRIBUTION OF THE LAND AND THE LAND'S GOODS, to parallel the Jubilee obligation to redistribute the land: redistribution of agricultural holdings from the few to the many through the breakup of excessively large holdings into family operations, cooperative operations, and communal operations (through such means as a progressive land tax to redistribute lands, and parity prices to family agriculturalists in order that they might remain on present or redistributed lands); promotion of minority (Black and Hispanic) land ownership; a just and equitable resolution of the land claims of native peoples, as implied in the treaties signed with them; the maintenance (and extension, where required by stewardship) of public lands such as national parks, forests, seashores and wilderness areas; and cooperative regional ownership of energy reserves.

Under such a New Jubilee, promulgated in the best biblical spirit, civil ownership of the land would pass from the few to the many, the land itself would be cared for in the present and in the future, and human societies, as one family of God's children, would share equitably in the bounties of God's creation. The New Jubilee would imply, as did the old Jubilee, not only that large-scale landholdings would be redistributed, but also that people—and their representatives in government—would rededicate themselves to care for the earth, God's garden.

The New Jubilee would require the recognition that *cooperation* is better than *competition*, that "individualism" and "independence" are only myths in agriculture, business, and commerce, and that people's organizations and transformations in economic structures are necessary to overcome the injustices of agricultural, industrial, commercial, financial, and political systems operating mainly in the interests of the wealthy few. One objective of popular efforts to transform the economic system should be that workers—agricultural and industrial—should become, as much as possible, the owners of the enterprise for which they work. Another objective should be regional public ownership of key energy resources soil, natural gas, coal, uranium, solar, wind, water, and geothermal): energy resources are part of the commonwealth and common wealth, and should be used for the commonweal.

Principles of Land Stewardship

If the New Jubilee and the new cooperativism are to be realized in our nation, we must impart anew to North Americans an understanding of the biblical teachings that pertain to the nature of our relationship with the earth, with each other, with other life forms, and with the cosmos as a whole. I would like to suggest that those biblical insights might be embodied in three basic moral theological principles of land stewardship. These principles are

The earth is God's.
The earth is entrusted to humanity,.
The earth and her fruits are to be shared equitably through the ages.

Observance of these principles would imply acknowledgement that God is the ultimate owner of the land, that God has entrusted that land to human caretakers who are responsible to God for that trust, and that God has intended that the earth provide first for the *needs* of all living beings, now and into the future, before any other individual or corporate or ethnic or national appropriation of the earth and her goods.

Feudalism on the land will be the inevitable retrogressive result of unchecked capitalism and racism. This trend toward a feudal system is apparent today, when formerly independent family farmers throughout the country are becoming the tenant managers and serfs of agribusiness lords, and when forest, mineral, and energy resources primarily benefit a few shareholders instead of the people as a whole. Capitalist and racist economic practices across America today are promoting a feudal economic system that, when fully in place, will be a new type of soviet collectivism: the corporate millionaires, not the communist party elite, will control the labor of, and live from the sweat of, tenant farmers, farmworkers, miners, foresters, fishers, and factory workers—while proclaiming all the while that we live in a democratic and free society, with "liberty and justice for all."

The survival of the earth and of all her creatures requires a new and better future for the land and for the peoples of the land. In order to envision and to work for that better future, people must explore their relationships with their Creator, with each other, with all the earth's creatures and with the earth herself, and better those relationships. They must begin anew to *build* barns, not *bulldoze* barns.

The promulgation of a New Jubilee would be a theoretical and practical way to effect a congruence between religious values and social reality, and to realize a vision of a productive, bountiful and peaceful earth for generations to come.

Notes

1. U.S. Catholic Bishops, *Economic Justice for All: Catholic Social Teaching and the U.S. Economy*, (Washington, D.C.: National Conference of Catholic Bishops, 1986).

2. The midwestern Catholic bishops of a twelve-state region chose this insight from Leviticus as the basis for their statement on land issues, *Strangers and Guests: Toward Community in the Heartland* (Des Moines, Iowa: National Catholic Rural Life Conference, 1980).

3. A more in-depth analysis of biblical values regarding land ownership and use is contained in John Hart, *The Spirit of the Earth: A Theology of the Land* (Mahwah, N.J.: Paulist Press, 1984), pp. 65–82.

II.B.
Rural Communities and Rural Women

THE PREVIOUS SECTION approached the exploration of agriculture's practitioners through an examination of issues concerning who owns and who manages the land. This viewpoint will not tell the whole story, however. It does not reveal the community context of agriculture, nor does it speak about the special contributions of any particular group of producers. The papers in this section take up the further vantage points offered by the study of rural community life and farm women. (Again the emphasis is on the present-day United States.)

The first of the papers comprise excerpts from a classic comparison of two sorts of farming communities—one serving many small-scale family farms and another serving fewer larger farms. As Walter F. Goldschmidt argues in his study "Small Business and the Community," scale of farming seems to make a significant difference to rural communities. This difference shows up in ways that Americans value, namely, in terms of physical amenities, "material possessions, social democracy, and economic opportunities."

Goldschmidt found farming around both communities to be modern, specialized, and industrialized. However, farm size differed significantly, with the apparent results that the two communities, Arvin and Dinuba, differed significantly in living conditions, social services, quality of public facilities such as schools and parks, number of individuals self-employed and self-governed in the community, and the amount of retail trade. Goldschmidt considers and rejects the possibility that these differences are due to factors other than farm size. And, he goes on to argue that although farm size itself can be partly explained partially by environmental factors, differences in the settlement periods of the two communities, and differences in the products grown around them, farm size can still help explain why Arvin and Dinuba differ in valued ways. As Goldschmidt shows, much of that explanation revolves around the simple fact that fewer farms means a concentration of wealth, influence, and effective demand for public services. In response to these concentrated demands and influence, social amenities are targeted on fewer individuals or else are acquired by the privileged few outside of the farming community. Perhaps this same story could be told to explain what is reported in the next paper.

Sam M. Cordes, in his discussion "The Interface Between the Health Care System and the Rural Environment" is concerned particularly with the rural availability of quality health care. Characteristic of rural areas is a relatively low population density. Perhaps, then, just as relatively low populations due to large farms deprived Arvin of many social amenities, the low population density of rural areas generally has hurt them when it comes to the availability of quality medical care. Perhaps. But the reader suspects that Cordes would urge us away from such sweeping generalities to a more contextual appraisal of health care in the United States. For, according to Cordes, the primary characteristic of rural America as it has evolved in the last twenty to thirty years is its diversity. As he points out, rural areas differ from each other in population, economic base (many of them enjoy major industrial employers), and such things as the availability of health care.

In the face of such diversity and with his expressed ethical commitment to policies that will serve basic human needs, perhaps the clearest lessons that Cordes could teach are the ethical need for equity and the documentable tendency toward non-equity in health care. After exploding several myths about rural America, including the view that its citizens are among the country's healthiest, Cordes shows that there are desirable connections between rural health care services and efforts toward rural development. As this demonstration makes clear, not only is equity in rural health care defensible on the grounds of serving basic needs, it is also defensible as a part of the constellation of factors (such as the availability of jobs and money for education) that will improve rural life in general. Someone moved by these considerations to champion equity in rural health care might wonder what political miracle will spare sparsely populated rural areas from the national rigors of cost containment. Cordes' article closes with a discussion of ways people can work at various levels on behalf of equity in rural health care.

No doubt efforts to support rural health care will call for differential spending that favors rural areas in at least per capita expenditures. How in the name of justice and equity can such differential spending be justified? Some philosophical dimensions of this question are addressed by Mary Gore Forrester in her paper "Some Considerations of Justice in Rural Health Care Delivery." Forrester begins by defining equality of health care as the same care to meet the same need, regardless of the patient's ability to pay and regardless of other considerations unrelated to health, such as gender and race. She identifies the basic principle of equity as the source of such a view. On this principle, health care is just one good in which people are equally deserving.

Still, are we to achieve equal distribution of health care by taking from some to give to others? Would differential or redistributive public support for health care be justifiable for the rural areas? Forrester notes that some would say "yes," while others would disagree. Further, she notes that while equality is sometimes served through respecting property and rewarding merit, it may also be served by redistributions to repair unequal distributions, or to ensure that people share equally in social benefits as well as social burdens. Thus equality pushes us in both directions with respect to the question whether or not differential assistance for rural health care is justified.

In spite of this appearance of dual tendencies in the notion of equity, Forrester shows that two concerns, that burdens and benefits be equally shared and that property and desert be equally protected, will argue for special public assistance for rural health care. Some of the details of what forms that assistance might take are discussed.

The remainder of the paper carefully defends these conclusions against objections that might be raised. In particular, Forrester considers whether all are obligated to share the burdens of rural agriculturalists and their neighbors, whether just living in a rural area is not itself compensation enough for relatively poor health care, and whether the extra cost for rural health care will not lower everyone's medical well-being unjustifiably. In the end she concludes that none of these objections prevails. Of course, not everyone can be assured of every medical advantage, but still, Forrester argues, additional assistance for rural medical services is justified on the grounds of equity.

Cornelia Butler Flora in her article "Women and Agriculture" leads in another direction and to lands other than the United States. Her concern is with the history of the changing terms of women's farm labor and their other contributions to agricultural production. Flora's analysis concentrates on women's access to and control of land capital and labor for agricultural production. She makes quite clear that we have moved from a time of male-female complementarity when females performed such crucial tasks as seed selection, planting, cultivating, and harvesting (along with the household tasks and childcare), to a time when women came to serve agricultural export development schemes much as did men did—by selling their labor for standardized tasks—or by continuing as subsistence agriculturalists even though they were disadvantaged relative to the men who were selling their labor or involved in cash crop production. More recently in developing countries where food crop farming has been replaced largely by export farming of nonindigenous food crops, even these changed roles, including subsistence farming, elude women. Low demand for exports, and loss of the traditions of subsistence farming have left women without wage labor and without subsistence activity in agriculture.

This sequence of subsistence, colonial plantation or hacienda, and then cash crop export farming shows the continuing disempowerment of women in agriculture outside of the United States. Their role as partner has changed to one of irregularly employed laborer, economically handicapped subsistence provider, or unemployed, unskilled, and landless agricultural laborer.

Flora closes with recommendations of how agricultural development should recognize and accommodate both the contributions women can make to agricultural production and the close links such contributions will have to women's reproductive contributions. Finally, she concludes with a reminder of the ways in which women's work in agriculture generally, in both food and nonfood production, in labor both on and off the farm, can increase a farm's productivity and help see it through the economic valleys that will be encountered in the internationally interdependent conditions of today's food and fiber markets.

This point, the strength and resiliency given to the farm-home unit by diversifying production through women's labor, is also emphasized by Christina H. Gladwin in her discussion "Values and Goals of Florida Farm Women: Do They Help the Family Farm Survive?" Gladwin concentrates on the contemporary picture in one area of the United States, reporting an empirical research that she and others have undertaken. Results indicate that many men are working off the farm to help make ends meet, leaving more farm work to women, who are coming to see themselves more as farmers than as spouses of farmers. Women's work, both on and off the farm, was found to complement men's work.

Gladwin's study covers farm women's motives for being on the farm, and for working off the farm. In addition, she studied perceptions of the source of difficulties facing farmers and the best ways to cope with these. The results of these studies lead Gladwin to conclude that it is for the sake of the family and the continuation of the family farm that women contribute to the farm enterprise. Gladwin ends on a pessimistic note as she takes up the question whether the values represented and nurtured by women who farm can survive in the face of economic pressures on the small family farm in the United States.

Both Flora and Gladwin emphasize with apparent approval the complementary character of men's and women's contributions to the farming enterprise, yet both emphasize the differences between these contributions. Perhaps this quiet approval indicates a belief in the basic value of partnerships in family living. The family farm would be defensible, then, not so much as an efficient means to the basic human needs of its residents and ultimate customers, nor as an arena in which individuals live their lives in a family on the land. Rather the family farm would be the only, or perhaps just one, setting for the intrinsically valuable life of cooperative familial reproductive and productive enterprise. If so (and this suggestion is only offered as food for thought), then, looked at through the eyes of many farm women, the nature and value of the farming enterprise would be akin to what Montmarquet (if not also Berry) suggests as a new agrarianism. The values underlying assessments of agricultural policy and practice would lie, ultimately, in the characteristically human activity of cooperative familial production and reproduction. Certainly this is not the only ethic compatible with what Flora and Gladwin report and the conclusions they draw. But it is one possibility worth keeping in mind as we investigate other issues connected with agricultural policy and practice.

Small Business and the Community

A Study in Central Valley of California on Effects of Scale of Farm Operations (Excerpts)

Walter F. Goldschmidt[1]

THE COMPARATIVE ANALYSIS OF ARVIN AND DINUBA, communities of large and small farms, was predicated under the following hypothesis. Within the framework of American tradition, what effect does scale of farm operations have upon the character of the rural community?

Essentially the technique has been to establish the area of similarity and difference between the two towns, assuming that the qualitative differences in social life rest upon fundamental causes in the economy of the communities. . . . [The analysis leads to] . . . an explanatory hypothesis which will account for all known difference without either calling upon mystic and undefined causes or doing violence to accepted understanding of human social behavior.

Essential Cultural Similarities

The differences between Arvin and Dinuba are differences within a broader framework of similarities. The necessary emphasis upon divergent social characteristics should not obscure this fundamental fact. Both communities belong to a common cultural heritage, so that, strictly speaking, the conclusions can have validity only in terms of that common tradition. They are, as a matter of fact, not so much differences in culture as they are differences in quality. The social conditions which have particularly attracted our attention are between good living conditions and bad, relative degrees of social equality, relative amounts of social homogeneity and participation, relative amounts of social services and of economic opportunity. These are differences on a scale of values, and acceptance of their significance implicitly recognizes that physical comfort, material possessions, social democracy, and economic opportunities are all desirable qualities in a community. Nobody imbued with American culture can cavil with such a scale of values.

The important thing here is that the two communities, therefore, do not have divergent value systems and social customs, but rather that they meet their own values with different degrees of success.

Essentially, Arvin and Dinuba are part of a common system of agricultural production, best understood as industrialized. Both also partake of a single culture pattern which, in turn, can best be described as urbanized.

By industrialized farming is meant the system of producing crops intensively, solely for the cash market, with a high degree of farm specialization, utilizing great quantities of capital and requiring a large input of labor hired on an impersonal basis. Large-scale operations tend to intensify these qualities, but the pattern is not dependent upon large units. It seems probably, however, that the existence of large-scale—particularly of corporate—operations within the broader area and with which the small farmer must compete is an essential element in developing the industrial pattern.

The urbanized culture pattern that results clearly reflects the social behavior of the cities and follows from the industrial nature of farm production. Its primary characteristic is the general acceptance of pecuniary standards of value and a social status system based upon money wealth. Such a set of values inevitably leads to a more or less closed class system based upon economic status, and expressed to the individual largely in terms of occupation. These features are common to Arvin and Dinuba, though the degree of social segregation and the social distance between occupational classes are markedly different. Urbanized culture has further effects. As a result of class stratification, and because of the complexity of society, there is a tendency toward developing social action in terms of special interests rather than on a community-wide basis. For that reason associations of like-minded persons tend to play a very important part in the functioning of the community. While specific differences have been noted, here again we get a common fundamental pattern. This aspect of urban culture is reflected in the specialization of the activities and interests of the individual—the tendency to be concerned with a single and very partial role in the total functioning of the economy. The farmer has traditionally held out against this aspect of the industrialization of the world. The farmer as jack-of-all-trades is the accepted American picture. Yet in the economy of agricultural production in the irrigated areas of California, the farm operator, like his city-dwelling cousin, has become specialized in his operations. The 40-acre farmer as well as the operator of 4,000 acres will show such specialization, though obviously there will remain considerable difference in degree.

It is against a background of such common cultural characteristics that the divergence between Arvin and Dinuba must be examined.

Recapitulation of Social Differences

Within the framework of cultural similarity, the differences between Arvin and Dinuba take a clearer meaning. The picture in Arvin may be contrasted with the Dinuba situation in the following way:

1. The greater number of persons dependent upon wages rather than upon entrepreneurial profit.
2. The lower general living conditions as measured by level-of-living scale and the subjective evaluation of households.
3. The lower degree of stability of population.
4. The poorer physical appearance and condition of houses, streets, and public buildings.
5. The relative poverty of social services performed by the community.
6. The poorer schools, parks, and facilities offered youth.
7. The relative dearth of social organizations serving the individuals in the community and the community as a whole.
8. The fewer religious institutions.
9. The lesser degree of community loyalty expressed.
10. The apparently fewer decisions on community affairs made by the local community and the apparently smaller proportion of the population participating in such decisions.
11. The apparently greater degree of social segregation and greater social distance between the several groups in the community. (This and the preceding items have been labeled apparent because neither is amenable to statistical evaluation, though considerable evidence is at hand to indicate their existence.)
12. The lesser amount of retail trade, the fewer business establishments, and the low volume of trade in those classes of merchandise most generally accorded a high place in social values.

This constitutes a rather imposing list of social and economic factors, reflecting the quality of the society in the two communities in which the one fulfills rather well our normal expectations of social life and the other consistently fulfills them less satisfactorily. The number of items and the consistency in their implications can hardly rest on purely fortuitous grounds.

Possible Causative Differentials

However, as already indicated, other differences between Arvin and Dinuba than the scale of farm operations might be invoked as the cause for the qualitative differential between Arvin and Dinuba. While many of these differences are functionally interrelated, a listing of them under major headings will serve to clarify their importance. Obviously they are not all of like importance—some clearly are secondary reflections of more fundamental factors while others would appear to throw the advantage in the wrong direction. Differences in physical environment, cultural and demographic features, community history, agricultural production, and farm organization are listed. (see Table 1)

Under these five headings are included fourteen separate items, some with great differences, such as farm size and age of community; some with large differences, such as tenancy and major crops; some with practically no difference, such as intensive land use and value of production; and a few where the advantage would appear to lie with Arvin, such as available good land, other resources, and seasonality of employment. . . .

Environmental Factors

Factors in the environment are more impressive for their similarities than their divergences. . . . The only factor of the environment which is markedly divergent is the water resources. . . .

The situation with respect to water has . . . had an effect upon size of farms in the Arvin area. The requirement for deep and expensive wells with large water flow has made it necessary to irrigate fairly large tracts with each pump—about 200 acres for efficient operation. Many farms in the Arvin area get water from wells owned either cooperatively or corporately, so that it is possible, even with this water situation, to operate small units efficiently; furthermore, most of the land is in units which are larger than the water requirements of single wells, and therefore farm size is not clearly dependent upon the need for deep wells. Nevertheless, this high initial investment has inhibited the development of small units and contrariwise been influential in the creation of larger ones. Furthermore, the depth to groundwater held up the intensive use of Arvin lands till efficient pumping plants were developed by engineers, so that the water situation was responsible for the late growth of Arvin. Summarizing, the water supply has had little or no effect upon the economic welfare of operating farmers that could create social poverty, but it has had some influence upon the size of farm units and upon the period of development of Arvin lands.

TABLE I

Differences between Arvin and Dinuba

I. Environmental Factors	*Arvin*	*Dinuba*
1. Land:		
(a) Area served	64,000 acres	43,000 acres
(b) Land in farms	46,000 acres	34,000 acres
(c) Intensive uses	22,000 acres	24,000 acres
(d) Land of soil classes 1 to 3	59,000 acres	31,000 acres
2. Water		
(a) Source	Pumped	Surface suplemented with pumps
(b) Cost	$6.92 per acre	$4 per acre
3. Other resources:		
(a) Minerals	Oil leases general	None
(b) Recreation	Little or none	Little or none
II. Cultural and demographic factors:		
1. Population of community	6,000	7,400
2. Cultural Origins:		
(a) American Origin	88 percent	81 percent
(b) Native Californian	4 percent	19 percent
(c) Dust Bowl migrants	63 percent	22 percent
(d) Median length of residence	less than 5 yrs.	15 to 20 yrs
3. Educational attainment (average for family heads)	7.6 yrs	8.4 yrs.
4. Economic status:		
(a) Median income bracket	$1,751–$2,250	[same]
(b) Wage labour as proportion of family heads	81 percent	49 percent
III. Historic factors:		
1. Age of community (as of 1944)	31 years	56 years
2. Decade of major growth	1930–40	1910–20

IV. Agricultural production factors:

1. Value of production (1940)	$2,438,000	$2,540,000
2. Type of farming:		
(a) Proportion irrigated land in orchard and vineyard	36 percent	65 percent
(b) Proportion in row crops	41 percent	11 percent
(c) Proportion in cotton	29 percent	7 percent
(d) Proportion of farms in fruit	35 percent	79 percent
(e) Proportion of farms in field crops	40 percent	17 percent

V. Farm organization factors:

1. Tenure:		
(a) Tenancy	42 percent	14 percent
(b) Absentee ownership	36 percent	16 percent
2. Labour requirements:		
(a) Man-hours of labour required	2.9 million	3.5 million
(b) Requirement for hired labour	2.3 million	1.4 million
(c) Minimun labour requirement as percent of maximum	25 percent	20 percent
(d) Maximum outside seasonal workers required	1,175	1,595
3. Size of farm operations:		
(a) Number of farms over 160 acres	44 percent	6 percent
(b) Acreage in farms over 160 acres	91 percent	25 percent
(c) Average farm size	497 acres	57 acres
(c) Average value of production	$18,000	$3,400

The availability of surface water in the Dinuba district and the relatively simple engineering and low investment in water resources made it possible to develop that area early. Establishment of an irrigation district under the original Wright Act made it advantageous to subdivide and sell the land. Thus the Dinuba water supply was a responsible agent in establishing farm size in that community.

Cultural and Demographic Factors

In Arvin 8 out of 10 families depend upon wages for their livelihood. In Dinuba 5 out of 10 are wage earners. These workers, especially those who are agricultural workers, have little economic or social investment in the community. Furthermore, they do not supply the leadership for social activities, which almost without exception comes from farmers and white-collar workers. The fact, therefore, that in one community there are approximately 1,000 families which make up the category from which such leadership normally arises, while in the other only about 250 families are in that position, is extremely important. It influences other demographic factors as well as the development of social institutions. This differential is, in turn, very largely a direct result of farm size—a simple arithmetical certainty, for the number of farmers that can be supported by a given resource base is a direct function of the amount of resources each one controls. The influence of size of farm on size of the merchant and other white-collar categories is less direct, but there is good reason to believe that such influence exists, as will be developed below.

Historic Factors

There are two pertinent facts about the history of the two communities which have an influence upon the character of their social institutions. These are: (a) The relative age of the two towns, and (b) the different epochs or periods in which they came into being.

It is difficult to say what point in time represents the beginning of a community. In Dinuba the year 1888 is generally accepted. It was in this year that the Alta Irrigation District was formed, that the post office was created, and the town officially inaugurated. . . . Nineteen hundred thirteen, the year prior to the establishment of the Arvin school, is most comparable to that of 1888 for Dinuba and places the two towns just 25 years apart in point of origin. . . . (see Table 2)

The effect of age on community per se—as distinct from the effect of the epoch of growth—can be eliminated if we examine the time at which facilities were developed with respect to the growth of the town. In table 2 are the approximate dates of these basic developments in Dinuba, the date of comparable developments in Arvin, and the calculation of the age of the community at the time of each development. Five of the items cited for Dinuba have not been developed in Arvin at all, though all took place in Dinuba prior to 1920. Three others—park, bank, and high school—had not actually been brought to fruition at the time of field study though action had been initiated in each. Had these all been developed during 1944, they still would not have had a growth record comparable to that of Dinuba. In most of those items which Arvin has acquired, there were 10 or more years' difference in age, and only in a single instance did Arvin acquire improvements as soon as Dinuba, and in no instance sooner.

[Table 2 shows that] . . . according to the growth of Dinuba there has been ample time for the development of fundamental physical improvements and social services which have not come about and that virtually every feature which Arvin has was obtained at a later stage in growth than comparable ones in Dinuba. . . .

The most probable effects of the historic recency of Arvin as compared to Dinuba are these: The relative newness is contributory to the fact that a large portion of the population is relatively young, while the old-age brackets are underrepresented. Since Arvin grew during a period of migration of destitute persons from the Dust Bowl, the period of growth accounts in part for the preponderance of persons from that area. It seems likely that, despite the fact that other communities of like age have developed them, the influence of the automobile inhibited the growth of local social and economic services. At least it has made it possible for a community to function despite their absence.

Agricultural Production Factors

The specific difference between Arvin and Dinuba with respect to farm production is that Dinuba is overwhelmingly a fruit—specifically grape—producing area, while Arvin is dominated by row crops, mostly cotton. Several measures of this difference have been presented. In terms of intensive land use Dinuba has nearly twice the proportion of orchard and vineyard (65 percent as against 36 percent) and only a fourth the proportion of row crops (11 percent as against 41 percent). In terms of value of production, Dinuba fruit is again twice as great as Arvin (69 percent compared to 36 percent), cotton is a third as great (7 percent compared to 20 percent), and all row crops a fifth (8 percent compared to 41 percent). Forage crops and livestock are, roughly, comparable in extent, while grain production is far more im-

TABLE 2

Date of Civic Developements in Arvin and Dinuba

Development	*Approximate date of initiation*		*Age of community at intiation*		*Age difference*
	Arvin, 1913	*Dinuba, 1888*	*Arvin*	*Dinuba*	
Community hall 1938	About 1900	Before	25	12	13
First newspaper	About 1938	1898	25	10	15
City park	1944[3]	1898	31	10	15
High school	1944[3]	1899	31	11	20
Second newspaper		1902		14	Over 17
Water system as public utility	1938	1902	25	14	11
First bank	1944[3]	1902	31	14	17
Incorporation		1906		18	Over 13
Second bank		1910		22	Over 9
First paving		1915		27	Over 4
First sewer	1940	1915	27	27	0

portant in Arvin than in Dinuba. The financial important of this class is minor, but the area of land use is greatest of any single class in Arvin. . . .

[This comparison suggests some interesting questions:] Is the association between impoverished social milieu and cultivation of cotton a direct one, or does it result from the further association between cotton, on one hand, and, on the other, the existence of an economically destitute and socially impoverished labor class and/or the speculative cash production of the enterprise? Formulated this way, the questions permits of but one answer—the latter. Yet this raises a real problem, if cotton per se is to be explanatory. The detailed analysis of farm production shows that both communities engage in production for the cash market and, furthermore, that the amount of labor required is higher in the grape-producing area of Dinuba than in the more diversified Arvin community. Requirements for labor are, therefore, not the differentiating factor and cannot explain the divergence between Arvin and Dinuba. . . .

Cultivation of cotton and other "row" crops, especially potatoes, may be partially responsible for the large operations in Arvin. Insofar as this is the case, the type of production is responsible for the proportions of farmers and farm laborers. However, the proportion of row-crop farms in the lower size categories is almost as great as the proportion of fruit operations, and some of the largest units are devoted chiefly to fruit production. Like the water situation, the kind of crops grown is therefore partially responsible for the size of farm pattern in Arvin.

Farm Organization Factors

Three aspects of farm organization attract our attention as possible causative factors in determining the differences that exist between Arvin and Dinuba: tenure pattern, labor requirements, and size of farm operations.

Arvin has a high proportion of tenants whereas Dinuba has far fewer. Likewise, the proportion of absentee owners in Arvin—here defined as owners reported living outside the county—is over twice that in Dinuba. In general, it is expected that owner-operators and resident-owners are more concerned with community welfare and social services than are tenants and absentee owners. While nothing in the present study either corroborates or refutes this, it may generally be accepted as a working hypothesis.

It is therefore accepted that in some measure the relative social poverty rests upon tenure pattern. This difference in tenure pattern is partially the result of historic timing and outside social forces. It is also in considerable measure a function of scale of farm operations and social poverty. Table 1 shows that tenancy is more frequent on large farms, over 160 acres, than on small farms. It has also been shown that the general social conditions in Arvin have caused some owner-operators and other natural leaders to leave the community. How influential these forces are in creating the tenure pattern of Arvin cannot be assessed, but certainly they are not wholly negligible.

The second aspect of farm organization is the labor requirements of operation. This has been touched upon in the discussion of occupation structure. At that point, we saw that occupation structure is a very important aspect of the difference between two communities. The question therefore arises as to whether differences in labor requirements on farms in the two communities create that differential in occupation structure. The answer is an unqualified no. For the production of commodities in Arvin requires just under 3 million man-hours of labor while the Dinuba production, reaching the same growth value, requires 3½ million man-hours of work. That the labor structure is a function of scale of operations becomes clear when we examine item V.2.b under this heading in Table 1. Only a small fraction of Arvin labor is absorbed by farm operators while in Dinuba three-fifths of the work can be performed by farm operators. . . .

Size of farm operations is the third characteristic of farm organization, and the one that the present study was designed to test. We find that the differences between average size of farm are great—in the neighborhood of 9 to 1 when taken on an acreage basis, 5 to 1 in value of products, and 3 to 1 if adjusted for intensity of operations. Nine-tenths of all farm land is operated in units of 160 acres or more in Arvin as against one-fourth in Dinuba.

Repeated allusions have been made to this factor. We have seen that water resources, historic timing, and type of farming were each to some measure responsible for the large farms in Arvin and the small ones in Dinuba. We have also seen that scale of farming operations had an effect upon the demography of the population, farm tenancy, and, above all, on the requirements for hired labor in each area and the occupation structure of the two communities. It is also true that throughout the intensively cultivated areas of the state, those communities with large-scale farming generally offer fewer economic and social services than those with moderate-sized farms. There remains no question that size of operations is therefore an important factor in establishing the kind of social environments found in Arvin and Dinuba. The place of this factor in the causal forces will be presented in detail in the succeeding section of this chapter.

An Explanatory Hypothesis

It is now possible to formulate a hypothesis of the chain of causative forces which were responsible for the divergence of social conditions between the two communities whose fundamental cultural heritage and economic circumstances are similar. In formulating such a hypothesis all the pertinent known facts should be explained and their forces understood in terms of recognizable social process. Naturally such a formulation cannot be complete and final but can approach that only insofar as social processes are presently recognized and understood.

The physical landscape and the geographic position of Arvin and Dinuba are sufficiently similar to produce an agricultural base to support communities equivalent in facilities offered, except that the water supply in Arvin created special circumstances. The necessary depth of the water level and the attendant need for larger capital investments delayed the intensive development of Arvin soils until adequate pumps were produced, and inhibited somewhat the growth of small farms. The delay in development made the land available to big operators at a time when industrialized fruit production in California was at its inception. Therefore, the water situation was doubly responsible for the fact that Arvin was a large farming community. It should be noted, however, that the water supply did not prevent small farms, and a few such units came into the community early and have been farmed continuously ever since. It is doubtful if the water supply had any other direct effects, though its cost may have created specific hardships in an earlier era. It is probably that other causes were contributory to the development of large-scale operations and the belated development of the area, but such causes are not readily apparent and were not the subject of specific analysis. High investment for farm development because of the water situation may also have been a contributory cause to the high tenancy in Arvin, since owners could rent to operators who irrigated several pieces of land from a single well.

The scale of operations that developed in Arvin inevitably had one clear and direct effect upon the community: It skewed the occupation structure so that the majority of the population could only subsist by working as wage labor for others. It probably had some effect upon the development of row crops. The relatively late development of Arvin placed it in a period of growing demand for vegetables and other row crops as contrasted with fruit. These two forces combined to give Arvin a large proportion of row crops, though fruits were also developed to a considerable extent. The large need for labor, and the period of major growth, resulted in the aggregation of a large proportion of destitute white migrant labor with poor social and economic background. . . .

The occupation structure of the community, with a great majority of wage workers and very few persons independently employed and the latter generally persons of considerable means, has had a series of direct effects upon the social conditions in the community. These effects are applicable only given the total cultural situation that exists in America and particularly in California agriculture. The large labor population inevitably means large groups with poor economic circumstances, for the conditions of wage work in agriculture have permitted of nothing else. This in turn means poor housing, low level of living, existence of slum conditions and little money for community improvement. It means that a large portion of the population has little vested interest—economic or social—in the community itself. Such lack of ties, together with the seasonal nature of wage work in agriculture, results in a high turn-over of population (or instability of residence). The laboring population does not take leadership in general civic action and rarely supports organizations that exist, out of a usually well substantiated feeling of ostracism that results from the large differences in economic status. Thus general social facilities do not come into being for lack of leadership and support. This tendency is furthered by their own lack of funds and by their instability as residents in the community.

The occupation structure leaves few who are in an economic and psychological position of leadership. These few consist largely of people who can afford to engage in the social activities of urban centers and who regularly do so. This mobility tends to drain their social interests away from local activities and renders them a less valuable asset to local community welfare than are less well-to-do farmers, though their value to the broader area of activity may be equally great.

This social mobility engendered by their well-being was made possible by the fact that the automobile gave them physical mobility as well. That this mobility was available to them from the outset made it unnecessary to develop local satisfactions, whereas if they had once been developed they would likely have continued. Thus the period of development of Arvin was a contributory cause to its social poverty.

The fact that the large farming community is of necessity made up of large groups of laborers with low incomes on one hand, and a small group of well-to-do persons on the other, tends to impoverish its social institutions of the leadership they require. It also impoverishes retail trade. For the farm laborer is generally unable to make a normal complement of purchases for family living because of his poverty, while the farm operator tends to make his purchases, as he does his social contacts, in the city. Thus the merchant group does not grow proportionate to the population, but lags behind it. This again reduces the proportion of independently employed.

The lack of economic and social facilities in the community has a continuative effect. The poor conditions tend to repel those very people who are most needed to enrich it. It was pointed out by farmers, merchants, and laborers alike that persons did not plan to make Arvin their home because of this very lack of facilities. It is very probably one cause for the high tenancy ratio in Arvin, since landowners will often prefer to live elsewhere and live off their rentals. It is possibly a cause for the fact that the average educational attainments of farm workers are below those in the same occupations in Dinuba.

The occupational structure has some influence upon political life in the community. The failure to develop real local interest in community affairs is a prime factor in this causal relationship. The mutual exclusiveness of the two major strata of society also inhibits the development of the community solidarity that would be expected in a more homogeneous group and thus prevents the development of a civic organization. The fact that the group from which natural leadership arises represents but a small minority, while those whose position is relatively insecure forms an overwhelming majority, is a further reason for the failure of Arvin to incorporate. The existence of a strong and rich county government contributes to the fact that such political institutions were not developed.

The high rate of tenancy and absentee ownership may reduce further the proportion of persons who are willing to assume leadership. No information on participation by tenure, other than the operator-laborer dichotomy, was obtained. While such effect of tenure pattern upon the social organization is not supported by empirical evidence, the reverse effect, that the social environment increases tenancy, does receive some support.

. . . The scale of farm operations only creates the occupational structure found under the assumption that land is individually owned and requires hired labor. Cooperative farming would have a different effect. . . .

Finally, cursory examination of other communities in California's intensively cultivated agricultural areas substantiates this point of view. In general, the following are associated: new communities, the cultivation of row crops, and large-scale operations. Where they are so found, communities in the Arvin pattern are found. But where the former two are found with small-scale operations, these communities acquire most of the characteristics of Dinuba. On the other hand, none of the towns whose agriculture is made up predominantly of large-scale operations has these amenities.

The study of Arvin and Dinuba shows, therefore, that quality of social conditions is associated with scale of operations; that farm size is in fact an important causal factor in the creation of such differences, and that it is reasonable to believe that farm size is the most important cause of these differences.

Notes

1. The text given here is comprised of excerpts from Chapter 7 of Professor Walter F. Goldschmidt's classic study, *Small Business and the Community, A Study in Central Valley of California on Effects of Farm Operations*, Report of the Special Committee to Study Problems of American Small Business, U.S. Senate, 79th Cong., 2d sess., Senate Committee Print no. 13, December 23, 1946 (Pursuant to Senate Resolution 28, Extending S. Res. 298—76th Congress), Chap. 7, pp. 91–114. The editor has tried to make clear Goldschmidt's line of argument for his main conclusion concerning the relation be-

tween size of farming operation and locally available amenities. Space restrictions prevent a full presentation of the argument. For a more complete account, the reader is referred to the entire text of the report and other work by Walter F. Goldschmidt.

Questions of Equity in Health Care and Other Amenities of the Countryside

Sam M. Cordes

A QUALITY INFRASTRUCTURE WITHIN RURAL AMERICA is essential to meet the basic human needs of the existing rural population, and to help ensure a bright future for rural America. This infrastructure includes a variety of services, among them transportation, education, public safety, and health care. Health care has become of increasing concern for those who study the quality of life in rural America. The reason for the concern is obvious: many indicators suggest a disproportionately larger need for health services in rural areas, while many rural areas have fewer health care resources available to meet their more extensive needs.

Given the underlying theme of rural health care issues, this chapter considers five questions: What is rural? What are some of the salient characteristics of rural America? What relationship exists between rural health and rural development? How will megatrends in the nation's health industry affect rural areas? How can individuals affect rural health service delivery?

What is Rural?

To some extent rurality is a relative concept or a psychological state. For example, in New York state a community of 60,000 located some distance from any major city would probably be viewed as small, remote, and rural by most New Yorkers. A community of the same size located in Wyoming would be that state's largest and would not be viewed as small, remote, and rural by the Wyoming citizenry.

Apart from the relative or psychological dimensions of rurality, official definitions do exist. Two approaches are used. One approach defines rural in terms of those persons who live in towns of less than 2,500 or in the open country. The second approach categorizes counties as either metropolitan or nonmetropolitan, depending on the presence of a population center of 50,000 or more people. Counties that are contiguous to a county with such a population center are often also classified as metropolitan, depending upon such factors as commuting patterns.

There is a single common thread that underlies any definition or conception of rural. That common thread is low population density. In recent years, areas of extremely low population density have been called "frontier areas." "Frontier areas," defined as those with fewer than six persons per square mile, are located almost exclusively in the Great Plains and western U.S.[1] However, the real meaning of frontier can be illustrated by the following three facts:[2]

—A significant proportion of "frontier states" do *not* have more U.S. representatives than U.S. senators. These states are Alaska, Idaho, Montana, Nevada, North Dakota, South Dakota, and Wyoming.
—The state of Delaware would fit within the Great Salt Lake, but this giant lake takes up less than 3 percent of the state of Utah.
—Vermont is considered rustic and rural and has a total population comparable to Wyoming's. However, Vermont has more than ten times as many persons per square mile as Wyoming.

The ultimate importance of low population density lies in its tremendous impact on communication and transportation patterns, sense of community in terms of networks and interactions with family, friends, and neighbors, and the existence—or lack thereof—of specialized services and complex organizations and institutions. Population density is also at the heart of many of the unique aspects of rural health care needs and issues. For example, it often leads to fundamental differences in the delivery of health services, such as the use of airborne ambulances, telecommunication links between remote outposts and secondary care centers, and satellite care centers staffed with physician's assistants and nurse practitioners.

Low population density may also affect health care needs as well as health care delivery. For example, recent research suggests that alcohol abuse and suicide may flourish in rural areas because "great physical distances between people can make social networking and the formation of psychological support groups difficult to establish and maintain."[3]

What are the Characteristics of Rural America?

A tremendous amount of folklore and mythology surround rural America. In reality, rural America is dramatically different from what it was twenty to thirty years ago. However, our perceptions have not kept pace with the changing reality, as shown by the contrast between myth and reality.

MYTH 1:
RURAL AMERICA IS SHRINKING
In 1984, over 60 million Americans were living in towns of less than 2,500 or in the open country; in 1986 more than 55 million Americans were living in nonmetro counties.[4,5] Never in the history of our country have more people lived in either rural or nonmetro areas.

MYTH 2:
RURAL AMERICA IS SYNONYMOUS WITH FARMING
Although the rural population has been growing steadily, the farm population has been declining steadily. Today, less than 10 percent of the rural population live on farms.[6]

MYTH 3:
NONMETROPOLITAN AMERICA RELIES HEAVILY ON THE FOLLOWING NATURAL RESOURCE INDUSTRIES: FORESTRY, ENERGY, FISHING, AND MINING
Only 5 percent of the total employment in nonmetro counties is in these four industries.[7] Today, the largest employer in nonmetropolitan America is the manufacturing sector.[8]

MYTH 4:
THE INDUSTRIAL STRUCTURE OF NONMETROPOLITAN AMERICA BEARS LITTLE RESEMBLANCE TO THE INDUSTRIAL STRUCTURE OF METROPOLITAN AMERICA
The overall industrial structure of rural and urban America is quite similar. Employment in both metro and nonmetro areas is characterized by private wage and salary workers, although this proportion is somewhat higher in metro areas than in nonmetro areas (78 percent compared with 70 percent). Within the wage and salary category, a somewhat greater proportion of nonmetro employment, compared to metro employment, is associated with goods-producing industries. Conversely, a somewhat small proportion of nonmetro employment is associated with service-producing industries. Self-employment in nonmetro counties is significantly higher than in metro counties, but is a relatively small proportion of overall employment in both types of

counties.[9] In sum, any differences in the economic structure between rural and urban America are greatly overshadowed by the similarities that exist.

Myth 5: Rural America is isolated and insulated

A common perception about rural America is that it is somewhat outside the mainstream of modern society, and that its basic structure remains fairly stable. This perception, like most of the other perceptions about rural America, includes more fiction that fact.

From the standpoint of economics, any particular rural area tends to specialize in a single type of economic activity. Moreover, many of today's specialized rural economies are tied closely to international forces. For example, in the early 1980s, the strengthening of the dollar, a worldwide recession, and the growing competitiveness of newly industrialized countries (e.g., Brazil, Taiwan, and Hong Kong) worked against several rural industries—manufacturing, energy, forestry, and agriculture—that tend to export heavily and face substantial amounts of foreign imports.

Because most local rural economies are highly specialized, when their primary economic activity is under stress, other industries are not available to take up the slack, as typically happens in a larger, more diversified urbanized economy. Furthermore, the institutional structure within which rural America operates has changed substantially. For example, "deregulation" and "privatization" have been major national policy themes in recent years, and nowhere have their effects been greater than in rural America.

What point is to be made in dwelling on international economics and the infatuation of policymakers with deregulation? These examples illustrate how the world has been turned upside down for rural areas. There was a time not that long ago, when the major problem in rural America was, in fact, isolation—physical, social, economic, and cultural. To be sure, isolation may still be an occasional problem. However, for the most part it has been replaced by problems associated with interdependency. Most of the problems faced by today's rural America exist not because of isolation, but precisely because the rural economy and its institutions are inextricably interwoven with the national and international scene. Hence, a war in the Persian Gulf that affects the price of oil, coal, and other energy sources will almost certainly have more impact on the economy of an energy-dependent community in Wyoming than will a rural jobs program.

The fact that rural America is no longer isolated and insulated has tremendous implications for health care. For example, current Medicare reimbursement policies may be at least as effective in closing rural hospitals as the rural-oriented Hill-Burton Act of 1946 was in constructing these same hospitals. As another example, the instability of rural economies means economic disruption is commonplace, and the social fabric and networks of a community can be torn apart overnight. This suggests that mental health services should be at least as high a priority as medical services.

Myth 6:
Rural America is homogeneous

Probably the most prominent single characteristic of rural America is its diversity, and the differences among nonmetro areas are almost surely greater than the differences among metro areas. Indeed, when one disaggregates the nation's rural population or its nonmetropolitan counties, the striking characteristic is not similarity, but dissimilarity. For example, in 1980 the population of the smallest nonmetro county in the U.S. was 91 (Loving County, Texas), and the population of the largest nonmetro county was 155,435 (San Luis Obispo County, California).[10] As another example, a substantial number of nonmetro counties have no physicians, and therefore a physician-to-population ratio of zero. On the other hand, Montour County, Pennsylvania, has a population of about 17,000 and has some 250–300 physicians because of the Geisenger Medical Center. Hence, the standardized physician-to-population ratio for Montour County is *not* just the highest among nonmetro counties, it is also far above the ratio found in any metro county in the U. S.

This tremendous diversity within rural America is *not* to be confused with the earlier point that the economic structure of rural and urban America is similar. Both are true. In the aggregate, the economic structure of rural and urban America is much more similar than most people realize, but the much greater diversity within rural America means *individual rural communities and counties* often bear little resemblance either to urban areas or to other rural counties.

Myth 7:
Rural America, Unlike Urban America, is Populated With Healthy, Happy People

The notion that rural people are invariably strong, robust, healthy, and happy needs to be dispelled. The data simply do not support these misconceptions. For example, the prevalence of the following chronic conditions is higher in nonmetro than in metro counties:[11] diabetes, epilepsy, kidney trouble, bladder disorders, prostate disease, rheumatic fever, heart disease, hypertension, cerebrovascular disease, chronic bronchitis, and emphysema.

Data on mental health status in rural areas are less adequate than the data on physical health. However, it is common practice to glorify the rural life-style, and to argue that this superior life-style contributes to superior mental health. Morton Wagenfeld has compiled virtually all of the studies available and concludes that

> There appears to be a pervasive amount of evidence that the pristine picture of country life is, if not manifestly incorrect, at least open to some serious challenges.[12]

Additionally, the homicide and suicide rates in nonmetro areas are surprisingly high and the death rate from motor vehicle accidents exceeds that of metro areas.[13]

What Relationship Exists between Rural Health Care and Rural Development?

In recent years, rural development has received increasing attention. Rarely, however, has there been adequate recognition of the contribution health care services and institutions can make to rural development. At least five avenues exist. First, investment in health is an investment in human beings that may result in tremendous economic gains. The flip side of this coin is a study that found that health problems were the greatest single barrier to participation in the labor force in rural areas.[14]

Second, health care influences the ability of rural communities to attract and retain businesses and people. A community with adequate health care will surely be more attractive to potential employers than a similar community with inadequate health care. Similarly, retirees may be influenced by the availability and quality of services, and rural America has a disproportionately large number of elderly. When retired people migrate, taking their retirement income with them, the economic impact on the community can be severe.

Rural health care makes a third contribution to rural development through the cash and short-term investments held by hospitals, clinics, and other health-related institutions. For example, the analysis of an eight-county nonmetropolitan area in Pennsylvania revealed that the cash and short-term investments associated with the area's hospitals totaled more than $6 million.[15] Moreover, 90 percent of these funds were held in local financial institutions. Such holdings provide a substantial source of funds that can be used for investment by local business and individuals.

Fourth, rural health development stimulates development of local leadership. One researcher who has studied this process notes that

> The leaders of health fairs and clinics become recognized as doers, the community begins to think better about itself, providing a boost in mental health, specific skills such as fund-raising are revived, and new skills such as proposal writing can be applied to additional problems such as housing, roads, and water systems.[16]

A fifth and critical factor is the employment associated with the health care sector. In the Pennsylvania study noted above,[17] a hospital in a town of 7,700 population was estimated to generate nearly 700 jobs, including those indirectly associated with the hospital's economic activities. Hence, it is not unrealistic to argue that rural hospitals are often the community's largest single employer, and may account for one-fourth of the community's jobs.

What is the Impact on Rural Areas of Megatrends in the Nation's Health Industry?

In the same way that rural people and the rural economy are no longer isolated and insulated from outside forces, neither is rural health care. Today, *generic* changes in the nation's health care industry have a tremendous impact on rural areas. Examples of generic changes include the methods and structure of Medicare reimbursement for hospitals, whether or not a relative value scale is used to reimburse the nation's physicians, whether or not malpractice and insurance liability reform are undertaken, the quantity and type of physicians that will be recruited and trained in the future, and eligibility criteria for Medicaid. Decisions in these areas may have more impact on rural services and rural people than will decisions directed toward rural-specific programs, e.g., the National Health Service Corps and the Indian Health Service program.

The one common theme at the national level that hurts rural areas is the need to reduce health care expenditures. Efficiency and cost containment are, of course, laudable goals; however, an equally laudable goal is reasonable access to services. In rural America, the "health care crisis" is largely synonymous with access, and since improving access requires additional spending, the current emphasis on cost containment does not bode well for rural America.

How Can Rural Health Service Delivery Be Influenced?

The list of megatrends affecting rural health services is lengthy. It is important that rural advocates and others be aware of their impacts and of the opportunities and avenues for influencing them.

For example, as an economist, I am attracted to measures that attempt to stem rapid growth in health care spending. However, in our zeal for cost containment I also feel a need to make certain we don't throw the baby out with the bathwater. I have two particular concerns. First, in a developed and civilized society we should have the sensitivity and the wherewithal to be at least as concerned with the goals of equity and access as with the goal of cost containment. The appeal of this broader perspective is enhanced when one realizes it is not the savings that may be realized from the nation's small hospitals that make the real difference in the nation's health care bill. In other words, the battle will not be won or lost in the corridors of Warren (Minnesota) Community Hospital or in the hallways of Weston County Memorial Hospital in Newcastle, Wyoming. Instead, the cost containment battle will be won, or lost, in the nation's giant hospitals and medical school complexes, and by those who must struggle with the enormous cost of heart transplants and other technological "marvels."

But exactly how can the political and policy-making process be influenced? One avenue involves collective action through three types of organizations useful in advocating rural needs. The National Rural Health Association in Kansas City, Missouri, formed by a merger of two other organizations, focuses exclusively on rural health issues.

The other two avenues of involvement are, first, health organizations that have a rural component and, second, rural organizations that have a health component. An example of the former is the American Public Health Association, a large and powerful national association with a rural constituency group. An example of a rural-oriented organization that happens to be concerned with health issues is the American Farm Bureau Federation.

Involvement in the political process is not simply a matter of hard-headed negotiations, debates, and political trade-offs. Much of what is needed is simply education and awareness, for example, that not all rural areas are alike. As noted earlier, perhaps the most outstanding single characteristic of rural America is its diversity. For example, the rural South has a high proportion of low-income blacks, but the Midwest does not. The rural Northeast is dotted with villages and hamlets, but communities are few and far between in the rural West.

Similarly, while rural areas tend to have few health resources, some rural communities are on a par with many cities. What this diversity means is that what is needed and what will work in McConnelsville, Ohio, may not be what is needed or what will work in Lusk, Wyoming, or in Tonopah, Nevada. Policymakers must be continuously reminded of this fact.

Another example of the lack of awareness by federal policymakers involves the use of infant mortality rates as a way of allocating certain federal funds. Infant mortality is calculated as the number of infant deaths per one thousand live births. In certain sparsely populated areas, only a few births occur per year, and because the numbers are so few it is highly unlikely in any given year that an infant will die. Hence, the infant mortality rate in most years will be zero, but in the occasional year when a death occurs it will skyrocket to a level that is comparable to that found in Bangladesh. This statistical instability created by such a small population base was never considered when the infant mortality criterion was first put in place.

When policy is being formed by those who lack knowledge and awareness of rural America and its diversity, it is inevitable that unfortunate biases and problems will emerge. Awareness and your educational efforts can help prevent this from happening.

At the local and state level, it is important to be able to adjust to or counter the problems created by a rapidly changing external environment. Suppose, for example, continuation of a full-service hospital is not a likely scenario for a particular community. In this case, the questions should be: How can the community's resources be modified to meet its health needs? What is needed, and what is affordable? There are many options available, ranging from small clinics and emergency centers, small acute care facilities with only several beds, or maybe simply a first-rate transportation system.

Summary and Conclusions

If local citizens wish to maintain some semblance of control over the destiny of their communities and insure adequate health care services, there will be no room for petty turf issues and the type of geographical provincialism that has characterized so much of rural history. Instead, there is a need for cooperative, creative, and innovative planning for a future that involves very strong external forces.

In coping successfully within this strong external environment, local activists must be knowledgeable about the dynamics of rural America and of the dramatic changes that have occurred in the past quarter century, why health care is an integral part of the larger issue of rural development, and how trends in the health industry impact rural services. In addition to learning how to cope successfully within such a dynamic environment, rural citizens and rural advocates must simultaneously invest in a second activity—active involvement in trying to shape the future environment, rather than passive acceptance and attempts to cope within that environment. Rural activism can be expressed through many avenues and organizations. The future vitality of rural America depends in no small part on fostering such activism.[18]

Notes

1. Frank J. Popper, "The Strange Case of the Contemporary American Frontier," *Yale Review* 76 (Autumn 1986): 101–21.

2. Barbara Bailey, "Frontier Health Care" (Paper presented at the Wyoming Rural and Community Health Conference, Casper, 1987).

3. R. H. Seiden, "The Youthful Suicide Epidemic," *Public Affairs Report* 25 (February 1985), p. 25.

4. I. T. Elo and C. L. Beale, "The Decline in American Counter-Urbanization in the 1980s" (Paper presented at the Annual Meeting of the Population Association of America, New Orleans, 1988).

5. Ronald C. Wimberly, "Agriculture and Rural Transition," in *New Dimensions in Rural Policy: Building Upon Our Heritage* (Washington, D.C.: Joint Economics Committee of U.S. Congress, 1986), 39–45.

6. Wimberly, "Agriculture and Rural Transition," cited in note 5.

7. Bruce A. Weber, Emery N. Castle, and Ann L. Shriver, "The Performance of Natural Resource Industries," in *Rural Economic Development in the 1980's* (Washington, D.C.: USDA, Economic Research Service, 1987), 5–1 to 5–37.

8. Bureau of Labor Statistics, in *New Dimensions in Rural Policy: Building Upon Our Heritage* (Washington, D.C.: Joint Economic Committee of U. S. Congress, 1986), 144–57.

9. Bureau of Labor Statistics, "New Dimensions," cited in note 8.

10. U.S. Department of Commerce, Bureau of the Census, *County an City Data Book, 1986* (Washington, D.C.: GPO, 1983).

11. Catherine H. Norton and Margaret A. McManus, "Background Tables on Demographic Characteristics, Health Status, and Health Services Utilization," *Health Services Research* 23 (February 1989): 725–56.

12. Morton O. Wagenfeld, "Psychopathology in Rural Areas: Issues and Evidence," in *Handbook of Rural Community Mental Health*.

13. Norton and McManus, "Background Tables," cited in note 11.

14. Loren C. Scott, Lewis H. Smith, and Brian Rungeling, "Labor Force Participation in Southern Rural Labor Markets," *American Journal of Agricultural Economics* 59 (May 1977): 266–74.

15. R. A. Erickson, N. I. Gavin, and S. M. Cordes, *The Economic Impacts of Pennsylvania's Hospitals* (University Park, Pennsylvania: Center for Research, College of Business Administration, The Pennsylvania State University, April 1984).

16. Richard A. Couto, *Streams of Idealism and Health Care Innovation: An Assessment of Service-learning and Community Mobilization* (New York: Teachers College Press, 1987).

17. Erickson et al., "Economic Impacts," cited in note 15.

18. Adapted from the Keynote Address at Wyoming's Statewide Health Care Conference, 1986.

Some Considerations of Justice in Rural Health Care Delivery

Mary Gore Forrester

AS PROFESSOR CORDES HAS SHOWN in this volume, rural areas fare less well in the field of health care than urban areas. My question is the extent to which this poses an ethical problem. Rural-urban differences in the quality and quantity of health services *do* seem, at least to some, to be wrong. According to them, we ought to provide equal health care opportunities to all our citizens. This claim is by no means uncontroversial. It can be criticized on grounds of both utility and justice.[1] Space does not permit examination of both types of considerations here, so I shall discuss only those of justice.

"Equality of health care" may be defined as apportionment according to need of the opportunity to obtain health care. For the same health needs, the same care would be available, regardless of the patient's ability to pay. Other variables such as race, age, and sex would be relevant only to the extent that they make a difference in a person's health care needs.[2] To provide equality of health care, the public sector must pay at least for those who cannot afford required services.

Arguments in favor of providing equal health care are based on the principle of *equality* (EQ). Most people believe that since people are of equal worth, the good, interests, or well-being of every person should be given the same consideration as that given to the good, interests, or well-being of anyone else. Still, there is considerable disagreement as to what such equality implies in practice. Many liberals want to see goods distributed in such a way that people come as close as possible to being equally well-off. For them, using the resources of the better-off to improve the lot of those who are worse-off is morally right. Those holding a more conservative view of equality contend that by taking from X to give to Y just because X is better-off to start with, we are not treating X and Y equally. Rather, we are benefiting Y at X's expense, thereby giving their interests *un*equal consideration.

An observation that tends to favor the more liberal interpretation of equality is that charity is universally approved, at least where the recipient is unable to help him- or herself. We believe it good for those with more to give to those with less. This in itself is by no means sufficient to justify the conclusion that it is morally acceptable to *take* from the well-off to give to the poor. Nevertheless, it is an indication that people in general think there is some moral value in redistributing goods in a more equal manner.

EQ may, however, be overridden by other considerations. If X has more than Y, we can make them equal just by destroying whatever goods make the difference between them. Such a procedure would surely be considered wrong by virtually everyone. What we might call the principle of *nondeprivation* (ND) is the belief that the only condition under which it may be morally acceptable to deprive a person of some good is if doing so benefits another. ND does not, by itself, forbid taking something from one person in order to give it to another. Thus it does not necessarily prohibit taxing the public to provide health services for those who can't afford them. However, EQ, together with ND, puts some constraints on the extent to which such a procedure would be justifiable.

EQ underlies the principle of *entitlement* (EN). This is that we ought to compensate those who benefit others by giving up goods of their own. For example, labor, which presumably brings goods to others but costs the laborer time and energy, deserves compensation. Without it, the others would benefit at the laborer's expense. This compensation becomes his *property*. Thus the notions of property and rewarding of merit are based on the idea of maintaining equality.

If a person's property is to be of any use to him, he must have some protection in using it as he sees fit. Consequently, the principle of entitlement (EN) implies that to take away something a person has earned we need a justification. We have a *prima facie* obligation not to interfere with a person's property. If everyone were born with equal resources, then justice considered simply as entitlement and desert would be adequate. For everything that any person contributed in the way of tangible or intangible goods, he would receive exact compensation from those his contributions benefited, and those who took from others would be punished by having retribution exacted to the extent that they had harmed others. But of course we are not born equal in this way, and the world is such that those having more to start with are in a position to acquire even more, while those starting with less are at a progressively greater disadvantage. This consideration underlies our belief that assistance to the needy, to compensate for natural or social handicaps, is morally good. Satisfaction of EQ appears to require more than distribution according to entitlement and desert.

Another application of EQ is the principle of *sharing* (SH). If a group of people benefit from something, they ought to share both the benefit and the burdens necessary to produce that benefit. Otherwise, some will benefit at the expense of those others who bear an unequal proportion of burdens relative to benefits. In the absence of other considerations, both benefits and burdens should be shared equally. This is true with respect to both public services and social institutions. For example, since, presumably, everyone benefits from roads and armies, everyone ought to pay taxes. The keeping of promises benefits everyone. Yet unless a large proportion of promisers do honor their commitments, the institution of promising cannot be sustained. Hence keeping promises, which is often inconvenient, is a necessary burden, which it is only just that everyone share. Those who do not pay taxes and keep promises benefit from the institutions in question without taking on part of the burdens, thereby increasing their own level of well-being at the expense of those who *do* share the burdens. Thus they contribute to inequalities, and thereby offend against justice.

Both SH and EN have implications for what society ought to do about rural health services. If society as a whole benefits by having people live in rural areas, SH requires that society share the burdens involved. And if rural people undergo hardships as a result of being rural, EN requires that these hardships be minimized or compensated. There are at least three distinct advantages to society in having a rural population. First, food production requires large areas of land unencumbered by houses, factories, and so forth, and therefore a less dense population. Secondly, if all of our people lived in cities, this would undoubtedly result in greater unemployment and crowding. Finally, most of us value having large areas of undeveloped land for recreation, but to some extent this requires upkeep and protection, and therefore people to live and work nearby at a distance from metropolitan areas.

Given that the nation as a whole benefits from having some people live in sparsely populated, i.e., rural, areas, SH suggests that all citizens should share in the burdens involved with having a rural populace, and that these burdens should not fall entirely upon the people living in these sections of the country.[3] One such burden—even for the relatively wealthy, but especially for the rural poor—is surely the greater difficulty of supplying such health services as emergency medical care and specialized diagnostic, treatment, and rehabilitation facilities.

The same conclusion may be argued using EN. Because people in rural areas make certain sacrifices that result in benefits to the rest of the country, the rest of the country owes them something. Just compensation can include making available certain services, such as health care facilities, which are admittedly more expensive for the total value they produce than the same services in an urban area.

Examples of such services are the following. First, helicopters could be provided to all hospitals that serve large areas single-handedly. These would bring in emergency patients from remote areas and airlift them to larger medical centers if they need additional treatment. Secondly, as Professor Cordes has pointed out, rural hospitals cannot pay their own way, and federal subsidies may well be needed to keep them open and able to provide high-quality care. Thirdly, it is convenient for physicians to practice, if not in formal groups, at least in areas where they have colleagues with whom they can exchange such services as taking night and weekend calls, and with whom they can consult. In rural areas it may not be feasible to have more than one physician, and doctors are understandably reluctant to serve such regions. The reluctance could be minimized, however, if special incentives were offered by the government. These might include a substantial salary over and above the fees the physician would normally collect, physician extenders to do much of the routine work, provision of a locum for occasional relief, paying specialists to make periodic visits to the area, and installation of computer hookups to medical data banks.

In short, the government has done much, could do more, and by the principles of justice ought to do more, to bring the quality of rural health services up to the level of urban services. Some objections and qualifications to this claim need to be considered, however.

First of all, the philosopher Robert Nozick has argued against the principle that sharing in the benefits of a social institution obligates one to share the burdens.[4] Second, it might be that society does not owe the rural population any compensation, because the natural compensations of rural life suffice. And finally, many have maintained that efforts to force people to contribute to the well-being of others results in a diminished level of welfare for all. Let me consider these in order.

Nozick argues that the mere fact that someone benefits from an institution does not obligate him to contribute to the upkeep of that institution. Suppose neighbors take turns broadcasting programs over a public-address system. If one individual obtains some mild enjoyment from the programs, but does not wish to take his turn presenting one, he has, Nozick says, no duty to do this. Because he cannot reasonably be expected to avoid the benefit, it is in a sense forced on him. He is not obliged to contribute to the upkeep of the p.a. system, for he has not *consented* to either the benefit or the burden. Thus in addition to the fact that someone benefits from an institution, he must also have consented to participate, if he is to be obliged to share its burdens.

I agree with Nozick that the passive listener to the p.a. broadcasts does not have an obligation to present a program himself. The reasons, however, are not those he presents. In a large and complex society, many different institutions contribute in varying degrees to the quality of life of its members. As a rule these all require for their functioning some effort on the part of a number of people. Also, as a rule they bring some benefits to persons who do not contribute. We may classify these institutions in a number of ways, three of which are relevant to our purposes here. One is by their importance—i.e., the degree of good they produce (and the harm that would be suffered without them), the second is the extent to which they can survive freeloading, and the third is the degree to which consent to both benefits and costs is obtainable. The more important the institution, the harder it is for it to function when some beneficiaries fail to contribute, and the easier it is to obtain consent, the stronger is the obligation to contribute to its upkeep.

On all the above counts the obligation of the passive enjoyer of the p.a. entertainment is very weak indeed. If everyone supported all such marginally beneficial institutions, their efforts would be so greatly spread out that each individual's contribution would be ineffective. It is more efficient to have everyone committed to working for a few beneficial, but nonessential, institutions, while sharing the benefits of many. In this way different individuals could utilize their own specific interests and talents in an effective division of labor.

On the other hand, there are institutions whose abolition would result in marked reduction of good for almost everyone: e.g., government, family, truth telling, and promise keeping. While such institutions can survive a certain amount of freeloading, this is limited. Consequently, it would be *unfair* of people not to contribute to their upkeep.

In short, it appears that there are certain social institutions that are extremely important and that can tolerate little freeloading. For some of these it is not possible to obtain consent to either benefits or burdens. If, however, the benefit in question is so great that many would suffer real harm by losing it, then lack of consent may surely be overridden.

As far as our immediate topic is concerned, the benefits of food production, the limitation of urban blight, and the preservation of wilderness recreation are not easy to avoid receiving, regardless of consent. Nevertheless, they are—the first especially—highly valued by most people. Thus compensation to rural populations, supported by everyone, and including compensation through additional health care, is called for, despite Nozick's claims.

A second argument against the view that rural people are entitled to compensation in the form of health services is that they already have compensation.[5] Living in sparsely populated regions offers advantages of its own, which may be equal to or surpass those of urban life. At any rate they are not obviously inferior, certainly not to those who choose to live there.

To this objection there are several rejoinders. First, people's choices of where to live are rather more limited than the argument suggests. Job opportunities, skills, and family responsibilities probably play a larger role than do personal preferences in determining location. Second, one of the most widespread social phenomena of this century has been the migration of rural people to cities. This suggests that for many, urban life has a higher expected utility than does rural life. Whether the advantages of the city actually exceed those of the country, it seems they are so perceived by most. Third, it is difficult to calculate whether the advantages of any region compensate for its disadvantages. There is little doubt that whether they do or not is a highly individual matter, depending upon many factors such as personality, tastes, matching of interests with opportunities, and perhaps most of all on income. Presumably there are benefits to all of us in having people live in areas of differing population densities. If partial remedies for these disadvantages are feasible, then it seems reasonable to suppose that equality is more likely to be achieved by using those remedies than by relying on the natural advantages of living in a given area to compensate for its disadvantages.

A final argument against the position I am presenting is that by providing equal access to medical services, we either put so many restrictions on freedom of action and incentives, or we bring about such an enormous inflation of medical costs, that the quality of medical care in general will decline. If so, everyone will be deprived, the poor as well as the rich.[6] If this is true, the nondeprivation principle would indeed forbid such a program. Space permits only some initial reflections on this matter. As John Rawls has acknowledged, some inequalities may result in everyone's being better-off, especially those least well-off initially; such inequalities may be permissible.[7] I would go farther and say that ND entails that such inequalities ought to be promoted. Not to do so will deprive some, or even all, of good without helping anyone.

What sorts of inequalities in the health care system might be justified in this manner? One suggested type is to provide everyone with the means to purchase a "decent minimum" of services through vouchers, but allow the purchase of additional medical care by those with the income to afford it. Proponents of this approach argue that, despite resulting inequalities in health services, there would be gains for all.[8] While the well-off would admittedly gain disproportionately more, this system would cost less than one that provided equal health care. Presumably the savings might be used for increased benefits in either health care or other areas. If so, this would be an instance in which inequality might be justified on Rawlsian grounds.

An objection to the voucher system has been proposed by Gutman.[9] Such procedures would result in a two-tiered system—low-quality public care versus high-quality private care. The enterprise of approximating equality of access to health services will be aborted as a result. Her reasoning is that the better practitioners will siphon off those who can pay for better care, leaving the poor with inferior services.

Another objection, particularly germane to the issue of rural health care, is raised by Arras.[10] He points out that even the well-to-do in rural areas may be unable to obtain high-quality health care because the facilities they need are not available. That this is so is supported by the observation that average Medicare payments (in the 1970s) in rural areas were half those made in urban areas, and that, while 50 percent of those eligible for Medicaid live in rural communities, only 30 percent of Medicaid payments were made to persons in these regions.[11]

Clearly, in order to deal with these issues, we need to distinguish between types of inequalities. If we tried to eliminate all inequalities by providing for every citizen every possible service obtainable by anyone, we would bankrupt the nation. Surely it would be wrong thus to make ourselves unable to prevent foreign attack or educate our children. We would have violated ND by achieving equality at an enormous reduction of well-being for all.

Each country has limits upon the resources it can afford to spend on health care, and it must choose what it will pay for and what it will not on the basis of what its people consider most important. It must weigh medical services not only against each other, but against other valued items. Since no society can afford to give everyone everything they may want, and since no society has succeeded in stamping out all inequality of resources, even by the most repressive and costly measures, it seems likely that some inequalities in health care will have to be tolerated.

It does not follow, however, that we should tolerate widespread inequality. Many inequalities breed further inequalities. In large urban areas, for example, many private hospitals refuse to take indigent patients. These patients are shunted to the municipal hospitals, which are often overcrowded and understaffed. Patients who can afford a private hospital with its better services and more pleasant surroundings naturally choose one. This further deprives the municipal hospitals of income, making it still more difficult for them to attract the best personnel and improve their facilities. A vicious circle is created, which reinforces the two-tiered system against which Gutman warns.

A rural hospital that is the only one serving a large area does not contribute to inequalities of this sort, since it must take everyone who enters its doors. If it cannot provide sufficient services, however, it may lose income from wealthier patients who will, except in emergencies, seek care in larger and better-equipped urban medical centers. The small rural hospital is, then, in much the same predicament as the large municipal hospital. In both cases, the inequalities between the medical care available to those with higher incomes and that which the poor can obtain are perpetuated and increased. The government helps to some extent, of course, with, for example, Hill-Burton funds, Medicare and Medicaid. But more could be done—perhaps by requiring *all* hospitals to accept a substantial proportion of indigent patients and by subsidizing their care, and by paying more for poor rural persons to seek in urban medical centers health care that is locally unavailable.

These would be expensive measures. On the other hand, money could be saved by generous expenditures on preventive programs, such as prenatal care, well-baby clinics, screening for such diseases as diabetes, hypertension, and cervical cancer, and programs to enable people to break destructive health habits.[12] Still more might be saved by increasing government coverage of home health care, which could decrease more expensive stays in hospitals or nursing homes by the elderly and chronically ill.

My conclusions, then, are as follows. Absolute equality of health care is not practicably obtainable, and, even if it were, it would not be in accordance with principles of justice. On the other hand, seeing that everyone is able to obtain, if needed, as many of those health services as the society is able to afford and considers necessary for or major contributors toward attaining a good life, is required by considerations of justice. To reach this end, we must pay particular attention to rural health care. Because of the services rendered by rural people, society owes it to them to provide certain goods, including assistance with health care, which offset some of the disadvantages of rural life.

Notes

1. See, for example, Norman Daniels, "Health Care Needs and Distributive Justice," *Philosophy and Public Affairs* 10 (1981); Amy Gutman, "For and against Equal Access to

Health Care," *Milbank Memorial Fund Quarterly/ Health and Society* 59 (1981): 542–60; and Dan E. Beauchamp, "Public Health as Social Justice" *Inquiry* 13 (1976): 3–14.

2. See the discussions by Mark Siegler, "A Physician's Perspective on a Right to Health Care," *Journal of the American Medical Association* (Oct. 3, 1980): 1591–6; Charles Fried, "Equality and Rights in Medical Care," *Hastings Center Report* 6 (1976): 29–34; Gutman, "For and against," cited in note 1; and Beauchamp, "Public Health," cited in note 1.

3. One can also argue that the public should provide certain services to its urban population. Since it is in all of our interests to have cities, and since living in cities has certain disadvantages, we all ought to share in helping to offset these disadvantages.

4. Robert Nozick, *Anarchy, State and Utopia* (New York: Basic Books, 1974), pp. 93–95.

5. For insisting that this point must be discussed, despite limits on space, I am indebted to James Forrester.

6. For insisting that this point must be discussed, despite limits on space, I am indebted to James Forrester.

7. John Rawls, *A Theory of Justice* (Cambridge, Mass.: Harvard University Press, 1971), pp. 60–90.

8. See Alain Enthoven, "The consumer choice approach to National Health Insurance: Equity, the marketplace and the legitimacy of the decision making process," in William Roy, ed., *Effects of the Payment Mechanism on the Health Care Delivery System* (U.S. Dept. of Health, Education and Welfare, 1978), 4–10; and Charles Fried, "Health Care, Cost Containment and Liberty," *Hastings Center Report* 6 (1976).

9. Gutman, "For and against," cited in note 1.

10. See John Arras, "Health Care Vouchers and the Rhetoric of Equity," *Hastings Center Report* 11 (1981).

11. Edward Martin, "Consumer choice health plan: Impact on rural America," in William Roy, ed., *Effects of the Payment Mechanism on the Health Care Delivery System* (U.S. Dept. of Health, Education and Welfare, 1978), 45–50. One of Charles Blatz's many helpful comments on this paper was his suggestion that there might be alternative explanations for the underutilization of Medicaid in rural areas—for example, pride, or ignorance of the program.

12. See Martin, "Consumer choice," cited in note 11.

Women and Agriculture[1]

Cornelia Butler Flora

AGRICULTURE IS AN ENTERPRISE that often engages resources of land, labor, and capital from all family members. Agriculture is unique in the way it combines these resources and, thus, unique in the kind of commitment demanded from family members. The role of women—and of men—in agriculture can best be understood through analysis of the relationships of each household member to land through ownership or use right; to labor through provision of labor at key times and for key elements in the production cycle; and to capital, both mobilization of inputs and allocation of the surplus produced.

Mann and Dickinson have identified a major characteristic which distinguishes agricultural production from industrial production: the disjuncture between production time and labor.[2] In agricultural production, the rhythm of biological processes determines the time between sowing to harvest, or from insemination to birth to market. Thus the time labor is actually applied to the production of crops and livestock is less than production time, which includes the growth process. Labor time is organized differently in agriculture than in other types of production, in that farm operations take place sequentially rather than simultaneously.[3] All the factors of production must be mobilized with special attention to the limiting aspects of sequential and irregular production cycles and the risks produced by nature, including variations in rainfall, temperature, and pests.[4]

In most precapitalist agricultural situations, family and communal organization of land, labor, and capital reduced the risk inherent in agricultural production. Land was rotated or shared through use right rather than formal individual ownership. Capital, in the form of inputs, also was shared and produced within the family or tribal unit. And labor was organized in multiple stock, crop, and craft activities. The intrafamilial division of resources involved multiple enterprises and multiple production units. There were his, her, and their crops. Intricate exchange relationships and hierarchies emerged, and women and children were often the resources on which male hierarchies were based.[5]

The formations and strategies that developed were highly diversified. Yet peasant agriculture evidenced certain regularities. Everyone worked, with social division of labor by sex and by age. Men's and women's work was highly complementary—each depended on the work of the other in order to complete their agricultural endeavors. For example, men might clear the land and plow, while women selected the seed and planted. Women and children would weed, and all would participate in the harvest, with the men reaping and the women threshing and winnowing. If one's husband was derelict in his agricultural activities, other men (brothers, uncles, or cousins) might substitute for him.

Men's activities, particularly those related to livestock production, often contributed more directly to status than did women's activities, yet women's agricultural and reproductive work, which were highly intertwined, were not devalued. Separate male and female cultures gave parallel systems of status, as well as separate enterprises which allowed for reduction of risk and rationalization of resource use over the agricultural cycle.

The linkage of peasant agricultural systems to larger economic systems disrupted the sexual complementarity of labor. Access to the factors of production by sex, which previously allowed both men and women to control or use land, labor, and capital, was altered, giving men dominance over all the resources, when the control was not entirely removed from the native peoples.

Links to larger economic systems varied: sale of agricultural products, exploitation of minerals, or sale of labor. In establishing this flow of materials, colonial powers imposed new forms of production on mining and agriculture, which disrupted the traditional peasant farming systems. The new linkages and the demands they made on the family production system placed ever-greater burdens on female producers, while at the same time women had less access to the resources necessary to successfully carry out their responsibilities. New crops were introduced to increase the wealth of the colonial power. Many of these crops were raised under the conditions of plantation agriculture.

The mines and the plantations required labor, slave and free. Males were usually recruited. By using only adult men, the costs of reproducing the labor force were borne by the sending populations, the subsistence agriculture sector. Women were left by default to provide the reproductive necessities of the labor force, including food through subsistence agriculture. The more mobile men were pulled to mines and plantations by the wages offered and pushed by the need for cash to pay cash taxes imposed by the colonial powers. Examples of such motivational tax structures were present in both Africa and Latin America. In Guatemala, a tax payable only in cash was instituted to get Indian men to work in the banana plantations.[6] The British protectorate of Bechuanaland (now Botswana) introduced a poll tax at the turn of the twentieth century, to be paid in cash, requiring that young men seek work in mines or farms in neighboring countries. Expatriate male labor left women even more firmly in charge of agricultural production, although older men kept control of cattle, the principal form of wealth in a society where most land is still communally held.[7]

These linkages of farmer households to larger markets, through the sale or expropriation of male labor for both mineral and plantation agricultural production, upset the traditional complementarity of agricultural production. Male provision of cash afforded greater status than female provision of food, increasing incipient sex inequality. Women's ability to produce food was severely modified by (1) lack of available male labor to perform the traditional male tasks, (2) male retention of decision making power over the utilization of capital, making investment in food production extremely difficult, and (3) the lack of resources and technology aimed at the special conditions of female farmers. Most of the credit and extension services established by colonial powers and later by national governments assumed that men were the primary agricultural producers.[8]

Plantation agriculture was particularly detrimental for women through its disruption of the family as an agricultural production unit. Sugar- and banana-based plantation agriculture in Latin America utilized primarily males, often African slaves, in contrast to the North American plantation system, which was cotton based and which recruited kidnapped males and females from different parts of Africa in order to reproduce its own labor force. In plantation areas, the tradition of permanent female-headed (*de jure*) households emerged much earlier than in other parts of the world, where, with more temporary male migration, temporary female-headed households (*de facto*) were more common. In the African and Latin American circumstances of high male participation in plantation agriculture, women often had to leave agriculture entirely, becoming traders and craftspersons, since they lacked access to land and capital, as well as male labor.

Other production systems utilized family labor to produce crops sold on the world market. In areas such as Costa Rica and Colombia in Latin America and Ghana in Africa, small producers maintained land ownership, but changed its use from food crops for home or local consumption to cash crops for export. A market-based, family-farm agriculture was created. Land relationships became formalized under the liberal reform movements of the late nineteenth and early twentieth century. Family use rights to land were changed to male property rights. Men were generally in control of cash crop production and the income it generated, in part because the colonial buying agents who helped introduce the crops held the male-dominant assumptions based on the Victorian ideal of womanhood.

Hacienda agriculture involved appropriation of the land by the colonial power, who then deeded it to those who had provided the crown with enough wealth or conquest to justify their new landed status. The indigenous people on the land were part of the package in the *encomienda* system. The peasants, now bound to the land by complex systems of legal and debt peonage, provided labor and received the use of a parcel of land for their own subsistence production. *Hacienda* agriculture was much more self-contained than plantation agriculture, with little market orientation. Both male and female labor was used, often extremely cruelly. However, the labor and land relationships meant that the complementarity of male and female agricultural labor, both for the *hacienda* and in the subsistence plots, was not challenged. Women were crucial in production for both the *hacendado* and the family.[9]

Flexibility that allowed the family to reproduce itself in times of economic crisis was present in peasant, female subsistence, *hacienda*, and family farm production. The family had access to the land, whether owned or not, to produce food when wage work for international markets declined. Although women were disadvantaged in these systems, they provided a variety of family survival strategies.

Raw materials were exported to the colonial powers, which, even after political independence, retained economic hegemony in their previous colonies. In turn, manufactured goods were exported from the central industrialized countries to their former colonies and new client states. The markets were never large, as skewed income distribution reduced the purchasing power of the vast majority of the populations. But the traditional elite and the small but growing middle-class groups imported consumer goods, from perfume to toothpaste and shoes, as well as capital goods from the industrialized nations. When the world economy was growing and export crops were selling well, elites could import consumer goods. When the economic situation was bad, and prices for export products were low, elites cut back on consumption. The agricultural workers in such times shifted their labor to subsistence crops, if only in exchange for services rendered, a share of the crop, or a cash rent. The depression of the 1930s had a muffled impact in developing compared to industrialized countries. A large part of their economy was not linked to international markets. Subsistence agriculture was an ever-present alternative, even in areas of highly concentrated land ownership. Women's access to the factors of production and their share in them, while not great, was crucial for family survival among peasant and semi-proletarianized workers—workers that had small plots for agricultural production and worked for wages at irregular intervals in response to cycles in export crops.

After World War II, the nationalism that led to political independence addressed economic independence as well. In Africa and parts of Asia, the two movements coincided, while in Latin America, political independence movements preceded economic independence by as much as 100 years. The move for economic independence first attacked the major symbols of dependency—the importation of manufactured consumer goods. Why, it was reasoned, should we not produce these articles in our own country? Such production would keep scarce foreign exchange at home and create alternatives to agricultural employment—urban employment for males. That strategy of import substitution industrialization requires a reorganization of capital, and labor relations, under the aegis of a strong state.

Factories had to be built to make national products. They required machinery which had to be acquired in the international market, using foreign exchange—generally U.S. dollars. Loans, either to private industrial groups or to governments, were the major source of capital. But even if the factories were successful in replacing foreign goods (and the state ensured that they would be, by enacting strong tariff barriers to manufactured products), the loans could not be repaid through profits from domestic sales. Those sales were in local currency, unacceptable in the international market place. Foreign exchange must be generated—and the only sources were the traditional export sectors—minerals and agriculture.

Reorganization of the urban-based economy thus required reorganization of the rural-based economy. Land, capital, and labor in agriculture had to become more productive.

Modernizing elites, particularly in much of Latin America, instituted a land reform. Its goal was to increase agricultural efficiency of the traditional agricultural landlords rather than increase agricultural equity.[10]

Land reform gained a veneer of equity because the 1960s was a period of heightened peasant organization and protest. In Latin America, the success of the Cuban revolution in 1959 underlined the dangers of ignoring inequality. The forces of international development also were put behind the land reform effort.

Import substitution did not have the desired results; despite heavy investment, relatively few jobs were created. The biggest increase in urban employment was in the informal sector, where women are over-represented.

At the end of over two decades of land reform, agricultural land in most Latin American countries remains as concentrated as it was in 1960.[11] Women's access to resources was further decreased by formalized land relationships, which, when land was titled to peasants, titled it to men. Further, the land deeded to peasants was not the productive, centrally located land they coveted, but newly opened frontier land, often isolated, with little infrastructure and fragile soils. Women in the colonization areas often lost the female support groups that they had in their traditional villages. They often had to join previously male field work, in addition to their traditional agricultural and household work. Because the agricultural system was radically different, these peasant women were unable to use the skills they had acquired from their mothers in seed selection, soil preparation, and food preservation. When such knowledge was made available through government and international colonization programs, it was made available to the men.

The shift to export agriculture used land more intensively than ever before. No longer could small plots be ceded to peasant families for their own subsistence production. The risk-reducing strategy of the *hacienda* involved mixed crop and livestock systems with a relatively small gap between total production time and total labor time, if peasant plots were also counted as part of the production system. Export crops tended to be planted in monoculture, requiring large labor inputs at key junctures. It was difficult to shift the year-round *hacienda* labor force into a seasonal agricultural labor force, although it did occur with one of the new export crops, cotton. Peasants previously involved in their own production systems and in *hacienda* production migrated to urban areas. Large farms increased their capital intensivity—and their need for foreign exchange—by mechanizing. Government subsidies of agricultural inputs for export agriculture of themselves reinforced this trend. In many countries in both Africa and Latin America, total agricultural production rose while food production fell and food imports increased.

The advent of capital-intensive export agriculture created a rural labor force totally dependent on sale of its labor. Many peasants lost their use right to land, as a strategy of major landowners to make sure peasants had no claim on the land in case land reform was really taken seriously. The large rural labor force forced wages down. Women and men increasingly sold their labor for the same tasks, including the harvesting of coffee (a traditional source of temporary rural employment for women in peasant families) and cotton and for weeding and other cultivation tasks in row crops.

The year 1973 was a landmark for developing countries, as events were set in motion that greatly affected the structure of agriculture around the world and the role of women within that structure. It was the year of the world oil crisis, with increasing oil prices that shifted world terms of trade.

Class distinctions in the rural sector increased with different roles in agriculture for women in the distinct emerging classes. Carmen Diana Deere,[12] among others, shows how, in Latin America, the sexual division of labor in agriculture declined for the rural proletariat and peasants, as it increased for women in the upper rural classes, who tended to be removed entirely from agricultural production. In other areas, it left women in charge of subsistence production, with less access to land, labor, and capital.

The economic depression of the 1980s was worldwide, the worst crisis since the 1930s. But while in the 1930s an economic cutback meant that the elites and the middle class cut back on consumption of imported goods, now decreased consumption also meant fewer jobs. Urban industrial workers lost their jobs, hit by the double whammy of decreased local markets and inefficient, protected enterprises that were not able to compete in an increasingly difficult world market. Total demand decreased, and loans became impossible to roll over. Export crops, already affected by increasing world production, earned less and less. And the option for peasant families to fall back to small plot subsistence production to sustain themselves during a crisis had been eliminated by the transformation of agriculture. Many developing countries had favored export agriculture over food production and maintained a cheap food policy through imports. So even the remaining peasant farmers and family farmers had little incentive to grow food. Programs aimed at food production often did not address the major policy issues, and even fewer addressed their efforts to the women, who by default often were left raising the subsistence crops.

Debt crisis in developing countries is compounded by stagnant economy, worsening declining value of exports; increasing unemployment; increasing public deficits; increasing balance of payment deficiencies; and increasing inflation. As a result, imports decreased, particularly imports of food that provide subsidized maintenance for urban female-headed households disrupted by temporary and permanent male migration. Contradictions abound, particularly for women. To solve the long-term problem of production disincentives, food costs must rise. An increase in food costs hits most heavily at the poor. Women and the children in the households they head are most likely to be poor.

In developing countries, the role of women in agriculture continues to be vital, but hidden. While affected negatively by planned change, it is the unplanned change that most directly breaks down the complementary roles in agricultural production and increases the disparity between the landless peasants and the major landowners.

The productive activities of female farmers, their differential access to land, labor, and capital, and the fact that their productive activities must almost always be combined with their reproductive, or household-based, activities—which include cooking and other forms of food processing, gathering fuel, and carrying water—should be part of planned change. As high debt and international agencies .such as the International Monetary Fund combine to limit the potential of developing countries to import food and maintain cheap food policies, recognition of the key role of women in food production and the disadvantaged conditions under which they participate must be part of the national calculus.

Because of women's household work and their multiple activities in agricultural production, particularly small farm production, women as agriculturalists tend to minimize the gap between production time and labor time. Household, handicraft, off-farm labor, as well as a variety of animal and crop enterprises, including gardening and egg and milk production, contribute to providing necessary labor when peak labor times in crop or animal production occur. Further, women's multiple enterprises help rural families reduce the risk that linkage to international markets, including credit, inputs, and sales, entails. When women are excluded from agriculture, however unintentionally, the farm family's ability to overcome the built-in difficulties of agriculture as a form of production are decreased.

Notes

1. Kansas Agricultural Experiment Station Contribution 85-227-J. A version of this article appeared in *Agriculture and Human Values* 2 (1985): 5-1.

2. S. A. Mann and J. M. Dickinson, "Obstacles to the development of a capitalist agriculture," *Journal of Peasant Studies* 5 (1978):466–81.

3. John M. Brewster, "The machine process in agriculture and industry," *Journal of Farm Economics* 32 (1950):69–81.

4. Max Pfeffer, "Social origins of three systems of farm production in the United States," *Rural Sociology* 48 (1983):540–62.

5. Karen Ericksen Paige and Jeffrey M. Paige, *The Politics of Reproductive Ritual* (Berkeley: The University of California Press, 1981).

6. Andrea Brown, "Land of the few: Rural land ownership in Guatemala," in *Revolu-*

tion in Central America, ed. Stanford Central America Action Network (Boulder: Westview Press, 1983), 232–47.

7. Alex Campbell, *The Guide to Botswana* (Gaborone: Winchester Press, 1980), 230.

8. Kathleen Staudt, "Uncaptured or Unmotivated? Women and the Food Crisis in Africa," *Rural Sociology* 52 (1987): 37–55.

9. Lucia Carrion, *La mujer en la hacienda lechera encuadoriana* (Quito: CEPLAES, 1983).

10. Osvaldo Barsky and Gustavo Cosse, *Tecnologia y cambio social: Las haciendas lecheras del Ecuador* (Quito: FLASCO, 1981).

11. Alain de Janvry, *The Agrarian Question and Reformism in Latin America* (Baltimore: The John Hopkins Press, 1982).

12. Carmen Diana Deere and Magdalena Leon del Leal, *Women in agriculture: Peasant production and proletarianization in Colombia and Andean Peru* (Geneva: International Labor Organization, 1982).

Values and Goals of Florida Farm Women

Do They Help the Family Farm Survive?[1]

Christina H. Gladwin

We pitch in and help; we do whatever needs to be done to keep the farm going and family together. . . .

THE CONTRIBUTION OF FARM WOMEN AND FAMILY LABOR to the survival of the family farm in the U.S. and Florida has been an ignored aspect of farm entrepreneurship until recently.[2] In Florida as in many agricultural states of the U.S., however, the contribution of the farm wife or agribusiness woman has assumed a new importance as inflationary pressures on land, equipment, and operating expenses force the male, able-bodied farmer on the small and medium-sized family farm to seek off-farm work to support the family and subsidize the farm.[3] The comanagerial role of the farm woman became even more important in the farm crisis of the 1980s, when between 65 and 88 percent of all U.S. farms were or became part-time farms.[4]

A recent survey of labor allocation on the family farm in North Florida has shown that farm women are doing more of the farming now, as compared to the 1920s and 1930s.[5] The data suggest that although farm men are indispensable (and are doing more farm work and off-farm work than the women), Florida farm women are now farming an average of 22 hours per week, as compared to the 11 hours per week estimated by the time-use diaries of the 1930s.[6] This increase in time spent farming may be due to previous underreporting of women's contributions to agricultural production,[7] or it may be an actual increase resulting from a decrease in their time spent on housework. Due to technological change in the production of household appliances during the past 50 years, time spent doing housework decreased from an average 50 to 26 hours per week.[8] This released time has allowed modern farm women to increase either their farm work or off-farm work. Although some women choose to spend that time off the farm, in our sample at least an equal proportion of them choose to farm.

As a result, evidence also shows that more farm women perceive themselves to be *farmers* rather than farmers' *wives*: 56 percent of the 50 farm women interviewed considered themselves to be full- or part-time farmers, while 36 percent perceived themselves to be farmers' wives.[9] The Florida data thus agree with National USDA data which showed that in 1980, 55 percent of U.S. farm women considered themselves to be a "main operator" of the family farm.[10]

Although women are doing more of the farming now, evidence also shows that farm women's contributions to the Florida family farm *complement*, rather than *compete with*, those of farm men on almost every work dimension. Data show that some Florida commodities are mainly women's commodities, because most of the work done to produce them is usually done by women. These include chicken houses (both layers and broilers), goats, pecans, assorted poultry, and the garden.[11] These commodities usually complement men's commodities, which include row crops, cattle and hogs, pasture, timber, and hay, as well as the "joint commodities" which are joint ventures of both husband and wife and include tobacco, cotton, vegetables, and nursery operations.

Rather than focusing attention on which commodity is whose, however, it is more instructive to look at who within the family does what task.[12] On the farm, both national and state data show that some tasks are mainly women's tasks, which typically include bookkeeping, caring for small animals, gofering, and chauffeuring.[13] These tasks complement the traditionally male tasks such as plowing, marketing, and the repairing of farm equipment. Finally, data on the off-farm work involvement of Florida farm women show that it also *complements* rather than competes with the farm work and off-farm work involvement of their men.[14] Women work off the farm full-time when off-farm income is needed and they have better paying off-farm jobs (or job training) than do their husbands; oftentimes they work part-time on the farm in addition to holding an off-farm job.

Feminists or Defenders of Family Ownership

Given the evidence that more women are now farming in North Florida, we must ask why. What are their goals and reasons to farm? Are they asserting themselves as individuals or feminists by farming? Or, as happened on the Western frontier in the nineteenth century,[15] are they farming simply to alleviate a temporary labor shortage? Are they partners or draftees, a reserve labor force called upon in times of high labor demand? If so, do they recognize or resent their function?[16] Alternatively, as C. Flora asserts, are they farming to defend their families, as part of their commitment to the collective called the family?[17] Rather than being part of a feminist struggle, are U.S. farm women part of a class struggle, defending the farm and preserving the land that has been in the family, often for generations?

Results from Florida

To answer these questions, a sample of 50 farm women in Baker and Gilchrist Counties, North Florida, were asked in an open-ended way to describe why they farmed, why they worked off the farm, and what they hoped to achieve from both kinds of work.[18] By means of the same kind of open-ended questions, they were then asked to describe the main reasons farmers cannot make a living farming today, and the major strategies used by experienced farmers to make a living. The responses were coded, and patterns were found in the responses, where possible. The sample of women were chosen such that both the counties and farms within each county were representative of the population. Based on the variety of farming systems found on the sampled farms and the distance of the counties from a major urban center, the counties were judged to be representative of North Florida farming communities. Within each county, the farms sampled were also representative, relative to the distribution of farms in the county by operating size, according to the 1978 Census of Agriculture.[19]

Why Do They Farm?

Table 1 summarizes the reasons Florida women farm.[20] Generating an income from farming and earning enough to pay off big debts is the predominant goal mentioned. One woman sums it up, "Our goal is to get everything paid for, land and equipment, so we can have an income coming in." To get out of debt, farm families try to reinvest farm earnings back into the farm, "to build up the cow herd, to have enough cows to cover the expense of keeping them." The goal of earning money from farming is not always achieved, however. One woman sadly reflected, "I enjoyed farming until we couldn't make a profit from it."

Children-centered goals (raising children right, helping older children start farming) were the next most frequently mentioned reasons women farm. Some farm women are concerned about raising

TABLE I
Farm goals

	*No. of Responses**	*Percent*
1. Generation of income	29	28
2. Children-centered goals	26	25
a. helping children - 16		
b. raising children - 10		
3. Rural residence/lifestyles	18	17
4. Personal autonomy	15	14
5. The farm is a goal in itself	13	13
6. Subsistence/self-sufficiency	3	3
	104	*100*

*Number of responses do not sum to sample size because respondents often reported more than one goal and all goals were recorded.

---

children in a healthy environment where the mores and values of neighbors are known and shared. Maintaining a rural residence and lifestyle, satisfying the desire to "stay where you are . . . ," to live in the country, and enjoy farm life is another frequently mentioned goal. Other farm women are accumulating land and equipment for children, encouraging them to farm, and planting timber for their children's future use. Only one woman said she did not want her sons to farm, but wanted them to have other job opportunities.

Farming is a goal in itself for some families. As one woman puts it, "The goal of farming is building a farm; everything else is secondary." Choosing an appropriate enterprise mix is a means to achieving this goal. One woman visualizes a time in the not so distant future when she would have the chicken farm built to the point that her husband can quit his off-farm job. Another woman hopes to have the farm built up and paid for, so they can sit back and enjoy themselves. One woman simply said, "if I didn't farm, I'd be lost." Another farm woman testifies: "When you live on a farm and enjoy it, you're already ahead of the game."

The need for personal autonomy and some control over the timing and level of one's own productivity and achievement is another goal: "You're your own boss. You can go to work today if you want to, or you can stay home, or you can go out there at 6 o'clock and stay out there until midnight."

Being self-sufficient in food, "knowing what we are eating . . . ," and keeping out of the grocery store is another major goal of Florida farm women. For them, "having a large enough garden for the whole family, having vegetables all year round, and growing your own . . ." are good reasons to farm.

Why Off-Farm Work

Given the evidence of the increasing importance of off-farm work to bigger and bigger farms, we asked farm women why they held off-farm jobs. The replies of this sample, 74 percent of whom had some off-farm income coming into the family and 58 percent of whom held off-farm jobs themselves at the time of the interview, are summarized in Table 2.[21]

The most frequently mentioned goal motivating off-farm work for 41 percent of the respondents was an increase in family income. Off-farm work allows farmers to achieve and maintain a lifestyle and standard of living that farm income alone cannot support. It pays for luxuries such as vacations and home improvements, and also provides fringe benefits such as health insurance. One woman admitted, "with the standards we have, we have to have off-farm work, to make more money and support the life style we are accustomed to." While farm women stress that off-farm work is "necessary, stable, and financially more important," they also claim that it is "not as rewarding" as farm work nor "their first choice." It does, however, pay the bills and help make ends meet.

A sizable minority (18%) of farm women work off the farm (or are now in school) to satisfy their own career goals. Some of these women are planning to start or resume a career (as a lawyer, writer, teacher, musician, or nurse) which had been deferred earlier in order to build the farm and family.

For 16 percent of the women, off-farm work helps subsidize the farm business. Sometimes it is used to pay for farm equipment; always it is perceived as a *temporary* means to achieve the couple's real goal to farm full-time—together. As one woman said, "What I've worked for has all gone back into the farm and home." Another woman cautioned:

> Off-farm work is important, but our eyes must be on the same goal. If that is farming and building a farm, then everything else is secondary. Women cannot allow off-farm jobs to pull them from the farm, making it a half venture. Farming cannot be a his-and-her venture.

TABLE 2

Goals motivating off-farm work

	*No. of Responses**	*Percent*
1. Supplement farm income and support a life style	20	41
2. Fulfill career goals	9	18
3. Subsidize the farm	8	16
4. Maintain social contacts	7	15
5. Provide for children's needs	3	6
6. Assist in community service	2	4
	49	*100*

*The number of women reporting goals motivating off-farm work do not necessarily sum to the sample size because first, not all farm women in the sample have off-farm income, and second, those who did often reported more than one goal.

Establishing social contacts on the off-farm job, earning money for children's special needs, and providing service to the community are other reasons women work off the farm. Meeting new people and having relationships with co-workers are aspects of off-farm work that often-isolated farm women look forward to. Some jobs, such as nursing, driving a school bus, or working in a school cafeteria allow women to provide valuable community service and at the same time be sociable.

The main reason farm women seek off-farm work, however, is to maintain the family's standard of living and keep the farm going. The need to seek off-farm income-earning opportunities usually means that farmers face problems making a living on farm income alone. Do Florida farmers perceive this to be the case?

Problems Farmers Face

A person can't start out in farming today and make it. If I were to give my children my whole place, all the equipment, and two years time, the way things are going now, they'd be a lost cause.

Why can't full-time farmers make a living farming today? To answer this question, farm women were asked to respond to two open-ended questions. First, "What are some of your major problems, needs, and concerns on the farm?" Second, "People say that one can't make a living on the farm. What do you think?" Because there are recurring themes in the responses to the two questions, the responses were combined and are seen in Table 3.[22]

The problem which heads the list of concerns is the skyrocketing cost of production inputs, including land, equipment, and credit. In today's inflationary economy, farmers are caught in a bind between high interest rates and high production costs on the one hand, and low product prices on the other. In the opinion of one woman: "Practically everything on the farm costs money; but food is the cheapest thing in America." The result is that "people who farm and stay out of debt are not very affluent."

Other women voiced concern over the difficulty in getting loans from Farmers Home Administration (FmHA) for capital repairs to their chicken houses. One woman undertook a sit-in at the local FmHA office after months of regular, frequent, and unsuccessful visits. Still others were concerned about increasing property taxes. One woman said that although the size of the exemption to the federal estate tax has been raised, "Inflation has made a mockery out of that."

The price farmers receive for their products is the second most cited problem:

> If they don't do something to preserve the family farm, one of these days Purina or a big company like that is going to own everything and people are going to pay for their food. If you look at it right now from the government's standpoint, they're depending on the farmer to keep the cost of living down. Everybody is guaranteed a minimum wage except the farmer; we're guaranteed nothing.

Women mentioned low prices as a problem for chickens, vegetables, and livestock. According to one chicken house grower, they realized more money eight years ago, when every third paycheck from the chickens could be put in the bank. Today's low prices, moreover, are accompanied by continual capital investments in chicken house equipment demanded by the poultry companies; otherwise, no contract is awarded. Likewise, vegetable growers claim the market is now so restricted that they don't have many options. And livestock producers claim, "Farmers cannot control prices they sell at and they can't control prices they buy at; so most of the time they just break even."

Related to this problem is the need to expand farm size to cover increasing costs of production. "Too small a farm size" in addition to

TABLE 3
Why farmers can't make a living farming

	*No. of Responses**	*Percent*
1. Inflation, high cost of inputs, credit, and taxes	44	32
2. Lack of a market, low prices received	14	10
3. Too-small land size	13	9
4. Uncertain future of the small farm, lack of government help	12	9
5. Scarcity of time and labor	11	8
6. Not producing high-enough yields	10	7
7. "We survive, but can't get ahead"	9	6
8. The need for off-farm income	9	6
9. Health, safety, retirement concerns	6	4
10. Risks involved in farming	5	4
11. The need to diversify	3	2
12. Energy self-sufficiency	1	1
13. "We can't hunt any more"	1	1
14. "The government shouldn't subsidize farms"	1	1
	139	*100*

*The number of respondents does not sum to the sample size as some respondents gave more than one response.

lack of control over product and input prices lead women farmers to conclude, "We survive, but we can't get ahead."

Time and labor availability is cited as another problem. One woman mentioned that she is on the phone all the time trying to locate parts for farm equipment. Another woman would like to see her husband take a hand in the bookkeeping. Several women are concerned that their kids will be leaving home soon: "the help is running off to school."

Concerns of others are over health, insurance, and retirement, and the inability to pay medical bills because of the lack of health insurance. One woman took her first "public" job at age 50 in order to get health insurance for her husband who had heart trouble; after working the night shift as a guard at a prison, she farmed at least four hours a day. Contemplating retirement, another woman asked, "We never learned to play; what do we do with time if we retire?"

Finally, in the opinion of one woman, the federally subsidized FmHA loan program, created especially to help small farms survive, is a problem and not a solution:

> Many farmers are FmHA farmers. They are not productive, because it is not their own money in the venture. They get money, and if they make it, okay. If not, so what? They don't make the sacrifices farmers did. First they need a pickup truck with a CB radio, and then an air-conditioned tractor. They are not building anything. They farm with other people's land, with other people's money, and with a high mortgage. I can't blame the farmer; they have a good thing going. But they are to be blamed for going into debt and not working their way out.

How Farmers Can Make a Living Farming

After the same group of women were asked to advise beginning farmers on how to be successful in farming, their replies were compiled into the list in Table 4.[23] The revealed patterns clearly show that survival on the family farm requires hard work, dedication, and commitment. Not surprisingly, "Use family labor efficiently" is the most frequent piece of advice given to young farmers. One woman warns, "Don't expect things to come easy." Another cautions women to expect hard work at the wrong time: "The wife should be willing to work long, hard hours, as and when work needs to be done." Many women were of the view that farmers can make a living farming today; but people are getting lazy and don't like to work hard.

Other women stressed the need to be committed to the farm. According to them, "You have to want it and be willing to do it most." Another advises, "If you try and make a go of it, you can. If you have a will and a mind and want to do it bad enough, you'll do it." The advice others give is that the whole family should work together, have one goal, and channel all energy and money in one direction: "The husband and wife must work together; they can't pull apart."

Choice of appropriate land use and commodity is the next most frequently mentioned way to be successful. Although many families started farming by clearing timberland and buying farmland piece by piece, most now advise young farmers to rent land, given present-day interest rates. Some advise that a diversified operation is essential for a

TABLE 4
How farmers can make a living: advice to young farmers

	*No. of Responses**	*Percent*
1. Use family labor efficiently	48	28
2. Choose the appropriate enterprise mix and land use	33	19
3. Expand slowly, be frugal in use of capital and credit	31	18
4. Manage carefully	25	14
5. Be prepared for a decrease in income	8	5
6. Expect risks	7	4
7. It depends on government intervention	6	4
8. Get a good off-farm job	5	3
9. Farm with others	4	2
10. Be self-sufficient	4	2
11. It depends on the state of the economy and commodity prices	2	1
	173	*100*

*Again the number of respondents giving advice does not sum to the sample size, as some farmers gave more than one piece of advice.

---

small farm, while others say to depend on a good money crop. One experienced woman farmer recalls:

> Tobacco was our cash crop when we first started farming. You need a cash crop to accumulate a cash flow to work with. We grew 2½ acres. I worked in Jacksonville for an insurance company then. I'd come home and hoe or plant, and work until 10 to 11 at night and then get up in the morning and go to work again.

Reports are mixed, however, concerning which of today's crops constitute "money crops." Still others mention that it now takes more land and equipment to farm than they have.

Another popular piece of advice is: "Be frugal; cut costs by saving every which way you can." Although initial capital is needed to get started farming, they urge young farmers not to overextend themselves by going too much into debt. Because the best equipment is not always necessary, farmers should shop around for good deals and buy second-hand equipment. Farm earnings should be reinvested into the farm, and each year's debt paid off. The general consensus on credit use is to "go slow, grow into farming," and use capital and equipment efficiently. Management skills are considered crucial to survival on a small farm. Farmers are advised to keep up with innovations and use all available resources: the university, agricultural extension, and other farmers. Farmers should keep farm records and do budgets to "figure out what you are getting into." As one woman put it, "Don't get excited about things that haven't been proven, for example, sunflowers and buckwheat. Try them out in a small way first."

To make a living farming, farmers should expect risks and a decrease in income. In one woman's opinion, "It is hard for young people to farm nowadays because they were raised differently from us. They can make a living but it's not the standard of living they are used to. They were raised in affluence." The risks of farming go with the profession, and as one woman frankly said, "I'd like to see young people take it on the chin like we did."

The role of government in the future of small farms is crucial, according to four percent of the respondents. Both governmental and agricultural leaders need to encourage young people to help themselves. The government should provide tax incentives to farmers, and support better prices for their products. One woman's view is that "government is not letting farmers get their share of the food dollar."

The need for off-farm income was stressed again. One woman claims, "A husband and wife can work 16 hours at a job and get double incomes, and still have 16 hours to devote to farm work!" Still other women mentioned the need for financial backing from relatives or a well-established older farmer. Some advised "growing your own vegetables, raising your own meat, and making your own jams and jellies. Farming means growing what you eat rather than buying it."

Only 1 percent of the respondents mentioned that the state of the economy determines whether a farmer can make a living farming: "If the economy is good, if the market is good, and if interest rates don't go up," it will be possible to make it in farming.

Conclusion

"Farming cannot be a his-and-her venture."

What do farm women's values and goals tell us about them? Are they farming more today because they are individuals and feminists? Alternatively, are they farming due to economic necessity and the desire to safeguard their families' land and production? Evidence from North Florida family farms clearly show that the latter motivation, to defend their families' material well-being, is more in tune with farm women's expressed goals and values. Indeed, only with respect to their own off-farm work do farm women perceive themselves as individuals with individualistic goals. And even then, they caution that "off-farm work is important, but our eyes must be on the same goal . . . , if that is farming and building a farm."

Clearly, these values and goals serve to strengthen the family's resolve to keep the farm going during adverse times. Further, they are values which are emotionally and ideologically charged,[24] because the family farm is the last vestige of independent land ownership and production control in the U.S. today. The farm woman's role in maintaining and reproducing these values in her family is thus a crucial one. As witnessed by recent popular movies (*The River*, *Country*), the women are not just following but are actually leading the charge to defend the farm and family from creditors in times of financial crises. In Flora's terminology, they are in charge of ideological as well as biological reproduction: they are the ones who instill the values required for family farming into the next generation.[25] Part of their job as farm wife and mother is to actively defend their family farm and their class interests, and even show more strength than men in times of farm crises.

Farm women, therefore, have multiple roles to play in helping the farm survive. Some women help the farm survive physically by actively farming to alleviate a labor shortage (due to crop seasonality or husband's off-farm work, illness, or death). Others help by bringing in necessary off-farm income which complements men's farm work. Our results show that women also help the farm survive by inculcating "survival values" into their children and male kin. If they don't, the farm (and often the family) may break up. The role played by women in instilling these values may thus be more important than the role they often play as substitute laborer in time of need.

Implications

The implications of these results are straightforward. Given the present farm crisis in the Midwest and debate about the 1989 farm bill, attention has once again been focused on the question of the survival of the family farm. Buttel suggests, however, that rather than explaining the demise of the family farm,[26] ". . . a much more interesting and enduring question concerns why the family-labor farm can be so persistent in an advanced capitalism dominated by large-scale corporate production".[27] Sachs attempts to answer that question via a provocative treatise on farm women, domesticity, and patriarchy, and the political economy of U.S. agriculture. In her rewrite of the history of the family farm from a feminist perspective, she attributes the continued survival of the family farm in part to "under-consumption and overwork by the entire family."

> The low standard of living and exploitation of family labor are factors that explain the viability of the family farm at the present time. Also, the continuation of subsistence production largely performed by women on the family farm allows the family to survive on less cash income.[28]

Part-time farmers' use of unpaid family labor, coupled with their tendency to hang onto land at much personal cost, as well as their use of other "survival strategies" such as direct marketing, gardening, entering into informal partnerships, keeping debts low, practicing frugality, renting rather than buying land and equipment, and cutting back production and increasing off-farm work during bad times,[29] has allowed small farms to exist side by side and compete with larger corporate farms.[30] As Hyden has shown for the peasantry in Africa, small may be more powerful than large because to a great extent it can exist outside the normal marketing system in an "economy of affection."[31]

The purpose of this paper has been to show that women's values and goals drive that "economy of affection" and keep it going. The question that remains is: how much longer can these values of hard work, dedication, and commitment to the farm be maintained and reproduced at such an intense level, given present farm income crises? In North Florida at least, it is clear that more and more younger farmers are pushed off the farm by high production costs and capital requirements, and pulled off the farm by off-farm work. As experienced women farmers testify, they are not willing to make the sacrifices their less-affluent parents did a generation ago. Instead, they have become "FmHA farmers." It is debatable whether the old values will last to insure the future survival of the U.S. family farm.

Notes

1. This paper was made possible by the gracious hospitality of Florida farm women in Baker and Gilchrist Counties, the cooperation of Extension Directors Pat Smith Barber and Marvin Weaver, the dedication of Dr. Masuma Downie and Ms. Janet Weston, who interviewed, coded, and tabulated data in Baker and Gilchrist Counties respectively, and funds provided by National Science Foundation Grant No. BNS-8218894 awarded to Christina Gladwin. The paper is reprinted with permission from *Agriculture and Human Values* 2, 1 (Winter, 1985): 40–47.

2. See Elise Boulding, "The Labor of Farm Women in the United States: A Knowledge Gap" (Paper prepared for the American Sociological Association session on Women and Work, Boston, 1979). Masuma Downie and Christina H. Gladwin, *Florida Farm Wives: They Help the Family Farm Survive* (Gainesville, Fla.: University of Florida, Food and Resource Economics Dept., 1981); and Carolyn Sachs, *The Invisible Farmers: Women in Agricultural Production* (Totowa, N.J.: Rowman and Allanheld, 1983).

3. See Elsa Chaney and Martha Lewis, "Women, Migration, and the Decline of Smallholder Agriculture," USAID-WID Report prepared for the Office of Women in Development, USAID, 1980; and Christina Gladwin, "Off-Farm Work and Its Effect on Florida Farm Wives' Contribution to the Family Farm," *World Development and Women*, vol. 2, M. Rojas, ed., (Blacksburg, Va.: The Virginia Tech Title XII Women in International Development Office, 1982); and Wallace Huffman and Mark Lange, "Off-Farm Work Decisions of Husbands and Wives: Joint Decision Making" (Ames: Iowa State University, mimeograph, 1984); and Rachel Rosenfeld, "Off-Farm Employment of Farm Wives and Husbands" (Paper presented at the Wingspread Seminar on Women's Roles on North American Farms, Racine, Wisc.: 1982); and Eugene Wilkening and Nancy Ahrens, "Involvement of Wives in Farm Tasks as Related to Characteristics of the Farm, the Family, and Work Off the Farm" (Paper presented at the Rural Sociological Society Meetings, Burlington, Vt., 1979.

4. Carl Zulauf, "Changes in U.S. Agriculture During the 1970s and Early 1980s: An Examination Based on Constant Dollar Sales Categories" (Columbus: Ohio State University, Dept. of Agricultural Economics and Rural Sociology, ESO 1146, 1985).

5. Downie and Gladwin, *Florida Farm Wives*, cited in note 2, p. 68; Gladwin, "Off-Farm Work," cited in note 3.

6. Gladwin, "Off-Farm Work," cited in note 3, p. 4; also see Joanne Vanek, "Time Spent in Housework," *Scientific American* 23, 5 (1974): 116–20.

7. Sachs, *Invisible Farmer*, cited in note 2, p. 20.

8. Vanek, "Time Spent," cited in note 6, p. 118.

9. Christina H. Gladwin, "How Florida Women Help the Farm and Agribusiness Firm Survive," Florida Cooperative Extension Service Circular 613 (Gainesville, 1984), p. 5.

10. Calvin Jones and Rachel Rosenfeld, *American Farm Women: Findings from a National Survey*, National Opinion Research Center, Report no. 130 (Chicago, 1981).

11. Downie and Gladwin, *Florida Farm Wives*, cited in note 2, p. 34.

12. Carol Mukhopadhyay, "Testing a Decision Process Model of the Sexual Division of Labor in the Family," *Human Organization* 43, 3 (1984): 227–42.

13. Gladwin, "How Florida Women Help," cited in note 9, p. 7; Jones and Rosenfeld, "American Farm Women," cited in note 10, p. 18.

14. Gladwin, "Off-Farm Work," cited in note 3, p. 8.

15. Sachs, *Invisible Farmers*, cited in note 2, pp. 13–20.

16. Ibid., pp. 99, 109.

17. Cornelia Flora, "Farm Women, Farming Systems, and Agricultural Structure: Suggestions for Scholarship," *The Rural Sociologist* 1, 6 (1981): 381–6.

18. Downie and Gladwin, *Florida Farm Wives*, cited in note 2, pp. 78–101.

19. Ibid., Table 1, p. 80.

20. Ibid., p. 80.

21. Ibid., p. 86.

22. Ibid., p. 90.

23. Ibid., p. 97.

24. Sachs, *Invisible Farmers*, cited in note 2, p. 70.

25. Flora, "Farm Women," cited in note 17, p. 386.

26. See Alain de Janvry, *The Agrarian Question and Reformism in Latin America* (Baltimore: John Hopkins University Press, 1981); and Christina Gladwin and Robert Zabawa, "Microdynamics of Contraction Decisions: A Cognitive Approach to Structural Change," *American Journal of Agricultural Economics* (Dec. 1984).

27. Frederick Buttel, "The Political Economy of Agriculture in Advanced Industrial Societies" (Paper presented at Canadian Sociology and Anthropology Association Meetings, Montreal, 1980), 10.

28. Sachs, *Invisible Farmers*, cited in note 2, p. 66.

29. Christina Gladwin, "Structural Change and Survival Strategies in Florida Agriculture," *Culture and Agriculture* 21, 3 (1983): 1–7.

30. Sachs, *Invisible Farmers*, cited in note 2, p.67.

31. Goran Hyden, *Beyond Ujamaa in Tanzania: Underdevelopment and an Uncaptured Peasantry* (Berkeley: University of California Press, 1980).

II.C.
Agricultural Research

MANY OF THOSE ENGAGED IN AGRICULTURE are not occupied with the actual work of production. However, this does not mean that they exercise no control over that work. One such removed but controlling group is that of agricultural researchers. This group, perhaps more than any other, has come under fire in recent years. The criticism has focused on the activities of both crop and animal researchers. It has been leveled against those engaged in genetic biotechnological research and those engaged in more traditional work. It has taken researchers to task for such problems as favoring large-scale capital-intensive production programs, mistreating animals in production research, and serving those in developing nations at the expense of our own farmers. While discussions in subsequent sections take up further charges against researchers, these are the issues of interest in the following articles.

Vernon W. Ruttan's essay begins this section with a reminder of some of the complaints against agricultural researchers. Mechanization in the fields, like mechanization in grain processing, has put laborers out of work. Fertilizers and pesticides have harmed the environment just as surely as they have increased productivity and strained marginal lands. The consolidation of farms has harmed rural community life even though (as Cordes tells us above) there is as a result less difference between rural and urban life. No doubt people are more alert to such issues, and complaints will continue to be heard. The question Ruttan raises is how we are to assess and respond to these complaints as ethically justifiable. Ruttan pursues that question in connection with two important cases: the famous tomato harvester suit in California, and subsidies for the production of tobacco, which Ruttan describes as addictive and lethal.

While Ruttan urges that society does have a right to ask for protection and relief from the deleterious effects of research, he still holds that society should not greatly fault the research community. If it does, it will miss out on the new economic opportunities provided by agricultural research. Similarly, society should recognize that it is such economic opportunities that induce research efforts, and so researchers should not be asked to concentrate on economically infeasible research initiatives. For example, cropping research should not and cannot be expected to be suited to the small-scale family farm when government policies favor larger-scale production units.

In the face of these realities, research directors are given a dual responsibility in return for societal tolerance. On the one hand they must be prepared to defend their programs in the political arena in terms of social costs and benefits, and on the other hand they must alert the general public to certain social impacts expected from the products and techniques they are developing. In both of these endeavors, Ruttan seems to be saying, the researcher will be playing a critical role in constructing a political and ethical consensus in terms of which new products and techniques will emerge as ethically justifiable.

Overall, it appears that Ruttan is concerned with maximizing social welfare and that some sort of utilitarian ethic is driving his discussion. Society will be better off only if new chances for employment and the pursuit of wealth are allowed to open up, although just which ones can be a matter for debate and consensus building in an informed society. Still, whether this is the ethical perspective at work here is not so clear. Ruttan closes with suggestions of the mutual responsibilities of researchers and society. Some of the constraints he would put on researchers, such as aesthetic concerns with the environment and a concern for future generations, are not the usual urgings of either classical utilitarianism or neoclassical economic theory.

The next article shows the same uneasiness with the central values of neoclassical economics, but is more clearly ready to depart from them in assessing agricultural research. Patrick Madden, in "Values, Economics and Agricultural Research," offers an economist's critique of economic assessment of agricultural research. Madden questions whether social welfare is served by continuing research aimed at increasing productivity, and he is skeptical about the possibility of constructing a responsible consensus on whether potentially harmful products or techniques should be developed or put into practice. But his concern is not just with these questionable assumptions underlying the assessment of research. Madden wants to explain why some economists tend to accept these assumptions and pinpoint the consequent ethical problem.

Madden reviews three sorts of economic evaluation of agricultural research. The first is an assessment in terms of the ratio of consumer and producer benefits to the research and development cost of the product or technology. The more consumers and producers benefit at a cost equal to or lower than the development cost, the better some product or technology might be and the more worthwhile the research leading to it. Such an assessment seems to be consistent with Ruttan's viewpoint. However, Madden points out that it favors those who adopt new technology early, while ignoring important social and environmental impacts.

The second kind of evaluation tries to assess the worth of research by determining the increase in total productivity that it promises. Problems in estimating productivity and questions about the adequacy of research alone for increasing productivity make this assessment difficult.

Third, by designing mathematical models of the operation of production units or sectors, researchers can compare new technologies with existing ones with respect to production and income. This form of assessment has the benefit of leaving a place for environmental, if not ecological, considerations.

Madden goes on to critically review the basic value assumptions of neoclassical economics. In the spirit of giving a real place to altruistic concerns for both human needs across generations and also the environment, Madden suggests that the third form of assessment might be the most defensible. Like Ruttan, Madden sees the need to move beyond the standard values of economists in assessing agricultural research.

Nancy Matheson, Dave Oien, and Al Kurki, in "Still Learning to Farm: Agricultural Research and Extension in the 1980s," offer the perspective of a grassroots producers association interested in sustainable agricultural systems. They consider how land-grant university research and extension programs must be modified to assist farmers and ranchers with production techniques that accommodate the ecosystem, rather than destroy it.

The first point the authors make deals with what some philosophers call the "problems of accessibility." Only if the various disputants in an ethical debate see the problem in ways that the others at least understand is there any hope of a reasoned and reasonable solution. Commonality of language is essential. The problem of accessibility is part of the legacy of reductionistic and atomistic research methods that cannot yield an ecologically sensitive picture of new crops, livestock, or techniques. Overcoming this legacy will require large and bold investments of funds and leadership to change the vision of university research from atomistic to holistic. Oddly enough, it is farmers themselves who are forging ahead in the necessary leadership roles. If this continues, one new role for extension systems could be to transfer the results of farm-based holistic research between farmers and back to the university researchers themselves. To accompany this effort, the authors suggest a new kind of federal research grant, open to farmers themselves, as a first step in the democratization of agricultural research decisions.

The ethical basis of these recommendations is not altogether clear. The authors believe that the current research programs in land-grant universities devastate productive resources. They also agree with Richard Haynes insofar as he calls for site-specifically informed research. Their concern for an ecologically sensitive research program could coincide, however, with a basic utilitarian concern for human well-being, a concern for meeting basic human needs equitably, a belief (expressed below in Leopold's "Land Ethic") that it is inherently wrong to abuse the resource, or a belief that ultimately we should serve harmonious living among autonomous individuals. That their beliefs accommodate all these ethics may in itself be welcome to these authors.

The ethical perspective is much clearer in the next two discussions as we turn to questions of genetic biotechnology. Paul Elihu Stern is concerned with "Legal Aspects of Biotechnological Research and Development." Recognizing that commercially directed research can conflict with the role of the university in creating and disseminating knowledge, the biotechnology researcher can be expected to be party to a variety of legal and, more generally, ethical constraints imposed both by the university and by society.

After indicating the range of these constraints, Stern reminds us of the current federal guidelines for recombinant DNA research. The history leading up to the National Institutes of Health guidelines is reviewed, as is that of the period after publication of a Coordinated Framework for Regulation of Biotechnology, proposed by the executive branch of the federal government. In spite of these efforts at coordinating regulation, questions remain about such issues as field-testing of genetically engineered organisms. In the aftermath of field trials that have been conducted with and without approval by the NIH or other agencies, it is still unclear just who is accountable to whom and for what. Stern's analysis indicts certain government agencies for taking the opportunity to expand their regulatory scope and power without coordinating their activities for the public good.

To guide us out of this morass of research outside the laboratory, and to protect the rights of researchers, Stern endorses the view that all research not now requiring permits or licenses be subject to the NIH guidelines up to the point of commercial development, when licenses should be required. The USDA is now working on this sort of idea.

It is clearly by the neoclassical economic values of growth and productivity, and the values of civil order and the right to free exchange of information that Stern justifies a properly regulated biotechnological research endeavor. Other ethical concerns could be invoked to justify much more caution in allowing such research. Jeffrey Burkhardt, in "Biotechnology, Ethics, and the Structure of Agriculture," explores some of these concerns and the question of what research limits they justify.

Burkhardt is interested in how biotechnology will affect the question of who is to be on the land. He is also interested in the dangers Stern kept foremost in his discussion—namely, the possible consequences of biotechnology for human and environmental well-being. Burkhardt considers the responsibilities of researchers for the negative consequences of their work, beginning with the famous frost-retarding bacterium, which has been rendered benign by genetic engineering. Since the bacterium is benign, opposition to its release cannot be justified on the basis of a threat to human health. But what of the threats to the environment? No doubt, as Stern argued, regulation of development and release is necessary to protect human and environmental well-being. Still, if Burkhardt is right, arguments do not yet exist to justify curtailing the research to address concerns about health.

Do socioeconomic issues demand limits on genetic biotechnological research? In considering bovine growth hormone, Burkhardt takes up this possibility, examining arguments tied to the importance of the dairy industry, the proper treatment of small producers, and the balance of power in setting agricultural production goals.

Regarding social welfare, Burkhardt argues that researchers must show that this potentially dangerous research promises benefits that outweigh risks. Burkhardt also urges that improving the human condition through agricultural research requires a social conscience and public accountability. Thus, there is a basic moral obligation to develop these meliorating conditions. This view is similar to that of the philosopher G. J. Warnock, according to whom part of the very meaning of the term "moral" is an action or rule of conduct that promises to ameliorate the human condition. If this is what Burkhardt intends, then he shifts the debate away from an undifferentiated ethical concern to limit biotechnological genetic research in the name of social welfare toward the claim that this is the very meaning of "morally responsible research."

Bernard E. Rollin, in his discussion "The Legal Status of Farm Animals in Research," takes us back to the question of legal constraints. However, Rollin suggests that we review the legal and social constraints to get at our moral views. Rollin finds that in the earliest animal welfare laws the concern for cruelty to animals was derived from a concern to prevent cruelty among humans. Research animals were eventually covered in anti-cruelty laws in England, but it was not until very recently that the USDA sponsored comparable legislation. That legislation, however, neither covers most farm animals nor affords those covered very great protection.

Farm animals were no better off under NIH research guidelines than under the USDA-sponsored legislation. The laxity of these regulations hurt more than the animals, however, since it did not protect the scientific integrity of research involving farm animals.

Rollin and others have tried to remedy this situation with model legislation that spells out illegal behavior and a system of compliance and accountability. Some of the model provisions have been adopted, but farm animals in agricultural research are still de jure excluded while to some extent de facto included in the resulting NIH guide and compliance procedures. However, a USDA guide for agricultural animal research is now in the works. Rollin emphasizes the need to legislate away certain cruel practices used on agricultural animals so that similar restrictions on agricultural animal research have some hope of taking hold, as they have in some other countries. Many of Rollin's prescriptions make sense only if the idea of animal rights is accepted. This subject is taken up in more detail in Part III.B.

Paul B. Thompson, in "Aid and Trade: Conflicts of Interest, Conflicts of Value," takes up the last set of issues that might call for constraints upon researchers, specifically, those whose work would use U.S. funds but would aid other countries. Any research and development efforts that would make other countries more competitive with the United States are considered. Thompson first reviews the history of the pertinent legislation and then the two arguments that supporters could give for limiting such research: it is not just that the interests of U.S. farmers are hurt by aid to foreign competitors; it is also that this aid is itself wrong on moral grounds. The moral argument is developed first through a Hobbsean, and then through a Lockean, social-contract view of the legitimacy and duties of governments as described by both. A Hobbesian contract would favor the research-limiting legislation, while a Lockean view might not, Thompson concludes.

Thompson next takes up what he calls the true interests thesis, the claim that increasing agricultural production abroad will later help producers at home. Whether these two arguments from the social contract might come off is a question mooted by an explanation of what Thompson calls the true interests thesis, the claim that increasing agricultural production abroad will later help producers at home. Thompson details how this thesis is itself open to question, how its acceptance and rejection would affect the social contract arguments against research aid, and how the thesis would have to be reformulated if its defense is ultimately going to support the humanitarian goals of assistance to developing countries through agricultural research. The truth of the true interests thesis is taken up again in Part IV with a discussion of research that favors it.

Thus, concerns for material human well-being, social welfare, individual autonomy, animal well-being, and social justice within the context of a contractually legitimated government might all justify limits upon agricultural research. The same ethical considerations arise over the conduct of agricultural production, as we shall see below.

Moral Responsibility in Agricultural Research

Vernon W. Ruttan

THE PRODUCTIVITY OF MODERN AGRICULTURE is the result of a remarkable fusion of technology and science. In the West this fusion was built on ideological foundations that, from the early Middle Ages, has valued both the improvement of material well-being and the advance of knowledge.

This fusion did not come easily. The advances in tillage equipment and cropping practices in Western Europe during the Middle Ages, and well into the nineteenth century, evolved entirely from the practice of husbandry and insight into mechanization. "Science was traditionally aristocratic, speculative, intellectual in intent; technology was lower-class, empirical, action-oriented," (White 1968, 79; Asimov 1979; Boulding 1966; Hannay and McGinn 1980). This cultural distinction persisted in the folklore regarding the priority of basic science over applied science long after the interdependence of science and technology had eliminated the functional and operational value of the distinction.

The power that the fusion of theoretical and empirical inquiry has given to the advancement of knowledge and technology since the middle of the nineteenth century has dramatically increased their impact on the integrity of traditional institutions and non-natural environments. It is not unrealistic to argue that agronomists, along with engineers and health scientists, have been the true revolutionaries of the twentieth century.[1]

The Agricultural Scientist as Hero and Villain

It has not been difficult to discover heroic qualities in the pioneers who have carried the banners for the agricultural revolution. We can recall many examples:

—Liebig battling to establish the theory of the mineral nutrition of plants, and Mendel patiently deriving the elementary laws of genetics from the color of peas in his monastery garden.
—Harry Ferguson, the self-taught mechanic, applying basic physical principles to the integrated design of tractors and tractor equipment.
—Donald Jones escaping from the orthodoxy of the corn breeding program at Illinois to the obscurity of Connecticut to find the freedom to explore the potential value of hybrid vigor.
—The intellectual and physical commitment of Vavilov, the great plant pathologist, geneticist, and wheat breeder, in protecting the integrity of the Institute of Plant Breeding against the ideological opportunism of Lysenko.

But agricultural scientists have been reluctant revolutionaries! They have wanted to revolutionize technology but have preferred to neglect the revolutionary impact of technology on society. They have often believed that it would be possible to revolutionize agricultural technology without changing rural institutions. Because they believed, they have often failed to recognize the link between the technical changes in which they took pride and the institutional changes that they either did not perceive or that they feared. As a result, they have often reacted with shock and anger when confronted with charges of responsibility for institutional change—in labor relationships, in tenure relationships, and in commodity market behavior—that were induced by technical change.

In the 1960s and 1970s a new skepticism developed about the benefits of advances in science and technology. A view emerged that the potential power created by the fusion of science and technology—reflected in the cataclysm of war, the degradation of the environment, and the psychological cost of social change—is obviously dangerous to the modern world and to the future of man. The result was serious questions about the significance for human welfare of scientific progress, technical change, and economic growth.

Agricultural science has not escaped these questions. Some interpret the mechanization of land preparation or harvesting as a source of poverty in rural areas rather than as a response to rising wage rates. The milling of grain by the use of wind and water power was counted as progress in twelfth-century Europe. But today's critics view the substitution of rice milling for hand pounding as destructive of opportunities for work in twentieth century Java. There are those who regard the use of fertilizers to increase food production as poisoning the soil rather than removing the pressure of agricultural production on marginal lands and fragile environments. The new income streams that flow from more productive farms are viewed as destroying the integrity of rural communities rather than enabling rural people to participate in a society in which the gap between rural and urban income, life-styles, and culture has narrowed.

What should the agricultural scientist or science administrator make of these charges? Can they be dismissed as the mistaken or malicious rhetoric of romantics, populists, and ideologues?[2] How can fruitful dialogue about the role of science in society take place in an atmosphere so politically and emotionally charged?

A first step is to recognize that similar economic and social forces have generated both the drive for technical change—leading to advances in the productive capacity of plants, animals, machines, and men—and the drive for institutional change—designed to achieve more effective management of the direction of scientific and technical effort and capacity. The increased scarcity of natural resources—of land, water, and energy—continues to create a demand for technologies capable of generating higher levels of output per worker, per hectare, and per kilocalorie. The rising value society places on the health of workers and consumers and on environmental amenities such as clean water, clean air, and clean streets, continues to create a demand for effective social controls over the development and use of agricultural technology.

Responsibility for Research Results

The enhanced sensitivity to the moral and esthetic as well as the economic implications of technical change imposes greater responsibility on both public and private decision processes. There is a demand for more responsibility in the way the results of science and technology are put to use. Should government respond to this demand by changing the institutions that induce the generation of new knowledge and new technology? Should government assume a stronger role in directing and limiting the adoption and use of new technology? Should it attempt to encourage greater esthetic and moral sensitivity on the part of scientists, engineers, agronomists, and science administrators?

The difficulties that governments face in attempting to respond to the public demand for greater moral responsibility in the generation and use of new technology can be shown more concretely by specific examples. The controversy during the 1970s over the displacement of workers caused by the mechanical tomato harvester serves as one useful illustration. The case of research to improve tobacco is another. Tomatoes and tobacco are not necessarily the most significant examples that might be selected, but they dramatically illustrate principles that are much more pervasive.

Technical Change and Employment Displacement: The Tomato Harvester Case

The introduction of machine harvesting of tomatoes has been accompanied by an especially vigorous debate. It has been viewed as the product of a uniquely effective collaboration between mechanical engineers and plant scientists. It has also been vigorously attacked for its effect in displacing farm workers and small producers, (Rasmussen 1968; Schmitz and Seckler 1970; Friedland and Barton 1975; and Just, Schmitz, and Zilberman 1979).

In 1978 a suit on behalf of the California Agrarian Action Project and a group of farm workers was filed against the regents of the University of California, charging that they had allowed agribusiness corporations and personal economic interests to influence their decisions to spend public tax funds on the development of agricultural machines. The relief sought by the plaintiffs included an order compelling the university to use its income from machinery patents to help farm workers displaced by those machines. In December 1979, U.S. Secretary of Agriculture Bob Bergland announced in Fresno, California, that he intended to stop USDA funding for research that might put farm laborers out of work (Marshall 1980). The dean of the University of California College of Agricultural and Environmental Sciences at Davis criticized Bergland for attempting to impose restrictions on the freedom of academic research.

Clearly the farm workers displaced by labor-saving machinery deserve a reasonable degree of protection from unemployment. This is a legitimate claim on the new income streams—the productivity dividends—resulting from the adoption of the new technology. But who among the displaced workers deserves protection? Do the displaced workers who immediately found other employment have a legitimate claim on the new income stream? What about the workers who found other employment but at lower wage rates? And what about the tomato growers in Indiana and New Jersey who lost part of their market due to the lower costs in California? Who should pay the compensation? Should it be the inventors and manufacturers of the labor-displacing equipment? Should it be the farmers who captured the initial gains from lower costs or the processors who expanded their production as a result of their ability to expand their California operations? Or should it be the consumers who ultimately gained as competitive forces transferred the lower costs of production on to consumers?

The response is implicit in the questions. The gains of productivity growth are diffused broadly. The costs should be borne broadly—in the form of generalized rather than specific protection. In a wealthy society such as the United States, a worker should not have to prove specific displacement—that he or she was displaced by a tomato harvester or a Toyota—in order to be eligible for such protection.

The first line of defense against the impact of displacement is an economy in which productivity is growing and employment is expanding. Society has little obligation to compensate the worker who can readily find alternative employment. The second line of defense is a program of severance payments and unemployment insurance that is effective for all workers—those who are forced to seek seasonal or casual employment as well as those in more favored industries.

A society that provides generalized protection will be in a stronger position to realize the gains from technical change, and to diffuse these gains broadly, than a society that insists on specific or categorical protection. The failure to develop institutions capable of protecting farm workers from the effects of seasonal unemployment and technological displacement has resulted in the transfer of an excessive burden of displacement costs onto farm workers. This in turn, has induced a legal and political response that, if effective, could slow technical change and limit the gains from productivity growth.

In a society in which employment opportunities are expanding rapidly and protection from unemployment is adequately institutionalized, neither the individual researcher nor the director of the research team involved in the development of a tomato or a lettuce harvester needs to be excessively burdened by the moral implications of tradeoffs between the economic and social costs and the benefits of mechanization. Public policy has relieved them of that burden. But who should bear the burden of responsibility in a wealthy society-that forces the burden onto its poorest citizens?

Efficiency in the Production of a Health Hazard: The Case of Tobacco

Tobacco is a commodity that has been the subject of moral debate and political intervention since it first became a commercial export from colonial America. In the 1950s and 1960s conclusive evidence was produced of the association between cigarette smoking and lung cancer, coronary artery disease, chronic bronchitis, and emphysema. The source of the health hazard is nicotine and related alkaloids.[3] What are the moral responsibilities of agricultural researchers and research administrators regarding a crop that not only induces chemical dependency but which also kills people—a crop that has a high probability of shortening the life of those who consume products made from it?

One would, under these circumstances, think that efforts to develop tobacco varieties with low nicotine content would have the support of both farmers and consumers. Yet a successful effort in the early 1950s by Professor W. D. Valleau of the University of Kentucky to develop low nicotine varieties of tobacco was bitterly attacked by Kentucky farmers because of potential competition with burley tobacco (Hardin 1976). In retrospect, we have little difficulty in sympathizing with the objectives of Professor Valleau's research. Even a marginal contribution to the reduction of chemical dependency and health hazards of cigarette smoking would seem to be desirable. But what about the issue that underlies this judgment?

Should public funds be used for research to reduce the costs and improve the productivity of a product that induces chemical dependency or shortens life expectancy? What are the moral responsibilities of the director of the agricultural experiment stations in the states that support tobacco research? And what about the individual scientist who devotes his life to understanding the physiology or the nutrition of the tobacco plant? Is the farmer who grows the tobacco absolved from responsibility by the market demand for tobacco? Are members of the legislatures and experiment station directors absolved by the fact that tobacco has been one of the more profitable crops available to small farmers in the depressed areas of Kentucky or North Carolina? Are the scientists relieved of responsibility by an appeal to the freedom to do research? What are the moral implications for the tobacco breeder, whether employed by a private firm or a public research institution, of responding to market criteria—when the market is most effectively enhanced by inducing chemical dependency? What inferences can be drawn about moral responsibility from the behavior of a society in which the government spends billions of dollars on medical and health care made necessary by smoking, millions of dollars on research on tobacco-related disease and on campaigns to discourage smoking, supports research to improve efficiency in tobacco production, and legislates programs to support the incomes of tobacco producers?

There are, as in the case of the tomato harvester, institutional changes that would relieve research administrators and scientists of the moral dilemma posed by tobacco research. If a public consensus were to result in making the sale of tobacco products illegal in the U.S. it is doubtful that the directors of the Kentucky and North Carolina state agricultural experiment stations would allocate any more resources to tobacco improvement than they now allocate to marijuana research. There has not yet been sufficient convergence of opinion to take the steps that would be needed to limit the content of dependency-forming or carcinogenic substances in cigarettes. An attempt to move toward complete prohibition would require a careful balancing of the desirable effects on individual health against the undesirable effects of attempts to enforce prohibition.

Technology and Reform

The tomato and tobacco research cases pose extremely difficult moral problems for agricultural researchers and research managers. The centuries-long struggle in western society to free scientific inquiry from the constraints of the church make it unlikely that the answers to issues of moral responsibility for new knowledge and new technology will be sought from traditional religious sources.

Where, then, can the scientist or science administrator look for guidance on issues of moral responsibility? This is not the place to settle the matter. However, I can suggest how to begin.

A necessary step in any effective response to the public concern about the social impact of technical change is for the research community to agree that there can be no question about society's right to hold scientists, engineers, and agronomists responsible for the consequences of the technical and institutional changes set in motion by their research.[4] When credit is claimed for the growth in productivity generated by advances in agricultural technology, responsibility cannot be evaded for the effects on the distribution of income between suppliers of labor, land, capital, or industrial inputs. Nor can responsibility be evaded for the impact of, for example, pest-control chemicals on environmental amenities or on the health of workers and consumers.

Once the question of society's right to hold its scientists, engineers, agronomists, and economists responsible for the effects of the knowledge and technology they provide is accepted, it is then possible to deal with the more tractable question: what responsibility will a wise society impose on its research community? I argue here that *it is in society's interest to let the burdens of responsibility rest lightly on the shoulders of individual researchers and research managers*. If society insists that it be assured that advances in agricultural technology carry minimum risk—that agricultural scientists abandon their revolutionary role—society must accept the risk of losing access to the new income streams generated by technical change.

Society should, for example, exercise great care in insisting that research managers and scientists commit themselves to the realization of scientific or technical objectives that are unrealistic in terms of the state of scientific and technical knowledge. It was unrealistic in the 1950s to expect that utilization and marketing research could make a significant contribution to the solution of agricultural-surplus problems in the United States. The allocation of excessive research resources to these areas led both to a waste of research resources and to erosion in the credibility of the research enterprise.

It is equally wasteful for society to ask agricultural research managers and scientists to adopt objectives that are not revealed in the economic or political marketplace. It is unrealistic, for example, to insist that the California Agricultural Experiment Station direct its mechanization or biological research to the needs of the 160-acre farm—unless the state of California or the federal government is prepared to support the structural policies necessary to reverse the trends toward large-scale agriculture. A research system cannot be asked to produce knowledge and technology that will not be used without eroding the intellectual integrity and ultimately the scientific capacity of the research system.

It might be argued, against the above position, that policymakers should insist that research managers direct social science research to "discover" society's true objectives (a social welfare function) before they are "revealed" in the political or economic marketplace. This implies that the research manager should have on his staff the analytical capacity not only to assess the incidence of the benefits and burdens of the technical changes anticipated from a research program, but also to develop a set of normative weights (*shadow prices*) reflecting the true value society places on the welfare of each individual or group that may potentially be benefited or burdened by the results of the research. The incidence estimates and the welfare weights could then be combined in making decisions allocating research resources. This view suggests that research directors should allocate resources on the basis of a social welfare function before it is revealed by either the economic or the political system!

How do I suggest that research managers respond to the social concern about the impact of technology on society? I do insist that research directors should have access to the analytical capacity to gauge the potential incidence of benefits and burdens. This will enable them to enter into effective dialogue with the political system about research budgets and priorities. The research director who does not have access to or fails to use such capacity stands naked before critics and supporters. Research leading to a better understanding of the discrepancies or the disequilibrium in the economic, political, and social weighting system is essential. But the objective of such research should not be to provide research directors with the weighting system for internal research resource allocation. The objective should be to contribute to a political dialogue that will result in institutional changes leading to convergence of the several weighting systems. As these weighting systems converge, research directors will not be forced to choose among alternative responses to an arbitrary or inconsistent set of economic, political and social weights.

Research managers do have a clear responsibility to inform society of the impact of pricing systems and tax structure on the choice of mechanical, chemical, and biological technologies by farmers; on the incidence of technical change on the distribution of income among laborers, landowners, and consumers; on the structure of farming and rural communities; and on the health and safety of producers and consumers. They also have a responsibility to enter into the intellectual and political dialogues that are necessary if society is to achieve more effective convergence between market and shadow prices and between the individual and revealed preferences of its citizens.

If market and shadow prices for inputs and products can be made to converge, research directors can be given clear signals for the allocation of research resources. When market and "efficiency" prices diverge, it will be almost impossible to induce research planners to allocate their resources in a manner consistent with the shadow prices. If political processes can lead to greater consistency between revealed preferences and individual values, individual scientists and research managers might no longer be confronted by a situation in which cigarette smoking is branded as dangerous to health and at the same time public resources are appropriated for research on tobacco. In taking this position I wish to express one major qualification. I am aware of few research directors who make adequate use of the knowledge available to them within their own institutions to provide themselves with either the positive knowledge on what is scientific and technically feasible, or the normative knowledge about the potential value of the new knowledge and new technology.

Agricultural Research and the Future

What should society expect from agricultural science in the future? And what does agricultural science have a right to expect from society if it is to meet society's expectations?

Let me comment first on what society should expect from agricultural science.

First, society should insist that *agricultural* science maintain its commitment to expanding the productive capacity of the resources used in agricultural production. These include the original endowments of nature—soil, water, and sunlight; the agents that people have domesticated or adapted for their purposes—plants and animals and organic and mineral sources of energy; the agents that people have invented—machines and chemicals; and the people engaged in agricultural production themselves.

It is essential for the future of man that by the end of this century the capacity to maintain this commitment should be established in every part of the world. During the last two decades, the world has become increasingly dependent on the productive capacity of North American agriculture. This dependence poses danger both to the developing world and to North America. Effective agricultural science communities and institutions must be established that are capable of producing the knowledge and the technology to reverse the trends of the last several decades agricultural science in North America must remain strong enough and sufficiently cosmopolitan to contribute to and learn from the emerging global agricultural science community.

Second, society should insist that agricultural science embrace a broader agenda that includes a concern for the effects of agricultural technology on the health and safety of agricultural producers, a concern for the nutrition and health of consumers, a concern for the impact of agricultural practices on the esthetic qualities of both natural and manmade environments, and a concern for the quality of life in rural communities. Society should further insist that agricultural science consider the implications of current technical choices on the options that will be available in the future.

These concerns are not new for agricultural science. But they have often been viewed as peripheral or diversionary to the main task of agricultural science by the agencies responsible for the financial support of agricultural research. It is important for the future of agricultural science that these concerns be fully embraced. It is also important that a capacity to work on these problems outside of the traditional agricultural science establishment be maintained so that an effective dialogue can be achieved both within the research community and in the realm of public policy.

What should the agricultural science community expect from society?

First, agricultural science should expect that society would gradually acquire a more sophisticated perception of the contribution of agricultural technology to the balance between man and the natural world. The romantic view that agricultural science is engaged in a continuous assault on nature is mistaken. Society must come to understand that agricultural science can succeed in expanding productive capacity only as it reveals and cooperates with the laws of nature.

We are the inheritors in the West of a tradition that views material concern as a defect in human nature. This inheritance leads to a romantic view of man's relationship to the natural world. It also leads to a view that technology alienates man from both the natural world and from the natural community. Scientists, engineers, and agronomists have a right to expect the philosophers of society to achieve more sophisticated insight into man's relationship to technology and nature. It is time to recognize that the invention, adaptation, and use of knowledge to achieve material ends does not reduce experience but rather expands it.

Second, it is time for the science community in general to begin to follow the lead of the agricultural science community in embracing the fusion of science and technology rather than continuing to hide behind the indefensible intellectual and class barriers that have been retained to protect its privilege and its ego from contamination by engineering, agronomy, and medicine. This change will become increasingly important in the future as the close of the fossil fuel frontier joins with the close of the land frontier to drive technical change along a path that implies a much larger role for biological and information technology.

The 1970s was a period of declining growth in productivity in the United States and in several other advanced economies. These dangerous trends were more apparent in the industrial than in the agricultural sector in a number of developed economies. Rates of return to agricultural research have remained high. The evidence suggests that the institutional linkages that have provided effective articulation between science, technology, and agriculture have continued to be productive sources of economic growth in both developed and developing countries. There is much that can be learned from this experience by those who are not blinded by outmoded status symbols or cultural constraints.[5]

Notes

1. It will be useful, for the sake of brevity, to occasionally use the term "agronomy" to refer to the whole body of agriculturally related science and technology and "agronomists" to refer to the community of production-oriented agricultural scientists. In the United States the term agronomy has the more narrow connotation of field-crop production and management.

2. For an example of romantic criticisms, see Berry, 1977. For a populist perspective,see Hightower, 1973. For an ideological perspective, see Lappe and Collins, 1977. Also, Valliantos, 1977; George, 1977. For reviews of this literature, see Eberstad, 1980; and Hardin, 1979.

3. For a definitive review of the evidence, see U.S. Public Health Service, 1980.

4. This is constant with the view expressed by Mohr, 1979. Mohr notes that "... freedom of inquiry ... does not necessarily imply freedom in the choice of any particular goal; it implies, however, that the results of scientific inquiry may not be influenced by any factor extrinsic to science."

5. This paper draws on material published in Vernon W. Ruttan, *Agricultural Research Policy* (Minneapolis: University of Minnesota Press, 1982). Some of the issues have also been discussed in an article, "Agricultural Scientists as Reluctant Revolutionaries," *Interdisciplinary Science Review* 7 (September 1982): 170-77, and in a chapter, "Accountability in Research: Examples from Agriculture," *Optimum Utilization of Knowledge*, Lawrence Senesh and Kenneth Boulding, eds, (Boulder: Westview Press, in press).

References Cited

Asimov, Isaac, "Pure and Impure: The Interplay of Science and Technology," *Saturday Review* 6 (June 9, 1979): 22–24.

Berry, Wendell, *The Unsettling of America: Culture and Agriculture*, New York: Avon Books, 1977.

Boulding, Kenneth E., *The Impact of the Social Sciences*, New Brunswick: Rutgers, 1966.

Eberstad, Nick, "Malthusians, Marxists and Missionaries," *Society* 17 (September/October, 1980): 29–35.

Friedland, W. H., and A. E. Barton. "Destalking the Wily Tomato: a Case Study in Social Consequences in California Agricultural Research." Davis, Calif.: University of California Department of Applied Behavioral Research, Monograph 2, 1975.

George, Susan, *How the Other Half Dies: The Real Reasons for World Hunger*, Montclair, New Jersey: Allanheld, Osman, 1977.

Hannay, N. Bruce, and Robert E. McGinn, "The Anatomy of Modern Technology: Prolegomenon to an Improved Public Policy for the Social Management of Technology," *Daedalus* 109 (Winter 1980): 25–53.

Hardin, Charles M., *Freedom in Agricultural Education*, New York: Arno Press, 1976 (reprinted from the 1955 edition published by the University of Chicago Press): 56–61.

———, "Feeding the World: Conflicting View on Policy," *Agricultural History* 53 (October 1979): 787–95.

Hardin, Russell, *Collective Action*, Baltimore: Johns Hopkins University Press, 1982: 82, 83.

Hightower, Jim, *Hard Tomatoes, Hard Times*, Cambridge, Schenkman, 1973.

Just, Richard E., Andrew Schmitz, and David Zilberman, "Technological Change in Agriculture," *Science* 206 (December 14, 1979): 1277–80.

Lappé, Francis Moore, and Joseph Collins (with Gary Fowler), *Food First: Beyond the Myth of Scarcity*, Boston: Houghton Mifflin, 1977.

Marshall, Eliot, "Bergland Opposed on Farm Machinery Policy," *Science* 208 (May 9, 1980): 578–80.

Mohr, Hans, "The Ethics of Science," *Interdisciplinary Science Reviews* 4 (March 1979): 45–53.

Pasour, E. C., Jr., "Economic Growth and Agriculture: An Evaluation of the Compensation Principle," *American Journal of Agricultural Economics* 55 (November 1973): 611–16.

Rasmussen, Wayne D., "Advances in American Agriculture: The Mechanical Tomato Harvest as a Case Study," *Technology and Culture* 9 (October 1968): 531–43.

Schmitz, Andrew, and David Seckler, "Mechanized Agriculture and Social Welfare: The Case of the Tomato Harvester," *American Journal of Agricultural Economics* 52 (November 1970): 569–77.

U.S. Public Health Service, *Smoking and Health A Report of the Surgeon General*, Washington, D.C.: U.S. Department of Health, Education and Welfare, Public Health Service, HEW Publication No. (PHS 79-50006), 1980.

Valliantos, E. G., *Fear in the Countryside: The Control of Agricultural Resources in Poor Countries*, Cambridge, Massachusetts: Ballinger, 1977.

White, Lynn, Jr. *Machina Ex Deo: Essays in the Dynamism of Western Culture*, Cambridge: The MIT Press, 1968.

Values, Economics, and Agricultural Research[1]

Patrick Madden[2]

The Inevitability of Making Value Judgments

While most publicly supported research and extension personnel like to assume a posture of value neutrality, saying they are not biased for or against any philosophical orientation, the fact remains that neither extension nor research personnel can be value free.[3] This is true also of agricultural economists evaluating the work of those other agricultural researchers. Most of this evaluation has been carried out by rather orthodox neoclassical researchers who rarely ask how the value assumptions underlying their analysis influence the findings and their interpretation. Indeed, to ask them this question is perceived as close to heresy.

Heresy or not, however, public debate regarding the optimum mix of scientific autonomy and social responsibility in publicly funded research organizations has intensified in recent years. For example, a public interest organization, California Rural Legal Assistance, won a lawsuit against the University of California (UC) and the state's Cooperative Extension program with charges that funds were being misappropriated and the fundamental mission of the land-grant system betrayed in the choice of research objectives and extension methods. CRLA demanded as relief that UC be required to delay initiation of publicly supported agricultural research until the potential social impacts have been studied and a committee of noninvolved persons has approved the proposed research. A university vice-president responded as follows:

> This allegation fails to recognize the nature of the benefit [of agricultural research] and its distribution among producer, supplier, and consumer.
>
> The social impact analysis of contemplated research called for by

the plaintiffs would have a destructive impact on creativity and innovation in research. All research, whether in agriculture, engineering, physical science, medicine, the arts, humanities, or social sciences has potential positive and negative impacts on societal values and structural configurations.

The challenge to us as a people is not to stifle inquiry into the unknown, but to be wise enough to incorporate new knowledge into the fabric of living a better life within an organized society. Programs conducted by the Land-Grant Agricultural Experiment Stations and Cooperative Extension are undertaken on the assumption that an enlightened society will accept or reject findings and practices based on what it sees as being in its best interests.

The broadest participation in the benefits from a technologically based agriculture in the United States accrues to the consuming public. The national interests of the United States are served by supporting, through research, extension, and other actions, the efficient production, processing, and marketing of the products of agriculture.[4]

In this statement, the impact of agricultural research on lower prices for food is clearly emphasized. The contention that society will serve its own best interest by abundantly supporting agricultural research, with no "social accounting" strings attached, seems to be based on three implicit value assumptions:

1. The "greatest good for the greatest numbers of people" is assumed to be promoted by an ever-increasing abundance of agricultural commodities. Agricultural research that enables producers to increase production, productivity, and efficiency are assumed inevitably to enhance the welfare of consumers through greater availability at lower prices.

2. It is assumed that if emerging technologies carry detrimental side effects (pollution, social dislocation, unemployment, carcinogenic residues, etc.), then society will omnisciently anticipate these side effects.

3. It is further assumed that, in view of the anticipated impacts, entrepreneurs and other decision makers will automatically reach a rational decision as to whether these disadvantages outweigh the advantages; that is, if the social disadvantages are expected to outweigh the anticipated advantages of adopting a technology, that technology will not be adopted.

These assumptions have been subject to extensive criticism both from within and outside the agricultural research establishment. For example, the axiom that more is better than less can be questioned in view of agricultural surpluses costing billions in federal funds. It is reasonable also to question whether the human condition is improved indefinitely with successively higher levels of wealth and income, at a time when one of the leading causes of death, even among affluent teenagers, is suicide. Even the wealthy suffer from anomie, alienation, depression, disease, and drug addiction, etc. This incongruity does not imply, however, that efforts to further improve the income (equitably distributed) and employment of this and other nations should be suspended or even slowed. Rather, it raises the challenge of finding ways to enrich the meaning of life, its ethical and spiritual content, in addition to overcoming material deprivation.

The second and third assumptions have also been severely questioned. Predictions of the long-term effects of chemicals and other technology have frequently been found to be incorrect. And the adoption of technology by private decision makers is known to be affected more strongly by the promise of greater profits than by anticipated social and environmental impacts whose costs are not borne by the firm adopting the technology. Bonnen has summed up the situation:

> Organizations, foundations, legal advocacy groups, and others . . . now constitute a Greek chorus of criticism of the performance of U.S. agricultural institutions. Most cluster around the growing *externalities* of agricultural technology and public policy. These issues include *environmental degradation*; concerns for *animal welfare*, impacts on *health and safety of farmers*, agricultural workers, and consumers; adverse *nutritional effects* of production and processing technologies; the extrusion of *smaller family farmers* from agriculture, erosion of rural communities, and the concentration of agricultural production and economic welfare; adequate conservation and commercial exploitation of *fragile lands* that should not be in cultivation.
>
> Focusing R&D investment on productivity and ever-increasing growth is not enough today. Equity, but also safety, quality of life, stability, and preservation of the environment for future generations, to name a few, must become major goals of agricultural R&D, as well as productivity and growth.[5]

Thus, the assumptions underlying the argument for a laissez-faire approach to agricultural research are doubtful. Yet, at the same time, not every economist's evaluation of agricultural research will condemn that approach. To show this I will now review three modes of economic evaluation of agricultural research and development. Then I will attempt to isolate a source of the ethical trouble in the assumptions of modern neoclassical economics.

Valuing Agricultural Research

In evaluating the three types of studies, the value assumptions and value judgments that influence the direction, form, and content of their inquiries can be categorized only in a very general way. (a) Those studies most nearly keyed to neoclassical economic theory are based on consumer surplus or producer surplus, and estimate an average rate of return to research. (b) The second major category of studies, those employing some form of statistical inference method involving regression, seem less closely tied to economic theory and are more pragmatically based. (c) The third general category, mathematical programming studies incorporating comparative analysis of agricultural technologies, are intermediate between the first and second types in regard to their dependence upon neoclassical theory. In this approach, however, important value positions are taken in the selection of the optimizing criterion, technologies analyzed, and constraints imposed on the models, as discussed below.

Consumer and Producer Surplus

The consumer and producer surplus approach has been very widely used in economic analysis of agricultural research productivity.[6] Consumer surplus represents the total satisfaction consumers as a whole receive from buying a product at a given price when some of them would have been willing to pay a higher price rather than do without the product. Producer surplus is conceptually defined as the summation of "satisfactions" gained by all producers who would have been willing to produce their share at a price lower.[7]

As applied to analysis of changes in agricultural productivity associated with technological change, the consumer and producer surplus approach entails estimation of two quantities: the market value of purchased input saved because of the more efficient production technology, and the lower market price consumers pay for their current level of consumption as a result of the improved technology. The discounted present value of the future streams of changes in consumer and producer surplus are combined into a monetary benefit, which is then compared with some estimate of the cost of research and development. The research best by this test, roughly, will show the most favorable ratio of consumer and producer benefits to research and development costs.

Ought we favor research which receives high marks on this grading system? Well, first note that this research will not favor all producers, but only those capable of early adoption of the resulting technology. Further, it will not favor consumers immediately, but only after the new technology is widespread. In his discussion of the distribution of benefits from agricultural technology, Sundquist notes that it is primarily the early adopters of the new technologies that tend to reap major gains in income, but later on as total output is increased enough to suppress prices, consumers become the beneficiaries.[8]

In addition, this approach might ignore such negative impacts of agricultural technologies as employment losses due to mechanization, environmental degradation due to excessive soil erosion and misuse of chemicals, and taxpayer burdens due to the high cost of dealing with massive surpluses.

Another flaw pointed out by de Janvry et al. was that the analysis had assumed that all cost savings were passed along to the consumer in terms of lower food costs, with none of the savings being captured by producers, processors, wholesalers, or retailers in the form of monopoly profits.[9] They contend this assumption is inconsistent with the obvious oligopoly power within the tomato processing and distribution industry.

It remains unclear how "non-monetary" considerations are to be weighed or otherwise combined with monetary values in evaluating research. Decisions on this matter, of course, involve important value judgments. In most economic evaluations, these considerations are ignored, based on a value assumption that they are unimportant or not measurable.

Regression Studies

The second general approach to economic evaluation of agricultural research mentioned by Norton and Davis (note 6) is the estimation of production functions featuring research as a variable, permitting an estimate of the "marginal rate of return to research." Many examples of such research are found in the literature. The dependent variable in these studies is usually some measure of agricultural productivity; independent or explanatory variables include, among others, various measures of research activity. Problems of discounting future streams of benefits and costs are avoided with this approach, because an array of annual data are used, typically at the state level rather than the national level of aggregation.

Let us first consider the dependent variable. In his seminal study of the impact of research on agriculture, Ruttan notes the distinction between increases in production versus increases in productivity.[10] An increase in production is simply an expansion of output, which can result from planting more acres or milking a larger herd, or it can be caused by an increase in productivity—such as higher yield per acre or milk production per cow. Productivity is a ratio whose numerator is production and whose denominator is input. When a single input is used in the denominator, the resulting "partial productivity" ratio can be misleading. For example, an increase in crop yield per acre can be the combined result of increased levels of fertilization, a more effective herbicide, and an improved seed variety. An increase in one partial productivity ratio may be accompanied by a decrease in another, as when higher milk production per cow is accomplished by increasing the number of times each cow is milked per day, thereby reducing the milk output per labor-hour.

In an attempt to overcome this confusion, economists have constructed a measure of "total productivity," where the numerator is an estimate of the current market value of production, and the denominator is some measure of total inputs. Ordinarily, the various classes of inputs, such as fertilizer, labor, seed, and so forth, are aggregated into an index using market prices of the inputs as weights—in other words, the total cost of the inputs valued at market prices. Valuation of land and of operator and management inputs is always a sticky problem, and no universally satisfactory method has been found to deal with it. In the case of estimating the productivity of research, the denominator is an estimate of the total costs of the research, or in the more detailed studies, the total cost of researching, developing, and transferring the new technology.

A widely accepted but nonetheless questionable procedure used in the measurement of productivity is the inclusion of government payments as part of the numerator, value of output. Conceptually, if the effect of research on agricultural productivity is to be measured, then only those components of increased value of production attributed directly to it (or, if indirectly, at least by some tangible linkage) should be permitted in the accounting. Government payments to farmers, either directly or through overt supply control programs, are a result of political rather than scientific activity, and should be accounted for accordingly.

Other conceptual difficulties are inherent in the way agricultural productivity is measured for purposes of evaluating agricultural research in regression studies. One of these difficulties has to do with the accounting of costs. Only out-of-pocket cash costs are taken into account; the market prices used in making these calculations fail to reflect externalities associated with environmental degradation or the health impacts resulting from adoption of the new technologies, as well as the preferences of future generations.

Bonnen (note 5) points out that some observers of agricultural research contend that the necessary and sufficient condition for enhancing agricultural productivity is basic or disciplinary research. Taking issue with this belief, Bonnen argues that basic research is necessary but not sufficient, requiring linkages to applied or problem-solving research, extension, and farmer education. I totally agree.

It is perhaps in recognition of this principle that Dean Hess of the University of California at Davis strongly advocates what he calls "targeted basic research," wherein some of the scientists with a bent for basic research are housed with those deeply immersed in subject matter, problem-solving, or technology-generating research in the various departments of the university.[11]

Ruttan notes that "Science-oriented research does not have a significant independent effect. The high payoff to science-oriented research is achieved only when it is directed toward increasing the productivity of technology-oriented research."

Mathematical Programming Approaches

Another important way in which economists "evaluate" agricultural research is to include the results of that research in their mathematical programming models in ways that permit comparisons of new and previous technologies. The scope of individual studies varies from the individual farm to the national level. For several decades, farm management researchers and extension experts have incorporated the financial implications of emerging new technology into their analysis of farm plans, to determine what effects various technologies may have on farm income and production of various commodities. The results of agricultural research are implicitly introduced into the analysis in the form of changes in yields, resource requirements, and costs.

When the analysis is done at the farm level, it is ordinarily reasonable to assume that the prices of the farm commodities and purchased inputs remain constant. That is, the decisions made by an individual farmer or small number of farmers are assumed to have an insignificant effect on total market supplies or the demand for farm inputs. This assumption historically has been valid, since farms have been very numerous and "atomistic," meaning that each farm accounts for a minute fraction of the total market. As the trend toward fewer or larger farms continues, however, this assumption will eventually become erroneous; it already may be naive in the case of highly concentrated industries such as poultry and eggs.

Crowder analyzed the effects of farming methods not only on soil erosion but also on pesticide and nutrient pollution of streams and underground water.[12] Soil erosion was limited to three tons per acre, since this was considered the "tolerable" limit for most Pennsylvania farms. Annual losses of nitrogen and phosphorus in surface runoff were constrained to 14 pounds and 6.5 pounds per acre, respectively. Crowder admits these limits may be too high, possibly posing ecological problems, but he felt these levels were "practical." Simulated soil losses of plant nutrients (nitrogen and phosphorus) and pesticides as well as tonnage of soil erosion were fed into a linear programming model to select among alternative cropping systems.

The scope of this study could have been extended to consider other alternative cropping systems (such as organic or regenerative methods, for example). And the levels of all pollutants could have been limited to ecologically harmless levels (established or presumed). Nonetheless, studies such as this illustrate the potential contribution of ecology-oriented economic analysis to informed decision making by farmers considering alternative rotations or tillage systems, and by policy makers concerned about limiting non-point source pollution in ways that do not destroy the profitability of farming. This trend is hopeful in view of T. W. Schultz's axiom, "An economist who is only an economist is likely to be a nuisance if not a positive danger."[13] An economist who is aware of ecological relationships can incorporate them into his/her analysis in ways that yield useful results.

Economists recognize that adoption of new technologies by vast numbers of farms (or even by a small number of gigantic ones) can change total output of farm commodities by amounts large enough to affect prices. In a similar vein, the prices of inputs can be changed. This realization has led to development of analysis beyond the farm level, featuring regional or even national aggregates of production and demand. These studies are termed "spatial equilibrium" or "interregional competition" studies. Historically, most of these studies have looked exclusively at the financial implications of various production technologies and public policies (via changes in prices and permissible levels of acreage or other restrictions or inducements).

In recent years, spatial equilibrium studies have undergone a metamorphosis reflecting changes in public policy concerns. Starting with the petroleum price escalation of the 1970s, studies began to examine the impacts of technology changes and policy options, not only with regard to farm income and prices, but also considering energy requirements. And more recently, these studies have considered soil erosion.

Value Assumptions of Neoclassical Economists

These trends reflect the value assumption by economists that their research should be useful in addressing emerging policy concerns. This is consistent with the findings of Busch and Lacy that agricultural economists report "importance to society" is the leading criterion for selection of research topics.[14] Economists are thereby making the value judgment that, other things being equal, it is better to be useful. Not a bad position to take. In seeking to become more socially useful, however, economists need to be aware of the value assumptions hidden in one of their favorite tools, called the neoclassical paradigm, which uses market supply and demand as the basis for determining the value of goods, services, and resources.

Many economists, notably those called resource economists, institutionalists, and labor economists, are acutely aware of the strengths and limitations of the neoclassical paradigm. Others, termed "doctrinaire neoclassical economists," do not question, nor are they aware of, the value assumptions imbedded in their paradigm, their way of thinking about the world and the affairs of men doing business as producers and consumers of goods and services. Elsewhere I have unpacked these value assumptions in considerable detail.[15] Briefly, some of the key value assumptions are reductionism and mathematization, the enthronement of greed and consumer sovereignty, efficiency and productivity, and intertemporal equity.

Reductionism and Mathematization

As economists have sought to be respected and rewarded in academic and other professional circles as "true scientists" they have honed their quantitative skills to a fine edge, with increasingly sophisticated and mathematical techniques. Criticizing the propensity of economists to substitute compactness and obscurity for simplicity and clarity, Leontief has stated: "Uncritical enthusiasm for mathematical formulation tends often to conceal the ephemeral substantive content of the argument behind a formidable front of algebraic signs. . . . it is the empirical validity of the assumptions on which the usefulness of the exercise depends." Leontief also contended that the tendency to increasingly mathematize economics has distorted the values of the academic community: "Continued preoccupation with imaginary hypothetical, rather than with observable, reality has gradually led to a distortion of the informal valuation scale used in our academic community to assess and to rank the scientific performance of its members. Empirical analysis, according to this scale, gets a lower rating than formal mathematical reasoning." He goes on to observe that an economist is likely to earn a higher professional status by devising a new statistical procedure for estimating an unknown parameter (often from data whose exact meaning and validity remain unclear to the analyst and to readers), than by performing a successful quest for more and better data "that would permit us to measure the magnitude of the same parameter in a less ingenious, but more reliable way."[16]

Enthronement of Greed and Consumer Sovereignty

The key value assumption here is that the individual consumer is the best judge of what goods and services will satisfy him. Neoclassical demand theory implies "more is better." As Kamarck has described it: "it is assumed that consumers are rational and selfish: they know which commodities will satisfy them best and they spend their money accordingly."[17]

Another value assumption central to much of neoclassical economic theory is that the greatest good for the greatest number of people will result naturally from an economic system governed by consumer sovereignty. This is coupled with faith in Adam Smith's "invisible hand" of greed among producers striving to increase their profits by satisfying consumer wants.[18]

But Schumacher wisely distinguishes between human needs and wants.[19] The poorest of the poor, for example, have unmet food and housing needs which may threaten their very existence, but because they lack purchasing power, these needs are not translated into demand in the market place.

Another problem is that consumer demand and market prices are not strictly based on the "wants" of *all* persons. Rather, demand is principally driven by the preferences of contemporary (as opposed to future) consumers who have ample money and will to spend it on certain categories of goods and services. The wants (much less the needs) of the very poor and of future generations are imperfectly registered in the market place.

Modern economics, it seems, has become largely a science of greed. As Schmid, a prominent institutional economist, has pointed out: "Modern Western economics has tried hard to make love superfluous for the working of the economy. The competitive market is thought to be a system where welfare is maximized without anyone caring for anyone else."[20] The engine driving a capitalistic economy is greed. The engine is sparked by sales promotional activity (such as advertising) which creates greater and greater wants, inducing a sense of dissatisfaction with things of the past.

While the value assumption of "economic rationality" underlies the logical structure of most neoclassical economic models of behavior, many economists slip into yet another value judgment, the habit of equating such rationality (read selfishness) with intelligence, the virtue most highly esteemed by academics. Anyone who refrains from acting in ways that maximize his own material "well-being" is considered irrational and *ipso facto* defective and inferior. Thus, the more doctrinaire neoclassical economists have enthroned the vice of greed as a cardinal virtue.

Efficiency and Productivity

The typical economist embraces the value assumption that increases in productivity are good, "other things being equal." In some instances, however, serious detrimental side effects accompany the increases in productivity—faster soil erosion, chronic unemployment, environmental pollution by farm chemicals, culturing of resistant strains of germs through routine feeding of antibiotics to livestock, etc. Such "side effects" are often ignored by those doctrinaire neoclassical economists who are unaware of the social and physical environment in which the economy operates. Other economists have made serious efforts to deal with *externalities*.[21]

Intertemporal Equity

Economists have sought rigorous (not always valid) ways of equating past, present, and future economic values through mathematical compounding and discounting formulas.[22] Both the compounding rate and the discount rate are ordinarily keyed to some appropriate market rate of interest in evaluating the future benefits and costs of public projects and investments. This discount rate has been a political football between conservationists and Congressional "pork barrelers."

Boulding observes that the "real" dollars of constant purchasing power so widely computed in benefit-cost analysis of social alternatives is a "dangerously imperfect measure of the quality of human life and human values."[23] Furthermore, benefit-cost analysis is highly vulnerable to manipulation to suit the prejudices of the persons hoping to influence the policy decisions.

Overview and Suggestions

The value assumptions inherent in alternative approaches to economic analysis of agricultural research have been explicated. The consumer and producer surplus approach was found to carry the strongest value assumptions; findings of such studies are subject to considerable doubt as to their proper interpretation. Measurement problems plague all economic analysis, not least the analysis of agricultural research. Difficulties have been noted in regression estimates of the impact of agricultural research. Mathematical programming (economic simulation or optimization model) constrained by reasonable ecological considerations such as soil erosion and runoff of agricultural chemicals, while not without deficiencies, was found to be a promising approach to the estimation of the potential impacts of alternative technologies and, *ipso facto*, of research and development work and technology transfer efforts required for the widespread adoption of that technology.

In the usual conduct of public and private decision making regarding agricultural research, economic analysis inevitably is and should be taken into account. As the economist becomes more acutely aware of the value assumptions underlying his/her analysis, and as alternative assumptions are incorporated into their studies, decision makers will be given a richer and more useful basis for choice. The task of envisioning society as it can and should be must not be left to economists or academics alone, however. All who have a stake in the outcome should become informed as to the choices and their implications.

The challenge before the agricultural research establishment is to organize itself and conduct its work in ways calculated to create science and technology that will lead to a "better" society, better according to ethics and values far beyond those embodied in current market prices. With sensitivity to that broader set of norms, as well as to the integrity of natural and living systems, economic analysis can illumine many decisions by predicting the outcome of alternative courses of action.

Notes

1. This chapter is a somewhat condensed and modified version of this author's chapter, "Beyond Conventional Economics: An Examination of the Values Implicit in the Neoclassical Economic Paradigm as Applied to the Evaluation of Agricultural Research and Productivity" in K. A. Dahlberg, ed., *New Directions for Agriculture and Agricultural Research* (Totowa, N.J.: Rowman and Allanheld Publ., 1986), pp. 221–58.

2. The author is professor of agricultural economics at The Pennsylvania State University. He also serves as manager of a national program, Low-input Farming Systems Research and Education, based in Washington, D.C.

3. James H. Laue, "Value-Free, Objective Educators," in *Coping with Conflict: Strategies for Extension Community Development and Public Policy Professionals* (Ames, Iowa: North Central Regional Center for Rural Development, 1979), pp. 1–6.

4. J. B. Kendrick, "Agricultural Research is on Trial," *California Agriculture* 38, nos. 5 and 6 (May-June 1984): 2.

5. James T. Bonnen, "Agriculture's System of Developmental Institutions: Reflections of the U.S. Experience." (Paper presented at Symposium on Rural Economics, University of Laval, Quebec, Canada.) See also "Historical Sources of U.S. Agricultural Productivity: Implications for R & D Policy and Social Science Research," *American Journal of Agricultural Economics* 65:958–66.

6. George W. Norton, W. L. Fishel, A. A. Paulsen, and W. B. Sundquist, *Evaluation of Agricultural Research*, Proceedings of NC-148 Workshop, University of Minnesota, Agricultural Experiment Station, Misc. Pub. 8 (Minneapolis, 1981). See also George W. Norton and Jeffrey S. Davis, "Review of Methods Used to Evaluate Returns to Agricultural Research," in G. W. Norton *et al.*, eds. *Evaluation of Agricultural Research* (Minneapolis: University of Minnesota Agricultural Experiment Station, 1981), pp. 26–47.

7. David W. Pearce, *The Dictionary of Modern Economics* (Cambridge: MIT Press, 1981).

8. W. Burt Sundquist, "Technology and Productivity Policies of the Future," in *The Farm and Food System in Transition*, Report FS4 (East Lansing: Michigan State Cooperative Extension Service, 1983).

9. Alain de Janvry, Philip LeVeen, and David Runsten, *Mechanization in California Agriculture: The Case of Canning Tomatoes*, Inter-American Institute of Agricultural Sciences, Misc. Pub. 223 (San Jose, Costa Rica, 1980.)

10. Vernon W. Ruttan, *Agricultural Research Policy* (Minneapolis: University of Minnesota Press, 1982).

11. Irwin Feller, Lynne Kaltrieder, J. Patrick Madden, and Dan E. Moore, *Agricultural Technology Delivery System: A Study of the Transfer of Agricultural and Food Related Technologies*, Final report to USDA, vol. 1–5 (University Park: Institute for Policy Research and Evaluation, The Pennsylvania State University, 1984).

12. Bradley M. Crowder, Donald J. Epp, Harry B. Pionke, C. Edwin Young, James G. Beierlein, and Earl J. Partenheimer, *The Effects on Farm Income on Constraining Soil and Plant Nutrient Losses*, Agricultural Experiment Station Bulletin 850 (University Park, Pa., May 1984).

13. Irving Hock, "Retooling the Mainstream: Discussion," *American Journal of Agricultural Economics* 66, 5 (1984):793–97.

14. Lawrence Busch and William B. Lacy, *Science, Agriculture, and the Politics of Research* (Boulder, Colo.: Westview Press, 1983).

15. P. Madden, "Beyond Conventional Economics," cited in note 1.

16. Wassily Leontief, "Theoretical Assumptions and Nonobserved Facts," *American Economic Review* 61 (1971): 1–7.

17. Andrew M. Kamarck, *Economics and the Real World* (Philadelphia: The University of Pennsylvania Press, 1983).

18. Kenneth E. Boulding, *Economics as a Science* (New York: McGraw-Hill, 1970).

19. E. F. Schumacher, *Small is Beautiful—Economics as if People Mattered* (New York: Harper and Row, 1973).

20. A. Allan Schmid, *Property, Power, and Public Choice: An Inquiry into Law and Economics* (New York: Praeger, 1978).

21. Emery N. Castle, "The Market Mechanism Externalities, and Land Economics," *Journal of Farm Economics* 47 (1965): 542–56. See also Emery N. Castle, Maurice M. Kelso, Joe B. Stevens, and Herbert H. Stoevener, "Natural Resource Economics, 1946–75," in Lee R. Martin, ed., *A Survey of Agricultural Economics Literature*, vol. 3 (Minneapolis: University of Minnesota Press, 1981), pp. 393–500.

22. Robert C. Lind, Kenneth J. Arrow, Gordon R. Corey, Partha Dasgupta, Amartya K. Sen, Thomas Stauffer, Joseph E. Stiglitz, J. A. Stockfisch, and Robert Wilson, *Discounting for Time and Risk in Energy Policy* (Baltimore: John Hopkins University Press, 1982).

23. See K. Boulding, *Economics as a Science*, cited in note 18.

Still Learning to Farm
Agricultural Research and Extension in the 1980s

Nancy Matheson, David Oien, Al Kurki

Introduction

Agricultural research and extension institutions were much scrutinized and criticized during the convulsive years of the 1980s. While farmers were losing their land to spiraling costs and lower commodity prices, other consequences of production-oriented agriculture were also emerging. Increasingly severe and frequent incidents guaranteed that ground- and surface water degradation, on-farm human and wildlife exposure to toxic substances, pesticide contamination of foods, and soil erosion would become unavoidable issues.

Publicly funded research and extension institutions generate much of this country's agricultural technology and are a primary source of information for farmers. A number of technologies developed through public research have played a major role in the resource depletion and degradation we are witnessing.

What obligation do these institutions have to reshape agricultural research and extension to address pressing social and environmental issues for agriculture? What role should the public have in that reorganization process? What are some of the institutional and systemic barriers to developing research activity or models meaningful to farmers who seek to become better stewards of the land?

Land-grant university officials and members of a public interest group in the West have addressed these and other questions during a four-year process of negotiating program and policy changes within the land-grant institution. The discussion began in 1984 when a small group of Montana farmers affiliated with the Alternative Energy Resources Organization (AERO), a Montana-based, grassroots citizen organization, initiated a dialogue between Montana State University (MSU) officials and AERO-affiliated farmers. The dialogue was soon formalized through state legislation calling on MSU to "develop comprehensive research and extension programs in sustainable agriculture." The farmers and MSU representatives (researchers, extension specialists, and administrators) then had the public mandate, if not the money, to engage in a serious discussion about modifying university research and extension priorities.

Those first four years of working to bring about changes in the research priorities of Montana and other land-grant universities taught AERO farmers some valuable lessons. They learned much about the process and dynamics involved in working with researchers and administrators to further the goals of sustainable agriculture—lessons that are examined in the following section. The result of personal experience, the discussion presented here explains the particular issues and problems the conversion from conventional to sustainable agriculture poses for both the public, and agricultural research and extension institutions.

Face-to-Face: The Public and Its Research Institutions

"2,4-D is an organic chemical."

One of the first challenges facing those approaching the conventional agricultural research community on issues of sustainable agriculture is finding a common language. The sustainable agriculture movement is a social phenomenon with its own history, cast of characters, events, and seminal texts. As such, it has developed its own "language. " Not surprisingly, some of the words overlap those used by the agricultural science community, though the meanings often do not. Terms such as "organic," "chemical," and "synthetically compounded" have particular and, in some cases, precise scientific meanings for an ag researcher. For the sustainable agriculture producer or advocate, they can have very different, but no less lively, connotations.

Ultimately, debate limited to semantics would be unproductive. Nonetheless, the development of a common language is a prerequisite for a productive relationship between the sustainable agriculture and research communities. Attempts to develop a common language are occurring, as is evident in the many movement names being used—alternative agriculture, ecological agriculture, organic ag, sustainable ag, regenerative agriculture, agroecology. That each term has its proponents and detractors, while all reflect a new perspective, points to the fact that, by whatever name, the agricultural research community is dealing with something more than another set of practices or techniques that can be substituted for current practices. What the language changes reflect is a new approach to agriculture—a holistic, ecological, or systems approach.

Since the agricultural research and extension community is in the cultural mainstream, its tendency is, and will continue to be, to redefine the sustainable agriculture language—incorporating it into the existing research and extension framework. Two dangers exist. The first is the trivialization of the language. Now that the concept of a more benign agriculture is gaining popularity, and funding for research is becoming more available, there is a temptation simply to rename faculty positions, research projects, or entire academic departments for political or financial reasons, with little or no substantive shift in program or research direction. The second danger is the trivialization of the issues—the redefinition of the issues raised by sustainable agriculturalists to fit institutional understanding and goals. Agricultural research and extension's early choice of the term "low-input" rather than "sustainable" is indicative of that tendency. To encourage, for instance, decreasing a farmer's costs without building the farmer's soil is to treat the symptoms, while the real illnesses that afflict modern agriculture go untreated.

"We already do sustainable ag research: In our control plots we apply no treatments at all."

The second challenge facing the research community is conceptual. As an heir to the logical-positivist tradition, the conventional ag scientist will attempt to understand sustainable agriculture in terms of existing mechanistic models. This worldview holds that it is possible to understand the whole by understanding its parts. Agriculture—even sustainable agriculture—can be studied and categorized by such models, but it is unlikely to be understood and enhanced by them. AERO farmer Stephen Elliott finds it hard to break down and judge by categories his farming practices. For example, Elliott explains, "To judge the effects of composting without considering the effects of crop rotations or other cultural practices is obviously silly." Likewise, Elliott contends that farming practices cannot be separated from the goals and philosophy of the farmer.[1]

Historically, we have viewed our farms as factories and applied the laws of efficiencies, economies of scale, and economics as if agriculture were an industrial process. The near collapse of the production agricultural system is a warning, not that we need to fine-tune our approach and apply those laws more stringently, but that our entire concept of agriculture needs to be re-examined. Applying the industrial model has, in itself, contributed much to the agricultural malaise.

The voice of sustainable agriculture calls to agricultural institutions to consider farming and ranching within its biological, social, and economic context. Another AERO farmer, Zane Zell, speaks for many when he says he wants his farming operation to evolve ecologically and economically to the point where the quality of the soil, water, food, and wildlife habitat become the determining factors in its management.[2] Zell's success criteria are a far cry from traditional standards. Historically, programs, research, individual farming operations, or agriculture as a whole have been assessed in terms of how many bushels of wheat or pounds of meat can be produced with a given amount of resources. That is not enough. We must also ask: What are the consequences of such production? What are the demands on limited resources? What are the environmental costs or benefits? What are the long-term effects on farm families and rural communities? What are the health effects on those producing the food or fiber and on those eating or using the produce?

Sustainable agriculturalists contend that agriculture is not practiced and cannot be understood, taught, or researched in isolation. Individual plants and animals, fields, farms and agriculture as a whole exist as part of a biological, social, and economic system and can be truly comprehended only by way of an ecological or holistic perspective—one that recognizes the whole to be greater than the sum of its parts, one that insists that the parts cannot be understood without understanding the whole. The task of shifting world views is tremendous and may well require major reorganization of agriculture departments, programs, and evaluation criteria.

"Find us funding and we'll research whatever you want."

A third challenge facing the agricultural research community is methodological. Generally, research is conducted on the presumption that the narrower the parameters and the fewer the variables, the more valid the results. Ironically, farming—at least the best farming—is just the opposite. Diversity is favored over specialization, polyculture over monoculture, interseeding over pure stands—in short, biological complexity over simplicity. For instance, conventional experimental design plots usually focus on a narrow aspect of a production system and are unable to shed more than dim light on how that aspect will affect the entire operation.

The methodology itself (for example, the reduction of the "competition" variable by application of a herbicide to an alfalfa forage plot) means that a whole range of factors impacting a farming operation are ignored (the effects of chemical residues on livestock or farmer health, the nitrogen-fixing capability of the plant, the potential for groundwater contamination or the quantity and disposal of toxic waste that is a co-product of herbicide manufacture). A whole host of concerns increasingly important to farmers and the broader public—concerns beyond reduced yields because of weeds in a field—are not addressed.

The holistic view that sustainable agriculture is based on asks ag researchers to use the wide-angle lens and telescope as well as the microscope. For that to happen, it will be necessary to develop a methodology that not only recognizes but addresses the biological and socioeconomic complexity inherent in a sustainable agricultural system.

For many producers, the reasons for implementing particular practices are more manifold than conventional research might assume. For example, a farmer may introduce alfalfa into a rotation for many reasons: livestock forage production, nitrogen fixation for subsequent crops, production of green manure, disruption of weed and other pest cycles, soil conservation and water quality. A farmer asking which variety to plant will likely find that university research and extension recommendations will be useful for the first and maybe the second reason given, but certainly not for weighing the trade-offs among all of them. If a farmer aware of all the goals above asks which variety to plant for a seven-year mixed rotation that uses no pesticides, the best information will likely be an educated, but nonetheless wild, guess.

The challenge is great. Ag research has, for the most part, asked the same questions producers have historically asked, but the sustainable agriculture movement is an indicator that producers are starting to ask different questions, and different types of questions. Increasingly, agricultural research will need to address secondary as well as primary consequences of practices, and whole systems as well as individual technologies. It may well require new, or not customarily employed, methods of observation, experimental design, and analysis. Agricultural research must meet these needs if it is to reflect and be responsive to the emerging agriculture and the public it services.

Getting from Here to There

"But what is a farm if it is not a research center?"

The message sustainable agriculture practitioners are emphasizing is that farms and ranches are not neat packages. All farms are real-world experiments producing tremendous amounts of biological, economic, and social information. AERO farmers recognized this fact when they asked themselves how they could move forward even if land-grant universities never did a day of research on sustainable farming systems. They decided to look to farmers and ranchers who have made and are making the transition to sustainable production, whose operations represent a vast untapped source of data about ecological farming practices in the context of the biological, economic, and social systems they are a part of.

In 1987, AERO undertook a project to gather information about what farmers are doing—about what interactions are at work—on regenerative and transitional operations in the semiarid northern Rockies and intermountain plains. What AERO found was that farmers are generating the very information they are most seeking in their shift away from resource-depleting, high-cost, and energy-intensive farming systems.

The transfer of information and technology from farmer to farmer—and from farmer to researcher—is one readily available means of effecting a more sustainable agriculture. It is an immediate alternative to waiting for the nation's and the region's land-grant research priorities to shift; it offers a systems approach to making long-term changes on farms and ranches, and it holds promise for helping shape scientific research programs and methodologies now and in the future. It also suggests a new role for extension—to facilitate the transfer of information and technology among farmers, and between farmers and researchers.

Farmers formerly on the "fringe" are now innovative leaders— in pest control, soil fertility, water conservation, and marketing. Yet they and the public who benefits from a more ecological approach to farming and ranching and to food production and processing, remain largely outside the circle of decision making that sets agricultural research priorities. While the role of researcher or extension specialist has been reserved for scientists, the setting of research and extension priorities has largely been reserved for university administrators, agribusiness, and commodity groups in a process mediated by federal and state policy makers. Broader public participation often comes too late, if at all, and then relies on adversarial processes.

One way to expand the circle is by setting aside public funds at the federal, state, or local level for allocation on a competitive-bid basis to the public and the private sectors for research projects meeting a particular set of goals. These goals and project criteria would be established through a public process involving consideration of the direct and indirect, short- and long-term, economic and ecological effects of new technologies. Those with the greatest capacity to achieve results meeting the predefined goals would have the opportunity to undertake the research—even farmers.

If new research priorities are to emerge from the country's recognition of its own long-term economic, social, and environmental needs, a widening of the decision making circle is imperative. Without that widening, the continuation of research that focuses on increased production—historically, at almost any cost—is inevitable.

And, just as a more democratic approach to setting research priorities holds promise for meeting the needs of a broader public, so it holds promise for the development of new research methodologies and approaches that are truly interdisciplinary and holistic.

Conclusions

"The exact sciences, however complex their implications, traditionally have been obliged to limit their immediate attention almost entirely to the simple."[3] This statement sums up the limitations conventional agricultural sciences have imposed on our understanding of agricultural systems. More specialized information does not necessarily lead to increased understanding.

The sustainable agriculture movement is challenging agricultural research and extension institutions to develop increased understanding of agriculture as a system. The dialogue that has begun has demonstrated that meeting this challenge will require a shift in world views, and the reorganization of departments, programs, methods of observation, experimental design and analysis, and evaluation criteria. It will require shifts in funding. It will require a more democratic process for determining research priorities. And it will require a redefinition of who the "experts" are. Practitioners of sustainable agriculture and the farming systems they are a part of have much to offer toward meeting that challenge.[4]

Notes

1. Stephen Elliott, 1988. Alternative Energy Resources Organization survey of sustainable agriculture farmers.

2. Zane Zell, 1988. Alternative Energy Resources Organization survey of sustainable agriculture farmers.

3. Timothy Perris, "Our cosmic decoder," *The Nation* (August 13/20, 1988).

4. Nancy Matheson, ed., *AERO's Guide to Sustainable Agriculture in the Northern Rockies and Plains* (Helena Montana: Alternative Energy Resources Organization, 1989), pp. 1–100. The authors would like to thank the members of the AERO sustainable agriculture task force for initiating the dialogue with Montana State University that is the subject of this paper. We would also like to thank Dr. Jim Welsh and Dr. LeRoy Luft for their willingness to commit MSU to the dialogue.

Legal Aspects of Biotechnological Research and Development

Paul Elihu Stern

Introduction

Since the early 1970s, the world has witnessed a scientific revolution. Within this very short time, the tools of molecular biology have been harnessed to provide technologies that promise to improve our ability to treat disease, to clean up the environment, and to supply food and fiber. These advances in science, broadly referred to as *biotechnology*, include such powerful techniques as recombinant DNA and cell fusion. Most significant is the development of laboratory methods to combine genetic material from diverse species. The biotechnology revolution has generated a new industry comprising established companies along with innovative ones. The biotech industry has spurred numerous relationships between universities and private companies, causing concern for traditional university values. At the same time, the race to create profitable new products through biotechnology has forced governments to devise rules, regulations, and guidelines to assure the public that potential dangers are minimized and to reduce its fear of the unknown.

The Role of Patent Law

A major catalyst in the advance of biotechnology has been the patent law, which gives patent owners in the United States the exclusive right to make, use, and sell a new discovery for seventeen years. In 1982, many observers were shocked when the Supreme Court of the United States ruled in a 5 to 4 decision that genetically engineered living bacteria were patentable. Even though nothing in the patent law suggested that such organisms would not be patentable, it had been generally assumed that, other than plants, living things were not subject to patent protection. The fall of 1985 saw the general (or "utility") patent laws extended to plants, which were previously protected only under the Plant Variety Protection Act and the specific plant patent section of the Patent Act. This development has significantly broadened available protection for new varieties of plants. Additionally, in the spring of 1987, the United States Patent and Trademark Office announced that animals,too, are subject to protection under the patent laws. The valuable protection accorded by the United States Patent Act provides an attractive incentive for business development in biological products.

Universities and Industry Working Together

The promise of valuable commercial products, subject to protection through the patent laws, has stimulated a flurry of activity that has produced new relationships between private industry and university scientists. Universities have acquired vast amounts of knowledge through research in biotechnology. Researchers have used the knowledge generated in university laboratories to set up companies to develop new products. Many large pharmaceutical and chemical companies have tapped university resources through collaborative and contractual arrangements. These relationships, ranging from simple consulting agreements to elaborate cooperative arrangements, have intensified many ethical considerations surrounding traditional university functions, especially those at public universities.

As the gap between research activity and commercial development of consumer products has become narrower, many legal and ethical questions have arisen. The fundamental purposes of the university are to educate students and to exchange and disseminate information. Public universities are further restricted by the notion that public funds may only be expended for public purposes. Generally, universities permit professors to spend some of their time consulting with private firms. However, when the objectives of private industry—i. e., the creation of products for profit—begin to influence the direction of research performed with university funds in university facilities, a conflict of interest may surface. To remedy these conflicts, several alternatives are available. At one extreme, a university professor whose work is being greatly influenced by private sources might be forced to choose between his university post and private employment. In less extreme situations, the university employee may be forced to take leave without pay to pursue the private interests. Minor relationships may only require disclosure of the activity to university administrators to resolve any ethical problems. All these relationships must be examined very closely to avoid conflict of interest and unwarranted expenditures of university funds. The goal is to maintain the integrity of the university by keeping its educational objectives prominent.

Cooperative research agreements between universities and industry can take many forms. Generally, however, they concern a particular area of university research that a company hopes to exploit. The university, on the other hand, hopes to obtain funding for research and, in some cases, for new facilities and even academic positions. University/industry agreements may entail many contractual aspects, such as sharing patent and other intellectual property rights, licensing of newly developed products, and determining publication rights. Research agreements with private companies must be tailored to fit within various state and university policies. These policies may establish the extent to which a university will give up patent rights to inventions developed on its campus, the amount of delay it will tolerate before publication of research results while patent protection is being evaluated, the acceptable manner of licensing patents, the use of the university name in advertising, the kind of insurance protection, and many other issues that vary among institutions. As a result, these arrangements assume myriad forms.

Development of Governmental Oversight

The progress of research in biotechnology, whether performed in university laboratories, by private industry, or through cooperative arrangements between the two, will be impeded to some extent by governmental regulation and oversight. Although no specific dangers or risks have been proven to be directly related to biotechnological techniques, the federal government has attempted to establish a uniform policy to regulate biotechnology. The safety of biotechnology, especially recombinant DNA techniques, has been emphasized from the earliest use of these new methods in the laboratory. The scientific debate over the safety of biotechnology has been highly publicized, and the public has participated since the initial discussions. Proper advancement of the biotechnology industry demands that public concerns for safety be recognized and responded to. Regulatory activity has been concentrated at the federal level, which has attempted to regulate biotechnology under existing laws and rules.

In 1976, the National Institutes of Health (NIH) published the Guidelines for Research Involving Recombinant DNA Molecules. Through these guidelines, a system has been established whereby laboratory experiments are reviewed by safety committees (institutional biosafety committees, or IBCs) at each research institution. Most research is now exempt from review, and research that is considered especially risky (for example, experiments using infectious or toxic agents) is scrutinized by a national panel of experts (the Recombinant DNA Advisory Committee, or RAC) at NIH that makes recommendations to the director for or against approval, as required by the NIH guidelines. Laboratory research has proceeded safely under the NIH guidelines, which have been continually amended in response to the latest scientific knowledge.

Development of the NIH guidelines was preceded by worldwide concern over the safety of recombinant DNA manipulations. Soon after methods to combine genetic material from dissimilar species were developed, the very scientists studying the techniques questioned their possible implications. They were unsure whether organisms with unknown virulence and survivability could escape laboratory containment, creating dangers that could not be anticipated or mitigated. This uncertainty was followed by an informal moratorium on certain genetic manipulations until a meeting of the leading scholars in molecular biology and others, including laymen and the press, could meet to consider the future of this exciting technology. This meeting, the International Conference on Recombinant DNA Molecules, convened in Pacific Grove, California, at the Asilomar Conference Center in February 1975. Out of the conference came a working paper intended to lift the voluntary moratorium and to guide further experimentation. The working paper that evolved from the Asilomar Conference was used by NIH in formulating the Guidelines for Research Involving Recombinant DNA Molecules recommendations that have assured safe laboratory experiments from 1976 to the present.

The NIH guidelines have provided a sound method for ensuring public confidence in the safety of recombinant DNA research while allowing progress to continue at a reasonable pace. The guidelines apply to all federally funded research, and the penalty for noncompliance is the loss of funding. Private companies have participated under voluntary compliance provisions. The NIH guidelines do not represent regulations in the strict sense that each project must be licensed or inspected by a government body before proceeding. They do, however, constitute more than self-regulation in that activities are governed by federally sanctioned safety recommendations, and the review procedures are open to public observation and scrutiny.

On December 31, 1984, the Office of Science and Technology Policy (OSTP) in the Executive Office published the Proposal for a Coordinated Framework for Regulation of Biotechnology in the *Fed-*

eral Register. This document arose in response to the extensive commercial activity in biotechnology that had developed by that time. It was produced by an interagency working group established in April 1984 by the Cabinet Council on Natural Resources and the Environment to study and coordinate the government's regulatory policy for the products of biotechnology. The *Federal Register* notice provided an index of United States laws potentially related to biotechnology, a proposed scientific advisory mechanism for assessment of biotechnological issues, and policy statements from the Food and Drug Administration (FDA), the Environmental Protection Agency (EPA), and the Department of Agriculture (USDA).

The Proposal for a Coordinated Framework for Regulation of Biotechnology received significant public comment and initiated a period of adjustment within the federal government. The major United States agencies responsible for regulating, conducting, or funding research in biotechnology—FDA, EPA, USDA, NIH, and the National Science Foundation (NSF)—grappled with the issues as they attempted to sort out the public comments and policy differences among the agencies.

Finally, on June 26, 1986, the Coordinated Framework for Regulation of Biotechnology was published in the *Federal Register* for public comment. This document outlined a plan coordinated among the agencies to regulate both existing and anticipated uses of biotechnology. Policy statements were included from FDA, EPA, USDA, NIH, and the Occupational Safety and Health Administration (OSHA). This set of regulations is a noble attempt to pull together the diverse responsibilities of several agencies and to guide the public. However, U.S. policy on biotechnology remains difficult to understand and comply with.

Regulation of Biotechnological Applications in the Environment

The most difficult area addressed by the coordinated framework was the testing of genetically engineered organisms in the open environment. Although biotechnology research has proceeded safely in the laboratory, testing and using recombinant organisms in the open environment present serious questions. It is the lack of certainty that creates public anxiety. To many people, bacteria are simply "those microscopic things that cause disease, multiply at an alarming rate, and spread throughout the environment invisibly." This is the public to which scientists must explain the fate of genetically engineered organisms in the environment. The public is concerned that new genetic material inserted into bacteria may be transferred to other organisms. Are the recombinant organisms as safe as the multitude of organisms that have been developed through conventional means and released into the environment as crops, ornamental plants, and pest control agents?

Notably, two recently published studies on the future of introduction of genetically engineered organisms into the environment have concluded that, while there are reasons to be cautious in releasing such organisms, there is enough knowledge to permit acceptably safe experiments. The first of the two reports, "Introduction of Recombinant DNA-Engineered Organisms into the Environment: Key Issues" (National Academy of Sciences, 1987), concluded that there remain substantial concerns which must be assessed in light of scientific knowledge and accumulated experience, but that "there is adequate knowledge of the relevant scientific principles, as well as sufficient experience with R-DNA-engineered organisms, to guide the safe and prudent use of such organisms outside research laboratories." The second report, "Field-Testing Engineered Organisms: Genetic and Ecological Issues," is the third in the series *New Developments in Biotechnology* (Congress of the United States, Office of Technology Assessment, May 1988). The Office of Technology Assessment document concludes that we must remain cautious in the introduction of genetically engineered organisms, but there is no cause for public alarm; "adequate review of planned introductions is now possible."

Some data has already been amassed through reviewing environmental applications of biotechnology. The first field test of a microbial pesticide has already been performed, and researchers are evaluating the data. This experiment, which involved the application of genetically altered bacteria to induce frost tolerance on crops, was first submitted under the NIH guidelines, before the coordinated framework was released. After NIH approved the field test, EPA assumed jurisdiction after it determined the bacteria were pesticides under the Federal Insecticide, Fungicide, and Rodenticide Act (FIFRA). After several field tests, developers of a genetically engineered vaccine for pseudorabies in pigs have obtained a USDA license to market the vaccine. The USDA has also issued several permits for the transportation of genetically engineered organisms under the Plant Pest Act.

However, this experience has not been gained without controversy. In reviewing the field test proposal for an "experimental use permit" under FIFRA, EPA learned that certain tests had been performed outside contained facilities without its knowledge. Although the experimenter was fined for this infraction of FIFRA, the experiment was ultimately allowed. Some controversy surrounded the granting of the pseudorabies vaccine license when it was discovered that the researchers had not received approval from an IBC or the NIH, as required by the NIH guidelines, before conducting field tests. Furthermore, the documents required of USDA by the National Environmental Policy Act were not prepared on time. Field experiments by researchers from the United States have also been performed in Argentina and New Zealand to avoid regulatory hurdles in this country. It is not entirely clear that these incidents involve deliberate attempts to avoid regulations, but they do warrant investigation.

Recently, a scientist performed an experiment with a genetically altered strain of a bacterium in hopes of eliminating Dutch elm disease (see the discussions in *The New York Times* of September 2, 1987, p. 11; and September 4, 1987, p. 1r). The experiment was not reviewed under the NIH guidelines nor by any other governmental agency. Although this experiment was described as a deliberate act of civil disobedience, there was still a question of the precise regulatory requirements applicable to the experiment. In fact, NIH subsequently determined that its guidelines were not violated, but under EPA's FIFRA policy, the experiment required an "experimental use permit." The researcher was reprimanded by EPA, and limitations have been placed upon his subsequent research activity.

The development of the Coordinated Framework for Regulation of Biotechnology and subsequent implementation of the regulating agencies' stated policy has been, in reality, somewhat less than coordinated, as described above. There has been some interagency dealing, and the regulating agencies have appointed liaison agents to work with one another. There have been shared reviews of certain projects with overlapping regulatory requirements, but the results amount only to compromise directed toward salvaging the powers of the respective agencies. The government has managed to cloud the major issues, while expanding its regulatory jurisdiction.

The major premise of the coordinated framework is that the techniques of biotechnology are not dangerous in themselves, therefore, it is not necessary to regulate the "process." It was generally concluded by the federal agencies that since regulation should depend on the product of the technology, not the technology itself, Congress does not need to enact any new laws.

Nevertheless, in the coordinated framework, EPA announced its intention of regulating all introductions of recombinant microorganisms into the environment and eliminating the exemptions that had existed for research activities. This was justified on the basis that the agency was not singling out recombinant microbes, because other microbes would be reviewed as well, and that microorganisms pose greater hazards than chemicals.

EPA derives its jurisdiction over recombinant organisms from the Toxic Substances Control Act and the Federal Insecticide, Fungicide, and Rodenticide Act. These statutes were enacted to offer protection to public health and the environment from chemical substances and pesticides. With the prospect of new biotechnological products, EPA found that their jurisdiction could be expanded by construing their statutory authority to include these organisms. So, bacteria protecting plants from frost became "pesticides," and recombinant microorganisms became "new chemical substances." At this point, the agency could justify massive expansion of its regulatory kingdom to cover research involving biotechnology.

Similarly, USDA expanded its authority over research by including "organisms and products altered or produced through genetic engineering which . . . there is reason to believe are plant pests" within its regulatory scope. Like EPA, USDA claims not to be singling out organisms because they have been created through biotechnological techniques, but only exercising its authority to protect the country from introductions of plant pests. The Plant Pest Act confers authority on USDA to control the introduction of plant pests from abroad and the movement of plant pests across state boundaries. USDA has construed "introduction" and "movement" to include "release into the environment," because the organisms released might cross state boundaries.

The issue pertinent to regulatory jurisdiction should not be whether the agencies can "legally" assume authority over activities involving biotechnological techniques, but whether they are acting in the best interest of the nation. What results is that a vast amount of research and experimentation that has traditionally been conducted under safeguards outside the federal regulatory community becomes entrapped within a regulatory maze. Researchers are not prepared to comply with regulations that were not established to control research. Likewise, the regulatory agencies cannot adequately apply their rules to research, because the statutory language under which they are operating was not designed to affect the conduct of research. Progress in this vital and promising field now must be delayed while researchers wait to receive licenses and permits.

This is not to say that research should be free from safety standards or regulatory requirements. However, much important research is conducted with no view to a commercial product. If a plant pest is to be transported into the country or across state lines, if hazardous materials are to be transported, if experiments with laboratory animals or humans are to be conducted, or if other regulated materials or organisms are to be used, permits or licenses should be required. But researchers should not be forced to receive permits or licenses to proceed with the research itself. That amounts to an unnecessary and unreasonable intrusion upon the right of free expression and investigation.

Although it has been stated by the regulatory agencies and others that biotechnology poses no inherent risks, it is clear that biotechnological techniques are unique to some extent. However, that quality does not warrant intrusive regulation of research. The revolutionary advances promised by biotechnology coupled with massive public involvement in its development do warrant special consideration. The mechanism already exists for rational oversight of biotechnological research; it has been operating for more than a decade in the form of the NIH Guidelines for Research involving Recombinant-DNA Molecules. The success of the oversight system operated by NIH since 1976 cannot be disputed. It should be extended to all research activity until an identified commercial product is being developed, or commercial-scale testing is being conducted. At that point, regulatory licenses and permits should be sought by the promoters of the particular product.

Such a system is being promulgated by the research arm of USDA. First presented to the USDA assistant secretary for science and education by the Committee on Biotechnology of the Division of Agriculture, National Association of State Universities and Land-Grant Colleges, in March 1985, the USDA Guidelines for Research with Genetically Modified Organisms Outside Contained Facilities were designed to mirror the NIH guidelines. The USDA guidelines will establish a system like that of NIH for experiments taken out of containment. The Agricultural Biotechnology Research Advisory Committee, already in place within the department, will serve the same function as the Recombinant DNA Advisory Committee in NIH. Institutional biosafety committees would be used, and little alteration of those IBCs set up for the NIH guidelines would be necessary. It is anticipated that the USDA guidelines would be flexible enough to respond to developments in biotechnology, so that the most recent knowledge could be applied, ensuring the utmost safety. At the same time, the accumulation of knowledge concerning experimentation outside the laboratory would allow review to be concentrated at the local level.

The USDA guidelines would apply to microorganisms investigated for their pesticidal properties, to organisms with plant pest characteristics, and to those with other potential uses in agriculture. The guidelines apply to *research*. If the USDA guidelines become as generally accepted as the NIH guidelines, the nation will have a rational procedure for the oversight of environmental releases and the protection of human welfare and the environment. By following the NIH example, the USDA guidelines will cause minimal intrusion into the research process. The review system defined by the USDA guidelines would also provide a sound record of research for use by regulatory agencies when research proceeds to commercial production. The USDA guidelines will provide the best possible scientific review and lay evaluation of research, while ensuring public access to the review process and its records.

Conclusion

Biotechnology does not create monsters; biotechnology is not an activity in need of strict regulation. Biotechnology is a powerful tool that people have developed for their benefit. Still, scenarios can be depicted that show the need for caution. Because all the ecological effects that may accompany releases of recombinant organisms into the environment are unknown, we must build assurances into the technology. The public should feel confident that progress in biotechnology is accompanied by proper safeguards, and scientists must be aware of the public concerns.

The USDA Guidelines for Research with Genetically Modified Organisms Outside Contained Facilities will eliminate the need for civil disobedience, for experimentation abroad without scientific justification, or for hurried governmental regulation. Scientific investigators will be presented with a clear and concise system similar to one with which they have been working, i. e., the NIH guidelines. Finally, the nation will acquire a system that builds confidence in the safety of experimentation by allowing public input and scrutiny.

References Cited

Coordinated Framework for Regulation of Biotechnology; Announcement of Policy and Notice for Public Comment. Federal Register vol. 51, June 26, 1986, pp. 23302–50.

National Academy of Sciences. *Introduction of Recombinant DNA-Engineered Organisms into the Environment: Key Issues* (Washington, D.C.: National Academy Press, 1987).

National Institutes of Health (U.S.). U.S. Dept. of Health, Education, and Welfare. Public Health Service. National Institutes of Health. 1976. 1 v.: RID.gp 77-003396.

Guidelines for research involving recombinant DNA molecules. Proposal for a Coordinated Framework for Regulation of Biotechnology; Notice. Federal Register vol. 49, December 31, 1984, pp. 50856–907.

U.S. Congress. Office of Technology Assessment. *Field-Testing Engineered Organisms: Genetic and Ecological Issues*, New Developments in Biotechnology, no. 3. Washington, D.C.: U.S. Government Printing Office, May 1988.

U.S. Dept. of Agriculture. Office of Agricultural Biotechnology. *USDA Guidelines for Research with Genetically Modified Organisms Outside Contained Facilities* (draft).

Biotechnology, Ethics, and the Structure of Agriculture

Jeffrey Burkhardt

THE PURPOSE OF THIS PAPER is to provide an analysis of some of the major ethical issues associated with agricultural applications of the "new biotechnologies"—recombinant DNA (rDNA), cell fusion, and tissue culture (cloning). Agricultural applications of these techniques are presently high in priority on the national agricultural research agenda, in part because these technologies promise to increase efficiency and productivity in food and fiber production.[1] However, there is a growing number of critics of both biotechnology and the entire agricultural research agenda. Some critics object to the whole ideology of "genetic engineering"—do we have a right, they ask, to "play God?"[2] Other critics ask more policy-oriented ethical questions: What specifically are the consequences of biotechnology research, development, and diffusion as biotechnology is currently practiced? When are particular products of biotechnology ethically justifiable? Although the ideological question always looms in the background, I want to focus on these latter issues; by sorting these out in some detail, we can address more precisely and directly the "rights," "wrongs," and responsibilities associated with biotech in agriculture.

There are three major domains in which criticisms or concerns about biotechnology arise: impacts on human health and the environment, the socioeconomic consequences of agricultural biotechnology, and the nature and extent of professional or scientific responsibility for biotechnology and the whole research agenda. I will briefly summarize ethical positions in the area of health and environment. Because many of the issues raised here resolve into those connected with socioeconomic consequences of biotechnology and scientific responsibility, the analysis will concentrate on these areas.

Effects of Biotechnology on Health and the Environment

There are a number of ethical foundations for the health/ environmental critique of biotechnology, ranging from anthropocentric to non-anthropocentric considerations,[3] and critics frequently do not distinguish among these considerations in their appraisal of biotechnology. Nevertheless, the conclusion reached through most of these arguments is the same: certain products of biotechnology should be prohibited from release into the environment, or from development in the first place.

The case of frost-retarding bacteria (in particular, "ice- minus") provides one good example of both the general health/environmental criticism as well as its different ethical foundations or directions. Ice-minus (*Pseudomonas syringae*) is one of a number of naturally occurring pathnogenic plant bacteria that have been recent subjects of genetic engineering. Pseudomonas disease is a severe problem for many crops, but one of the effects of pseudomonas infection in plants is that the destruction of cells by ice crystals is retarded, because the bacteria provide a matrix on the surface of the plant for water to crystalize upon. Researchers have been able to engineer (through rDNA) the disease-producing properties out of this bacterium. The goal is to produce a commercially feasible bacteria-containing solution that could be sprayed on crops by conventional pesticide application equipment to lengthen growing season for these crops.[4]

According to critics, the release of the bacterium into the larger environment is ethically unjustifiable. One possible reason could be that release risks human health: "do not risk the health or environmental quality of present generations," or "harm to people now living is morally wrong" would be the ethical principle underlying this judgement. Yet, while these present-directed anthropocentric principles may well apply to many biotech products and processes, particularly pharmaceuticals, they do not appear to apply in the assessment of this plant bacterium. This is true with respect to many of the *agricultural* applications of biotechnology. It is not really ourselves who are placed at risk, but instead the environment. The basis for the critique is therefore better stated as either a "future generations" or ecocentric principle.

The future generations argument begins with "do not risk the well-being of future generations," and invokes the environmental impact or environmental risk assessments performed for the bacterium. These suggest that although there is a very small probability that the bacterium will have larger ecological consequences,[5] the *degree* of harm could be severe were it to occur. At worst, we don't know what could happen if we allow bioengineered organisms into the system. The argument concludes that since risking ecosystem disruption threatens future well-being, release of bioengineered organisms is morally wrong. The concern here is not with health, but primarily with the resource base available to people in the future. There is, however, a problem with this argument, namely, that even though we risk ecological disturbance, tremendous environmental good might result from introducing ice-minus and many other bioengineered organisms into the system. In other words, uncertainties in our risk assessments weaken the "future environment" argument. Despite its general philosophical plausibility, considerably more analysis is needed before it can form an adequate ethical foundation for a general critique of agricultural biotechnology.

In fact, the strongest ethical basis for the environmental critique of biotechnology is a nonanthropocentric or ecocentric principle: because the complex web of ecological relationships embodies or displays a certain completeness and integrity,[6] destroying or risking some part of this web is inherently unethical. As intuitively appealing as this principle might be, it is on the one hand philosophically difficult to establish: Why is it, for example, that the ecosystem itself is entitled to respect? While the ecosystem does display a certain completeness or integrity, the dynamics of ecosystems include a significant amount of disturbance, degradation, decay, discomfort, death, and even extinction. Human interference, whether through farming or through plant and animal breeding, or now through microbioengineering, could in fact be construed as just another part of the dynamics of the larger ecosystem. On the other hand, as even defenders of ecocentrism admit, the specific ethical obligations that follow from this ideology are difficult to establish.[7] Indeed, nearly everything human beings do interferes with nature. A strong ecocentrist position may even forbid agriculture.

In most cases, the health/environmental critique attempts to highlight the uncertainties associated with environmental risk assessment: we simply can't be sure how engineered microorganisms will affect present or future humans or the environment, even though, as some scientists suggest, there are good models and analogies that can be used for assessing the nature and consequences of products of the "new" biotechnologies.[8] Nevertheless, given uncertainties, the "who should play God?" question immediately comes into play. I cannot hope to do justice to that issue here. What I will suggest, however, is that an *institutional* argument accompanies the health/environmental critique. This argument is that potential risks demand that health and environmental risk assessments are actually performed for these products by appropriate government agencies and research institutions.[9] Although few scientists or institutions enjoy or prefer submitting their products or processes for impact review and regulation in order to protect the public good, requirements such as this are ethically justifiable. Clear negative health or environmental impacts will suggest grounds for restriction or prohibition. Now, what is interesting is that impact assessments of some biotechnology products have concluded that the products will have profound negative *social* effects; nevertheless, the products not only have not been outlawed, but in fact are thought to be justifiable. Socioeconomic critics argue that these effects should be attended to, and bioproducts which bring them about should simply be prohibited from use.

Socioeconomic Consequences of Agricultural Biotechnology

There are three distinct, though interrelated, ethical arguments regarding agricultural biotechnology that fall into the socioeconomic category: the structural critique, the fairness critique,[10] and the corporate benefit critique. Although writers on the political economy of biotechnology tend to conflate these arguments in their indictments of biotech, they reflect quite different ethical concerns. To illustrate both similarities and differences in the general political- economic position, we will consider one recent focus of this critique, the bovine growth hormone.

Bovine somatotropin (BST), sometimes called bovine growth hormone (bGH), is a naturally occurring nonsteroid substance that regulates growth in cattle and also affects feed-to-milk conversion efficiency. Studies by dairy scientists have found BST to increase milk production in dairy cattle by up to 40 percent with only a 5–15 percent increase in feed consumption. Until recently, retrieving naturally produced BST was too costly to be commercially feasible, but now bovine somatotropin can be less expensively produced through rDNA methods. Since the chemical is not lactated, and in fact has been shown not to affect human health even when administered directly, it is considered safe for humans. Although it may negatively affect cattle in various ways, no long-term environmental effects have been associated with the drug.[11]

A 1986 technology impact assessment by the U.S. Congress Office of Technology Assessment (OTA), as well as a number of other studies, however, have suggested that there will be significant social effects of BST use.[12] In particular, the economics associated with the use of BST will tend to make smaller dairy operations less competitive. Despite the claims of some analysts and spokespersons for companies involved in research and development,[13] most experts appear to agree that diffusion of BST is highly likely to put many smaller dairy farms out of business. BST will increase the efficiency of production for those dairy farms that remain, but it is also expected to boost total milk output and lower prices at a time when there are already significant surpluses of dairy products and volatile prices, at least in the U.S.[14]

The structural argument holds that this product of biotechnology is illegitimate because of larger socioeconomic effects it will have: "do not negatively affect the present structure of agriculture" could be one statement of its major ethical principle, although this may be better stated as "do not risk agricultural security and sustainability." According to the argument, the development and diffusion of any technology is ethically wrong when it contributes to an increase in high-tech industrialized and concentrated agricultural production systems. Industrialized and concentrated agriculture is in turn illegitimate because it is less than secure and sustainable. Further, security and sustainability are constitutive of the social good associated with agriculture. This is thus a welfare-based or roughly "utilitarian" argument.[15] If the diffusion of BST further contributes to industrialization and concentration, it is ethically wrong.

There are, at least in theory, good reasons to think that the general argument that technological innovation contributes to industrialized and concentrated agricultural production is sound. The historical analogies are clear: nearly every efficiency- increasing innovation in technology over the past 100 years that has been introduced into agriculture and widely adopted by agricultural producers has contributed to the industrialization and concentration of agricultural production.[16] The predominant judgment on the part of the agricultural establishment (including farmers), as well as the implicit judgment on the part of consumers, has been that increased productivity, yields, and cheap and available food are the prime concern. Economics appears to dictate that this will be best (or only) achieved by high-tech, large-scale agricultural operations, so that technologies favoring this structure have been and probably will continue to be introduced into agriculture. Although some observers raise questions about whether BST will contribute to concentration,[17] to the extent that BST does increase efficiency as dairy scientists and agricultural economists say it will, some effect on agricultural structure is likely.

Nevertheless, the ethical component of the argument may break down. If structural change does not generate determinate negative environmental effects, or long-term negative social effects such as monopolization in ownership or control, what is wrong with technological innovations that contribute to that change? So long as healthy food can be produced for an indefinite period of time without damaging the environment, what's the problem with large-scale concentrated production? Indeed, the industrialization and concentration of *agriculture* may be no more insidious than the industrialization and concentration of the steel industry. If the greater good is served, the diffusion of these technologies can be ethically justifiable.

At this point, some socioeconomic critics raise a different issue: the "unfairness" of BST diffusion. According to this argument, a practice is unethical if it arbitrarily disadvantages a given group in society.[18] What "structural change" means is that many individual farms will go out of business as a result of the diffusion of BST and other products of biotechnology. Even efficient and profitable small operations may be affected: despite their best efforts, some dairy farmers will be harmed because of the availability of BST. The presumption is of course that "going out of business" constitutes a harm to those who do. The ethical point is that they are harmed against their will: this is not fair.

This point may be correct. Nevertheless, in the absence of a social consensus, embodied in legislation, against the unfair effects of either technologies or the operation of the market, one answer to the charge of unfairness would have to be that harms are not being *arbitrarily* imposed on particular farmers. Those that cannot afford BST or use it effectively simply cannot compete. Furthermore, a post hoc "returns to research" analysis may well prove BST to have the tremendous social value that is now associated with the mechanical tomato harvester.[19] As long as there are alternative employment opportunities for displaced farmers, that is, the social welfare associated with the innovation may be great.

Nevertheless, there is another argument that is advanced: the corporate benefit argument. BST and most of the other products of the new agricultural biotechnologies have been developed by multinational chemical or pharmaceutical companies or by public researchers funded by these companies.[20] These companies stand to gain from sales of these products regardless of who or how many farmers go out of business (certainly up to a point). According to critics, the only benefit associated with BST and many other biotechnology products is to increase corporate profits, market share, and control. The ethical issue is ultimately the justice of the distribution, not of immediate benefits or harms, but of power instead.[21] Despite industry claims to the contrary, the *result* of the development and marketing of many products of biotechnology will be to tie even those farmers that remain in business more closely to the chemical-industrial sectors of the economic system. This may have decided effects on our ability to *socially* control agriculture, either through market forces or through regulation. No longer would the larger society be able to set goals for agriculture, for example, adequate supplies of food at reasonable prices, sustainable production, or national food security. Goals for agriculture would instead be set in the corporate headquarters. This is not to say that companies necessarily intend this result. Further, in a market system, it is the farmer's decision whether to adopt a new technique or technology. Nevertheless, as agricultural economists have argued for years, the "treadmill effect" is particularly strong in agriculture: adopt the newest technology, or "fall off" the treadmill and "fall out" of business.[22] If multinational companies are in effect accelerating the treadmill solely for their own benefit, this is wrong.

Tremendous efforts have gone into promoting biotechnology as the next "revolution" in agriculture, over and above the capital invested in research and development. According to critics, we need to reassess our social commitment to biotechnology. We need to question the ethical justifiability of corporate involvement in agricultural research, particularly given the direction of that research. Biotechnology *might* be used to produce products and processes that would more directly benefit a secure and sustainable agriculture, for example, environmentally beneficial organisms or scale-neutral products—products not biased against small- to medium-scale farms—could be bioengineered.[23] However, socially or environmentally responsible biotechnology such as this may not be in corporate actors' interest.

Each of the socioeconomic criticisms, as well as the health/environmental ones, have some sound ethical points to make. If there is something socially or environmentally problematical with particular products of biotechnology, or with particular actions taken by individuals or institutions involved in agricultural research, these problems should be addressed. Perhaps, in addition to environmental impact assessment and regulation, *social* impact assessment and regulation should be institutionalized.[24] However, there is a tendency in discussions of the ethics of biotechnology to think that problems with biotechnology, if they are to be solved, must be solved somewhere in the halls of the U.S. Department of Agriculture, the Congress, or the executive branch's Office of Technology Policy. Indeed, many of the criticisms discussed conclude with the "*we* should do X, Y or Z" when everyone knows that "we" means "they," which means nobody. All too frequently, questions aren't addressed to individuals, but to "the system." In some respects this may be appropriate. However, the real question for biotechnology ethics has to be this: What do the critical points ultimately imply for individual moral agents—scientists, research administrators, corporate decision makers, policymakers at higher levels, and ordinary citizens?

The Nature and Extent of Scientific Responsibility for Biotechnology

Some of the pressing ethical issues associated with biotechnology arise simply because of the institutional nature of contemporary scientific research. Research goals and agenda have come to be set by the goals and agenda of "external" agents—e.g., the military and multinational corporations. This system sets the stage for actual or potential conflict between the professional scientist's intellectual concerns and the institutions' structure and goals. This conflict had been present long before biotechnology; however, it may now be exacerbated by the enormous amount of money that both public institutions and private corporations have made available for biotechnology research.[25]

Many questions arise here: should a scientist, particularly one working in a publicly funded university or agricultural experiment station, pursue or receive private or corporate funding while retaining his or her public role? A possible conflict of interest may occur. Should scientists and research administrators in publicly funded institutions pursue biotechnology research and development at the expense of other kinds of research, for example, traditional plant breeding? This may tend to contradict the mission of the governmentally instituted research effort—to serve agriculture. Is it legitimate for corporate decision makers to seek to control the public sector research agenda? Many of these problems may be prevented or resolved by a clear specification of relationships between public and private concerns over proprietary rights, sharing research results, and so forth. Some of them may require a more direct specification of the overall relationship between public and private research efforts. Some of these issues may simply require that scientists, administrators, and funding agents be honest with themselves and the public about the nature and consequences of specific research as well as the whole research agenda. This again may have little to do with biotechnology per se, though. One key scientific issue connected directly with biotechnological research and development that is rarely discussed is the professional-ethical requirement to abide by lab safety procedures and in general to act competently. If *some* biotechnology research and development does carry health or environmental risks, lab safety would seem to be scientists' and administrators' main ethical responsibility.[26]

The underlying ethical concerns are, first, whether an individual is aware of his or her role in the production of both knowledge and things. The second is whether one accepts the responsibility for engaging in research and development that produces things that have effects beyond the lab, beyond the firm, beyond the farm. One aspect of this responsibility involves awareness of the range of influences that affect research and development. Another aspect of this responsibility is accountability, literally, being prepared to give an account to the larger society regarding the goals and impacts of the research effort. Another is willingness to abide by whatever social consensus we arrive at concerning the legitimacy of either particular products of the new biotechnologies, or even biotechnology itself.

Far too often, administrators and policymakers talk in generalities about the "wonders of American agriculture" and the "promise of biotechnology" while failing to note possible inequities in the distribution of benefits and burdens of agriculture and agricultural research. Or, they fail to take seriously health, environmental, and socioeconomic risks such as those cited in critics' arguments. *If* biotechnology can provide a variety of products and processes that will serve the broader public good through serving agriculture, it is the responsibility of those who direct and fund such research to understand, address, discuss, and clarify these benefits and risks, and not simply sidestep the critics' points of view. This will also involve honesty with the public regarding the real promises of biotechnology as opposed to "hype." Not everyone shirks these responsibilities, to be sure, but more than a few administrators and policymakers, and more than a few professional and trade publications and promotional articles, display symptoms of irresponsibility in this regard.

Many scientists' first presumption is that science should be pursued, no strings attached, and that it is therefore simply illegitimate for others, particularly those not trained as experts in the "hard" sciences, to *question* the direction or nature of science and the technology development effort. Environmental and social critics are "anti-science" if not anti-*rational*.[27] A second presumption—or unconscious assumption—is that only technical matters are important: since scientists and technicians have contributed to our ability to reap the tremendous benefits of modern agriculture, then more technical knowledge, more information, more "engineering" will resolve whatever problems we now face. But that is not enough: as unpopular as it may be to say, every practicing scientist, whether in the physical, biological, or social sciences, has a moral responsibility to consider the implications of his or her work for contributing to the ultimate amelioration of the human condition. This means understanding technical scientific work in terms of the whole range of background values and goals that affect it, and the larger society that it affects. It also involves giving honest accounts to decision makers and to the public regarding the nature and "promises" of biotechnology.

In a market-oriented society, one of the assumptions people make is that markets function effectively to achieve the greater social good; further, markets are generally thought to be fair. This may be true, but only if market actors—individual producers and consumers, corporate executives, government regulators—undertake to act fairly in the marketplace, and with an eye toward the greater good. Competitive pressures or simply the business of making a living may appear to imply that any action, including technological innovation, that can increase profits or market share should be pursued. However, this is not true. Individual corporate actors have the same responsibilities as ordinary individual citizens—if not stronger ones due to economic as well as political power. In the case of agricultural biotechnology, this entails abiding by—and not undermining—whatever social consensus we arrive at concerning biotechnology's legitimate place in the agricultural research and production system.[28]

The responsibility for biotechnology is not solely that of the agricultural scientific establishment or the business community. Citizens and consumers have responsibilities as well. The first is to be aware, as far as possible, of the issues surrounding agricultural biotechnology such as those discussed above. The second follows from this. We should each maintain a healthy skepticism with respect to the arguments that are advanced, both in support of the new biotechnologies as well as those critical of them. Far too often policies and practices are presented to the public as a fait accompli; products and processes are offered on the market as fully safe, and socially beneficial. Alternatively, activist critics often have hidden agendas to push, and the object of their critique may be far removed from that ostensibly targeted. Neither the agricultural scientific establishment and multinational corporations, nor their environmental and socioeconomic critics, has sole possession of the truth. It is our responsibility to demand that they justify their efforts in explicitly ethical terms.

In a larger ethical context, particular harms or risks are occasionally acceptable in the interest of broader social goods or goals. However, the burden is legitimately placed upon the individual or collective actor who causes harm or risks harm to the larger society, or to future generations or the environment, to prove that that harm is socially necessary. We must not hastily conclude that no good will come from the new agricultural biotechnologies. However, neither should we conclude that anything that can be bioengineered should be bioengineered, or that anything that could increase efficiency and productivity is necessarily a good thing. If critics of biotechnology and of the agricultural research system have a constructive point to make, it is that care should be taken to rethink the broader ethical foundations of the research agenda, as well as the purposes and structure of the agricultural system that agricultural research is ostensibly designed to benefit. In the final analysis, it is the responsibility of each of us to ensure that the research agenda—whether in private or public hands—does indeed benefit agriculture, and that the structure of agriculture does indeed serve broader social interests in present and future human health, environmental safety, fairness, and the security and sustainability of food and fiber production.

Notes

1. United States Office of Technology Assessment (OTA), *Commercial Biotechnology* (New York: Pergamon Press, 1984); see Terry B. Kinney, Jr., "USDA Agricultural Research Service—Biotechnology in Farm Policy," *Notre Dame Journal of Law, Ethics, and Public Policy* 3, no. 1: (Fall, 1987).

2. The most vocal critic is Jeremy Rifkin. Rifkin's views are presented in a variety of places. His most complete expression is *Algeny* (New York: Penguin Books, 1984).

3. For a useful account of alternative philosophical approaches to environmental ethics, see J. Baird Calicott, "In Search of an Environmental Ethic," in Tom Regan, ed., *Matters of Life and Death* (New York: Random House, 1986).

4. See C. Norman, "Rifkin versus Gene Splicing: NIH wins a Round," *Science* 229 (1985): 252; R. Hilts, "Gene Altered Bacteria Tested in Berry Patch," *The Washington Post*, April 25, 1987, A5.

5. Martin Alexander, "Ecological Consequences: Reducing the Uncertainties" *Issues in Science and Technology* 1 (1985); for a more general account of bioengineered organisms in the environment, see David Lincoln et al., *Release and Containment of Microorganisms from Applied Genetics Activities*, Report to the Office of Research and Development, United States Environmental Protection Agency, 1983.

6. Rifkin, *Algeny*, cited in note 2; also, see the environmental section in Andrew Kimbress and J. Rifkin, "Biotechnology: A Proposal for Regulatory Reform," *Notre Dame Journal of Law, Ethics, and Public Policy* 3:1 (Fall 1987).

7. Callicott, "In Search," cited in note 3. See also Richard De George, "The Environment, Rights, and Future Generations," in K. Sayre and K. Goodpaster, eds., *Ethics and Problems of the 21st Century* (Notre Dame Ind.: Notre Dame University Press, 1979). Another attempt at providing a nonanthropocentric foundation for environmental ethics is Tom Regan, *All That Dwell Therein* (Berkeley: University of California Press, 1982).

8. See Albert H. Teich et al., *Biotechnology and the Environment: Risk and Regulation*

(Washington, D.C.: American Association for the Advancement of Science, 1985); and Joseph Fiksel and Vincent Covello, eds., *Biotechnology Risk Assessment* (New York: Pergamon Press, 1986).

9. Rifkin, *Algeny*, cited in note 6. Martin Kenney's analysis also suggests this. See *Biotechnology: The University-Industrial Complex* (Boulder Colo.: Westview, 1986).

10. Socioeconomic critical treatises include Jack Doyle, *Altered Harvest: Agriculture, Genetics and the Fate of the World's Food Supply* (New York: Viking Press, 1985); Jack Kloppenberg, "The Social Impacts of Biogenetic Technology in Agriculture: Past and Future," in G. Berardi and C. Geisler, eds., *The Social Consequences and Challenges of the New Agricultural Technologies* (Boulder, Colo.: Westview, 1984); Wendell Berry, *The Unsettling of America* (San Francisco: Sierra Club Books, 1977); David Dickson, *The Politics of Alternative Technologies* (New York: Universe Books, 1974); and Edward Yoxen, *The Gene Business* (New York: Harper and Row, 1983). Although each makes use of all three arguments, Kloppenberg best represents the structural critique, Berry the fairness argument, and Kenney, Doyle, and Yoxen the corporate benefit argument.

11. A symposium on the various biological and economic aspects of BST was published in *Journal of Dairy Science* 70 (1987). See especially C. F. Baile and F. C. Buonomo, "Growth Hormone-Releasing Factor Effects on Pituitary Function, Growth and Lactation," pp. 467–73. Also D. M. Bergenstal and M. B. Lipsett, "Metabolic Effects of Human Somatotropin and Somatotropin of Other Species in Man," *Journal of Clinical Endocrinology and Metabolism* 20 (1960), cited in C. J. Peel and D. E. Bauman, "Somatotropin and Lactation," *Journal of Dairy Science* symposium, pp. 474–86.

12. U.S. Congress, Office of Technology Assessment (OTA), *Technology, Public Policy, and the Changing Structure of American Agriculture*, OTA-F-285 (Washington, D.C.: U.S. Government Printing Office, March 1986). R. J. Kalter, "The New Biotech Agriculture: Unforeseen Economic Consequences," *Issues in Science and Technology* (Fall 1985); R. J. Kalter et al., "Biotechnology and the Dairy Industry: Production Costs, Commercial Potential, and the Economic Impact of the Bovine Growth Hormone," *Agricultural Economics Research* 85-20 (Ithaca, N.Y.: Dept. of Agricultural Economics, Cornell University, 1985).

13. See, for example, W. Wayne Withers and Patricia Kenworthy (Monsanto Corporation), "Biotechnology—Ethics, Safety and Regulation," *Notre Dame Journal of Law, Ethics and Public Policy* 3, no. 1: (Fall 1987).

14. R. J. Kalter, et al., "Biotechnology and the Dairy Industry," cited in note 12.

15. The classic utilitarian argument is by J. S. Mill. See *Utilitarianism*, vol. 10 of *The Collected Works of John Stuart Mill*, J. M. Robson, ed. (Toronto: University of Toronto Press, 1969). A good selection of modern accounts (and criticisms) is Amartya Sen and Bernard Williams, eds., *Utilitarianism and Beyond* (Cambridge: Cambridge University Press, 1982). One recent (there are many) utilitarian-economic approach to agriculture is Bruce Gardner, *The Governing of Agriculture* (Lawrence, Kan.: The University Press of Kansas, 1981).

16. L. Busch et al., *The Relationship of Agricultural R & D to Selected Changes in the Farm Sector*, Report to the National Science Foundation, 1983. Don Parlberg, "The Land-Grant Colleges and the Structure Issue," *American Journal of Agricultural Economics* 64 (1981). Howard Gregor, *Industrialization of U.S. Agriculture: An Interpretive Atlas* (Boulder, Colo.: Westview, 1982). Walter Goldschmidt, *As You Sow: Three Studies in the Social Consequences of Agribusiness* (Montclair, N.J.: Allanheld, Osmun, 1978). Richard

Merrill, ed., *Radical Agriculture* (New York: Colophon Books, 1978). For a more general account, see John Blair, *Economic Concentration* (New York: Harcourt, Brace, Jovanovich, 1872).

17. See F. H. Buttel, "Agricultural Research and Farm Structural Change: Bovine Growth Hormone and Beyond," *Agriculture and Human Values* 3, no. 4 (Fall 1986): 88–98. Also, OTA, *Technology and Public Policy*, cited in note 12.

18. The classic statement of the fairness principle is John Rawls, *A Theory of Justice* (Cambridge, Mass.: Harvard University Press, 1971). For agricultural applications, see J. Burkhardt, "Agribusiness Ethics: Specifying the Terms of the Contract," *Journal of Business Ethics* 5 (August 1986): 333–45.

19. Andrew Schmitz and David Seckler, "Mechanized Agriculture and Social Welfare: The Case of the Tomato Harvester," *American Journal of Agricultural Economics* 54, no. 4 (1970).

20. See Kloppenberg, "Social Impacts," cited in note 10, and Kenney, *Biotechnology*, cited in note 9. One classic statement of the potential injustice of power differentials is John Kenneth Galbraith, *The New Industrial State* (Boston: Houghton Mifflin Co., 1971). See also Michael Godlhaber, *Reinventing Technology* (New York: Routledge and Kegan Paul, 1986).

21. Robert M. Goodman (Calgene Corporation), letter to editor, *Bioscience* 36, 7 (July/August 1986), in response to M. Hansen, L. Busch, J. Burkhardt, W. Lacy, and L. Lacy, "Plant Breeding and Biotechnology," *Bioscience* 31, 1 (January 1986): 29–39. Also, F. H. Buttel, "Biotechnology and Agricultural Research Policy: Emergent Issues," Bulletin no. 140, Dept. of Rural Sociology, Cornell University, 1984.

22. Willard Cochrane, *The Development of American Agriculture: A Historical Analysis* (Minneapolis: University of Minnesota Press, 1979).

23. F. H. Buttel and I. G. Youngberg, "Implications of Biotechnology for the Development of Sustainable Agricultural Systems," in W. Lockeretz, ed., *Environmentally Sound Agriculture* (New York: Praeger, 1983); also, Buttel and Youngberg, "Sustainable Agricultural Research and Technology Transfer: Socio-political Opportunities and Constraints," in Thomas Edens, et al., eds., *Sustainable Agriculture and Integrated Farming Systems* (East Lansing: Michigan State University Press, 1985).

24. The term "social impact assessment" is William Friedland's. See "A Programmatic Approach to the Social Impact Assessment of Agricultural Technology," in Berardi and Geisler, *Social Consequences*, cited in note 10. Also, William Friedland, et al. *Manufacturing Green Gold: Capital, Labor and Technology in the Lettuce Industry* (Cambridge: Cambridge University Press, 1981).

25. J. Burkhardt, L. Busch, W. Lacy, and M. Hansen, "Biotechnology and Food: A Social Appraisal," in D. Knorr, ed., *Food Biotechnology* (New York: Dekker, 1986). Also, Hansen et al., "Plant Breeding and Biotechnology," cited in note 21.

26. This point was raised in a discussion by a microbiologist friend of mine whose major laboratory work has been doing "biotechnology," and who recently has been researching ethical issues in his field. Apparently, at no time in the orientation that beginning graduate-student lab assistants receive are they informed of the risks or standard operating procedures to reduce risks, *nor* are they provided with copies of the American Society of Microbiologists' code of ethics regarding lab procedures and "permissible" research projects. My friend suggests that this is probably due to oversight: every professor assumes that every other professor is providing at least some "ethics" guidance, so nobody does it.

27. This was personally brought home at a conference I recently attended on "commercial biotechnology." At one point, during a discussion led by a panel of eminent experts in biotechnology, a young man rose, and virtually screamed at me and a few others who were raising issues about "social consequences" for being "against science and reason." Ian Barbour, *Technology, Environment, and Human Values* (N.Y.: Praeger Publishers, 1980), especially pages 201–211.

28. On "social goals" for agriculture and agricultural research, see Paul Thompson, "The Social Goals of Agriculture," *Agriculture and Human Values* (Summer 1986); William Aiken, "On Evaluating Agricultural Research," in Kenneth Dahlberg, ed., *New Directions for Agriculture and Agricultural Research* (New York: Rowman and Allanheld, 1986); and Jeffrey Burkhardt, "The Value Measure in Public Agricultural Research," in L. Busch and W. Lacy, eds., *The Agricultural Scientific Enterprise: A System in Transition* (Boulder, Colo.: Westview, 1985).

The Legal Status of Farm Animals in Research

Bernard E. Rollin

THE HISTORY OF SOCIAL AND CONCOMITANT LEGAL ATTITUDES TOwards farm animals used in research—both agricultural and biomedical—provides an effective lens through which one can view both traditional and emerging moral norms relevant to human treatment of animals. The first encoded recognition of any moral obligation towards animals appeared in the early nineteenth century with the advent of anti-cruelty legislation. These laws, substantially unchanged from their inception until the present, may be viewed as indicative of the minimalistic, "lowest common denominator" ethic that was all that a society totally dependent on myriad forms of animal exploitation could countenance. Typical of these laws is the Colorado statute entitled Cruelty to Animals:

> A person commits cruelty to animals if, except as authorized by law, he overdrives, overworks, tortures, torments, deprives of necessary sustenance, unnecessarily or cruelly beats, needlessly mutilates, needlessly kills, carries in or upon any vehicles in a cruel manner, or otherwise mistreats or neglects an animal.[1]

At first blush, this law may seem to be quite adequate, since it addresses itself to all sorts of abuse. But a moment's reflection leads us to the conclusion that it is self-emasculating. The problem is of course the use of words like "needlessly" or "unnecessarily," and through this loophole, the interests of man pour, submerging the moral status of animals. One discovers that it takes very little to blunt the edge of this law. Subsequent cases that tested the law made this point quite clear and resulted in a ruling that asserts that:

> Not every act that causes pain and suffering to animals is prohibited. . . . Where the end or object is reasonable and adequate; the act re-

sulting in pain is necessary or justifiable, [as where] the act is done to protect life or property or to minister to some of the necessities of man.[2]

With very minor differences, virtually all U.S. state laws follow the pattern of the Colorado statute both in conception and in enforcement. Most patently, these laws exist to ferret out intentional, willful, deviant cruelty, "pulling the wings off flies"—the sort of cruelty which, as many judicial decisions interpreting these statutes make plain, could, if unchecked, spread to the treatment of humans. As one Colorado judicial pronouncement put it, these laws exist as much to preserve public morality as to protect the animals.[3] In other words, the aim of these laws is to isolate the deviant psychopathic or sadistic individual, not to minimize animal suffering generated by "normal" activities. Thus it is both statutorily and judicially plain that such activities as animal agriculture, scientific research, and fur trapping, having as their end the "ministering to the necessities of man," are exempt from the purview of anti-cruelty statutes, whatever attendant pain and suffering they might entail. It is for this reason that recent attempts by animal advocacy groups to utilize these laws against confinement rearing of veal calves and the use of the steel-jawed traps have been totally unsuccessful.

Yet in at least one area, social concern for animals has exceeded the boundaries of the anti-cruelty legislation. This is the area of scientific and biomedical research on animals, which has never in its history enjoyed the unqualified public acceptance that animal agriculture has. Indeed, almost as soon as animal research became established in England, public concern demanded the drafting of new legislation aimed at curbing its perceived excesses. This Act of 1876, unchanged until 1987, provided some meaningful constraints on animal use in science and medicine unparalleled in any other country.[4] Thus, for example, medical and veterinary students were prohibited from acquiring or sharpening surgical skills on live animals. So while the U.S. medical surgical curriculum, human and veterinary, was based on practice on experimental animals, the British learned through an apprenticeship program of watching and assisting.

Legislation in any way relevant to regulating biomedical research on animals did not appear in the United States until 1966, when the Animal Welfare Act was passed. And even this legislation was directed at allaying fears of pet owners, fueled by dramatic press coverage, that their animals could be kidnapped and sold to research laboratories. The law was a reflection both of inchoate and inconsistent social attitudes on animals and of the strong pressure coming from the research community to block any significant intrusion into the research process. The public's concern centered primarily upon pet animals, and upon animals perceived as cute, cuddly, or otherwise of sentimental concern to the general population. This was dramatically illustrated by the definition of "animal" in the Act.

> The term "animal" means any live or dead dog, cat, monkey (nonhuman primate mammal), guinea pig, hamster, rabbit, or such other warm-blooded animal, as the Secretary may determine is being used, or is intended for use, for research, testing, experimentation, or exhibition purposes or as a pet but such term excludes horses not used for research purposes and other farm animals, such as, but not limited to livestock or poultry, used or intended for improving animal nutrition, breeding, management or production efficiency, or improving the quality of food or fiber. With respect to a dog the term means all dogs including those used for hunting, security, or breeding purposes.[5]

Though the further specification of animals is left to the Secretary of Agriculture, the agency charged with interpreting and enforcing the Act through its inspectorate, the guidelines issued by that agency specifically indicated that rats, mice, and farm animals were not animals according to the Act, and that interpretation is still extant.[6] Thus, although the language of the law did allow for the possibility that farm animals used in biomedical research could be covered, as evident in the passage quoted above, the USDA chose not to issue that interpretation. And, of course, the statute specifically excludes from coverage animals used in agriculture operations or agricultural "food and fiber" research. Thus, according to the Animal Welfare Act as interpreted, a dead dog was (and is) an animal, while a live mouse, rat, cow, pig, sheep, or goat was not (and is not) an animal. In practical terms this meant that approximately 90 to 95 percent of the animals used in biomedical research were not animals for purposes of the Act, and *none* of the animals used in agricultural research of any sort were covered either.

Nor did coverage amount to a great deal. The Act specifically disavowed any concern with either the design or conduct of research:

> (6)(A) NOTHING IN THIS ACT—
> (i) except as provided in paragraph (7) of this subsection, shall be construed as authorizing the Secretary to promulgate rules, regulations or orders with regard to the design, outlines, or guidelines of actual research or experimentation by a research facility as determined by such facility;

(ii) except as provided in subparagraph (A) and (C) (ii) through (V) of paragraph (3) and paragraph (7) of this subsection shall be construed as authorizing the Secretary to promulgate rules, regulations, or orders with regard to the performance of actual research or experimentation by a research facility as determined by such research facility; and

(iii) shall authorize the Secretary, during inspection, to interrupt the conduct of actual research or experimentation.[7]

Where the Act did represent an advance was in its mandating of standards of housing, husbandry, shelter, and food and water for those animals falling under its purview. Since rats, mice, and farm animals used in any sort of research were excluded, they had little to cheer in the Act. Nor were inspectors empowered to force on researchers control of even unnecessary pain, i.e. pain not essential to a piece of research.

With one exception, the Animal Welfare Act, with all of its limitations, was the only mechanism demanding accountability in research use of animals. That exception was provided by the National Institutes of Health guidelines, "Principles for the Utilization and Care of Vertebrate Animals Used in Testing, Research, and Training," and the attendant *Guide for the Care and Use of Laboratory Animals,* first published in 1963. Unlike the USDA regulations, these principles were developed by the research community itself, through experts in laboratory animal care. In addition, they covered essentially all of the "higher" animals used in biomedical research, but not in agricultural research. Though not law, these NIH stipulations were allegedly binding on all research institutions receiving federal funds, by virtue of a mandatory contractual agreement entered into with NIH by those institutions. Breach of contract could result in freezing of all federal funding to the offending institution.

Though many aspects of the *Guide* were detailed and relatively thorough, the document was virtually mute on farm animals used in biomedicine, specifying standards of care comparable to those obtaining on "a well-run farm." The absurdity of such a criterion was patent. Aside from the fact that it was essentially vacuous, it is clear that a well-run farm is one which is economically profitable. As we have discussed elsewhere in this volume,[8] today's well-run farms do not assure a fit with the farm animals' natures, as technological "fixes" such as routinely used antibiotics allow us to make a profit while pressing the animals in ways that produce high degrees of what the confinement agricultural community calls "stress." Thus, even forgetting about animal welfare, the level of stress taken for granted in a "well-run farm" far exceeds the levels of stress acceptable in animals used to study sensitive biomedical parameters. It is well-known that stress has major effects on all aspects of physiology and metabolism,[9] and that therefore research results obtained on stressed animals are unreliable. Even minor disturbances, usually ignored by researchers, can wreak havoc with relevant variables; major environmental factors such as space, temperature, grouping, noise, and so on are well known to have major effects on animals.[10] Thus, the NIH *Guide* did little, even from a scientific point of view, to assure that research had control of "noise" arising out of stress and capable of skewing experimental results.

In any event, everything we have so far discussed as critical of the NIH *Guide* was rendered moot by the inescapable (and widely known) fact that NIH had no desire to enforce its own guidelines, nor machinery for doing so. Until the infamous Taub and University of Pennsylvania head-injury laboratory cases of the mid 1980s, which galvanized public outrage and brought significant pressure to bear on NIH, it had never seized funding from an institution for failure to comply with its rules. And noncompliance was patent, rife, and unconcealed. In the late 1970s, for example, I discovered that every veterinary school I visited was doing multiple survival surgery on animals to teach surgery—sometimes operating on an animal for a whole semester. Although such practice was forbidden by the *Guide*, institutions were unconcerned, and one veterinary school dean actually told me he had never even heard of the *Guide*! When I contacted NIH complaining of this cavalier disregard of its requirements, I was bluntly told that "we are not in the enforcement business." It was for these sorts of reasons that I was informed by the director of a major society of biomedical researchers that they tended not to encourage biomedical research on farm animals, because the standards of care and husbandry were too varied for research results to be predictably meaningful.

Such was the situation until the mid 1980s. Over the previous decade, for many reasons I have discussed elsewhere,[11] public concern with the welfare of animals used in biomedical research was growing exponentially. Great pressure, underscored by the highly publicized cases mentioned above, was brought to bear on the research community and on government to provide greater protection for laboratory animals, though the bulk of concern was again directed at familiar animals—dogs, cats, rabbits, and nonhuman primates. Rodents and farm animals were not a central focus; agricultural research was almost never mentioned. As a result, greater interest arose in the biomedical research community for using farm animals as a substitute for "companion animals." In an extraordinary article, one researcher urged investigators to switch to swine as against dogs wherever possible, as the public, which after all ate swine, didn't care about them.[12] In another famous case, the Department of Defense capitulated to unprecedented public outrage against a wound lab which would have involved shooting dogs to train surgeons in handling bullet wounds. This "capitulation" involved loudly abandoning the use of dogs and quietly replacing them with farm animals. At the same time, breeding laboratories supplying animals to research began to push the miniature swine as a viable alternative to the dog, on the grounds that swine were not of concern to public opinion, and unregulated by law.

The general inadequacy of extant legislation for both scientific reasons (e.g., standardization of husbandry for all experimental animals and control of stress variables) and ethical reasons (control of pain and suffering in animals) had been noted by a group based in Colorado, consisting of myself (a philosopher), two veterinarians and researchers, and an attorney. We therefore set out to draft model legislation that would have significantly extended legal constraints on the treatment of laboratory animals. In particular, we proposed extending coverage of protection to all vertebrate animals (we believed that legislatures would not seriously concern themselves with invertebrates), and augmenting that protection to legally guarantee at least the control of pain and suffering not essential to a research protocol. In addition, we hoped to eliminate the widespread practice of multiple survival surgery for teaching purposes, and of using paralytic drugs without anesthesia. These requirements were to fall under the purview of local animal care committees, charged with protocol review and subject to federal audit. These committees were to contain nonscientists, and it was our hope that the mandated deliberations would raise the ethical sensitivity of animal researchers, as had in fact already occurred with researchers using humans through the creation of local committees charged with protecting human subjects in research. After a decade of abortive attempts at passing such a law, generally blocked by the powerful biomedical research lobby, public concern had increased to the point where passage was inevitable. In 1985, two laws were passed embodying some of the principles we had proposed.

The first law, known as the Dole Amendment to the Animal Welfare Act, was irrelevant to the situation of farm animals used in either biomedical or agricultural research, for it shamefully failed to extend the class of animals covered by the Animal Welfare Act.[13] Thus rats, mice, and farm animals remain outside of the purview of the Animal Welfare Act, as does all agricultural research. The second law, popularly known as the NIH Reauthorization Bill, was more relevant, in that it made the NIH guidelines and *Guide* discussed earlier into federal law, and significantly increased the role of the institutional animal care committee to review and monitor animal use in research and teaching. And teeth were given to this law by the creation of NIH site teams empowered to "parachute" into institutions and review facilities, programs, and committee function.[14]

By virtue of the latter law, all animals used in biomedical research, behavioral research, and even wildlife research were now covered by the NIH guidelines. Thus the 90–95 percent of animals not covered by the Animal Welfare Act were now otherwise protected—rats, mice, pigs, sheep, goats, cattle, and others—as long as they were used in any type of nonagricultural research. Animals used in agricultural research were still exempt from monitoring. And thus was created a very bizarre situation as evidenced by the following scenario: Suppose one had a herd of pigs at a university, half of which were used for biomedical research (typically operationally defined as research funded by NIH), and the other half of which were used for agricultural research. And let us further suppose that half of a set of littermates fall into the NIH research animal category; the other half into the category of agriculture. Further, imagine that both sorts of research on the pigs involve castration at puberty. Those pigs deployed in the NIH protocol would almost certainly receive anesthesia, postsurgical analgesia, and surgery under aseptic conditions. Then litter mates used in agricultural research would receive none of these, and would be castrated as pigs are on the farm. Not surprisingly, this is widely viewed as absurd.

Furthermore, the NIH regulations regarding husbandry conditions for farm animals used in biomedical research continue to remain vague, sketchy and, in essence vacuous. On the other hand, the American Association for Accreditation of Laboratory Care (AAALAC), a private body under contract to NIH that certifies laboratory animal programs as fulfilling NIH standards and sends teams to inspect institutions, has sometimes asked to view even agricultural facilities, as have NIH site visitors.

These factors have galvanized a perception in the agricultural research community that some attempt must be made to address the incoherence arising out of the exclusion of farm animals used in agricultural research from any legal mandate. This attempt has taken the form of a set of guidelines produced by committees chartered by the agricultural research community and entitled *Guide for the Care and Use of Agricultural Animals in Agricultural Research and Teaching*. As of this writing, only a draft of the *Guide* has appeared, one which I have reviewed in detail for the USDA.

In my view, the very fact that such a document is in process bespeaks a major advance over the laissez faire attitude that, as we have seen, characterizes the history of agricultural research animals. But, at the same time, there are serious flaws in the current effort. Although modelled on the NIH *Guide*, often quite detailed on animal care and husbandry, and requiring an animal care committee to oversee protocols, the basic flaw is that ultimately these guidelines do not enjoy the force of law. Granted that current social pressures probably will militate towards greater compliance with these guidelines than the NIH *Guide* enjoyed prior to 1985, adherence to the guidelines will inevitably be less than if they were legally mandated.

Another serious criticism concerns the acceptance by the *Guide* of practices that would not be accepted on the same animals used in biomedical research—hot-iron branding, castration without anesthesia, dehorning without anesthesia, and other practices. Thus the incoherence exemplified by our earlier littermate example remains.

In my remarks to the USDA, I pointed out that levels of pain and suffering unacceptable for a set of animals used in one area cannot be acceptable for animals used in another area. One must seek the "highest common denominator." This is open to the response by the agricultural research community that they are only doing what is commonly done in agricultural practice, something society permits. And this accurate response leads me to a major, highly controversial, conclusion: Society in its biomedical legislation has said that certain levels of pain are unacceptable for animals. This, then, becomes the standard of practice in society, as participants in the recent American Veterinary Medical Association Panel on Pain and Suffering in Animals noted.[15] If we cannot accept a practice in biomedical research, we also cannot accept it in agricultural research, and thence, by implication, in agriculture. And, indeed, other countries have banned many agricultural practices that we take for granted.

Can the agricultural research community be held to a higher standard than the agricultural community itself without compromising its very raison d'être? Probably not. But what this in turn implies is not that agricultural research should have carte blanche, but that society must regulate agricultural practice, for indeed we have gone too far in technological confinement agriculture at the expense of the animals, at the same time as social concern for animals is at its highest point in history. Not only must we phase out through law the practices listed above, we must also call a halt to both agricultural practice and its attendant research that sees the animal merely as a metabolic machine. Pain and suffering must be controlled; not only the sort resulting from surgical procedures performed without anesthesia, but the more subtle sort that arises out of the failure of confinement systems to meet the psychological or behavioral needs dictated by an animal's nature. Such thinking is manifest in recent Swedish legislation that guarantees the rights of cows to graze. It is present embryonically as well in the 1985 Amendment to the Animal Welfare Act that mandates exercise for research dogs and environments for research primates that enhance their psychological well-being. All of these bespeak the fact that society has progressed well beyond the anti-cruelty laws. This progress must be mirrored in agricultural practice and its attendant research, assured by significant legal protection.

Notes

1. See the discussion in B. E. Rollin, *Animal Rights and Human Morality* (Buffalo, N.Y.: Prometheus Books, 1981), p. 78.

2. *Ibid.* 3. *Ibid.*

4. R. French, *Antivivisection and Medical Science in Victorian Society* (Princeton, N.J.: Princeton University Press, 1975).

5. Animal Welfare Act, Public Law 99.198, 1966, Section 2 (g).

6. See B. E. Rollin, "Laws relevant to animal research in the United States," in A. A. Tuffery, ed., *Laboratory Animals* (London: John Wiley, 1987), pp. 323–33.

7. Animal Welfare Act, Public Law 99.198, 1966, Section 13 (6A).

8. B. E. Rollin, "Social ethics, animal rights, and agriculture," this volume.

9. See B. E. Rollin, "Moral, social, and scientific aspects of the use of swine in research," in M. E. Tumbleson, ed., *Swine in Biomedical Research*, vol. 1 (New York: Plenum Press, 1986), pp. 29–39.

10. D. Gärtner *et al.*, "Stress response of rats to handling and experimental procedures," *Laboratory Animals* 14 (1980):3.

11. A. Rowan and B. E. Rollin, "Animal research—for and against: a philosophical, social, and historical perspective," *Perspectives in Biology and Medicine* 27 (1983):1.

12. J. C. Russell and D. Secord, "Holy dogs and the laboratory," *Perspectives in Biology and Medicine* 28 (1985):3.

13. See B. E. Rollin, "Laws relevant to animal research in the United States," cited in note 6.

14. *Ibid.*

15. *Journal of the American Veterinary Medical Association*, 191 (10):1186–92.

Aid and Trade

Conflicts of Interest, Conflicts of Value

Paul B. Thompson

IN NOVEMBER 1985, Senator Dale Bumpers first offered an amendment (No. 1129) intended to prohibit the funding of foreign aid that would assist the export of agricultural commodities that compete with U.S. exports. Now commonly referred to as the *Bumpers Amendment*, it became law in May 1986.[1] In Bumpers's words, the act is to "prevent American tax dollars from being used to help foreign countries who are trying to take our export markets."[2] Under this law, the U.S. Agency for International Development (USAID, or AID) is required to suspend research and implementation projects that could enable poor foreign farmers to increase commercial production of commodities (such as meat, maize, or wheat) that are exported from the United States, and also of commodities (such as palm oil) that, while not produced for export in the United States, may substitute for U.S. commodities. How can the Bumpers Amendment be defended on philosophical grounds? The answer given below is based on social contract theory, but it raises further questions about the goals and purposes of publicly funded agricultural research, and about how moral values are to be projected into the international sphere.

Public Research for Foreign Competitiveness: The Moral Issue

The Bumpers Amendment reflects a sentiment regarding AID science policy that has surfaced before.[3] An Aug. 1, 1985, mailing to members of the American Soybean Association (ASA), the soybean producers' trade association, pegged U.S. public support for international farm production research at $341,137,588; angry letters to government officials followed quickly. The thrust of the ASA criticism was that AID's support of agricultural research in developing countries harmed the already weakened U.S. foreign trade in agricultural commodities, and hence the incomes of agricultural producers.[4] AID questions the accuracy of ASA reports, concluding that the ASA could have arrived at their figure only by including amounts intended to be expended over a period of several years and by failing to distinguish accounts dedicated to health and nutrition projects from those dedicated to agriculture. Although fairness to AID demands accuracy in reporting programs, the argument made by AID's critics does not depend upon the technical accuracy of ASA figures. This argument can be broken down into two distinct themes. The first is an *interest argument* asserting that U.S. foreign agricultural assistance programs are in conflict with the interests of U.S. farmers. The second theme is a *moral argument* that the use of public funds to aid foreign producers at the expense of U.S. citizens overreaches USAID budgetary authority. Both of these themes were represented simultaneously in most statements of the criticism, though some individuals undoubtedly gave little thought to anything beyond their own interests. The argument cannot be interpreted as *merely* an interest argument, however, as the following analysis shows.

The Interest Argument

It is entirely appropriate that U.S. citizens should express their opinions (both in print and through personal communication) to lawmakers and government officials regarding the impact of government actions and programs upon their personal or commercial interests, and it is not only reasonable but necessary for government officials in a democracy to take these expressions of their constituents' individual interests under consideration in forming public policy. Public policy is in many instances an attempt to balance competing interests of individuals against one another. The principle that assures everyone of the right to have their own interests considered as this balance is struck in fundamental to democracy in a republic. This very picture of the policy process, however, entails that sometimes governments will inevitably act in ways that are *not* in the interest of some individuals, since it presumes that there will be occasions on which the competition among individual interests is irreconcilable.

There is, therefore, no *general* correlation between policies that conflict with individual interests and those that are illegitimate in the sense that they violate principles of ethics and justice. A claim asserting that the policy is unjust (or otherwise morally unacceptable) implies that the policy violates one or more of the moral standards that govern the use of state power. The simple claim that a given policy conflicts with individual interests does not do this, since there may be other interests at stake. These other interests might be regarded by everyone as at least equal to, if not more important than, those interests that are thwarted.

The basic distinction between a simple interest argument and an ethical argument can be illustrated by contrasting the case at hand, use of public funds to support research for foreign producers, with the more common case in which public funds are spent for research on commodities that compete with one another (either on a commodity-by-commodity or region-by-region basis) within the domestic agricultural economy. Sugar, for example, is produced from beets in some areas of the United States and from cane in other areas. A sugar beet producer can claim with some accuracy that government funds for research and extension services in sugar cane help the producers of these products, and thus harm any competitive advantages that a beet producer might otherwise enjoy. The beet producer might demand to be compensated (through funds expended for research and extension on sugar beets, for example) when such actions are taken. None of this, however, could be construed as a *moral* claim that government acts illegitimately when it helps cane producers in the Southeast, but rightly and with justice when it helps beet producers in the Northwest. Such a claim is so patently ridiculous that even the most ardent partisan supporter of the beet industry could utter it only in jest.

The Moral Argument

The corresponding claim (that the government acts rightly and with justice when it helps U.S. producers, but wrongly and illegitimately when it helps foreign commercial growers of the same products) needs to be (and is) made with all seriousness. Producers who criticize AID express an interest argument, to be sure, for they claim that helping foreign growers is contrary to the interests of American farmers, but they also make a moral claim that is philosophically distinct. While the Colorado beet grower who criticizes cane programs in Louisiana is somewhat placated by a policy that provides commensurate support for beets, the Illinois soybean grower would not be at all satisfied to learn that the government spends far more to support development of the Illinois soybean industry than it does to support the soybean industry of Brazil or Argentina. Such a response misses the point.

The criticism of AID's agricultural research that is implicit in the Bumpers Amendment claims that AID's program violates basic principles on the just use of government power. The moral sentiment implicit in the Bumpers Amendment can be found in social contract theory, particularly as it was expressed in the thought of Hobbes and

Locke. In the analyses of government given in the *Leviathan*[5] and the *Second Treatise of Government*,[6] contracting parties are clearly making arrangements for national states, with the resulting sovereign nations remaining in a state of nature, a situation of unrelieved competition, relative to one another. A primary duty of the national state is to shield its citizens from the uncertainties of the state of nature, but this duty does not extend to persons outside social contract. A national government has no *contractual* duty to aid the poor of other lands, though the question whether they ought or may do so for other reasons remains open. As such, an ethical objection to agricultural assistance programs does not follow directly from the relatively narrow scope of social ethics as they are defined by Hobbes and Locke. The fact that a government is not obliged to aid the world's poor at the expense of national competitiveness does not entail that they are never permitted to do so.

What would Hobbes and Locke have to say about foreign aid? First note how they differ over the character of moral action in the state of nature. For Hobbes, the state of nature is a place of unbridled competition and warfare; moral notions beyond an ethic of simple self-preservation simply do not apply. For Locke, on the other hand, individuals are morally bound by the law of reason and by the duty to respect the natural rights of others even in the state of nature. Morality for Hobbes is purely conventional, having no extension beyond the contract; the purpose of the contract is to establish the basis of morality. For Locke the contract fulfills a different role. Restrictions on individual action have moral force even in the state of nature, at least prior to the breakdown of civility that leads into a state of war; the problem is that every individual has equal authority to interpret and enforce the moral law, and this is an open invitation to conflict. It is the problem of authority, rather than that of morality per se, that Locke's theory of the social contract is intended to redress.

For both Hobbes and Locke, the social contract establishes a basis for national identity and the legitimacy of national policies. Since foreign assistance actions are intergovernmental and are intended to benefit people who are not party to the contract, the legitimacy of foreign aid is measured less by its effect upon the intended beneficiaries than by the internal standards of justice for the donor nation. For a Hobbesian view, these standards are likely to involve the question whether such policies yield home benefits, irrespective of any benefit or harm they may do for others. For a Lockean view, the fact that there is no authority to enforce the natural law in international relations does not obviate the duty to respect the natural rights of noncitizens. There is a slight proclivity toward extending the benefits of just society to parties outside the contract. The final standard for Locke, however, is procedural. Hobbes and Locke thus provide divergent rationales for the legitimation of a Bumpers-type law.

In following a Hobbesian account of the contract and the state of nature, no moral obligations (beyond those that have been explicitly contracted through treaty) to foreign poor or to their governments exist. The moral duty of a sovereign power is to justify its citizens' abnegation of sovereignty by returning benefits that exceed those they would have obtained for themselves in the state of nature. The rationale for a Bumpers-type law is, therefore, largely an empirical question for economic policy analysis. The farmers' (or their proxies') belief that foreign agricultural development assistance harms their commercial interests is ground enough to oppose the policy outright, since there are no (obvious) benefits returned to other citizens. The final determination depends upon whether this belief is, in fact, true. If it turns out that the farm interest groups are right in the perception of their interests, Hobbesian social contract theory provides the Bumper Amendment with a political justification fully consistent with the moral duties assigned to just governments.

The Lockean case is both more subtle and less conclusive. While the Hobbesian individual is motivated purely by self-interest, the Lockean individual at least aspires to the life of reason. The Lockean citizen will, therefore, be inclined to extend the benefits of contractual society beyond the strict limits of the national state. Individuals are thus to be praised for helping the foreign poor, and they are certainly permitted to press their government to do so as well, through the political process. It may be, for example, that a majority of citizens would prefer helping the foreign poor over protecting agricultural trade interests. If so, then the procedures for majority rule could lead to a policy of foreign aid. Such a policy, duly legislated and enacted by the just and agreed-upon procedure for determining government actions would itself be just, presuming it violates no minority rights.

To claim that their rights had been violated, the farm interest group would have to equate the decline in value of their crop to a property right that has been appropriated through government action, but this is a tenuous argument, at best. The alternative is for the farm group to work within the political process to change public opinion, arguing for the moral value of the family farm, perhaps, or convincing other citizens that strong farm trade is a crucial component of the economic strength that holds the contract together. While each of the individual arguments intended to generate political support can be analyzed on its merits, the merit of the arguments is not what determines the legitimacy of the policy. Those policies that result from the public debate have gone through a process governed by openness and representative democracy. It is not the substantive character of the policies that is just, but the policy process itself. A Lockean democracy might go either way on a Bumpers-type law. The law's appeal would depend upon the case advocates made for it in the political process, but once passed, the amendment would meet the test of legitimacy, at least until challenged in a new round of the policy process.

International Agricultural Assistance and the Interests of U.S. Agriculture

The Hobbesian case depends upon the truth of ASA claims, while the Lockean case depends upon ASA's ability to persuade others in political debate. A convincing case can be made for concluding that the objectives of the law would ultimately be thwarted were it to be enforced, but the critique also has the unintended effect of implying that the interest considerations of U.S. agriculture are indeed the crucial test for setting international agricultural research policy. Before these philosophical points can be examined, however, it will be necessary to review the basis criticism of ASA's point of view.

The True Interests of U.S. Agriculture

Theories of agricultural commodity trade and of economic development support the two-stage thesis that expansion of demand for U.S. agricultural exports is dependent upon economic growth in nonindustrialized, low-income countries, and the most likely route to economic growth in most such countries is through development of the agricultural sector. The linkage of these two theoretical tenets provides the conceptual basis for what I shall call the true interests thesis, that foreign agricultural development assistance does not hurt, but in fact helps, U.S. agriculture.[7] In addition to its theoretical basis, the true interests thesis is supported by a growing body of empirical studies on the correlation between development and agricultural trade patterns.[8]

The first component of the true interests thesis is implied by a basic postulate in agricultural economics. The demand for agricultural products in a closed economic system is virtually inelastic; consumption of agricultural products is, therefore, only moderately sensitive to price. People, that is, will buy what food they need, but they obtain very little additional benefit from having more food than they need to eat. One important exception to this general rule occurs when consumers make a dietary shift away from basic grains (such as wheat and rice) and toward meat, poultry, and dairy products, since animals are fed a larger portion of feed grains than would be consumed by a human eating a diet of basic grains. Such a shift in diet leads to an overall increase in the demand for agricultural products, and it also involves a shift in the type of products demanded. the other major source of increased demand comes from an increase in the number of consumers.

As it happens, the developing world holds promise for both sources of increasing demand. Diets in the developing world rely heavily on basic grains, but as incomes increase, many consumers will, it is expected, elect to increase their consumption of animal proteins. This will create a demand for animal feeds that far exceeds current demands for basic grains. In addition, the total number of consumers in the developing world will increase as these countries become more industrialized. People currently involved in subsistence agriculture (or too poor to provide themselves adequate diets, even in basic grains) will become consumers of agricultural products as they obtain cash income, either from industrial employment, or perhaps even from the commercial sale of agricultural commodities (such as cotton or tobacco) that do not provide the grower with complete food needs. General economic growth in the developing world is, therefore, one of the few sources for expansion of agricultural exports.

But how to achieve economic growth in the developing world? Theories of economic development from the 1950s recognized the importance of industrialization in general economic growth. Early development plans stressed the formation of manufacturing capabilities in developing countries, but investment in capital-intensive manufacturing industries created severe political problems in many developing economies. Wealth tended to accrue to relatively small elites, while industrial workers (and the urban poor lured to cities by false expectations of industrial growth) expended a high percentage of their incomes upon basic necessities. Agricultural sectors still organized for plantation production of commodities for export (and subsistence production of commodities for personal use) were unable to meet the food needs of the new urban proletariate. Government attempts to supply urban food needs through cheap imports (or food aid donated by the West) depressed markets for indigenously produced food and exacerbated problems in foreign exchange.[9]

Some of these problems might be avoided by reversing the assumption that agriculture is relatively unimportant for general economic development. Investment in agriculture should spread capital (and, hence, return on capital) across many more people in the developing economy than does a single large investment in industrial manufacturing. The multiplier effect of increasing incomes throughout the economy is greater when more incomes are increased, even if by relatively smaller amounts. Furthermore, increases in rural income are less likely to be expended upon imported luxury items, thus easing pressures on foreign exchange. Finally, the increased production of food and improved efficiency of farming should release labor for industrialization (thus creating demand for purchased food) at the same time that it increases the supply of basic foods available on commercial markets. Agricultural development does not replace industrial development under such a scenario, but it *is* seen as equally important in contributing to overall economic growth.[10]

Agricultural Interests and the Moral Argument

The true interests thesis must address both the interest argument and the moral argument reflected in criticisms of AID. It is impossible to be specific about the time frame required for this expansion to be effective, but it is reasonable to think that it will be at least ten, and probably twenty, years before the development efforts described in the true interests thesis result in significant increases in demand for agricultural imports. The true interests thesis can be interpreted as a trade-off response of the sort frequently made when people object to a policy on the ground that their interests are harmed. Just as the harms to sugar cane producers are offset by benefits to sugar beet producers in the example discussed above, the true interests thesis suggests that harm to farmers producing today and in the coming years will be offset by benefits to farmers producing ten, twenty, or more years in the future. This makes the policy question one of deciding how to weigh the present day interests of U.S. farmers with those of farmers who will be producing in the first half of the twenty-first century. Even framed in these terms, the ethical issues do not go away. Some farmers who are expected to make sacrifices today will be retired or forced out of farming by the time benefits to U.S. agriculture begin to accrue. Are the future benefits greater than the lost opportunities for income, and if so, should policymakers choose the greater good? Should benefits (and harm) to foreign producers be included in the calculation? Should present-day farmers be compensated for their sacrifice? These questions are crucial to the success of the true interests thesis as a response to the interest argument, and none of them will be easy to answer.

Under the Hobbesian interpretation of the moral argument, government should seek the interests of constituents in international affairs, and give no standing to the interests of foreigners. The true interests thesis, however, makes it more difficult to ascertain constituents' interests. Stated as a conflict between two forms of domestic interest, there are no clear moral grounds on which the conflict can be resolved within Hobbesian political theory. Locke's theory, however, endows all persons with natural rights, rights that give noncitizens moral standing in their relationship with foreign governments. Rights of noncitizens, however, are not rights that governments are required to protect as matters of justice. This means that there may be morally compelling reasons for American citizens to request that AID (as an agency of the United States government) assist poor farmers in the developing world, but that there is nothing in the social contract (or, indeed, in the United States Constitution) that would require such assistance. Other citizens would be within their rights to oppose it, perhaps on the ground that public funds ought to go beyond national borders only for reasons of national security, and, perhaps, dire emergencies.[11] The final policy should reflect majority opinion as formed in the workings of the democratic process. By making the issue into a conflict of domestic interests, however, the true interests thesis alters the moral terms of the debate. Service to interests of domestic constituencies have implicitly been accepted as legitimate criteria on which to evaluate AID's agricultural research program. The debate turns from being one over whether foreign development assistance is generally the sort of thing that a democratic government ought to be providing into one over whether there are payoffs for Americans, and how they ought to be distributed.

If we assume, with Locke, that the political process decides whether foreign agricultural research should be supported, the true interests thesis can be expected to have a dual effect on AID science policy. First, to the extent that farm groups are persuaded to seek long-term goals, they can be expected to join with those who have humanitarian motives in supporting AID, but they will support AID not because they feel it is morally right for the government to help foreign farmers, but because it serves their own pecuniary goals. Second, to the extent that their effects upon U.S. farmers come to be interpreted as valid criteria for evaluating AID programs, AID will be forced to conduct research under an extremely tenuous mandate composed of the altruistic goals of humanitarian supporters and the self-serving goals of farm groups. While these goals may coincide in practice, they are undeniably contrary in spirit. Even if the true interests thesis succeeded in persuading farm interests to support foreign agricultural research, then it would do so in a way that made the administration of that research fraught with tension, jealousy, and second-guessing from its competing constituencies.

While the contract theories of Hobbes and of Locke thus provide some basis for the arguments that were advanced on behalf of the

Bumpers Amendment, the case for it is inconclusive. The true interests thesis has enough plausibility to muddy the waters on interpreting the interests of American farmers. Nevertheless, the true interests thesis does not succeed as a defense of the research efforts that AID has traditionally undertaken. Far from providing a defense of the moral ground on which one might advocate development assistance, the true interests thesis implicitly undercuts the moral legitimacy of humanitarian goals and subjects AID research to an unwieldy and philosophically ambiguous mandate.

If the case for the Bumpers Amendment is inconclusive, what, then, can be said of the case for AID's traditional research program? Sadly, an answer to this question exceeds the limited scope of the present analysis. Attempts have been made to establish the philosophical basis on which humanitarian assistance is founded,[12] but humanitarians would typically be unreceptive to the self-interest reasoning of the Bumpers Amendment and the true interests response. What is needed is to rethink the moral imperatives in a way that underscores the consistency of genuinely humanitarian efforts to aid foreign nationals and the national interests of sovereign powers. If the true interests thesis can be interpreted as a component of *national* interest, rather than simply the occupational self-interests of farmers, it can play an important role in building this bridge. To the extent that the true interests thesis demonstrates the links between trade and world development, it can serve as a component of that longer philosophical argument, one intended to build a moral community on a worldwide scale.

Notes

1. U.S. Senate, Report 99-301, Urgent Supplemental Appropriations Bill 1986, May 15, 1986, p. 56.

2. *Congressional Record - Senate*, June 6, 1986, S7028.

3. cf. Grant M. Scobie, "The Demand for Agricultural Research: A Colombian Illustration," *American Journal of Agricultural Economics* 61 (1979): 540–45; and especially Dana G. Dalrymple, "The Demand for Agricultural Research: A Colombian Illustration: Comment," *American Journal of Agricultural Economics* 62 (1980): 594–96.

4. cf. John Baize, "Farmers must fight for world market share," *Pennsylvania Farmer* (Sept. 14, 1985): 48. Baize is an ASA executive based in Washington, D.C.; also, "World Bank Loans Stir Ire of U.S. Farm Groups," *The New York Times*, June 5, 1986, p. A9.

5. Thomas Hobbes, *Leviathan* [1651], C. B. Macpherson, ed. (New York: Viking Penguin, Inc., 1969).

6. John Locke, *Two Treatises of Government* [1697], Peter Laslett, ed., 2d ed. (Cambridge: Cambridge University Press, 1967).

7. John Mellor, *The Economics of Agricultural Development*, (Ithaca, N.Y.: Cornell Uni-

versity Press, 1972); George E. Rossmiller and M. Ann Tutwiller, "Agricultural Trade and Development: Broadening the Horizon," *United States Agricultural Exports and Third World Development: The Critical Linkage*, (Boulder, Colo.: Lynn Reiner for The Curry Foundation, 1987).

8. Earl Kellogg, Richard Kodl and Philip Garcia, "The Effects of Agricultural Growth on Agricultural Imports in Developing Countries," *American Journal of Agricultural Economics* 68, no. 5 (1986); Robert E. Christiansen, *The Impact of Economic Development on Agricultural Trade Patterns*, Economic Research Service, U.S. Department of Agriculture, ERS Staff Report no. AGES861118 (January, 1987); C. Christensen, M. Lofchie, and L. Witucki, "Agricultural Development in Africa: A Comparison of Kenya and Tanzania," *United States Agricultural Exports and Third World Development: The Critical Linkage*, (Boulder, Colo.: Lynn Reiner for The Curry Foundation, 1987); and K. L. Bachman and L. A. Paulino, *Rapid Food Production Growth in Selected Developing Countries: A Comparative Analysis of Underlying Trends, 1961–1976*, (Washington, D.C.: International Food Policy Research Institute, 1979).

9. Michael P. Todaro, "Ethics, Values, and Economic Development," *Ethics and International Relations*, Kenneth W. Thompson, ed. (New Brunswick, N.J.: Transaction Books, 1985), 75–97.

10. John W. Mellor and Bruce F. Johnston, "The World Food Equation," *Journal of Economic Literature* 22, no. 2 (June 1984): 531–74; John W. Mellor, "The New Global Context for Agricultural Research: Implications for Policy," *IFPRI Report 1986* (Washington, D.C.: International Food Policy Research Institute, 1986), pp. 7–14.

11. Cf. Michael Walzer, "The Distribution of Membership," *Boundaries*, P. Brown and H. Shue, eds. (Totowa, N.J.: Rowman and Littlefield, 1981).

12. Cf. Peter Singer, "Famine, Affluence and Morality," *Philosophy and Public Affairs* 1 (1972): 229–43; Arthur Simon, *Bread for the World*, (New York: Paulist Press, 1975); Thomas Nagel, "Poverty and Food: Why Charity Is Not Enough," *Food Policy*, P. G. Brown and H. Shue, eds. (New York: The Free Press, 1977), pp. 54–62; C. Ford Runge, "American Agricultural Assistance and the New International Economic Order," *World Development* 5 (1977): 725–46; Henry Shue, *Basic Rights*, (Princeton: Princeton U. Press, 1980); William Aiken, "World Hunger and Foreign Aid: The Morality of Mass Starvation," *Values in Conflict*, B. Leiser, ed. (New York: Macmillan Publishing Co., 1983), pp. 189–201; Onora O'Neill, *Faces of Hunger*, (London: Allen and Unwin, 1986).

III.
Agriculture's Conduct

III.A.
TREATMENT OF CROP RESOURCES

PARTS I AND II VARIOUSLY PRESENT THE IDEA that we ought to be careful with land and other resources because we hold them in trust for the common good. The first article in Part III goes further, to argue that land has ethical standing on its own. Aldo Leopold's "The Land Ethic" urges that we see land (including all of agriculture's productive resources) in an ecological light. As Leopold speaks of "land" here, he means biological communities. These must be understood not atomistically as a collection of parts, but holistically as complex systems whose features and operations are not reducible to those of individual components of the system. We must come to see the land not as an immense resource to consume, but rather as an organism to sustain. Forestry, as practiced by conservationists, and biotic farming fill the bill.

Accepting the intrinsic value of the land as an organism and adjusting farming, silviculture, and other agricultural activities accordingly is a natural next step in our social evolution. Leopold stops short of detailed descriptions of what will emerge from that evolution, however.

Sara Ebenreck, in her discussion "Caring for Soils," discusses one of the specific problems in our treatment of the land. Soil is treated not as part of an organism that needs careful nurturing for its sustenance, but as a resource to be mined in the process of growing food. The role of soil in food production can be seen as analogous to that of coal in the production of electrical energy. Ebenreck begins with a brief inventory of soil loss around the world and with a broadly acceptable argument against soil abuse. She then goes on to describe some of the complex questions and issues involved in moving to just soil-conserving farming practices. Following Leopold, she considers as a guide values that are ecological, aesthetic, economic, and non-maleficent.

The discussion concludes with an examination of the practical impediments to the wide adoption of soil conservation. Ebenreck considers educational reform, an appropriate federal conservation incentive and penalty program, and cropping techniques such as conservation tillage.

This specific technique of soil conservation is taken up by Charles Little in "Beyond the Mongongo Tree: Conservation Tillage and the Environmental Tradeoff." Little contrasts the ecologically sensitive attitude with a manipulative, ecologically insensitive one, and with the middle ground of conservation tillage (CT). After distinguishing the various forms of CT, Little examines whether the soil-conserving promise of CT depends on increased chemical use to control weeds. While that has been true in the past, he argues, new techniques promise to dramatically reduce the environmental impact of herbicide use. Little explores some of the surprising number of alternatives to chemical pest controls, including intercropping and allelopathic cover crops. While this is indeed good news for those interested in the environment, it makes two points clear: First, in any real-life cost-benefit analysis of soil-conserving technology and production strategies, there is considerable detail that we might be unprepared to deal with, despite the need to make decisions and proceed with research, development, and production work. Second, we need, as a constraint on these decisions, an ethic of ecological sensitivity. The forces of the market will not serve the ends of conserving soil and minimizing pollution. We need some societal limits that come from a clearly articulated ethical stance. But what underlies that stance?

Similar problems might confront the individual who wants to conserve water while allocating it for agricultural production and rural community life. Here, however, the market is more and more widely regarded as the best means of water allocation. Terry L. Anderson and Donald R. Leal explore the desirability of such an approach in their paper "Going with the Flow: Expanding the Water Markets." Beginning with a traditional view reminiscent of the work of Frederick Hayek, the authors praise the market as a means of water allocation that responds to the greatest amount of pertinent information (both general and site-specific) and the greatest number of individual preferences.

This benefit requires a legal control friendly to the sale and resale of water rights. Just how much alleged good lies within our reach in such a context is clarified as the authors discuss a proposal to conserve irrigation water and sell the surplus to California's population centers. However, current federal management of water resources is more of an impediment than an asset in pursuing such benefits. The basic water allocation would be according to a prior appropriation doctrine (or, first use, first right), with allowance for market transfer of water rights.

The authors argue that such a scheme would avoid many of the current problems surrounding in-stream flow and groundwater allocation: individual frustration, environmental degradation, and wasteful management. If so, then the responsible individual aim serving that underlies the suggested scheme would be a strong ethical consideration in its favor.

However, it is clear that the authors see profit maximization as the predominant individual aim to be served, and their scheme seems to lack a clear way to redress unjust or inequitable distribution patterns. For example, can "mining" an aquifer be "appropriate," as the authors hold, if it is required to maximize profit or to derive the greatest economic value from the water? What if past policy and the prior allocation of opportunity was not equitable? Ought we to perpetuate that legacy through the marketplace, favoring those most economically advantaged? Despite the appeal of market allocations of water shares, some would put equity first.

Helen Ingram, Lawrence Scaff, and Leslie Silko address the last of these questions in their article "Replacing Confusion with Equity: Alternatives for Water Policy in the Colorado River Basin." Their approach is in fundamental contrast to that in the previous article, for Ingram et. al. begin by justifying their view of water as a social good that should not be allocated by private rights of ownership and that should be held and managed in trust (in the U.S.) by the federal government. They recognize the need for conflict-resolving rights of private use and benefit, but these are circumscribed by the concern for the public interest. The public interest is apparently something the public must construct itself, since Ingram et. al. seek to understand public interest in the procedural terms of a highly participatory democracy, rather than through a set of rules or principles that define end-states to be reached by following universal policy directives designed for context-free, standardized problems of water allocation and use.

The procedures that serve the public interest while responding to the special characteristics of water distribution will respect five principles that in various combinations will define "equitable water policy." These principles define a water allocation system in which the costs and benefits of water distribution are shared across society, while the differing values of users are respected. Broad participation in the allocation process is guaranteed and negotiated promises are kept. Finally, responsibility to future generations of water users accompanies equitable water use.

Ingram et. al. discuss four areas where equity has broken down through failure to respect one or more of these principles. These problems focus on the water rights of Native Americans, of Mexico vis a vis the United States and of the states of New Mexico and Colorado vis a vis other U.S. water users.

One of the issues that Ingram and her fellow authors raise in identifying problems of equity are upstream-downstream relations. Mexico, for example, is at a disadvantage in being downstream of the U.S. in the flow of both water and technical information. The authors point out that ethical theory addressing water must recognize the varying geographical, cultural, and occupational settings of water resource problems. Donald Scherer's discussion "Toward an Upstream-Downstream Morality for Our Upstream-Downstream World" enables us to appreciate the complications in the ethics of water and other natural resources whose quality downstream can be affected by upstream behavior removed in space and time.

According to Scherer, moralities that see individuals in isolated groups cannot adequately deal with real water problems. Individual liberty and equity across a society are not unimportant, but the upstream-downstream relationships of water users today provide a context different from the one in which liberty and equity are usually understood.

The central ethical issue occupying Scherer is how to understand and construct norms that regulate upstream-downstream relations in a way promoting responsible action. In responsible action, the source of untoward consequences is avoidable, and the individuals involved will seek to avoid or minimize the untoward consequences of their actions. The basic question is how in an upstream-downstream world can reciprocity be ensured? Market approaches to water allocation and management restrict reciprocity by externalizing many costs. Also, certain features of upstream-downstream relations, such as specialization of roles and threshold effects in potentially harmful acts, be changed to reinforce responsible agency.

Much of what Scherer discusses deals with airborne as well as water-borne pollution. Some of this pollution is traceable to agricultural chemicals. The last two articles in this section are concerned specifically with ethical issues in pesticide use and resulting soil, water, and air pollution.

Kristin Shrader-Frechette considers two arguments, the realism argument and the threshold argument, in discussing the need to eliminate dependence on agricultural pesticides. The realism argument rationalizes pesticide use on the grounds that danger exists everywhere. Shrader-Frechette counters this argument by considering how this risk is distributed and the degree of personal acceptance of that risk. The threshold argument states that pesticides have determinate thresholds at which they become dangerous, so subthreshold use should be morally defensible. However, the combined effects of pesticides and other phenomena, as well as unknown individual risk with respect to these phenomena, make it impossible to ethically assume that the population is standardized in terms of risk. If some are at greater risk, it would be morally indefensible to ignore this in pesticide policy and practices.

Thus, Shrader-Frechette sees serious ethical obstacles to the use of pesticides, obstacles related to the voluntary distribution of burdens in society and equal protection against risks beyond an agent's control. These concerns would not settle the issue if, for example, an imperative of survival dictated our continued use of pesticides. The paper concludes with an outline of an argument against such an imperative and for reduced use of pesticides.

Sara Ebenreck, in "Pest Control for a Whole Earth," further defines an "alternative ecological control model" for pest management. After reviewing the history and hazards of the present dependence on chemicals in pest management, Ebenreck articulates the ideal of an ecologically sensitive biological pest control approach. Three ethical considerations favor such an approach: a largely negative utilitarian concern with minimizing harm, a principle of respect for all of nature and a belief in the intrinsic ethical merit of living in harmony with other creatures, and a goal of rebuilding the ecosystem damaged by previous chemical pest management. While these principles are presented as of presumably equal weight, the possibility of conflicts between them and ways to resolve those conflicts are not explored. These principles are brought to bear on the questions, who is responsible to act, what policies are needed at the federal level, and how is an ethical imperative for human survival to be understood?

Soil and water are only two production resources whose use raises tremendous ethical questions. Perhaps the most controversial such resource is farm animals raised for food. Section III.B. will take up ethical issues in the rearing of such animals.

THE LAND ETHIC[1]

ALDO LEOPOLD

WHEN GOD-LIKE ODYSSEUS returned from the wars in Troy, he hanged all on one rope a dozen slave-girls of his household whom he suspected of misbehavior during his absence.

This hanging involved no question of propriety. The girls were property. This disposal of property was then, as now, a matter of expediency, not of right and wrong.

Concepts of right and wrong were not lacking from Odysseus' Greece: witness the fidelity of his wife through the long years before at last his black-prowed galleys clove the wine-dark seas for home. The ethical structure of that day covered wives, but had not yet been extended to human chattels. During the three thousand years which have since elapsed, ethical criteria have been extended to many fields of conduct, with corresponding shrinkages in those judged by expediency only.

The Ethical Sequence

This extension of ethics, so far studied only by philosophers, is actually a process in ecological evolution. Its sequences may be described in ecological as well as in philosophical terms. An ethic, ecologically, is a limitation on freedom of action in the struggle for existence. An ethic, philosophically, is a differentiation of social from anti-social conduct. These are two definitions of one thing. The thing has its origin in the tendency of interdependent individuals or groups to evolve modes of co-operation. The ecologist calls these symbioses. Politics and economics are advanced symbioses in which the original free-for-all competition has been replaced, in part, by co-operative mechanisms with an ethical content. . . .

The first ethics dealt with the relation between individuals; the Mosaic Decalogue is an example. Later accretions dealt with the relation between the individual and society. The Golden Rule tries to integrate the individual to society; democracy to integrate social organization to the individual.

There is as yet no ethic dealing with man's relation to land and to the animals and plants which grow upon it. Land, like Odysseus' slave-girls, is still property. The land-relation is still strictly economic, entailing privileges but not obligations.

The extension of ethics to this third element in human environment is, if I read the evidence correctly, an evolutionary possibility and an ecological necessity. It is the third step in a sequence. The first two have already been taken. Individual thinkers since the days of Ezekiel and Isaiah have asserted that the despoliation of land is not only inexpedient but wrong. Society, however, has not yet affirmed their belief. I regard the present conservation movement as the embryo of such an affirmation. . . .

The Community Concept

All ethics so far evolved rest upon a single premise: that the individual is a member of a community of interdependent parts. His instincts prompt him to compete for his place in the community, but his ethics prompt him also to co-operate (perhaps in order that there may be a place to compete for).

The land ethic simply enlarges the boundaries of the community to include soils, waters, plants, and animals, or collectively: the land.

This sounds simple: do we not already sing our love for and obligation to the land of the free and the home of the brave? Yes, but just what and whom do we love? Certainly not the soil, which we are sending helter-skelter downriver. Certainly not the waters, which we assume have no function except to turn turbines, float barges, and carry off sewage. Certainly not the plants, of which we exterminate whole communities without batting an eye. Certainly not the animals, of which we have already extirpated many of the largest and most beautiful species. A land ethic of course cannot prevent the alteration, management, and use of these "resources," but it does affirm their right to continued existence, and at least in spots, their continued existence in a natural state.

In short, a land ethic changes the role of *Homo sapiens* from conqueror of the land-community to plain member and citizen of it. It implies respect for his fellow-members, and also respect for the community as such. . . .

The Land Pyramid

An ethic to supplement and guide the economic relation to land presupposes the existence of some mental image of land as a biotic mechanism. We can be ethical only in relation to something we can see, feel, understand, love, or otherwise have faith in.

The image commonly employed in conservation education is "the balance of nature." For reasons too lengthy to detail here, this figure of speech fails to describe accurately what little we know about the land mechanism. A much truer image is the one employed in ecology: the biotic pyramid. I shall first sketch the pyramid as a symbol of land, and later develop some of its implications in terms of land use.

Plants absorb energy from the sun. This energy flows through a circuit called the biota, which may be represented by a pyramid consisting of layers. The bottom layer is the soil. A plant layer rests on the soil, an insect layer on the plants, a bird and rodent layer on the insects, and so on up through various animal groups to the apex layer, which consists of the larger carnivores.

The species of a layer are alike not in where they came from, or in what they look like, but rather in what they eat. Each successive layer depends on those below it for food and often for other services, and each in turn furnishes food and services to those above. Proceeding upward, each successive layer decreases in numerical abundance. Thus, for every carnivore there are hundreds of his prey, thousands of their prey, millions of insects, uncountable plants. The pyramidal form of the system reflects this numerical progression from apex to base. Man shares an intermediate layer with the bears, raccoons, and squirrels which eat both meat and vegetables.

The lines of dependency for food and other services are called food chains. Thus soil-oak-deer-Indian is a chain that has now been largely converted to soil-corn-cow-farmer. Each species, including ourselves, is a link in many chains. The deer eats a hundred plants other than oak, and the cow a hundred plants other than corn. Both, then, are links in a hundred chains. The pyramid is a tangle of chains so complex as to seem disorderly, yet the stability of the system proves it to be a highly organized structure. Its functioning depends on the cooperation and competition of its diverse parts.

In the beginning, the pyramid of life was low and squat; the food chains short and simple. Evolution has added layer after layer, link after link. Man is one of thousands of accretions to the height and complexity of the pyramid. Science has given us many doubts, but it has given us at least one certainty: the trend of evolution is to elaborate and diversify the biota. Land, then, is not merely soil; it is a fountain of energy flowing through a circuit of soils, plants, and animals. Food chains are the living channels which conduct energy upward; death and decay return it to the soil. The circuit is not closed; some energy is dissipated in decay, some is added by absorption from the air, some is stored in soils, peats, and long lived forests; but it is a sustained circuit, like a slowly augmented revolving fund of life. There is always a net loss by downhill wash, but this is normally small and offset by the decay of rocks. It is deposited in the ocean and, in the course of geological time, raised to form new lands and new pyramids.

The velocity and character of the upward flow of energy depend on the complex structure of the plant and animal community, much as the upward flow of sap in a tree depends on its complex cellular organization. Without this complexity, normal circulation would presumably not occur. Structure means the characteristic numbers, as well as the characteristic kinds and functions, of the component species. This interdependence between the complex structure of the land and its smooth functioning as an energy unit is one of its basic attributes.

When a change occurs in one part of the circuit, many other parts must adjust themselves to it. Change does not necessarily obstruct or divert the flow of energy; evolution is a long series of self-induced changes, the net result of which has been to elaborate the flow mechanism and to lengthen the circuit. Evolutionary changes, however, are usually slow and local. Man's invention of tools has enabled him to make changes of unprecedented violence, rapidity, and scope.

One change is in the composition of floras and faunas. The larger predators are lopped off the apex of the pyramid; food chains, for the first time in history, become shorter rather than longer. Domesticated species from other lands are substituted for wild ones, and wild ones are moved to new habitats. In this worldwide pooling of faunas and floras, some species get out of bounds as pests and diseases, others are extinguished. Such effects are seldom intended or foreseen; they represent unpredicted and often untraceable readjustments in the structure. Agricultural science is largely a race between the emergence of new pests and the emergence of new techniques for their control.

Another change touches the flow of energy through plants and animals and its return to the soil. Fertility is the ability of soil to receive, store, and release energy. Agriculture, by overdrafts on the soil, or by too radical a substitution of domestic for native species in the superstructure, may derange the channels of flow or deplete storage. Soils depleted of their storage, or of the organic matter which anchors it, wash away faster than they form. This is erosion.

Waters, like soil, are part of the energy circuit. Industry, by polluting waters or obstructing them with dams, may exclude the plants and animals necessary to keep energy in circulation.

Transportation brings about another basic change: the plants or animals grown in one region are now consumed and returned to the soil in another. Transportation taps the energy stored in rocks, and in the air, and uses it elsewhere; thus we fertilize the garden with nitrogen gleaned by the guano birds from the fishes of seas on the other side of the equator. Thus the formerly localized and self-contained circuits are pooled on a worldwide scale.

The process of altering the pyramid for human occupation releases stored energy, and this often gives rise, during the pioneering period, to a deceptive exuberance of plant and animal life, both wild and tame. These releases of biotic capital tend to becloud or postpone the penalties of violence. . . .

The combined evidence of history and ecology seems to support one general deduction: the less violent the man-made changes, the greater the probability of successful readjustment in the pyramid. Violence, in turn, varies with human population density; a dense population requires a more violent conversion. In this respect, North America has a better chance for permanence than Europe, if she can contrive to limit her density.

This deduction runs counter to our current philosophy, which assumes that because a small increase in density enriched human life, that an indefinite increase will enrich it indefinitely. Ecology knows of no density relationship that holds for indefinitely wide limits. All gains from density are subject to a law of diminishing returns. . . .

Land Health and the A-B Cleavage

A land, ethic, then, reflects the existence of an ecological conscience, and this in turn reflects a conviction of individual responsibility for the health of the land. Health is the capacity of the land for self-renewal. Conservation is our effort to understand and preserve this capacity.

Conservationists are notorious for their dissensions. Superficially these seem to add up to mere confusion, but a more careful scrutiny reveals a single plane of cleavage common to many specialized fields. In each field one group (A) regards the land as soil, and its function as commodity production; another group (B) regards the land as a biota, and its function as something broader. How much broader is admittedly in a state of doubt and confusion.

In my own field, forestry, group A is quite content to grow trees like cabbages, with cellulose as the basic forest commodity. It feels no inhibition against violence; its ideology is agronomic. Group B, on the other hand, sees forestry as fundamentally different from agronomy because it employs natural species, and manages a natural environment rather than creating an artificial one. Group B prefers natural reproduction on principle. It worries on biotic as well as economic grounds about the loss of species like chestnut, and the threatened loss of the white pines. It worries about a whole series of secondary forest functions: wildlife, recreation, watersheds, wilderness areas. To my mind, Group B feels the stirrings of an ecological conscience.

In the wildlife field, a parallel cleavage exists. For Group A the basic commodities are sport and meat; the yardsticks of production are ciphers of take in pheasants and trout. Artificial propagation is acceptable as a permanent as well as a temporary recourse—if its unit costs permit. Group B, on the other hand, worries about a whole series of biotic side issues. What is the cost in predators of producing a game crop? Should we have further recourse to exotics? How can management restore the shrinking species, like prairie grouse, already hopeless as shootable game? How can management restore the threatened rarities, like trumpeter swan and whooping crane? Can management principles be extended to wildflowers? Here again it is clear to me that we have the same A-B cleavage as in forestry.

In the larger field of agriculture I am less competent to speak, but there seem to be somewhat parallel cleavages. Scientific agriculture was actively developing before ecology was born, hence a slower penetration of ecological concepts might be expected. Moreover the farmer, by the very nature of his techniques, must modify the biota more radically than the forester or the wildlife manager. Nevertheless, there are many discontents in agriculture which seem to add up to a new vision of "biotic farming."

Perhaps the most important of these is the new evidence that poundage or tonnage is no measure of the food value of farm crops; the products of fertile soil may be qualitatively as well as quantitatively superior. We can bolster poundage from depleted soils by pouring on imported fertility, but we are not necessarily bolstering food value. The possible ultimate ramifications of this idea are so immense that I must leave their exposition to abler pens.

The discontent that labels itself "organic farming," while bearing some of the earmarks of a cult, is nevertheless biotic in its direction, particularly in its insistence on the importance of soil flora and fauna.

The ecological fundamentals of agriculture are just as poorly known to the public as in other fields of land use. For example, few educated people realize that the marvelous advances in technique made during recent decades are improvements in the pump, rather than the well. Acre for acre, they have barely sufficed to offset the sinking level of fertility.

In all of these cleavages, we see repeated the same basic paradoxes: man the conqueror *versus* man the biotic citizen; science the sharpener of his sword *versus* science the searchlight on his universe; land the slave and servant *versus* land the collective organism. Robinson's injunction to Tristram may well be applied, at this juncture, to *Homo sapiens* as a species in geological time:

Whether you will or not
You are a King, Tristam, for you are one
Of the time-tested few that leave the world,
When they are gone, not the same place it was.
Mark what you leave.

The Outlook

It is inconceivable to me that an ethical relation to land can exist without love, respect, and admiration for land, and a high regard for its value. By value, I of course mean something far broader than mere economic value; I mean value in the philosophical sense.

Perhaps the most serious obstacle impeding the evolution of a land ethic is the fact that our educational and economic system is headed away from, rather than toward, an intense consciousness of land. Your true modern is separated from the land by many middlemen, and by innumerable physical gadgets. He has no vital relation to it; to him it is the space between cities on which crops grow. Turn him loose for a day on the land, and if the spot does not happen to be a golf links or a 'scenic' area, he is bored stiff. If crops could be raised by hydroponics instead of farming, it would suit him very well. Synthetic substitutes for wood, leather, wool, and other natural land products suit him better than the originals. In short, land is something he has "outgrown."

Almost equally serious as an obstacle to a land ethic is the attitude of the farmer for whom the land is still an adversary, or a taskmaster that keeps him in slavery. Theoretically, the mechanization of farming ought to cut the farmer's chains, but whether it really does is debatable.

One of the requisites for an ecological comprehension of land is an understanding of ecology, and this is by no means co-extensive with "education"; in fact, much higher education seems deliberately to avoid ecological concepts. An understanding of ecology does not necessarily originate in courses bearing ecological labels; it is quite as likely to be labeled geography, botany, agronomy, history, or economics. This is as it should be, but whatever the label, ecological training is scarce.

The case for a land ethic would appear hopeless but for the minority which is in obvious revolt against these "modern" trends.

The "key-log" which must be moved to release the evolutionary process for an ethic is simply this: quit thinking about decent land use as solely an economic problem. Examine each question in terms of what is ethically and esthetically right, as well as what is economically expedient. A thing is right when it tends to preserve the integrity, stability, and beauty of the biotic community. It is wrong when it tends otherwise.

It of course goes without saying that economic feasibility limits the tether of what can or cannot be done for land. It always has and it always will. The fallacy the economic determinists have tied around our collective neck, and which we now need to cast off, is the belief that economics determines *all* land use. This is simply not true. An innumerable host of actions and attitudes, comprising perhaps the bulk of all land relations, is determined by the land users tastes and predilections, rather than by his purse. The bulk of all land relations hinges on investments of time, forethought, skill, and faith rather than on investments of cash. As a land user thinketh, so is he.

I have purposely presented the land ethic as a product of social evolution because nothing so important as an ethic is ever "written." Only the most superficial student of history supposes that Moses "wrote" the Decalogue; it evolved in the minds of a thinking community, and Moses wrote a tentative summary of it for a "seminar." I say tentative because evolution never stops.

The evolution of a land ethic is an intellectual as well as emotional process. Conservation is paved with good intentions which prove to be futile, or even dangerous, because they are devoid of critical understanding either of the land, or of economic land use. I think it is a truism that as the ethical frontier advances from the individual to the community, its intellectual content increases.

The mechanism of operation is the same for any ethic: social approbation for right actions: social disapproval for wrong actions.

By and large, our present problem is one of attitudes and implements. We are remodeling the Alhambra with a steam shovel, and we are proud of our yardage. We shall hardly relinquish the shovel, which after all has many good points, but we are in need of gentler and more objective criteria for its successful use.

Note

1. This essay is a shortened version of Aldo Leopold's, "The Land Ethic," reprinted in *A Sand County Almanac with Essays On Conservation From Round River* (New York: Oxford University Press, Inc., 1966; New York: Ballantine Books, 1970), 237–64. Grateful acknowledgement is hereby given to Oxford University Press and the Aldo Leopold Shack Foundation for permission to reprint these portions of the piece. The editor takes responsibility for the fidelity of the selection to the original.

Caring for Soils

Sara Ebenreck

IN EARLY SPRING OF 1985, a national insurance company foreclosed on the loan of a Missouri farm family, taking ownership of land on which the family had lived and worked for thirty-five years. It was not an unusual action. Such companies held many farm mortgages, and plummeting incomes in a tight market had created intense economic pressure on American farms. But the "plow-out" that followed the foreclosure drew national attention. As one paper described it, a bulldozer operator appeared on the scene and leveled twelve soil-conserving terraces, two houses, a few barns, and tore out dozens of windbreak trees. The farm was then rented and planted to corn and soybeans, with a result predictable to anyone who knew farmland ecology: five-and-one-half foot gullies carved in the soil by stormwater runoff. Quite within the law, the land was being dramatically abused.[1]

Less visibly and in smaller amounts, but still steadily, much of America's idyllic-appearing farmland is today losing soil from its surface. In graphic terms, the U.S. Department of Agriculture reported in 1977 that for every pound of food consumed in the U.S. that year, over twenty-two pounds of soil were eroded from croplands.[2] The 1982 National Resource Inventory conducted by the U.S. Soil Conservation Service estimated that ninety-six million acres of cropland—about one-fourth of the national total—were losing soils at more than twice the rate at which they could be naturally replenished.[3] This erosion does not occur in equal amounts everywhere, of course. A large portion of this soil erosion is associated with about fifty million acres of cropland, largely concentrated in areas of Iowa, Missouri, and Texas.[4]

Worldwide, the figures for soil loss are correspondingly large. In India, one of the few other countries to compile a national estimate of soil erosion, scientists says that 60 percent of the cropland is eroding excessively.

Worldwatch Institute concluded in 1984 that the Soviet Union may be losing more topsoil than any other country. China, the fourth major food-producing country in the world, has now recognized that river siltation from soil erosion is a national threat.[5]

The results of such humanly induced soil erosion affects the future survival of both people and ecosystems. Soil lost and not rebuilt through careful land management can threaten long-range food and fiber production. Computer models have estimated that, at the extreme end of the spectrum, 100 years of soil erosion at current levels would decrease productivity by as much as 50 percent in portions of Virginia and California.[6] Although the United States' generous soil resources mean that the estimated national loss of productivity in such estimates is closer to 2 percent, leaving us far from crisis, the long-range implications of severe soil loss carry an unmistakable warning about the price we are asking future generations to pay for our methods of production.

More immediate are the environmental impacts of soil loss on the nation's waters. Soils washing into waterways carry phosphorus, nitrogen, and other farm chemicals. In 1982, pollution from agricultural fields was reported as a major remaining cause of reduced water quality by thirty-six of fifty states.[7] That loss can range from complete eutrophication in some lakes and rivers to the depression of plant and fish habitat in others. In one attempt to put dollar figures on the off-site costs of soil erosion from American cropland, the Conservation Foundation estimated net damage costs of $2.2 billion per year.[8]

If we consider the earth a living whole, as suggested by the Gaia hypothesis of scientist James Lovelock,[9] the soils of the earth are the planet's thin living surface on which all other life in the system depends. Although moon dust may be lifeless matter, healthy earth soils are quite the opposite. Along with minerals and decayed organic matter; they contain a swarm of microorganisms—millions to the teaspoonful, by common estimates. Plant, animal, and human life flows from this living skin of the earth, and returns to it. From this perspective, the way we value the soil says much about the way we value life itself. Thus, the choices leading to loss of farm soils raise basic ethical questions for a society suffering such losses.

Principles for Sound Land Use

Many ethical theories commonly invoked in western societies—utilitarianism, Kantianism, and rights-based theories, for example—accept the idea that actions that unduly harm others, when that harm can be easily predicted to follow a consciously chosen action, are morally questionable. So, in one sense, to show that soil erosion produces harmful effects for society's long-term future leads to a simple ethical argument. If knowingly harming others is wrong, and land uses that lead to excessive soil erosion do harm others, then choosing those land uses can, by simple logic, be said to be ethically wrong.

In practice, what follows from this ethical logic is not so simple. Consider the matter of highly erodible lands, for example. If the cropping of such lands creates severe and costly land degradation and water-quality problems, does a sound land ethic demand that their owners be treated like industrial polluters and face legal demands that pollution be stopped or at least held within defined limits? What if achieving that goal is costly, demanding either the construction of terraces or conversion to less profitable land uses such as forestry or grazing? Should society or the landowner pay for this conversion? Does it matter whether the landowner is wealthy or barely surviving? Does it matter that education about soil erosion has not taught all farmers the negative effects of what may appear to be a "normal" amount of soil erosion? What about federal commodity programs that have, by their one-sided support for certain crops, encouraged the use of land in ways unsuitable for its long-term health? Or sectors of the farm industry that may have profited from the misuse of land by selling farm "input" products or harvesting valuable crops? Or the failure of consumers, in their desire for cheap food, to ask essential questions about the long-term price of that food? Does it matter that land-use regulations fly in the face of several centuries of American resistance to mandatory federal land-use controls? Is it more ethical to regulate land use or to follow the long-standing practice of appealing to landowners to voluntarily shift their land-use practices?

In short, while it is fairly easy to argue that land uses leading to excessive soil erosion are morally wrong, reflection on actual situations suggests that responsibility for that wrong may be widespread, shared by government programs, farm industries, and consumers, along with landowners. Just solutions, then, demand programs that allocate the cost and responsibility for change among the responsible group.

Another line of questions also suggests the need to further clarify exactly what it is that is wrong with misuse of soils. Even if all off-site pollution could be controlled, should a society tolerate land uses that destroy any portion of the nation's cropland itself? Does the ownership of farmland imply a right to use it in ways that destroy its long-term capacity to grow crops? If not, would such an ethical demand prohibit not only the agricultural misuse of croplands but uses that radically change the future of land capacities—uses ranging from strip mining to the draining of wetlands for cropping? And what about the ethics of the complete conversion of farmlands to other uses, such as shopping centers or country homes? (In 1982, the U.S. Department of Agriculture estimated that about 1.5 million acres of agricultural land were being converted to nonagricultural uses each year.) If people are benefited, at least in the short term, by such conversions, and if these conversions do not lead to further off-site pollution, does this make them ethically good? If so, we have an odd logic: a farming system that does not conserve soils is unethical, while a complete conversion of the total soil surface to another use could be "good."

This series of questions places a soil conservation ethic squarely in the context of a land ethic in general. What principles and what vision, we must ask, ought to positively guide our use of and relationship to the land? And if we follow the negative injunction to not harm others, who exactly is it that we ought not to harm? Nonhuman life that is dependent on the soil, as well as human life? Future lives as well as present ones?

Aldo Leopold, the Wisconsin wildlife and forestry specialist whose 1948 essay on the land ethic outlined one basis for answering these questions, suggested a correction in the values that guide decision making about the land: Right the lopsided results of self-interested economics by attending to the ecological resiliency and beauty of the land, taken as a whole community. The economic value of land use has seldom been in question; it is attentiveness to the matter of ecological integrity, beauty, and the sense of the land community as a whole that have been lacking from our usual approaches, Leopold said.

Some simple reflections can lead us to see the interconnectedness of the set of values proposed by Leopold. As a nation, our wealth has been derived from the plentitude of forests, minerals, soils, and water. Everything we have, from furniture to pizza, as well as the profits that flow from its merchandising, ultimately traces back to the earth. But the long-range renewability of land resources, in turn depends upon uses that respect the nature of ecological systems. For farmlands, renewability could imply uses that regenerate soils, grow crops within limits of water availability, and protect diversity of plant and animal species, at least over farm regions as a whole. Moreover, farms can be seen as one land use within larger regional, national, continental, and even global ecological systems whose resilience we must understand, respect, and protect. This overall integrity of biotic systems must be balanced with economic goals in a sound land ethic, Leopold argues, both out of respect for the whole biotic community and out of a concern for human survival in the long run.

And what of beauty as a criterion for sound land use? Almost every person has experienced healing and renewal through the earth's beauty. The eutrophication of Lake Erie and countless other smaller lakes and ponds across the country through soil erosion is ugly as well as economically and ecologically disastrous. Our revulsion at the ugliness that follows from land misuse is deep and powerful. Curiously enough, it is arguable that from attention to ecological needs, beauty almost always follows. The aesthetically fine curves of soil conservation contours are commonly appreciated by air travelers. Kentucky writer and farmer Wendell Berry, commenting on an especially attractive Pennsylvania conservation farm that he visited just "to figure out how it all works," concluded that "the ecological pattern is a pattern of pleasure."[10]

A sound soil ethic also involves the dimension of time: the future generations who will inherit the land changed by its present uses. What counts as an ecologically resilient system is affected by the introduction of this long-term dimension. In the short term, for example, soils made fertile by the addition of synthetic fertilizers may mask the loss of productivity associated with soil erosion and produce yields equal to or even better than soils whose structure, moisture-retention, and nutrient level have been enriched by crop rotation and manure. But in the long term, the soils whose inherent fertility has been nurtured by sound land practices can be passed on as a heritage not matched by depleted soils. The inclusion of future generations in the ethical community also makes an even stronger case for social investment in protecting the interests of unborn persons who may or may not be the descendants of existing landowners.

Citing ecological, aesthetic, and economic values in association with long-term assessments does not provide instant answers for all ethical questions about land use. Aesthetics is a notoriously culture bound concept, and varied ideas exist about what exactly promotes the "health" of an ecosystem already influenced by people. If diversity is healthy, for example, just how much diversity is needed for an ethically sound land-use system? Will a five-year crop rotation do, or does ecological health demand livestock on the farm and provision of shelter, and for native wildlife? How much shelter for how many kinds of wild species? Despite these difficulties in application, when they are added to the ethical principle of "not unduly harming another," the three values provide a strong basis for positive goals in an ethical soil conservation program.

In response to the question raised earlier about conversion of farmland to homes and shopping centers, for example, Leopold's ethic would indicate that a nation should assess its best and most unique farmlands and take steps to protect both the land and soil for future use. If the ethic were taken seriously, this assessment would include the land's importance to our cultural heritage, to biological diversity, and to the open-space needs of an area—perhaps on a continental or even global scale. The current effort of some private groups to protect the habitats of migratory birds and waterfowl is one positive step in this direction. Still lying before us, however, is open debate about stronger public protection for such lands.

Individual landowners can and do act out of an ethic that regards the land as a community. But the tasks of research, education, and designing appropriate incentives or regulations for soil protection are likely to be public ones—deservedly so, given the broad responsibility for soil erosion suggested earlier in this article. For that reason, another need implied by the ethical approach outlined here is for educating the public in appreciation of soil and land. This ethic asks that all of us, not simply farmers, recognize that we are members of a community that reaches back to past and on to future generations, a community that is deeply interwoven with the natural world of soil, water, air, and other living creatures. The costs of an ethical response are not likely to be borne by citizens unaware of these interconnections.

Overall, these guidelines for a sound soil conservation ethic make clear the need for what philosophers such as Aristotle and Thomas Aquinas would call people of practical wisdom: people whose understanding of the principles, the land, and the people of the land enable them to discern right action. These people may be farmers; they may be conservationists, policymakers, or just plain citizens. As Leopold knew, it is an appreciative, lively, and curiosity-filled relationship of people with the land that allows the guidelines themselves to be resilient and responsive to changing conditions both in society and on the land.

A Declaration of Interdependence

In fact, our society has already taken major steps on the ethical path described here. Although our government has not been in the business of demanding soil conservation of farmland owners thus, the insurance company cited earlier acted legally, If not ethically, it has certainly been promoting soil conservation for over fifty years. Beginning with the response to the 1930s Dust Bowl, which led to the foundation of the federal Soil Conservation Service, soil conservation research, education, and promotion has been actively pursued by multiple government agencies, universities, and private and public groups, including farm groups. Although the insurance company was not legally challenged by any government agency, it was quickly called to public account for its action by an active group of Missouri citizens led by the nonprofit Land Stewardship Project.

Nationally, concern about soil erosion and its effects led in 1985 to the passage of unprecedented conservation legislation in the 1985 Food Security Act. This law provided conservation incentives for taking highly erodible lands out of production, combined with a longer-range threat: exclusion from federal farm programs after 1991 if adequate conservation plans were not in place on those lands. After three years, the result was impressive: twenty-eight million acres of such lands were planted to trees or grass or put in wildlife habitat with incentive funds provided by the federal government.

At least partially as a response to concern about soil erosion, farmers in the 1980s have moved steadily toward adoption of soil-conserving and economically efficient crop management methods called "conservation tillage" and "sustainable agricultural systems." Conservation tillage, which generally refers to keeping crop residues in place so that soils are less often bared to the eroding forces of wind and water, was in use on about 30 percent of American cropland in 1987. In addition, growing concerns about farm chemical contamination of water and food, as well as interest in lowering costs of production, have nudged many innovative farmers toward the use of crop rotations for restoring soil fertility and gaining pest control. Such management, by increasing field cover, also keep soils in place. As the decade comes to a close, sustainable agriculture programs, which recognize the importance of ecological and social as well as economic goals for agriculture, are increasing in popularity— and funding.

With such programs and trends established, will the problem of excessive soil erosion disappear, not only from farmlands, but consequently from the arena of ethical debate? If we are very lucky, the guidelines suggested by Leopold could become so integrated into our policy and behavior that maverick landowners would remain the only problem. As the data cited earlier indicates, we are not yet in that enviable position. The right mix of soil-conserving technology and incentives are not in place on many croplands, and many reports indicate that one obstacle is the inability of many farmers to recognize erosion on their own land.[11] The debate on the right balance between legal requirements and voluntary commitments is far from finished. And although individual farmers certainly appreciate the beauty of their land, beauty as a criterion for land use is seldom invoked in farm policy discussions.

In view of these needs, it is heartening to reflect that the pursuit and protection of common goods are at the very heart of American society. It was in the name of truths held to be self-evident and for the long-range common good of a free and democratic nation that the signers of the American Declaration of Independence pledged their lives, fortunes, and sacred honor. In 1776 there was, however, little awareness of the need to protect the nation's natural resources as an essential part of its heritage. Land, let alone its stewardship, is scarcely mentioned in either the Declaration of Independence or the U.S. Constitution.

Today, two centuries later, countless facts point to the link between stewardship of our natural resources and a resilient, secure society in the future. That we may achieve as a society a living ethic which recognizes the long-term importance of the fragile life-support layer of living soil on earth will demand a clear declaration of our interdependence and our willingness to pledge, in the cause of this ethic, at least some small portion of our lives, fortunes, and sacred honor.

Notes

1. Description taken from account in *The Land Stewardship Letter* (Summer 1987): 4, Stillwater, Minnesota.
2. Cited in Edwin H. Clark et al., *Eroding Soils: the Off-farm Impacts* (Washington, D.C.: The Conservation Foundation, 1985), p. 4.
3. U.S. Department of Agriculture, *The Second RCA Appraisal: Soil, Water, and Related Resources on Nonfederal Land in the United States* (Washington, D.C.: USDA, 1987), p.2-1.
4. Ibid., 1987, p. 4-21.
5. Lester R. Brown and Edward C. Wolf, *Soil Erosion: Quiet Crisis in the World Economy*, Worldwatch Paper 60 (Washington, D.C.: Worldwatch Institute, 1984).
6. *Second RCA Appraisal*, cited in note 3, p. 2-3.
7. Ibid., p. 10-2.
8. Clark, *Eroding Soils*, cited in note 2, p. 174.
9. James Lovelock, *The Ages of Gaia: A Biography of Our Living Earth* (New York: W. W. Norton, 1988).
10. Wendell Berry, *The Gift of Good Land* (San Francisco: North Point Press, 1981), p. 226.
11. cf. report on Kansas farmers in Cheryl Simmons, Lynn Osika, and Mary Fund, *The Barriers to Soil and Water Conservation: A Kansas Study* (Whiting, Kansas: The Kansas Rural Center, 1988).

Beyond the Mongongo Tree[1]

Conservation Tillage and the Environmental Trade-off

Charles E. Little

In human history, there have been two dominant kinds of food economies. One of them might be described as nonmanipulative, a natural economy of benefit to primitive tribes who could collect food from nature without disturbing its balances whatsoever. In his book *People of the Lake*, anthropologist Richard Leakey describes the !Kung people of East Africa as having a food economy of this kind. (The curious spelling of !Kung is to indicate a clicking sound made in the back of the throat, followed by a low musical "ooong.")

Leakey calls the !Kung gatherer-hunters rather than hunter-gatherers because the !Kung do not really hunt very much. Nor do they cultivate crops. These aboriginal people live mainly on the nut of the mongongo tree, which grows abundantly on the tops of the dune hills of the Great Rift Valley of Africa, where man arose as a species distinct from other primates over three million years ago. The average !Kung eats 300 mongongo nuts a day, a diet that contains the same amount of calories as two-and-a-half pounds of rice and as much protein as a fourteen-ounce steak. Moreover, mongongo nuts are easy to fetch. You just pick them up. There is no danger of overharvesting, for the greater part of the production of each tree rots uncollected beneath it. "Why should we plant," said a !Kung to one of Leakey's colleagues, "when there are so many mongongo nuts in the world?"

The other dominant food economy, unlike that of the !Kung, I would say is as manipulative as all get-out. It is *agricultural*, and though it may have started simply enough with the scattering of seed, it gave way in time to the plow. A plow-based food economy involves perturbing the soil in order to replace native plant associations with monocultures, usually of annual crop plants that are higher in food value or easier to harvest. The agricultural production of surplus food made cities possible, since food could be brought to an urban, non-food-producing population. "Where tillage begins," the great orator

Daniel Webster observed in an explanation of the origins of civilization, "the other arts follow."

And yet, the environmental impacts of plow-based agriculture have ranged from extreme to disastrous—from the desertification of large areas of the Mediterranean basin to the erosion that created the American Dust Bowl. Agronomist Edward Faulkner, in his 1943 bestseller *Plowman's Folly*, excoriated the plow as unnecessarily damaging to the "self-sufficiency of the soil." Forget the plow, said Faulkner, who offered instead a middle way—perhaps the most significant contribution to agricultural technology in modern times and one with major ethical implications—between the Mongongo and the moldboard. In his theory for a new ecology for agriculture, Faulkner wrote: "We already know by incontrovertible example that wherever man does not interfere crops grow spontaneously. It follows of necessity that if man duplicated in his farming the soil conditions which in nature produce such perfect results, he will be able to grow similarly perfect crops on cultivated land."

Thus, the ecological principle behind what we now call conservation tillage—for that is what Faulkner proposed—is to capitalize on, rather than eliminate, the natural properties of the soil that, if "conserved" by not plowing, can be beneficial in growing crops: structural integrity, moisture, porosity, tilth, fertility, and possible resistance to pests and diseases. Conservation tillage is officially defined (by the Conservation Tillage Information Center) as "Any tillage and planting system that maintains at least 30 percent of the soil surface covered by residue after planting to reduce soil erosion by water; or, where soil erosion by wind is the primary concern, maintains at least 1,000 pounds of flat, small-grain residue equivalent on the surface during the critical erosion period." The principal types of conservation tillage are "no till," in which soil is not tilled at all; "ridge till," in which permanent planting ridges are established and cultivation is used only to "sweep" the weeds and rebuild the ridges; "strip till," which alternates untilled soil with planting strips; and various forms of "mulch till" or reduced tillage, usually limiting cultivation to disking or chisel plowing, which does not turn the soil and keeps residue at or near the surface. Such conservation tillage techniques can reduce erosion by up to 90 percent, without any long-term sacrifice in yield, and often an improvement, due to reduced compaction (fewer trips across the field), increased soil moisture, and other factors. Today, conservation tillage is practiced on nearly a third of U.S. cropland.

There is, however, a major difference between the Faulkner method, developed during the 1930s, and the conservation tillage of today: herbicides, virtually all of which have been developed since

World War II. They became the key to moving plowless farming from theory to practice. Without herbicides, most authorities maintain, there would be no conservation tillage on a commercial scale. Apparently the only way for such techniques to succeed without inviting in a forest of weeds, at least for the first several plowless years, is to substitute herbicides for mechanical cultivation in eliminating weeds.

The ethical question that must be asked is this: Does the new agro-ecology of contemporary conservation tillage actually offer a middle way as promised by Faulkner; that is, a partial return to the ecologically benign realms of the nonmanipulative !Kung? Or does it simply substitute one kind of adverse environmental impact for another—more pesticides in exchange for less erosion—continuing, maybe even increasing, the serious environmental "externalities" of modern-day commercial farming?

This question is currently an issue: Agriculturalists argue that conservation tillage significantly reduces erosion and water pollution from agricultural runoff in return for a very small increase in chemical inputs. The environmentalists assert that conservation tillage, with its putative reliance on an arsenal of pesticides, might well produce more environmental impact (groundwater pollution, for example) than it eliminates, because conservation tillage is most often employed where erosion is not much of a problem anyway.

This is the "trade-off" argument. But the trouble with it is that it assumes the techniques of conservation tillage to be static, when, in fact, they are quite dynamic. It assumes that the intensive use of highly toxic herbicides is now, and will continue to be, the sine qua non of this new agricultural ecology. In this regard, environmentalists and the chemical companies are in unwonted, as well as inadvertent, agreement. The only difference between them is that the chemical companies believe this is wonderful ("No-till farming is our number one priority," said one Chevron executive at a national conservation tillage conference held in 1984), and the environmentalists think it's awful. Fortunately, recent events suggest that both may turn out to be wrong.

Many leading farmers and agricultural scientists agree that herbicide use does increase in the early years of conservation tillage, especially no-till. But as the seasons pass, and techniques are fine-tuned, the weed problem gets less and less, Faulkner predicted. This is partly because weed seeds are no longer turned up by plowing, so herbicide use may be reduced. But improvements in application methods can also reduce herbicide requirements. For example, the "Ro-Till"—a no-till planter with an in-row subsoiler that is used for strip-tillage in extremely compactible soils, especially in the South—is able to incorporate herbicides efficiently into the row via a "rolling basket," not possible with other conservation tillage implements. Incorporation reduces the herbicide load by "banding" the chemicals so that they work only on the target weeds, eliminating the need for an allover spray.

Ridge-tillage, in which permanent planting ridges are created, also reduces herbicide use substantially. Ridge-tillage combines mechanical tillage on the ridges and precision herbicide placement between them at planting. At midseason another pass is made to rebuild the ridges, completely clearing the row middles of weeds without using herbicides. As ridge-tillage techniques develop, this method of cultivation will probably use fewer chemicals—herbicides, insecticides, and fertilizers—than conventional Corn Belt tillage practices do.

New shielded sprayers now make spot applications of herbicides possible, eliminating the need for a wholesale preventive regiment. Another device used in a post-emergent spraying system is an electric eye. The sprayer releases herbicide only when the eye sees a weed in a row. Yet another technique has been developed for use with the very efficient systemic herbicides that work by "translocating" from the leaves throughout the vascular system, killing the weed to the roots. Obviously such herbicides cannot be sprayed in a field with a standing crop, since drift or bad aim will kill the wrong plants. Traditionally, the systemics have been used as pre-emergent herbicides sprayed on an entire field before planting. An applicator has now been developed that dangles a wick from a boom that brushes the tops of the weeds between (or even above) the rows. There is almost no possibility of runoff with this system, which uses only a fraction of the herbicide needed for edge-to-edge spraying.

Such advances in herbicide application are not yet commonly used, even though some of them have been around for a number of years. The vast majority of conservation tillage farmers still trundle out the tank and spray the fields. But the new techniques are taking hold, and the agricultural experts I have interviewed believe that environmentalists should learn about them. As Washington State University agronomist Robert Papendick told me, "I think we've got to squelch this idea that no-till is necessarily tied to increased use of pesticides. That may be the fact today, but it need not be the fact tomorrow."

Papendick has been working on new rotations, using new cover crops to control pests in conservation tillage. "We're going to have to pay a lot more attention to crop rotation systems with conservation tillage than we have with conventional tillage," he said.

In search of new ideas, Papendick journeyed to Australia where a biennial legume called "black medic" is used in rotation with sheep grazing and wheat. "What we're attempting to do," he explained, "is develop a system that is highly competitive with weeds so that we can minimize herbicides—use them only when there is a runaway epidemic." Another approach Papendick described was intercropping the area between wheat rows with legumes, which would compete with the weeds and provide nitrogen for the next season's crop. "The whole idea," said Papendick, "is to cut down on herbicides and fertilizer in conservation tillage."

A colleague of Papendick's, weed scientist Alex Ogg, whom I also interviewed, was particularly keen about a new generation of sulfonylurea-based herbicides developed by DuPont. "Some of the new products," Ogg pointed out, "use only 1⁄16th of an ounce per acre. Half a pound—200 grams—can handle a 100-acre field." While the molecules of these new compounds are "very active," Ogg noted that since a fraction of an ounce per acre is used, rather than the pints and quarts of traditional herbicides, the new compounds "should substantially reduce the potential for environmental contamination."

Another reduction in the environmental impact of herbicide use may come from coating herbicides directly on seeds, which could, Ogg told me, "reduce the total amount of pesticide per acre by a large margin." Moreover, Ogg is watching the development of biological herbicides with interest. One of these is a naturally occurring fungus that when cultured and sprayed can control the vicious sicklepod, a major pest in no-till fields in the Southeast.

Given these new techniques, the "hard herbicide" era of conservation tillage may be on the way out. Although anyone reading a farm magazine would be likely to conclude that chemical companies have a mortal lock on U.S. agriculture in general and conservation tillage in particular, in fact the grip is being loosened by agricultural chemical companies themselves. In a curious irony of free-enterprise economics (albeit one that is modified by EPA rules and regulations and a number of energetic environmental groups), the chemical companies, for the sake of staying competitive in the growing conservation tillage market, may be showing farmers the way toward a reduced "pesticide load," with safer, more efficient products that are no more expensive than the environmentally damaging compounds they replace.

While these are important improvements, conservation tillage is still far from "organic." Most organic farming people and most conservation tillage people have agreed that the two techniques must, inevitably, take separate paths to the reduction of erosion and agricultural runoff.

There are, however, some who believe in investigating the possibilities of convergence. Among them is Barney Volak of the Rodale Research Center in Kutztown, Pennsylvania. The center is part of

Rodale Press, publishers of *Organic Gardening* magazine and a national leader in the organic farming movement for many years.

Volak was testing alternatives to herbicides in conservation tillage regimes—different crop rotations, biological and predator controls, limited mechanical tillage, and weed control by competition from the crop. This last approach includes shading the weeds by a ground cover, using high-quality, vigorous cultivars, spacing plants more closely in the row, and moving the rows closer together. A preliminary finding reported by Volak was the achievement of "competitive yields from corn grown with alfalfa" in ridge-tillage and no-tillage tests.

Of great interest to organic farming experts as well as those involved in conservation tillage are the possibilities offered by *allelopathic* cover crops. The Rodale center is testing ways to join conservation tillage methods with allelochemicals—"natural pesticides," as Volak called them—to control weeds in corn fields.

Allelo is a Greek combining form indicating reciprocity, so *allelopathic* means plants that are inherently pathological to other plants. According to Douglas Worsham of North Carolina State University, simply planting a cover crop of annual rye, but leaving it on the surface after it dies rather than plowing it under, produces compounds that can slow the growth of weeds. Crops planted into the residue with a seed drill are not inhibited, since they are placed beneath the surface and out of harm's way. James D. Riggleman, a weed scientist from DuPont and president of the Weed Science Society in 1986, has suggested that new allelopathic substances might even be extracted from plants or produced synthetically for use as herbicidal sprays or for incorporation into the soil.

Riggleman has proposed, in fact, that "new ecological, biological and nonchemical methods of weed control" be a top priority for all weed scientists. "While biological control of a broad range of weeds is unrealistic at current levels of technology, we have positive examples in the control of single species." Riggleman has reported that biological control of five weed species is now feasible, and that by the year 2000, thirty more might be added to this list. One fascinating idea advanced by Riggleman in his 1986 presidential address to the weed scientists was that weed seed germination might be influenced biologically, which could, as he put it, offer "a remarkable new approach to weed control." If cocklebur seeds, for example, could "be forced to germinate very early or very late in the season, or even all at one time," said Riggleman, "the management of this pest would be greatly simplified."

Despite the long-term prospect of significantly reducing environmental impacts from agricultural herbicides, wholly nonchemical methods of dealing with weeds in conservation tillage, such as those proposed by Barney Volak, may seem wildly theoretical to most agronomists and farmers. However, at least two commercial farmers in the U.S. are trying "organic conservation tillage" with some success.

One of those is Dick Thompson, owner of a 300-acre farm near Boone, Iowa. "Herbicides have not been used on this farm since 1967," Thompson claims, but he has tested ridge tillage with a regular Buffalo till-planter anyway to see if he could adapt it to his kind of farming. "In three soybean growing seasons," he reports, "side-by-side comparisons have shown that conservation tillage, fall and spring, produced more weed pressure in both broadleafs and grasses. On the Buffalo ridge-strip-till plant plot it was easier to manage weeds than on the conventional plot, even without using herbicides."

A principal difference between Thompson's ridge-till system and those that apply herbicides is his use of a rotary hoe during the growing season. He also controls weeds by a light harrowing in the very early spring. Some crops are planted at a higher-than-usual density to provide better crop competition against weeds. The higher seed costs are offset by the savings on herbicides. In the fall, Thompson plants cover crops with allelopathic properties, including oats and rye. "Both crops control erosion and add valuable organic matter to our soil," he reports, "and we've found that they chemically suppress weed growth in the corn that follows. The oats winter-kill, and the small amount of rye left over is just enough to help control early weeds without clogging up the planter sweep." At harvest, Thompson gets competitive yields at a cost much lower than that of conventional tillage.

Another farmer working on the convergence of conservation tillage and organic farming is Richard Harter, a California rice grower. According to Patrick Madden, an agricultural economist at Pennsylvania State University who has studied the operation firsthand, Harter began experiments with no-till organic rice in 1982. He overseeded the rice into a legume, and by the next year he began using no-till for his entire "adobe ground" rice crop. His method, Madden has written, "is based on the same general idea that chemically oriented farmers are increasingly using to grow corn interplanted into an established sod crop. But instead of using herbicide to suppress the legume growth, Dick floods the fields."

For "upland" rice, in which fields are not flooded, Harter's no-till method is to mat down the residue of annual weeds from the previous year, seed heavily, and quadruple the amount of fertilizer (chicken manure). The result is a heavier stand of rice that can better compete with weeds.

Despite the work of pioneers like Thompson and Harter, it seems doubtful that commercial conservation tillage will ever be practiced widely on an entirely herbicide-free, organic basis, given the greater costs, labor requirements, and risks of lower yields. At the same time, these experiments suggests that the "truism" that conservation tillage simply substitutes herbicides for mechanical tillage is not really true at all. Nor is it a sound basis on which to evaluate the future, or even the present, environmental impacts of conservation tillage.

Edward Faulkner defined plowless farming as a "new agriculture which is in reality very old." Civilization has brought us well beyond the mongongo tree, but with the adoption of the new techniques of conservation tillage, we may yet recapture some of the environmental gentleness we have lost during the millennia we have been using the plow. Herbicides measured by the gram, new devices for applying chemicals, new biological weed controls, new rotations with allelopathic cover crops, and even *organic* no-till may mark the beginning of a new phase in the ecology of agriculture that will greatly reduce environmental impacts.

To be sure, there are some retrograde tendencies. The development of herbicide-tolerant crop plant cultivars via genetic engineering is one of these. This is not only backward thinking, in my view, but it is gratuitous, egregiously self-serving on the part of chemical companies, and utterly contradictory to even the most rudimentary system of agro-ecological ethics. The object of conservation tillage is to provide simplified cropping systems that are naturally resistant to weeds, for the sake of productivity, net farm income, and resource conservation. These objectives are not well served by complicated and attenuated technologies intended to create permanent dependence on costly chemicals for the sake of corporate profits. It seems to me that engineering plants to encourage a high level of herbicide use is an Edsel of an idea, the substitution of chromium for common sense, and deserving of a similar fate.

By contrast, the directions suggested by Robert Papendick, Alex Ogg, James Riggleman, Barney Volak, Richard Thompson, and Richard Harter seem, on balance, to promise that environmental quality will improve as conservation tillage matures. The work of these investigators suggests that the endless arguments about a "trade-off" may become, it is devoutly to be hoped, old hat. And then conservation tillage, conscientiously applied, will be accepted as both the most ethical and the most practical way that farming can work with nature, rather than against it, in the production of crops.

Note

1. This essay has been adapted from *Green Fields Forever: The Conservation Tillage Revolution in America* by Charles E. Little, with permission of Island Press.

Going with the Flow
Expanding the Water Markets

Terry L. Anderson and Donald R. Leal[1]

THE CURRENT POLITICAL, SOCIAL, AND ECONOMIC CLIMATE is ushering in a whole new era in western water. In the face of efforts to curtail runaway government spending and protect the environment, water institutions must foster the conservation and efficient allocation of existing supplies. They must also take water's growing recreational and environmental value into account. The crucial question is: Can the current water institutions meet today's requirements?

In many cases, the answer is "no" because regulation of water allocation evolved during an era when massive federal outlays for huge water projects made trade-offs unnecessary. The objective was to deliver enough water to make the desert "bloom like a rose" regardless of the cost. With water supplied by federal bureaucracies at highly subsidized prices, we have found that if water runs uphill to money, it gushes uphill to politics.

Though the era of centralized water allocation has created a deep suspicion of water markets, the New Resource Economics (NRE) paradigm is challenging traditional political controls. The traditional approach relies on the knowledge of a few experts to direct resource allocation. While the NRE does not deny the importance of such expertise, it stresses that efficient resource allocation is dependent on knowledge of individual tastes, experiences, and circumstances. Such information does not exist in cohesive, integrated form but is distributed among the members of society. "With knowledge conceived of as both fragmented and widely dispersed, systematic coordination among the many supersedes the special wisdom of the few." The NRE focuses on the importance of institutions and incentives generated by property rights and questions whether collective action can increase either efficiency or equity. Emphasis is placed on the production of information through the market and the importance of entrepreneurial activities to the market process. Thus, those who take the NRE approach continually ask how responsibility and authority could be conferred on individuals so as to coordinate their disparate knowledge.

The Case for Water Marketing

Consider how the NRE approach can be applied to water. Traditionally there has been an implicit reliance on (some would say a blind faith in the ability of the few decision makers within a centralized structure to act objectively, omnisciently, and responsibly in pursuit of the public interest. The NRE economists ask whether decentralized markets with well-defined property rights could do better. If property rights in water use were fully defined and transferable, each owner would incur the full costs and benefits of his actions. An owner who ignored the need to allocate water to higher-valued uses would see his personal wealth decrease. Thus, knowledge and incentives would be linked.

That is not the case when property rights in water are "owned" by the government. Irrigators may derive benefits from water supplied by public works projects, but they are not at liberty to transfer the water to nonagricultural uses—even when such reallocations would be of higher value. The actions of the "owner"—the agency official who authorizes water use—are not directed by the value of competing uses, as would be the case in a market setting, because he would not gain monetarily from such transfers and in fact could lose discretionary power. Disallowing voluntary trades and restricting water use to irrigation are ways of ensuring that agency control will be maintained.

There are other important differences between market and centralized allocation. Water markets would send supply and demand signals that would enable managers to conserve water and coordinate its use—precisely the type of information that is conspicuously absent under centralized allocation. Water markets would also allow decentralized knowledge to be brought to bear on water management decisions. As Rodney T. Smith explained, "A farmer can apply his firsthand knowledge of his land, local hydrology, irrigation technology, and relative profitability of alternative crops to decide how much water to apply and which crops to grow on his land."[2] Because they lack such information, public officials are typically forced to use comprehensive plans that are not appropriate under varying circumstances.

Water markets cannot exist, however, in the absence of a legal structure that supports private ownership rights. In particular, the riparian doctrine applied in the eastern United States cannot utilize water markets because property rights in water are coequal for landowners adjoining a watercourse and hence cannot be transferred to nonriparian uses.

The prior appropriation doctrine that evolved in the arid western U.S. offers the basis for efficient water allocation. To support agricultural and mining operations, it was necessary to transport water considerable distances from its source. Because that could not be accomplished by restricting water use to riparian landowners on a coequal basis, the early California gold miners, in the absence of a formal government, devised their own system for allocating water use. They determined how much water each claimant was entitled to divert by applying the prior appropriation doctrine—"first in time, first in right." Usage rights were well defined and transferable and were enforced by the miner's associations. A market for trading such rights evolved, and for a time the arid West had in place a legal structure that fostered market allocation of water among competing uses. That success was short-lived, however, as a series of court and administrative decisions led to the centralized restrictions and controls that currently hamper efficiency.[3]

It is becoming evident throughout the United States that if the legal impediments to water markets were removed, substantial benefits would result. Nowhere is this more apparent than in central California's San Joaquin Valley, which has 4.5 million acres of irrigated land, and in southern California's burgeoning Metropolitan Water District. Like farmers in other parts of the nation, San Joaquin Valley farmers are suffering because product prices are low. In addition, the quality of the soil in the valley is steadily deteriorating from years of salt buildup and high concentrations of trace elements, such as selenium, in the drainage water. Several years ago high levels of selenium in the irrigation water draining into Kesterson Wildlife Reservoir caused largemouth and striped bass, catfish, and carp to disappear and caused newly hatched waterbirds to develop crippling deformities. The reservoir had been transformed from a fish and wildlife sanctuary into an environmental disaster.[4] Selenium pollution now poses a serious threat to the San Francisco Bay, a critical wildlife and marine life habitat.

Solving such problems will require significant investments in water conservation and cleanup; the estimated costs range from $10 an acre-foot for scheduling irrigation and recycling tailwater to $175 an acre-foot for using drip-sprinkler systems. None of those investments, however, make economic sense to the region's farmers, who currently pay $5 an acre-foot for irrigation.[5] So where will the money for cleanup come from?

The solution to central California's pollution problems may be a proposed transfer of water from agricultural uses in the San Joaquin

Valley to urban use in southern California. The logic of that choice becomes apparent when one considers southern California's situation. It is a densely developed, highly populated, arid region heavily dependent on imported water. The prospects for meeting southern California's growing demands for water through increasing supply were diminished when a readjudication of the Colorado River reduced its share by nearly five-hundred-thousand acre-feet a year. Hence, studies of the Metropolitan Water District have forecast significant supply shortages during the 1990s unless new sources can be acquired.[6]

The proposed water transfer would thus benefit both regions. Southern California currently pays $200 an acre-foot for water for urban use and expects to pay as much as $500 an acre-foot for water diverted from rivers into proposed reservoirs. But southern California could continue to pay $200 an acre-foot if it purchased water from San Joaquin farmers—water that they had saved by practicing conservation techniques. The sale of water to southern California at $200 an acre-foot would mean that the valley's farmers could make a profit even if they invested $175 an acre-foot in drip-sprinkler systems. And they could improve the environment, too, by taking damaged land out of production and eliminating the toxic runoff from agricultural chemicals.[7]

Under current federal policy, however, such transactions are discouraged. The Bureau of Reclamation (BuRec controls the water, and San Joaquin farmers are not empowered to sell BuRec water without its consent. In essence, the bureau has become the water OPEC of the West. It has funded massive projects that supply 35 percent of the West's delivered water and holds contracts that govern the use of the water, most of which is sold to irrigators at heavily subsidized prices. Irrigators in the San Joaquin Valley, for example, pay only about 15 percent of the cost of their delivered water. Such subsidies have led to a large overinvestment in water storage and delivery, wasteful water management practices, and the overcultivation of farmland. The bureau's subsidies and ability to veto transfers are standing in the way of efficient water allocation.

Change is coming slowly because the bureau has traditionally depended on expensive structural solutions to sustain its substantial budget and its discretionary power. Supporting water transfers would reduce the need for the pork barrel and thus threaten the bureau's potency in western water management.

In all likelihood, major changes will be spearheaded by state legislatures. There are already signs that the states are moving in that direction. The legislatures of New Mexico, Colorado, Utah, and California have made it legal for one person or agency to temporarily transfer surface water rights to another and reclaim those rights in the future, thus providing additional opportunities for short-term transactions. California and Oregon legislatures have also taken a step toward encouraging voluntary water conservation by "vesting the senior right to saved water in the user who saves the water. The law enables him to dispose of that water as he wishes, subject to basic transfer legislation."[8]

There are also many indications that water-market solutions are being taken seriously in the policy studies arena. At a 1987 symposium on water policy, for example, one of the country's water experts stated that "regulatory and pricing measures can be contrasted with what promises to be a more effective approach, namely, facilitating voluntary market transfers of water"[9] and another that "the nation is approaching limits of what can be achieved by increasing supply. . . . This means introducing market devices into the equation."[10] Market allocation of surface-water use throughout the nation is clearly an idea whose time has come.

Extending the Paradigm

The same insights that have helped to refocus the debate on the efficacy of markets in the allocation of surface water use can be extended to the more complex task of allocating instream flows and groundwater.

Instream Flows

The management of instream flows was once restricted to the maintenance of flow levels sufficient for navigation and power generation, but today it encompasses the allocation of a broad range of stream uses. Adequate instream flow levels must be maintained to sustain fish and wildlife habitats. In addition, pollution from industrial wastes remains a threat to many inland waters, and maintaining adequate flow levels diffuses pollutants. The demand for recreational opportunities, which also require adequate instream flows, is growing. A U.S. Fish and Wildlife Service study found that the sportfishing population increased by 27 percent between 1970 and 1980 and predicted that it would reach one hundred million by the year 2000.[11] The value of instream flows is clearly rising; the problem is that institutional recognition of that value is difficult to attain.

In the absence of property rights in instream flows, instream flow protection is currently regarded as a responsibility of state agencies, which must balance competing uses. The task is difficult because traditional offstream uses can dewater streams, which in turn can "adversely affect and in some cases destroy valuable in-place commercial and recreational water uses."[12] Hence, instream flow interests have usually collided with agricultural, industrial, and municipal interests, who currently hold rights to divert water. Fearing that their rights are threatened, these interests have strong incentive to fight political allocations for instream flows. Understandably, state agencies hesitate to reserve instream flows in cases when such allocations would collide with existing diversion rights in fully appropriated (or nearly so) watersheds.

Such a situation means that fish populations in western rivers remain in "precarious" positions upon arrival of droughts. For example, on the Ruby River in northwestern Montana, excessive irrigation led to a large fish kill during a dry period in 1987. The problem could have been prevented had the flow of the river been increased by 150 cubic feet per second. The state's Department of Natural Resources and Conservation eventually obtained these flows—but not soon enough to save the fish. Furthermore, the modest action by the state created conflict with other diverters, who claimed they had the right to the water.[13]

A market for instream flows would have solved the problem if private property rights in the instream flows were allowed. A major stumbling block to this, however, is the legal precedent for postulating a relationship between diversion and beneficial use. Judicial and administrative bodies have established diversion as a prerequisite for beneficial use and in the absence of diversion have rejected all private appropriation claims to instream flows.

Sanctioning private instream flow rights could allow private organizations to preserve environmental and recreational water values. Organizations such as The Nature Conservancy, Trout Unlimited, and Ducks Unlimited could use their resources to purchase or rent water to preserve wildlife habitat. Change may be in the offing in Montana to protect instream flows because Trout Unlimited is beginning to lobby for legislation enabling it to rent water in dry years to prevent trout kills. Hopefully, such efforts to protect instream flows will be carried to other states.

Groundwater

Groundwater use has been increasing steadily for the last forty years. In the West groundwater accounts for 46 percent of the municipal and 44 percent of the industrial water supplies. Due to the steadily rising demand, extraction exceeds natural recharge in most of the West's groundwater basins. Kenneth Frederick has estimated that in western aquifers withdrawal exceeds resupply by more than 22 million acre-feet each year.[14]

Groundwater depletion is occurring in urban as well as rural parts of the United States. In Tucson, Arizona, the largest American city entirely dependent on groundwater, the water table has fallen by 50 meters since 1960; the water table beneath Dallas-Fort Worth has fallen by 150 meters. Similar conditions exist in California's San Joaquin Valley, in Houston, Texas, and in Savannah, Georgia.

Does such groundwater depletion make good economic sense? From an efficiency standpoint, the answer is not necessarily "no."[15] "Mining" a basin is appropriate if the future value of the water is expected to be lower than the current value. The real problem in groundwater management is to induce users to optimize the rate of extraction, which means that the net marginal value of the water currently being extracted is equal to the net marginal value of the water being left in a basin for future extraction.

A major difficulty in groundwater allocation is that the future value of water left in a basin is not captured solely by individuals who decide to conserve. Water left for the future is a common-pool resource; that is, its value can be captured by anyone. Suppose that an individual must decide whether to leave water in a basin in order to offset future shortfalls in precipitation or surface-water availability. Even if he believes that the current consumption value is less than the future insurance value, his incentive to leave water in the basin is reduced by the knowledge that other users can pump the water immediately. As in the case of several children sharing a soda, each individual realizes that anything he leaves behind will be consumed by others. In the absence of secure ownership claims, future value gets zero weight in an individual's calculus.

Groundwater users cannot optimize the rate of extraction unless the rights to water in a basin are clearly defined by water institutions and the courts. Only then can users calculate the current and future value of groundwater supplies accurately. Thus, the first step in solving the problem of depletion is to secure well-defined rights in groundwater use, which in turn will facilitate market transfers.

Pollution as well as overextraction is a problem of groundwater basins. The problem was highlighted in the 1970s when it was discovered that toxic chemicals had seeped through subterranean structures into homes near Niagara Falls, New York, and the chemicals were traced to the now-infamous waste disposal site known as Love Canal. Press reports on the Love Canal incident frightened local residents and created a national chemical pollution scare. That incident, coupled with such subsequent events as the discovery of the evil-looking "valley of the drums" in Kentucky and the dioxin pollution at Times Beach, Missouri, led to public demand for governmental action. Ultimately, the federal government complied; in 1980 it passed the Comprehensive Environmental Response, Compensation, and Liability Act—better known as Superfund.

Superfund, along with related toxic waste legislation, has led to the discovery of a myriad of pollution threats to underground water supplies. They come from point sources, such as abandoned or problem waste disposal sites—which already number over a thousand and continue to proliferate—and leaky underground gasoline storage tanks, and from nonpoint sources, such as pesticides and herbicides used in agriculture. The cleanup costs are projected to be in the tens of billions of dollars.

Unfortunately, Superfund creates an incentive for polluters to increase rather than decrease discharge because it lowers the cost to pollute. The legislative price tag for Superfund increased from $1.6 billion in 1980 to $9 billion in 1986, and with taxes footing the bill, parties guilty of pollution are spared the full opportunity cost of their acts. For that reason, Fred Smith, a former EPA official, suggested that Superfund, and legislation like it, are a "hazardous waste of taxpayer money."[16]

The depletion and pollution of groundwater are directly related to the failure of the institutions governing that resource to provide proper incentives and information, without which users are not likely to augment groundwater supplies or reduce pollution discharged into them. To gain an understanding of the present property rights structure governing groundwater, it is important to realize that the underpinnings of groundwater law are found in English common law. Because very little was known about the hydrology of groundwater, groundwater rights were assigned to the owner of the overlying land. As Frank Trelease, the dean of water law, has pointed out, "It was in the light of this scientific and judicial ignorance that the overlying landowner was given total dominion over his 'property,' that is, a free hand to do as he pleased with water found within his land, without accounting for damage."[17] When groundwater rights either are not assigned or are assigned on the basis of overlying land, the common-pool problems can become quite severe. A rule of capture applies to a migratory resource such as groundwater. Each individual achieves the greatest net benefits by pumping water earlier than the others because the lift costs increase as the level is lowered. The "tragedy of the commons" is that each individual has an incentive to pump water earlier than everyone else, so the supply is depleted rapidly. Moreover, if the groundwater basin is being used for waste disposal, the pollution flows away and becomes someone else's problem. Such poorly defined rights were harmless as long as there was little demand for groundwater, but the changes that evolved as the demand grew have not led to efficient groundwater use.

A creative alternative approach to groundwater allocation suggested by Vernon Smith is to issue property deeds for two rights in groundwater basins: a share of the total water stock in a basin and a share of the average annual recharge flow of the basin.[18] The maximum initial allocations of each component would be proportional to users' land overlying the aquifer. In order to enforce the rights once they had been defined, metered pumps could be used and periodic readings taken. At the end of each year, individual stock rights would be increased or decreased depending on whether an individual's use exceeded his recharge rights. Those who pump more than their combined stock and flow rights would be fined.

While this system might not be perfect, it would encourage efficiency because transfers of property rights in stocks and flows would force users to compare the opportunity costs of various present and future uses. Groundwater users could stabilize water levels by purchasing water from other sources during dry years and selling temporary shares during wet years. An additional benefit of the exchange system is that the risk of dry years would be distributed among many producers and consumers. Risk-averse parties would have an incentive to acquire or hold greater shares in groundwater stocks and flows. The water market would thus incorporate a voluntary savings plan that permitted users to guard against water shortages.

The assignment of property rights in stocks and flows will not solve all the common-pool problems because a holder of a title to a stock of water could still face high extraction costs imposed by the usage rates of other pumpers. Such third-party effects could be lessened through unitization, a contractual arrangement that evolved in oil recovery to mitigate common-pool problems.[19] Under such an arrangement, all parties would contract to use agreed-upon methods of extraction and delivery and share the costs. Some wells would be shut down and others would remain operational. For that reason, unitization might entail higher delivery costs, but it would also foster increased water conservation and thus lower lift costs.

In considering new institutions for groundwater allocation, it is important to remove, and refrain from creating, legal obstructions to the evolution of such arrangements. That means getting rid of overlying-land restrictions and reasonable-use criteria and choosing a set of rules that would enhance the specificity, enforceability, liability, and transferability of property rights.

Conclusions

Supply-side solutions to water allocation that have subsidized delivery and use must be replaced by policies forcing users to face the full costs of water. Water marketing provides this alternative.

In order to reap the advantages of the market, policymakers must find ways to define property rights in water, enforce them, and make them transferable. The prior appropriation doctrine provides those elements. By extending the application of the prior appropriation doctrine to instream flows and groundwater basins, policymakers could vastly improve the nation's water allocation system. Political coalitions that could bring about the necessary institutional reforms are possible because water marketing can reduce inefficient water use, environmental degradation, and budget deficits.

Notes

1. Terry L. Anderson and Donald R. Leal thank the Earhart Foundation for its support of their forthcoming book, *Free Market Environmentalism*, from which this paper is excerpted.

2. Rodney T. Smith, *Trading Water: The Legal and Economic Framework for Water Marketing* (Claremont, Calif.: Claremont McKenna College, Center for Study of Law Structures, 1986), p. 26.

3. Terry L. Anderson, *Water Crisis: Ending the Policy Drought* (Washington, D.C.: Cato Institute, 1983), pp. 27-28.

4. Richard W. Wahl, "Cleaning Up Kesterson," *Resources* (Spring 1986): 11.

5. Zach Willey, "Economic Common Sense Can Defuse the Water Crisis," *EDF Letter* (March 1987): 7.

6. Timothy H. Quinn, "Water Exchanges and Transfers to Meet Future Water Demands in Southern California" (Paper presented at the symposium "Water Marketing: Opportunities and Challenges of a New Era," Denver, Colorado, September 24-26, 1986), p. 2.

7. Willey, "Economic Common Sense," cited in note 5, p. 7.

8. Bruce Driver, *Western Water: Tuning the System* (Denver: Western Governors' Association, 1986) p. xi.

9. Richard W. Wahl, "Voluntary Market Transfers of Federally Supplied Water" (Paper presented at the Congressional Research Service symposium "Evolving Issues in Water Policy: The Agricultural Connection," Washington D.C., February 13, 1987), p. 2.

10. Kenneth D. Frederick, "The Legacy of Cheap Water" (Paper presented at the Congressional Research Service symposium "Evolving Issues in Water Policy: The Agricultural Connection," Washington D.C., February 13, 1987), p. 4.

11. Zach Taylor, "Hunting and Fishing in the Year 2000," *Sports Afield*, February 1986, p. 81.

12. R. W. Johnson, "Public Trust Protection for Stream Flows and Lake Levels," *University of California at Davis Law Review* 14 (1980): 256–57.

13. Terry L. Anderson and Donald Leal, "A Private Fix for Leaky Trout Streams," *Fly Fisherman*, June 1988, pp. 28–31.

14. Kenneth D. Frederick, "The Future of Western Irrigation," *Southwestern Review of Management* 7 (Spring 1981): 21.

15. For a more thorough discussion of the economics of groundwater, see Terry L. Anderson, Oscar Burt, and David Fractor, "Privatizing Groundwater Basins: A Model and Its Applications," in Terry L. Anderson, ed., *Water Rights: Scarce Resource Allocation, Bureaucracy, and the Environment* (San Francisco: Pacific Research Institute, 1983).

16. Lawrence Reed, "'Superfund' a Bonanza for U.S. Polluters," *Idaho Press-Tribune*, December 11, 1986, p. 4A.

17. Frank J. Trelease, "Developments on Groundwater Law," in Z. A. Saleem, ed., *Advances in Groundwater "Mining" in the Southwestern States* (Minneapolis: American Water Resources Association, 1976), p. 272.

18. Vernon L. Smith, "Water Deeds: A Proposed Solution to the Water Valuation Problem," *Arizona Review* 26 (January 1977): 7–10.

19. Stephen N. Wiggins and Gary D. Libecap, "Oil Field Unitization: Contractual Failure in the Presence of Imperfect Information," *American Economic Review* 75 (June 1985): 369.

Replacing Confusion with Equity
Alternatives for Water Policy in the Colorado River Basin

Helen M. Ingram, Lawrence A. Scaff, and Leslie Silko

Introduction

From its beginning the fate of civilization has been tied to water and the management of water resources. Regional development, shifts in population, the growth of trade, the ebb and flow of cultural influence have all depended in important ways on water transportation routes, sophisticated irrigation works, and uncontaminated supplies for consumption. In the semiarid American West we hardly need to be reminded of these universal facts of experience: our landscapes are dotted with the ruins of ancient cultures—the Hohokam, the Anasazi—forced to surrender to nature's privations. Theirs is a history we do not want to repeat.

Nevertheless, memories can be surprisingly short. We are quick to assume that modern society, supported by new technologies, will readily avoid past errors. But as the twentieth century comes to a close some of our more comfortable assumptions have been badly eroded. It has become naive to hope that we can continue to muddle through, merely react to crises as they arise, or expect that over the long run the maximum demands of all interests can be fully accommodated. There is increasing awareness that the destiny of people in arid lands depends far less upon technical understanding and physical structures than upon institutions and an appreciation of the *kinds* of political choices available to us and the contrasting consequences of those choices. For instance, in concluding a comparative study of six irrigation communities in Spain and the American West, Maass and Anderson point out that their observations about water policy "relate to the justice of institutions—to the relations in irrigation communities among popular control, distributive shares, economic growth, and farmers' concepts of fairness."[1] Significantly, the precise nature of these crucial relationships is not specified by the authors; they suggest that the "challenge remains" to find an acceptable "model" for justice, fairness or equity with respect to water distribution and management. A similar plea has been entered recently by Norris Hundley, Jr., based upon his searching review of the checkered legal and political history of water rights in the West, especially in light of controversies flowing from the Winters decision of 1908: we must "find a way of replacing confused law . . . with clear and reasonable principles. . . . The challenge is to replace confusion with equity."[2]

Of course, the concern for "equity" in the disposition of water resources is hardly a new issue, particularly in the Colorado River Basin. To examine the record of "dividing the waters" in this century is to encounter constant appeals from all sides to principles of "reciprocity," "rights," and "equity." This is as true of officials in the Western states and the Supreme Court, which defended its decision in *Wyoming v. Colorado* as "consonant with the principles of right and equity,"[3] as it is of those communities, like the Indians and Mexicans, that have generally been excluded from the decision making process. But today it is the perception of persistent inequalities and the attempt to assert "water rights," advanced especially by Indians, which is "the sword of Damocles that hangs over the West." In Philip Fradkin's words, "It threatens, like nothing else, to sever the complex web of laws, agreements, regulations, quiet understandings, and court decisions that, collectively known as 'the law of the river,' constitute the major determinant in the growth of the West—the white man's West, that is, since the Colorado is essentially a white man's river."[4] This may be strong language, but it only states what we know: In the West water has gone to those with political power, legal skills, technical knowledge, and sheer tenacity; others have been excluded. In light of this record and our common reliance on legal adjudication, the complex and troubling question of "equity" will surely not disappear; for the next generations it poses questions that will have to be confronted, whether we like it or not.

We are presented, then, with a double challenge: confusion and uncertainty at the level of principles, controversy over "water rights" within the social order. In these circumstances nothing could be more timely than the articulation of a principled understanding of what has come to be called the "equity perspective." Such an understanding does not yet exist, at least not with respect to the special domain of water distribution, use and management. Our aim is to develop a rational defense of "equity," calling upon both the general theoretical discussions of "distributive justice" and the particular circumstances and history of water policy in the West. The task it to identify and clarify those points of contact, of intersection between the general and the particular. In order to accomplish this aim we propose starting with observations about two aspects of the problem: the nature of water as a special kind of resource, a "social good"; and the nature of the American "democratic" political process and the principles and expectations associated with it.

Water as a Social Good

The fundamental social significance of water was acknowledged at the inception of our civilization. In fact, the earliest discussions of water as a special human resource emerged as part of a series of comments on the conditions appropriate to a "just" political community, to its health, defense, beauty, and legal arrangements. Thus, in several passages in *The Laws*, Plato sought to show that of all resources and necessities of life, water, because of its basic importance for human well-being and its vulnerability to "doctoring, diverting, or intercepting the supply," must always be subject to public regulation. Time-honored practices recognized "priority rights," but such rights were qualified by norms of "reciprocity" that were publicly enforced.[5] The same ideas recur in Aristotle's *Politics*, with the added reminder that despite its all-too-obvious importance for the "self-sufficiency" of a polis, the public management of water "is a matter which ought not to be treated lightly."[6] And a less familiar figure, Pausanias, writing in Roman times, scornfully dismissed the civic aspirations of a small town merely by noting that it has "no government buildings, no theater, no town square, no water conducted to a fountain." As if to underline the human consequences of such deprivation, he observed that "the people live in hovels like mountain cabins on the edge of a ravine."[7] The absence of visible water works and water institutions was a sure sign of the lack of public life and civilization itself.

As citizens of semiarid lands, writers from Plato to Pausanias were well aware of how capricious nature could be: droughts were inevitable, rainfall came during the wrong season, irrigation was a necessity. Scarcity raised basic questions about resource use and distribution, questions that could only be answered by institutionalizing a set of arrangements that would produce socially sanctioned decisions. Distributive problems were no less compelling for urban communities than for rural peoples. Everywhere water was caught up in a web of social interdependencies, and this meant that like other "social goods" it could be considered under the heading of distributive justice.

To adopt the long-standing conception of water as a "social good" is certainly not to suggest that water never be considered a natural resource. Of course it is *also* a natural resource, and it is this double identity that can create considerable perplexity. Our understanding suggests minimally that water not be seem simply as an economic commodity, subject to the usual market laws of supply and demand and to calculations or efficiency, but rather that it be viewed as a fundamental necessity that society chooses (for good reasons) to treat differently from other resources. Historically, the "water is different" conception has often prevailed: Spanish water law, from which much of our present Western water law is derived, in fact went to great lengths to protect the public interest and place it above parties seeking particular water rights, and even above claimants invoking the doctrine of prior appropriation.[8]

In the contemporary setting, Maass and Anderson capture the essence of the issue when they state that in actual experience the goal of "economic growth" often conflicts with other community objectives, so much so "that farmers typically refuse to treat water as a regular economic good, like fertilizer, for example." "It is," they say, "a special product and should be removed from ordinary market transactions so that farmers can control conflict, maintain popular influence and control, and realize equity and social justice."[9] If water is indeed different, as seems to be the case, then it is closer in its most significant aspects to being a social good than an economic good, or (if you will pardon the comparison, however excusable coming from educators) it is more like basic education or basic health care than fertilizer. It may seem surprising to speak of water in this way. Yet it should be neither surprising nor irrational that communities show considerable reluctance to surrender to the "market mechanism" decisions so closely tied to collective well-being as those associated with water distribution are.

Three important consequences follow from this distinctive understanding of water as a social good: a definition of government's role, a characterization of the function of "public interest" in relation to water rights, and an identification of the kind of "public ownership" that applies to water.

The Role of Government

Political communities are formed to provide certain basic services and protect certain basic rights that citizens could not secure by acting alone. We suggest that together with providing for common defense, security of life and property, and enforcement of law, one of the most basic tasks of a political community, acting through its government, is to oversee the maintenance and distribution of water supplies. There is a crucial sense in which government and its agents must function as "trustees," as the institutional locus of accountability. Attempts to shift accountability to individuals, private interests, or a market's "invisible hand" will, of course, tend to fragment this role and exacerbate conflict. The tendency increases in arid and semiarid environments where questions over water distribution among competing users are inherently conflictual and continually test the community's capacity to institutionalize negotiation and compromise. After all, as we have seen again and again in the West, a threat to the system for allocating water is perceived as a threat to communities' well-being or way of life. It may be a slight exaggeration to suggest (borrowing a page from Hobbes) that in the settlement of the West disputes over water rights made life "solitary, poor, nasty, brutish and short."[10] But we have it on the authority of Elwood Mead, an early observer of western irrigation practices, that until public institutions for adjudicating disputes were developed, "there was either murder or suicide in the heart of every member" of the irrigation communities.[11] In short, there was a clear interest in channeling private grievances into public institutions.

Public Interest

If government is to be assigned an activist role, then the category appropriate to its decision making is "public interest." However difficult it may be to decide what the public interest *is* in actual cases, there seems to be no acceptable alternative to thinking about water policy in terms of its imperatives. Moreover, we can begin to conceptualize these imperatives in terms of certain primary values that characterize the American political community, especially those which state belief in the inherent fairness of "open" and "democratic" political processes. The key to limiting confusion about "public interest" (which like many political concepts is open to partisan abuse) is to see that it attaches to process itself, not to a specific constellation of "right results." In addition, it functions to alert us to the fact that in situations where a "social good" such as water is under consideration, particular interests are subordinated to general interests, individual interests are secondary to common interests. Thus, it is justifiable to expect people to act in certain ways with respect to water, not because actions promote self-interest, but because they serve the public interest. The grounds for this justification must be sought in the notion of "equity" itself, as we shall suggest below.

Public Ownership

It follows from what has been said so far about water as a "social good" that, viewed as "property," water resources are owned by everyone—or by no one. That is, water is at best owned by the public, acting through its authorized political agents and institutions. When government grants or recognizes claims for water rights, it acknowledges a right for *use*, not ownership. There are no natural, innate, fixed, or absolute rights to the ownership of water, but rather rights to use that are contingent upon an implicit conception of "public interest" as developed by the political process. Water and its "status" as a "good" seem to be radically conditioned, once again, by social and political arrangements.

Politics as a Democratic Process

Having developed a perspective on water as a social good, we need to turn directly to our second theme, to the political context within which considerations of "equity" have become prominent. This context is profoundly shaped, we would argue, by certain deeply ingrained assumptions about that much-abused term, "democratic politics." Stated in a bold (and we hope not reckless) form, the enlightened experiment we call American democracy has operated under the expectations and constraints of two basic ideas about the political process: First, to Americans "democracy" has entailed respect for legal or constitutional rules and procedures arrived at in an "impartial" and "fair" manner. Second, our commitment to democratic politics has generally conveyed a sense of power being shared by members of a community organized as participants having equal access to the law, to social goods, and to political positions. The first idea expresses a procedural norm, the second a participatory norm; democracy in the first sense is a form of decision making, in the second a mode of association or "conjoint action."[12] When taken literally, both are unabashed precepts or ideals that we shall surely at best only approximate in partial and limited ways. Nevertheless (or perhaps for this reason), these ideals have provided the motive force behind the appeal for equity.

Both the procedural and participatory conceptions of democracy have assumed that the democratic public is essentially an association of individuals in whose collective interest policies are to be set. After all, in order to meet with approval, most would agree that democracy as a form of rule should operate for the benefit of individuals. But as a condition for securing potential benefits, it becomes necessary for individuals to have certain rights protected. One normally thinks of First Amendment rights in this connection, but of course there are other kinds of "rights," such as water rights, that may be just as controversial as their stand counterparts. In any case, the exercise of all rights, a hallmark of the democratic process, tends to produce two results: rights come into conflict with each other, individual is set again individual, one part of the political community is set against another part, and inequalities are generated, which in turn affect the ability of individuals to exercise rights. Beginning with two apparently satisfactory norms of democratic politics, we are led to a point at which inequalities in power, participation, and the practice of rights threaten to undo the norms themselves. Our conceptions of democratic politics seem to say one thing, whereas our practices seem to say another. Yet both are part of an unavoidable tension in the democratic process.

Controversies over water rights and the use and distribution of water invariably encounter this tension: current distributive practices are attacked in the name of principle, and principles are criticized in view of existing practices for distributing water. Here, then, is the problem of the democratic process, particularly with respect to water issues: How do we keep the political community functioning in a situation of severe conflict? How do we decide which inequalities are acceptable and for which categories of users? What principles can be proposed for correcting unacceptable inequalities? Indeed, are there any principles at all, consistent with our democratic expectations, that can establish once and for all the meaning of distributive justice with respect to water and thereby allow us "to replace confusion with equity?"

To raise these questions is to move toward the heart of the problem posed by the equity perspective. We need to call upon the general characterization of democratic politics to see whether particular lessons can be drawn concerning the meaning and application of equity.

The Problem of Equity

In the language of politics "equity" is dependent for its meaning on conceptions of equality that are rooted in general theories of distributive justice. Over the last decade, following upon the heels of John Rawls' well-known work,[13] we have seen an avalanche of such general philosophical theories and models of rational choice. These efforts have sought to answer questions like "what is justice?" or "what is equity?" by identifying principles and decision rules that are abstract, hypothetical, invariant, universal, and applicable to whole societies.

However, because of these characteristics the general theories of justice have had difficulty coping with areas of public policy, such as water policy, where all of the serious problems are of a different order, where the context of policy is established by relationships that are concrete, historically specific, changeable, particular, and applicable only in restricted settings.[14] Often it seems as though the relationship between "theory" and "policy" has remained about where Pausanias left it.

If we are to move toward a coherent understanding of "equity" in water policy, then two new assumptions seem to offer the greatest promise: It strikes us as reasonable, first of all, to categorize the issues of water resources and water rights as occupying what Walzer has recently called a "sphere of justice," that is, a particular area of policy and decision where society acknowledges the relevance of certain questions having to do with distribution and equity.[15] This "sphere" may have a family resemblance to other sphere, such as welfare, security, education, and the like, but the rules and history shaping its policies are different in important ways. Thus, what equity can mean in this sphere will depend importantly on the particular and even unique conditions characterizing water policy in the Colorado Basin. It follows, secondly, that what the equity perspective requires is an identification and logical ordering of practical principles that will fit the unique circumstances of water. There are no general postulates or theories of equity that will clarify policy in this sphere, and it is pointless to look for them. What we need are "middle range" generalizations, not grand theories, that might provide some practical guidance through this labyrinthine sphere of compacts, rights, laws, claims, and interests.

Now, it is unfortunate but true that equity (or equality) has long been recognized as a protean and paradoxical concept, hardly the most reliable instrument for our purposes. As we have suggested above, the problem is this: to affirm equity in one of its many forms—equality of rights, for example—is in fact to affirm *in*equality of results. That is, arguments for equity always end up at some point as rationalizations for "acceptable" levels and types of inequality among different categories of persons. In writing *The Promise of American Life* (1909) Herbert Croly already complained that "in so far as the equal rights are freely exercised, they are bound to result in inequalities; and these inequalities are bound to make for their own perpetuation, and so to provoke still further discrimination. Wherever the principle has been allowed to mean what it seems to mean, it has determined and encouraged its own violation."[16] But instead of abandoning Proteus to Croly's furies, we would be better off to see that in the messy and clouded political world, where things are often not as they seem, equity taken literally as an arithmetical relation of identity, is simply a myth. Any defense of equity must therefore be "complex": when inequalities arise or when differences emerge in the criteria used for resource allocation for given categories of users (as inevitably they must), we need to be able to defend them as "reasonable" or "fair." The equity perspective really refers to implicit claims about reasonableness and fairness; we hope to make such claims explicit.

Five Principles of Equity

In our view an acceptable "equity doctrine" can be explicitly formulated around five distributive principles that refer to what we propose to call reciprocity, value-pluralism, participation, promising, and responsibility. These principles are offered as a statement of "necessary and sufficient" conditions for equity, and in this sense they may serve as a "test" for equity in water policy.

Principle 1.

"Reciprocity" captures one sense of equity, namely the notion that *distributive advantages and costs should be shared by all members of the relevant community*. Yet the difficult problem is to decide how costs should be apportioned when the welfare of water resources is at stake. Reciprocity suggests some minimally applicable rules: In the first place, everyone should share in the burdens of a water system, as on a small scale in northern New Mexico where each spring the mayordomo enlists all able-bodied men for servicing the *acequia madre*, the main irrigation ditch, and for repairing diversion dams.[17] Also, as a general rule those emerging users who place a heavy marginal burden on the resource beyond what existing arrangements for allocation can accommodate must shoulder the burden of negotiating ways whereby their demands hurt neither the resource nor other users. Furthermore, in the case of water allocation those who use more should expect to have to sacrifice more in situations of scarcity.

Reciprocity is sufficiently complicated to deserve a brief comment. As used here it is actually a "balancing" principle that acknowledges the doctrine of prior appropriation ("first in time, first in right"), but is also committed to frugality and protection of third-party rights. The difficulty here stems from prior appropriation, which was invoked initially as a fair rule for protecting stability of allocation, security of investment, and reciprocity in the treatment of users. When pushed to an extreme, however, it can have negative effects. One of the most justifiable criticisms of Western states' water law is that in practice it often encourages waste or penalizes those who postpone resource use through operation of the "use it or lose it" formula, which is really the reverse side of the doctrine of prior appropriation.[18] Thus, we end up with the Navajo Indian Irrigation Project, which received tribal support not because a consensus formed in favor of using Winters rights for a marginal (and, it turned out, ill-advised) irrigation project, but rather because the Navajos believed if others successfully claimed and used the water, while they did not, their opportunity to use their water would be lost forever. As one councilman mused, "We will never see the water again if it goes over the mountain."[19] Just as prior appropriation needs to be modified by frugality, then, so it also needs to be modified by third-party rights. In this respect the record in the West is more promising. Regarding purchases of senior water rights by energy companies, for example, courts have often (and appropriately) invoked a doctrine of "no injury to third parties."[20] It seems consistent with the principle of reciprocity to expect costs for this kind of growth—rapid expansion of energy development in coal and oil shale that places additional demands on Colorado Basin water resources—to be borne by the agents of growth.

Principle 2.

Our second equity principle, value-pluralism, holds that *users' rights to employ water to pursue whatever values they consider legitimate should be respected, provided use does not degrade the resource or harm others*. This typically "liberal" assertion is important,[21] because like all complex human environments, the Colorado River Basin includes political communities with very different value orientations toward fundamental social goods, such as work, leisure, recreation, education, welfare, health, and water. The equity perspective is consistent with the view that different communities should be able to decide independently about such fundamental matters, including water resources use and development, assuming "no degradation" and "no harm to others" conditions are satisfied. Few would deny that such "negative" conditions may become quite restrictive, in which case value-pluralism is necessarily counterbalanced by the principle of reciprocity. Like the scales of justice, our first two principles exist in tension and must in fact be weighed against each other. On the positive side, however, our second principle has implications both for low-income rural communities, which should be able to pursue their own "values" without fearing arbitrary loss of access to water as a social good, and for the relative autonomy of the Western states. In its recent *Sporhase v. Nebraska* decision (1982) the Supreme Court appears to have adopted a contradictory position on this important aspect of equity, as we shall argue below. We think it unlikely that position can be maintained.

Principle 3.

The third principle of equity is derived from our statements about the participatory aspects of politics within democratic communities. In the view defended here, because of water's fundamental importance *members of society having claims consistent with other stated values should always be accommodated in resource allocation and in the decision process.* To have a share in water resources is a legitimate right of every member of society, and government has an obligation to protect that right. Similarly, to take part in allocative decisions is a right that should not be infringed. Thus, it does not seem equitable to attempt either to limit community membership by restricting access to water or to decrease the probability of technically "inefficient" decisions by restricting the circle of participants. Exclusionist policies of both kinds invite destabilizing conflict and further accusations of inequity. Accommodating a variety of claims will render the decision process more confused and tempestuous than under "authoritarian" conditions attributed by Wittfogel to "hydraulic societies,"[22] but such inconveniences necessarily accompany equity and are less damaging to public interest than the alternatives.

Principle 4.

As a fourth principle, we suggest that equity assumes the *obligation to obey promises agreed to in good faith in the course of negotiation and compromise.* In a sense, the politics of the Colorado River Basin are nothing more than a fabric of promises, incurred at different times, under different conditions, and often for different purposes. Despite such differences, promises express the shared social understanding of the meaning of water. In the Basin as a whole there appears to be a consensus that promises do matter precisely because they are the underlying metaphorical "social contract" binding members, communities, and government agencies together in a common fate.[23] This is a controversial principle, however, because promises come into conflict with each other and the circumstances change under which promises are made. Unfortunately, there is no single, unambiguous rule of equity for solving the dilemmas that appear at this point. Instead, emphasis should be placed on the need for flexibility and adaptation; we must be able to accept a built-in ambiguity in water decisions. Renegotiation of promises is always possible, but (and this is our main contention) only on the condition that our other four equity principles apply. Promises are inviolable, to be sure, but when "dilemmas" appear they may be qualified by the other principles we have proposed.

Principle 5.

Finally, we propose that the equity perspective is consistent with the view that *present use of water resources should be accompanied by responsibility for future generations*. It is important that use of a basic resource and social good like water not be part of a "Faustian bargain" which sacrifices future well-being to momentary pleasure. We need a kind of "ethic of responsibility" that will encourage attention to consequences, especially long-term costs of immediate short-term benefits. Of course, it is not always clear how the welfare of future generations might best be served. Economists have argued that among the finest gifts to be handed on by society are knowledge, technical advancement, and economic prosperity, and that these achievements may well depend upon the exploitation of resources.[24] Could such reasoning support allowing toxic pollution of groundwater supplied today in hopes that future users will have developed the technology to clean up aquifers, cure cancer, or find a substitute for water? We think not. Equity is also an ethical idea which imposes responsible restraint in the fact of very large risks to a social good whose fate is inseparable from human well-being.

These five principles serve as a concise summation of what has come to be called the "equity perspective." As should now be apparent, that perspective is not unitary, but consists instead of a variety of competing yet internally consistent principles that must be taken together and balanced against each other. Approached in this way, the five principles can be effectively used to analyze and assess Colorado River Basin water policy.

Application and Discussion

Difficult water reallocation decisions are facing the Colorado River Basin: rising demands are placing pressure upon dwindling supplies, long-standing interests whose use of water had been deferred are now pursuing their claims, new interests whose use yields relatively higher rates of return are demanding preferential treatment, and present water users are resisting any sacrifices. At the same time, the strategies currently being chosen to deal with these conflicts tend to be insensitive to the politics and principles of equity. Pricing schemes, market mechanisms, and quantification of water rights are placing high value on efficiency, permanence, and security at the expense of equity. Yet the unintended result of these strategies may well be to perpetuate and amplify inequities, thus unleashing further conflict instead of subduing it.

Consider the issue of treating water as a market commodity. In accord with a preference for unfettered interstate trade, courts have recently declared water an "article of commerce" and have held unconstitutional state anti-export statutes that place an undue burden on interstate commerce.[25] Such decisions depart from precedents where courts recognized the special status of water as a social good. For instance, in an opinion written by Justice Oliver Wendell Holmes, the Supreme Court found that "few public interests are more obvious, indisputable and independent of particular theory than the interest of the public of a State to maintain the rivers that are wholly within it substantially undiminished, except for such drafts upon them as the guardians of the public welfare may permit for the purpose of turning them to more perfect use."[26] Furthermore, the "article of commerce" designation is not entirely consistent with the Court's own language in *Sporhase v. Nebraska*. Representing the majority, Justice Stevens noted that the Court was "reluctant to condemn as unreasonable measures taken by a State to conserve and preserve for its own citizens this vital resource in times of severe shortage," citing four specific grounds for such reluctance.[27] Justices Rehnquist and O'Conner dissented on the grounds that "'commerce' cannot exist in a natural resource that cannot be sold, rented, traded, or transferred, but only *used*."

Importantly for our discussion, the treatment of water as an article of commerce erodes the value-pluralism principle of equity and places a special burden upon states that have chosen to husband resources and to develop economically at a slower pace. We have long assumed that states could follow the wishes of their own citizens in allocating water. The states' power to protect their citizens' values in regard to water is no longer secure.

The circumstances surrounding the anti-export statute struck down by the United States District Court particularly illustrates the equity problem. In contrast to Texas, New Mexico has closely regulated groundwater pumping in order to control overdrafts and conserve for the future. The City of El Paso, to which New Mexico is called upon to export water, is the fifth fastest growing city in the West, and currently residents use 200 gallons per capita per day. In the words of the *Albuquerque Journal*,

> El Paso has the problem and succeeded in making New Mexico's scarce and diminishing water resources the solution. That in turn has given New Mexico an even bigger problem—protecting its ability to govern its own resources. Quite simply New Mexico's border has been breached. Theoretically, outside municipalities or states—or anybody—can now apply to claim every unappropriated drop of New Mexico water. It is ironic because New Mexico has carefully guarded and conserved its water resources, only to lose a lawsuit to a city and state that take far less care of the resource.[28]

Claims of equity should not be allowed to protect mere hoarding of water resources, and laws that discriminate solely against out-of-state users cannot be justified. At the same time, it is consistent with respect for pluralism and the Court's longstanding recognition of water as a social good for states to be permitted to deny permits to pump water for export on bona fide, reasonable grounds of water conservation.[29]

The issue of Indian water rights is subject to enormous conflict and confusion; legal and historical scholarship has had only limited success clarifying the issue. It would serve little purpose here to tally the injustices committed on what Norris Hundley, Jr. has called "dark and bloody ground."[30] More useful, we believe, is a discussion of how present and future application of equity principles can help sort out Indian rights. In our view equity is weighing less heavily than it should in contemporary decision-making, and unless equity is served, decisions made in the name of finality are likely to be ephemeral.[31]

By any reasonable hierarchy of promises made about water in the Colorado River Basin, those made to Indian people must be placed near the top. Pledges given to Indians guaranteeing their water rights trace back centuries and have been frequently repeated. The obligation as stated in the Winters decision is sufficiently clear: When Indian lands were reserved, so were the rights of Indians to the use of water. These rights were described by the Court as paramount and continuing to exist, even though unused, against federal and state governments and all others granted subsequent rights.[32] Indians were also promised flexibility in accommodating their needs, which might expand in the future. The Court in another case stated:

> What amount of water will be required . . . may not be determined with absolute accuracy at this time; but the policy of the government to reserve whatever water . . . may be reasonably necessary, not only for the present uses, but for future requirements is clearly within the terms of the Treaties as construed by the Supreme Court in the Winters case.[33]

However uncomfortable it may be to other users of water in the Colorado River Basin, Indians have been promised that lack of water will not be allowed to hamper their future opportunities. We have promised to tolerate uncertainties in all water rights subsequent to the Indians' paramount rights. Is this to mean that all development that has taken place in the basin is vulnerable to the whims of Indian people who may decide to reclaim use of water? Certainly not, since Indians are bound by the same rules of equity as others: They have been promised what is "reasonably necessary." Reasonable necessity must be determined in the light of circumstances and must take into account adverse impacts upon others and upon the resource. It is important to state that paramount Indian water rights cannot be employed to make up for injustices in other realms, such as health, education, or general economic welfare.

Had the principle of full and fair participation in allocation decisions been followed in the past, many of the most troublesome issues faced today in Indian water rights would have been avoided. Indians have seldom been at the negotiating table when decisions crucial to their water interest were being made. Of course, the federal government agreed itself to represent Indians as a "trustee" (Chief Justice Marshall called Indian tribes domestically dependent nations and said that their relationship to the United States resembled that of a ward to a guardian).[34] Once having accepted this responsibility, the federal government was obliged to protect Indian interests, a job often poorly performed. To take only one instance, there is widespread agreement that in the 1920s the federal government badly neglected its obligation to protect the Paiutes' water rights in Pyramid Lake. Now, sixty years later, the Justice Department is correct in taking its trust responsibilities seriously.[35] No lasting settlement of water allocations at Pyramid Lake or on the Colorado is likely to be built upon perpetuated inequity.

Lack of full and fair participation has also deprived our relations with Mexico over the Colorado of the blessings of equity. The United States has had the decided advantage of being upstream and controlling dams and canals. It has also had superior information and expertise about the river and the implications of decisions. Bargaining from weakness understandably leaves the Mexicans dissatisfied with the equity of decisions and anxious to exploit whatever international situation might provide an opportunity to reopen issues. Rather than take advantage of Mexican weakness, Western states need to seek ways to empower Mexican negotiators with better information and more meaningful choices.

As the largest users of the river, Western states need to shoulder the burden for the welfare of the river, including its salinity, and for satisfying the Mexican Water Treaty obligation. For instance, the Colorado River Basin Project Act of 1968 makes the supply of water guaranteed by the Mexican Water Treaty an obligation of the national government. The provision was the product of byzantine Congressional politics and a common motivation among Basin states to relieve themselves of delivering Mexico its share of the river.[36] The provision implied that the United States would supply an additional quantity of water beyond that already allocated by the Colorado River Compact. Forcing the nation to seek water sources outside the Basin, from the Columbia Basin perhaps, has set the stage for further conflict and further perceptions of inequities. In the same vein, Basin states later shifted the burden for salinity control, causing the federal government to fund inefficient and environmentally damaging projects.[37] The conflict over the responsibility to deliver water of reasonable quality to the Mexicans is almost certainly only temporarily dormant.

The development of the Colorado River Basin has been enormously uneven. Upper basin states have lagged behind the lower basin, and within the lower basin the City of Los Angeles and the Imperial Valley have consumed vast quantities of water. This growth was made possible in part through the consent of upstream users who believed they would eventually have a turn in line for federally funded water development. The case of the state of Colorado in the upper basin was recently systematically laid out:

> Colorado's position consists of several elements: (1) that over a span of more than 60 years this State has cooperated generously with other states and with the Federal Government in fabricating a "law of the river"; (2) that through this carefully, although not flawlessly, crafted system of compacts and Federal statutes Colorado is entitled to make beneficial use of more than 3 million acre feet of water from the river system; (3) that Congress registered its unequivocal intent in every major act concerning the Colorado River to develop completely—that is to treat the entire basin as an integrated hydro-climatic system, not as merely a conveniently contrived collection of State development plans; (4) that as part of this overall plan, the Federal government had explicitly committed itself to construct and operate dams and reclamation projects in Colorado (by the terms of various acts); (5) that realistically Colorado's full compact share of the river system could only be made available to the people of the State if and when the Federal Government completed the promised projects at Federal expense; (6) consequently, the Federal Government and the other compact States have not only a statutory commitment but a

moral/historic obligation to support Federal development of water projects.[38]

What is the continuing obligation to the upper basin for promises made? We have already suggested that promises sometimes conflict and that renegotiation of promises is always possible. But the conditions of equity must apply. It is patently unfair for the claimants who have yet to develop to carry their entire burden for previous decisions overestimating the amount of water in the river and underestimating claims of Indians and Mexicans and the possible adverse environmental consequences of overbuilding on the river. The obligation for satisfying all legitimate claims that exist on the river belong especially to the lower basin users whose interests have been for so long so well served.

Conclusion

In this paper we have attempted to show that a coherent rationale for the "equity perspective" must rest on an understanding of water as a social good and on an appreciation of the democratic aspirations at work in the political process. Our practically oriented principles of equity have in fact led us to embrace an open-ended distributive norm: as a social good, water should *not* be distributed to persons who possess some other kind of good (such as wealth) merely *because* they possess that other good and without respect to the meaning of water as a *social* good.[39] And what is this meaning? As we have seen, water represents satisfaction of a socially defined and legitimated "need," but it also represents security, and it represent opportunity. All of these meanings are complex, but it is perhaps opportunity that is most intriguing, for as a password to potential economic and social development, it is closest to the core of the concern for equity. As far back as the Winters decision of 1908 we have heard of water as a means "to practice the arts of civilization." Unfortunately one group's opportunity to practice this art is not necessarily compatible with another group's security of investment, as the latest round of Supreme Court cases are demonstrating once again. Socially defined needs conflict and change under new circumstances; meanings clash. But from the perspective of equity, security must not be allowed to displace opportunity, and the uncertainties which results must be shared equitably.

Thus, our argument at the level of principles has implications for water policy and water institutions: Water is a social good and for that reason a public trust; private ownership of it is not desirable. "Public interest" must be protected by government, especially if water becomes part of a market exchange. But to treat water as a commodity is a mistake in our view. In addition, the use of "efficiency" alone is a poor rule for evaluation of water projects and for water allocation. Finally, quantification of water rights in the Basin, a temporary expedient to settle immediate conflicts among users, can be considered final only so long as the broad public interest is served. Equity claims will be with us for generations, and we will need to learn the democratic virtues of flexibility, toleration of differences, and compromise.

In sum, any solution to problems in the Colorado Basin which attempts to deny equity will increase already existing tensions and generate new forms of opposition. At the least it will breed piecemeal special interest legislation and more costly and protracted litigation, all of which will interfere with attempts at sound, long-range planning for river management and regional development. Or in the worst-case scenario it will lead to a kind of regional "Milagro Beanfield War" in a highly emotional and politicized environment. Time is running out. In present circumstances the "equity perspective" on Colorado River Basin issues is not just high-flown rhetoric or unworkable idealism. It simply is the assertion of common sense.[40]

Notes

1. Arthur Maass and Raymond L. Anderson, *And the Desert Shall Rejoice: Conflict, Growth, and Justice in Arid Environments* (Cambridge: MIT Press, 1978), p. 395.

2. Norris Hundley, Jr., "The Dark and Bloody Ground of Indian Water Rights: Confusion Elevated to Principle," *Western Historical Quarterly* 9 (October, 1978): 482.

3. Quoted in Norris Hundley, Jr., *Water and the West* (Berkeley: University of California Press, 1975), p. 178.

4. Philip Fradkin, *A River No More* (New York: Knopf, 1981), p. 155.

5. Plato, *The Laws* 844a–845e.

6. Aristotle, *Politics* 1330a–b.

7. Quoted in M. I. Finley, *Economy and Society in Ancient Greece* (London: Chatto & Windus, 1981), p. 3.

8. See Michael Meyer, *'Til the Wells Run Dry: Water and Water Law in the Hispanic Southwest*, (book manuscript, 1983) ch. 8.

9. Maass and Anderson, *And the Desert Shall Rejoice*, cited in note 1, p. 5.

10. *Leviathan*, I, 13.

11. Maass and Anderson, *And the Desert Shall Rejoice*, cited in note 1, p. 2.

12. The phrase is from John Dewey, *The Public and Its Problems* (Denver: Swallow, 1927), p. 149: in Dewey's more complete statement the democratic idea "consists in having a responsible share according to capacity in forming and directing the activities of the groups to which one belongs and in participating according to need in the values which the groups sustain" (p. 147). Like our second conception, this definition might be said to represent the "Jeffersonian" tradition in America. But in order to

achieve a comprehensive understanding, this tradition must be combined with the "Madisonian" emphasis on constitutional rules.

13. John Rawls, *A Theory of Justice* (Cambridge: Harvard University Press, 1971).

14. Not surprisingly, therefore, in the burgeoning philosophical literature on areas of public policy there is not a single discussion of water policy, nor even examples drawn from the numerous water rights controversies of the twentieth century. In policy discussions dealing with water, on the other hand, despite numerous casual references to "equity," there is not a single successful application of any of the general theories of distributive justice. From both points of view these failures seem extraordinary in light of the undeniable social importance of the water issue. The fault does not lie in the subject matter, we would suggest, but rather in the assumptions that have governed inferences drawn from the theory of justice.

15. Michael Walzer, *Spheres of Justice, A Defense of Pluralism and Equality* (New York: Basic Books, 1983), especially chap. 1.

16. Arthur M. Schlesinger, ed., *The Promise of American Life* (Cambridge: Harvard University, 1965), p. 189.

17. Sue-Ellen Jacobs, "'Top-Down Planning': Analysis of Obstacles to Community Development in an Economically Poor Region of the Southwestern United States," *Human Organization* 37 (Fall, 1978): 248.

18. Traditional Spanish water law, for example, clearly recognized that prior appropriation did not include a right to waste, even in the case of spring or well water originating on private property. Instead, when considering disputes, a conception of a socially defined need was often invoked: in the words of a Santa Fe decree of 1720, water judges should "divide the water always verifying the greatest need, . . . and giving to each one that which he needs" (Meyer, *'Til the Wells Run Dry*, cited in note 8, chap. 8, p. 6).

19. Quoted in Monroe E. Price and Gary D. Weatherford, "Indian Water Rights in Theory and Practice: Navajo Experience in the Colorado Basin," *Law and Contemporary Problems* (Winter, 1976): 121.

20. See Gary D. Weatherford and Gordon C. Jacoby, "Impact of Energy Development on the Law of the Colorado River," *Natural Resources Journal* 15 (January, 1975): 199–200; Gary Weatherford et al., eds., *Acquiring Water for Energy: Institutional Aspects* (Littleton: Water Resources Publications, 1982), pp. 65–66.

21. The classic expression of a similar principle is found in the first chapter of John Stuart Mill's *On Liberty* (1859).

22. Karl A. Wittfogel, *Oriental Despotism: A Comparative Study of Total Power* (New Haven: Yale University Press, 1957).

23. This idea is found not only in the Basin but in an authoritative tradition within political theory. For example, David Hume remarks that "the principal object of government is to constrain men to observe the laws of nature. In this respect, however, that law of nature, concerning the performance of promises, is only comprized along with the rest; and its exact observance is to be considered as an effect of the institution of government, and not the obedience to government as an effect of the obligation of a promise" (A Treatise of Human Nature, III, ii, 8).

24. See, for example, Harold Barnett and Chandler Morse, *Scarcity and Growth: The Economics of Natural Resource Availability* (Baltimore: Johns Hopkins, 1965).

25. See *Sporhase v. Nebraska*, 81 U.S. 613 (1982), and the report on *El Paso v.*

Reynolds, "Judge Rejects New Mexico Ban on Water Exports," *Albuquerque Journal*, January 18, 1983, pp. 1–2.

26. *Hudson County Water Co. v. McCarter*, 209 U.S. 349 (1908).

27. "Our reluctance stems from the "'confluence of several realities,'" Stevens continued: "First, a State's power to regulate the use of water in times and places of shortage for the purpose of protecting the health of its citizens—and not simply the health of its economy—is at the core of its police power. . . . Second, the legal expectation that under certain circumstances each State may restrict water within its borders has been fostered over the years not only by our equitable apportionment decrees . . . but also by the negotiation and enforcement of interstate compacts. Our law therefore has recognized the relevance of state boundaries in the allocation of scarce water resources. Third, although appellee's claim to public ownership of Nebraska ground water cannot justify a total denial of federal regulatory power, it may support a limited preference for its own citizens in the utilization of the resource. . . . Finally, given appellee's conservation efforts, the continuing availability of ground water in Nebraska is not simply happen-stance; the natural source has some indicia of a good publicly produced and owned in which a State may favor its own citizens in times of shortage."

28. *Albuquerque Journal*, January 21, 1983, p. 4.

29. Michael D. White, "Reasonable State Regulation of the Inter-State Transfer of Percolating Water," *Natural Resources Lawyer* 2 (September, 1969): 383–406.

30. Hundley, "The Dark and Bloody Ground," cited in note 2.

31. See, for example, the recent ruling of the Supreme Court in the continuance of *Arizona v. California et al.*, reported in *The Washington Post*, March 31, 1983, pp. 1, 11.

32. Norris Hundley, Jr., "The 'Winters' Decision and Indian Water Rights: A Mystery Reexamined," *Western Historical Quarterly* 13 (January, 1982): 17–42.

33. *Conrad Investment Co. v. U.S.*, 161F 831, 835 (9th Cir., 1908).

34. *Cherokee Nation v. Georgia*, 30 U.S. 16 (1831).

35. Charles R. Babcock, "Indian Tribes Discover Friends in Court," *The Washington Post*, April 13, 1983, p. 23.

36. Dean E. Mann, "Politics in the United States and the Salinity Problems of the Colorado River," *Natural Resources Journal* 15 (January, 1975): 117.

37. *Ibid.*

38. Conrad L. McBride, "Colorado Water Resources Development Politics" (Paper presented at the Annual Convention of the Western Political Science Association, Seattle, Washington, March 24–26, 1983).

39. Adapted from Walzer, *Spheres of Justice*, cited in note 15, p. 20.

40. This paper is reprinted, with the kind permission of the editors and the author, from Lee Brown and Gary Weatherford, eds., *New Courses for the Colorado* (Albuquerque: University of New Mexico Press, forthcoming).

Towards an Upstream-Downstream Morality for Our Upstream-Downstream World

Donald Scherer

ON THE AMERICAN FRONTIER during the nineteenth century, settlers followed the rule of thumb that water purifies itself in six miles. The rule was important because nobody treated sewage. Consequently, new settlers needed guidance about how far downstream they should stake claims in order to assure the quality of their drinking water.

Implicit in this simple bit of frontier history are several hints about the importance and difficulty of understanding upstream-downstream relations. At its opening, a frontier is sparsely populated: newcomers have choices among alternate tracts more than six miles downstream from any other settlers. The usefulness of water is plural: water is used for waste removal and for cleaning, as well as for drinking. The rule of thumb about water's self-purification, while generally true, was true relative to the uses to which humans put the water, upstream and downstream. No one was dumping toxic chemicals upstream, nor did downstream industrial processes require any special purity. The deep plowing of plains grasslands that contributed to the Dust Bowl of the 1930s was unenvisioned, and until the explosion of Florida's population in the 1960s, only a few academic theorists talked about aquifer salinization resulting from deep aquifer irrigation. How do these facts help us understand upstream-downstream relations?

While the independent choices of individual pioneers once sufficed for maintaining a safe and adequate water supply, communal systems reflecting complex technologies and regional planning are now the norm. The human population has quintupled to over five billion people within the past 150 years. Accordingly, population density has made atypical the naturally purified downstream niche. The norm of metropolitan sewage treatment plants has replaced the norm of settling at least six miles downstream.

Population density also intensifies the multiple uses of resources. Water, long used to carry human bodily wastes, now carries human industrial wastes. The water carries the residues of chemical fertilizers, and the wind carries the carbon dioxide and sulfur dioxide to its descent as acid rain. In Tucson and other arid areas, where population density means water scarcity, citizens begin to think about population control, while wondering how much more growth some new recycling technology will allow.

And, clearly, we lack stable patterns of resource usage, because intensified resource uses interact. Causation within ecosystems is hardly linear, and human understanding of causation in ecosystems is sketchy at best. Even though we know that human cancer rates increase as one moves from the tributaries of the Great Lakes to their mouths, we scarcely know what relationships of effluents cause the cancer. In many environments nobody knows the pollutants involved, much less their synergisms. Thresholds of risk are crossed from benign to harmful uses, synergisms of uses occur, and rules of thumb about the self-purification of water and air become useless as well as false.

The rise of cities teaches further lessons, because human habitats in rural environments are significantly different from those in urban environments. It is not merely the difference between wells and city water, nor is it simply the easier urban access to schools, doctors, and other cultural amenities. Resources like timber and ore flow from upstream to downstream environments where they are transformed into products. People commute from home to factory to effect the transformation. The resources are bought, transformed, and sold. Markets develop, and power comes to surround downstream centers of exchange.

With markets come the vicissitudes of change. If demand increases, the factory increases its pollution, straining to keep pace with demand. If demand declines, the lack of funds to pay workers ripples through a regional economy. If demand increases, more workers are drawn to the city, the demand for social services increases, and the provision of those services lags, in a classic pattern. If the demand declines, the economy flags, discouragement and crime increase, and human drug use—from alcohol to cocaine—rises. If demand increases, pressure builds for the construction of an upstream dam to assure a minimum flow rate high enough to sustain peak urban requirements. If demand decreases, upstream runoff, particularly of phosphates, increases water stagnation in the artificial lake and diminishes the value of the mass-market, lake-based recreation that replaced the solitary, individualistic, river-based recreation when the dam was built. If demand increases, the wealthy seek an upstream retreat, the mountain hike, or the vacation home, to remove themselves from the stress of downstream life. If demand decreases, potential vacationers rethink their finances, and the economy of economically downstream, geographically upstream vacation areas suffers.

Although a densely populated upstream environment magnifies downstream problems, we human beings mold our environments. While we think of our technologies as the molding forces, we should recall the prominent social dimensions of upstream-downstream problems, for we also mold our social environments. We know the molding power of credit cards, traffic signals, and alphabetical ordering, but we may fail to notice lake level covenants (or treaties), the lack of any regulation of the packaging that contributes heavily to overflowing landfills, or the absence from television programs of sympathetic characters concerned about downstream runoff accumulation. Clearly, our molding of the social environment can vastly modify the impacts of naturally upstream and upwind environments on their downstream and downwind counterparts.

Morality, we should realize, is an integrated and functional part of a system of norms, and has probably had survival value. Yet that survival value developed for independent human populations living in small bands. Consequently, a normative system functional for small, rather independent human populations might not prove functional for large, highly interdependent populations in upstream-downstream relationships. Upstream-downstream problems have intensified not merely because of technological development, but also because of our reliance on a social order not designed to serve upstream-downstream environments. Accordingly, in this paper I first sketch how, in upstream-downstream environments, our norms fail by failing to minimize wastes and internalize costs, and then I suggest some appropriate adjustments for a normative system in an upstream-downstream world.

The Anomalies of Upstream-Downstream Environments

An upstream-downstream relationship is one in which an action taken "upstream," that is, at a given point in time and space, has a significant effect "downstream," that is, at a later time or in a distant space. The characteristics of upstream-downstream environments themselves create problems in upstream-downstream relationships.

A central characteristic of upstream-downstream environments is that within them causation works, or is perceived as working, in only one direction. What happens upstream is perceived to cause effects downstream, but not vice-versa. Consequently, those who live upstream do not fear harm from downstream. In contrast, a fundamental reinforcer of human norms is "Someday you may be in my position and how would you like it if I . . ." Thus, when one human community is upstream and another down, the two communities will typically not perceive reciprocity as constraining their relationship.

Even without reciprocity, many human relationships are unproblematic because the interrelationship involves a quid pro quo. But upstream-downstream relationships, being perceived as unidirectional, do not strike people as providing a basis for a quid pro quo. In a particular case, the fortuitous fact may be, for example, that A is upstream of B with respect to water flow, while B is upstream of A with respect to prevailing winds, but upstream-downstream relations often lack this symmetry.

Indeed, the specialization of roles characteristic of urbanized human interactions is a central factor in minimizing apparent quid pro quo. The specialization of roles implies that the communities are linked by several interrelationships, most of which owe to the initiatives of different groups,[1] and multilateral relationships are not easily perceived as providing quid pro quos.

A further effect of the population explosion is the increased importance of thresholds. Many agents upstream may easily cause effects that none of them would have caused individually. Industrial chemical effluents, the runoffs of farmers' fields, and the Ohio State University Stadium-ful of trash the people of Ohio throw away every week are equally good examples of threshold problems. Here we see at work the historical limits of our assignments of responsibility. Responsibilities are obviously harder to assign and coordinate when the number of assignees is larger and unfixed and the identities of involved parties are not clearly known.

The problem of thresholds exhibits but does not exhaust another anomaly of contemporary upstream-downstream environments. Upstream-downstream environments often render insignificant the actions of persons, corporations, and governments. Many upstream-downstream problems that would be solvable under conditions of perfect coordination plague us today. Moreover, some of the most significant norms of contemporary life reinforce the difficulties of coordination. To the extent that the actions of individuals are anonymous, monitoring the acceptability of those actions is difficult. But of course anonymity is often the outgrowth of privacy and of traditionally broad concepts of liberty allied with narrow definitions of harm. The moral constraint on producers to meet consumers' needs is reinforced by norms of competition within free markets. The producer's need for efficiency is reinforced by an instrumental value of secrecy used to promote a competitive advantage. In the modern world, jurisdictions of government are used to protect the intrajurisdictional economy. Whether we are talking about acid rain pollution of eastern Canada, the exportation of products that do not meet U.S. safety standards, or thousands of other examples, the use of governmental coercion frequently prioritizes the protection of a local constituency over the long-term health of persons and ecosystems. But, given the plurality of jurisdictions and interactions, superior coordination is difficult to achieve and to maintain. Numerous "prisoner's dilemma"-like situations occur. Thus, even nations with considerable power can be coerced from actions their jurisdictional authority might otherwise coordinate.

Upstream-downstream environments are also characterized by ignorance. Upstream-downstream environments are, in parts, simply markets in which perfect information can not be realistically expected. In particular, how the actions of third parties will affect contemplated actions is often unknown. Our knowledge of ecosystems is still quite sketchy. While it is apparent that ecosystems tend to be resilient, many limits of an ecosystem's resilience are usually unpredictable except within a rather broad range. The evolutionary impact of fertilizers and pesticides continually introduces significant novelty (and thus unpredictability) into human waterways. These forms of ignorance work to excuse even more harmful consequences than they cause.

Moreover, upstream-downstream environments are problematic because of the interaction of the preceding characteristics. For example, consider the common maxim I discussed in connection with reciprocity: "How would you like it if you were in my position and I . . ." In addition to reciprocity, the use of this maxim often presupposes that we can identify a party whose causal role ties responsibility clearly to that party. The use of the maxim is limited not only by the specialization of roles we have in the world today but also by the threshold effects and the problems of ignorance typical of many macroenvironmental problems.

Restructuring the Human Normative Environment for Upstream-Downstream Environments

I take the problem of upstream-downstream relations to be this: in order to multiply the fruits of human society, human beings create not only technologies but also norms. The characteristics of upstream-downstream environments constrain many traditional human norms. Thus, human beings need to seek a restructuring of upstream-downstream relations through which traditional or new norms can foster for us today the beneficial coordinations human society makes possible.[2] How can the human normative environment be restructured to respond to the anomalies of upstream-downstream environments? The concern addressed is that moral norms have their efficacy within a framework of reciprocities and quid pro quos that upstream-downstream environments apparently undermine.

To the extent that social norms are strengthened by reciprocity it is important for people to structure environments so that any real reciprocity has a perceived salience. When middle class people escape to their vacation retreats and find, even in remote upstream environments, that they are still downstream from other environments, they can begin to sense the need for a higher level of personal responsibility. The new model of reciprocity must be not "You scratch my back and I'll scratch yours," but "What goes around comes around." This new model tells people that they cannot act with immunity, even when no one-to-one reciprocity constrains them, for we commonly fail to recognize reciprocities to which we are subject. Perhaps we are unacquainted with the other party to whom we are related, as when suburban homeowners in a drought run their automatic sprinkling systems at night. Perhaps the reversal of roles is based in differences of space, like so many recreational uses of water. Perhaps the differences are temporal, as when the farmers of South Carolina remember the hay that the farmers of Ohio sent south in 1984 and themselves send hay north during the Ohio drought of 1988. Perhaps the causation we perceive as linear is really systematic: human recreational uses pollute the lake sufficiently that ducks are attracted, to eat the snails that eat the pollution, but the duck hunters and the duck droppings reinforce the pollution. Certainly the normative structure is buttressed to the extent that people realize that, to some degree, everybody lives downstream.

In many ways, however, the wealthy of a community and of the world insulate their downstream environments and buy themselves upstream environments, so that upstream-downstream relations will not be reciprocal. The people of advanced nations do not begin to know how well they have managed to make their own environments atypical of those upon the earth. Consequently, the resolution of upstream-downstream problems must rely not only on a limited reciprocity but on quid pro quos as well.

Now, prototypically, upstream environments are characterized by resource abundance, resource manipulation, perceived purity, and personal opportunities for self-renewal. In contrast, downstream environments are characterized by product availability, consumption, pollution, and concentration of power. In other words, the relations between prototypical upstream and downstream communities are asymmetrical.

Yet this asymmetry is itself the basis for many quid pro quos. Water dammed upstream becomes electricity downstream, but upstream runoff contaminates downstream lakes with algae blooms and worse. Even though nonreciprocal relationships tend to predominate in a mass society, especially in a society where markets freely develop, quid pro quos nonetheless arise, strengthening the interdependence of individuals.

The efficiency of much of the role specialization we practice arises from the externalization of costs. An important aspect of the problem of pollutants is externalization of the cost of an exported pollutant. And yet, in a society of specialized labor, we far too easily accept role designations as defining acceptable delegations of responsibility, thereby exacerbating the problematic tendencies of upstream-downstream relations.

Consider the amazingly ubiquitous role of consumer in conjunction with the fact that as a society we generate five pounds of solid waste per person per day, even though we never seem to reach that average number of pounds of trash outside our homes on garbage pickup days. When, as consumers, we eat fast food, we let McDonald's handle the resulting litter. When patients enter hospitals, they accept the use of disposables that create over eighteen pounds of waste per patient per day. When fifteen thousand students come to Bowling Green State University, they let the maintenance department put their trash in three hundred thousand giant plastic bags per year. Even when we go to parties, we accept our host's decision to use paper plates and plastic eating utensils. All these role specializations create externalities. And an externality simply is a cost for which nobody accepts responsibility.

Downstream of these consumer decisions, municipalities across the nation are finding that nobody wants their trash. More and more communities cannot buy anybody else's landfill space. This scarcity is, of course, forcing the internalization of costs. States from New Jersey to Hawaii are now planning to reduce waste production by 90 percent within ten to twenty-five years.

Role specialization, then, is a two-edged sword. It creates real efficiencies through the economies of scale it brings into play, but it creates pseudoefficiencies by the externalization of costs. The normative structures we need to evolve, then, require not only that we eschew externalization to which upstream-downstream relations naturally tend, but also that we learn how to recognize when our delegation of responsibility externalizes costs.

Notice that responsibility is often delegated to parties who have incentives or obligations to minimize costs. Many hospitals are businesses trying to make a profit, and every party giver prefers to reduce party cleanup efforts. But these obligations and incentives move both the hospitals and the party givers to reduce costs by externalizing them.

Somewhat ironically, the traditional response to externalized costs within a community has been for altruistic organizations, like churches and service clubs, to sponsor events and do projects. Sometimes this may help, if, for example, we organize a walk with proceeds used to support research on ways to overcome the perceived deficiencies of no-till or low-till farming methods. Other times, however, we members of altruistic organizations have failed to notice that in our work and in our consumption we have accepted the duty and the desire to act in those ways that have, collectively, created the problems we now address in our altruistic organizations. Recycling has been popular with the Jaycees for many years, but who has stepped forward to say, "The mere fact that the technology exists to recycle junk mail is irrelevant if we cannot accept junk mail at our local recycling center"? And who has asked, "If plastic containers can't be recycled, how will we assume the responsibility for assuring that they are not used?" The highly interdependent society in which we live may well require altruistic organizations to determine how they can take on the new role of forestalling the creation of externalities for which communities cannot buy a fix.

At a popular level, the traditional moral response to the problem of thresholds has been "What would happen if everybody did that?" This question, of course, has been used to promote absolute prohibitions. But the model of emergency vehicles on city streets tells us that the fact that disastrous results would follow if everyone did something does not necessarily justify an absolute prohibition. The only reason for adopting an absolute prohibition would be the infeasibility of creating an effective rationing system for distinguishing acceptable below-threshold uses. A siren on an emergency vehicle is an effective means of making feasible the selective violation of generally desirable norms of vehicular movement.

Accordingly, when a little pollution is not a bad thing and there is a clear, inexpensive, and effective way of knowing what pollution is occurring, one acceptable option may be the sale of a pollution permit (which is, in essence, what a dumping fee at the local landfill is). But one of the differences between flowing water and a stationary landfill is in the greater difficulty of knowing the sources of water pollutants. Nonpoint pollutants here pose a serious obstacle.

Individual insignificance has for centuries been recognized as detrimental to socially responsible behavior. A traditional social response to individual insignificance has been to make the individual's response matter socially, so that the weight of that social response makes up for the physical insignificance of the individual's response. Conservative social theorists have long noted the value of integrating individuals into selective societies, for within those societies a weight quite significant to an individual may attach to actions that, on a larger scale or on other measures, are insignificant. Communities of all sizes therefore need to work very hard at making individuals aware of themselves as members of the community, so that identification with the community and its well-being can become a weight in the individual's decision making. Moreover, communities can be strongly reinforced for such identity-creating activities, because when community-minded identities are widespread, actions that were individually insignificant become community successes.

Here, however, the geographic expansiveness of upstream-downstream (and upwind-downwind) problems stands as a major detriment to such communitarian emphases. Proximate community is more readily perceived and proximate interactions are more intensely felt. Surely one of the most significant social dimensions of upstream-downstream relationships is their anonymity. And don't conservative theories require personal identification?

Certainly, in traditional small-town economies the reputation of a business is critical to business success. Reputability, after all, has a value in many transactions. Some years ago, the Cooper Tire Company recaptured some of that value by a mass advertising campaign in which Cooper tires were touted as the tire with two names inside, the name of the company and the name of the individual tire maker. The company wanted to use increased worker pride to improve product quality while using the image of old-fashioned craftsmanship to attract more customers. But their action suggests what could become a powerful general strategy of erasing anonymity. To the extent that customers can know producers, the producers are encouraged to take pride in their work and the customers are provided a social environment within which a basis for personal trust reemerges. Advertising campaigns, telephone sales, and computerized mailing lists are all high-tech means for personalizing human contacts. To the extent that anonymity promotes attitudes of nonresponsibility and irresponsibility, high-tech means should be exploited for re-creating and strengthening ties of responsibility.

Farm cooperatives, churches, and service organizations also have an important role to play in overcoming anonymity. Their belief systems, their convictions, their practices, and their conventions let their members identify each other. However unknown to us as individuals, the people in such organizations and their pride in belonging can provide a sense of sharing and a sense of the power of communities to overcome individual insignificance.

Ignorance is a problem to which there is no one solution, so I will confine myself to one suggestion for lessening the havoc that ignorance portends in a mass technological society. While there is much merit to the argument for a more thorough testing of products, I want to urge, independently, that different products be introduced into different environments. Such a generalized procedure has two advantages: we can better account for resulting changes in the environments into which the products are introduced, and, even more important, those environments effectively become test environments for various products, increasing safety and efficiency in their use.

Notice that these suggestions reinforce one another. If testers of new products bear public responsibility for conducting the tests and especially if the dangers of the product are not externalized, then community pressure will minimize danger in the conduct of the test. Further, if the tester has no vested interest in the outcome of the test, then the test results will not be tampered with. Or, if the tester is known to have an interest in the outcome of a test, then public knowledge of any dangers to the local citizenry will create pressure for an independent review of the testing process and outcome.

Let me then recollect some of what I have been saying about role specialization, thresholds, insignificance, and ignorance: Responsible responses are promoted when individuals are downstream of their own actions. So desirable products and commodities are those that do not spew their pollution downstream: any residues remain in the polluters' neighborhoods to affect them and to be known as their responsibility.

A morality capable of standing up to critical scrutiny is a morality whose norms promote responsible action. The density of human populations and efficacy of human technology mean that human actions can and do affect others outside of an individual's circle. Consequently, the norms of morality we require cannot rely on the simple reciprocities and quid pro quos of traditional agrarian and small-town life. But the vital ecological importance of water and land to human and nonhuman life implies that effective alternative norms must work their way into modern thought and practice. My suggestions should be carefully scrutinized for feasibility as well as for moral efficacy. I offer them in the hope that they may catalyze the development of norms that promote responsible action—that which maintains and enhances values—in an upstream-downstream world.

Notes

1. And this specialization of roles is reinforced in its effect by the population explosion, which magnifies the possibilities of interdependence without quid pro quos.

2. Here I work from the presumption that a goal of human coordination is to avoid having to choose between meeting human needs and maintaining those social practices that have enhanced human identity and enriched human society and human life. Ideal forms of action, then, maintain or expand supplies to meet demand (production incentives), control demanders to balance supplies (population control, rationing, and wage and credit controls), substitute materials and procedures that do not endanger the quality of human life (pollution control, where some pollutants are material, some social), and redistribute opportunities and materials so that failures in any of the above do not prevent people from having life's basic goods.

Pesticide Policy and Ethics

Kristin Shrader-Frechette

Introduction

One out of every four Americans dies of cancer, and the U.S. Office of Technology Assessment has claimed that up to 90 percent of those cancers are environmentally induced and hence "theoretically preventable" (Lashof 1981, 3). One of the most significant causes of these environmentally induced cancers is agricultural pesticides. Worldwide, 49,000 people are killed annually by these toxic chemicals, and in third world countries, one person suffers pesticide poisoning every minute (Mathews 1986, 48–49; see also Repetto 1985, 3 TT).

However, not only humans suffer the ill effects of widespread pesticide use, as a famous story of the World Health Organization (WHO) illustrates. Several year ago, the WHO used DDT to kill off malaria-carrying mosquitos in Borneo. The chemicals killed the mosquitos but not the roaches, which accumulated the pesticide in their bodies. When the long-tailed lizards, called geckos, ate the roaches, the DDT in their prey caused disorders in their nervous systems. The geckos became sluggish and fell victim to the village cats, who ate them and died from the DDT in the lizards. Rats, carrying the threat of a plague epidemic, moved in from the Borneo forests, and cats had to be flown into the villages to catch the rats. The cats controlled the rat population, but the roofs of the people's huts began caving in because the lizards, now gone, had formerly eaten the caterpillars that ate the roof thatching (Cole 1972, 233).

Because pesticides have effects on all living things, not just pests, their use continues to raise both ecological and ethical questions, questions concerned with issues such as the rights of future generations to protection from long-lived chemicals, and the equity of pesticide risk distribution. Answering such troubling questions is becoming more and more difficult. On the one hand pesticide use has doubled over the last ten years and continues to grow (Eichers and Andrilenas 1978, v, vi, 7, 16; Irving 1970, 1419; Bloom and Degler 1969, 1–2), yet the UN Food and Agriculture Organization wants to reduce food losses to pests by 20 to 30 percent, in order to achieve a fourfold increase in world food supplies (Bloom and Degler 1969, 1). Moreover, industry representatives maintain that government regulation, especially in the U.S., effectively ensures consumer protection from pesticides (Glasser 1976, 228–39; Kraybill 1975, 13–15; see also Jukes 1973). On the other hand, environmentalists claim that there are alternatives to agricultural chemicals, and that pesticides are one of the most immediately hazardous pollutants ever known, even when they are used as directed (see, for example, Harmer 1971, 11).

With Rachel Carson, I believe that the immediate solution to the pesticide problem is not to eliminate these chemicals completely but rather to use them with greater discrimination (Carson 1962, 12). Such use, however, presupposes that we understand both the risks they pose and the ethical constraints they place on our behavior. One way to clarify both the risk and the ethical issues is to see where and why the arguments in favor of pesticides go wrong. Although a complete analysis of this sort would involve a great many such arguments, let us consider only two of the most prominent ones. These are what I call the *realism argument* (RA) and the *threshold argument* (TA). The RA is that "although chemical pest control is hazardous, it is realistic to accept the minimal degree of risk it presents, since absolute safety is unattainable in any sector of life" (Kraybill 1975, 10, 16; Furtick 1976, 12). The TA is that "because there may be a threshold for injurious effects of chemicals, their use is not necessarily contrary to human well-being" (see Lowrance 1976, 84). Let's summarize where and why these arguments go wrong.

The Realism Argument (RA)

The realism argument (RA) is initially quite plausible because living is indeed a hazardous process that makes it impossible for anyone to attain a position of absolute safety (see Shrader-Frechette 1985, ch. 5). What is correct about the RA is that it recognizes that risks and benefits must be balanced. What is incorrect about the RA is, in part, that it presupposes that the moral acceptability of a hazard, like pesticide use, is a matter only of risk magnitude or degree of physical danger. (See Shrader-Frechette, 1985, ch. 6; and Shrader-Frechette, 1983, ch. 6, for criticism of this presupposition.)

Two other important parameters affecting the acceptability of a hazard are how equitably the risk is distributed and whether it is taken on voluntarily or imposed involuntarily. "Scientific evidence as to safety versus hazard" is clearly not sufficient, as Kraybill (1975, 16) has suggested, to determine what is an acceptable risk. Even if it could be proved that the carcinogenic (cancer-causing) and mutagenic (inducing genetic damage) hazard of pesticides were very slight, it would still have to be shown that this risk was equitably distributed to substantiate the claim that it was acceptable. (See Shrader-Frechette, 1985, ch 3; and 1984, ch. 7 for treatment of equity and equal protection.)

Suppose, for example, that a number of families live downwind of a large cotton crop regularly sprayed with pesticides. Government scientists indicate that 63 percent of all pesticides are applied by aircraft (Baker 1972, 9), that usually only 50 percent or less of the aerial spray distributed reaches its target (Reese 1972, 23), that chemical application efficiency is undercut primarily by wind drifts, and that no more than 2 percent of applied amounts of pesticide are effective (Reese 1972, 8, 13, 24; Baker 1972, 1–2, 70–73, 127–28). For all these reasons, it is plausible to assume that families living downwind of crops regularly subject to aerial pesticide application are likely to receive a much higher dose of these chemicals than are most Americans. In fact, statistical studies indicate that, in some farm counties in California, half of the children annually show one or more signs of pesticide poisoning (Harmer 1971, 49). If this is true, then the costs and benefits of the chemicals are not borne equitably. Whereas all or nearly all of Americans may be said to benefit from efficient growing of cotton, for example, a small subset of this group (e.g., those living downwind of aerially treated crops) may be said to bear a greater cost in the form of increased health risk.

If all Americans have legal rights to equal protection by virtue of the Fifth and Fourteenth Amendments, then it might be possible to argue that government regulation of pesticides jeopardizes these rights. It can also easily be argued that, to the extent that citizens affected by pesticides are given neither equal protection, nor due process, nor compensation, nor the opportunity to exercise informed consent over the pesticide risk that they face, imposition of pesticides on them is unethical. To make such an argument, one would have to establish that there are no morally justifiable grounds for discriminating, with respect to equal protection, on the basis of geography, e.g., how close one lives to an area of pesticide application. Such an argument would not be difficult to make, and indeed has already been made for many other issues. (For analogous arguments, see Shrader-Frechette 1983, chs. 2, 4; Shrader-Frechette 1985, chs. 3, 4; and Shrader-Frechette 1984, ch. 7.)

But if it is possible, on grounds of equal protection, due process, lack of compensation, and informed consent, to make a case that many applications of pesticides violate ethics, then the RA is, at best, an incomplete argument. Similar difficulties also plague the threshold argument (TA).

The Threshold Argument (TA)

The threshold argument is that "because there may be a threshold for injurious effects of chemicals, their use is not necessarily contrary to human well-being." Perhaps the most questionable presupposition in the TA is that a threshold for chemical injury from pesticides may exist. Several considerations suggest that acceptance of this presupposition may be unwise. For one thing, scientists who proposed in the past that there was a threshold for acute or chronic injury from radiation have now been proved wrong. We have known for more than a decade that any amount of ionizing radiation, however small, puts the person exposed in a higher risk category for carcinogenic and mutagenic effects (see Shrader-Frechette 1983, especially 97, 108–9).

Hundreds of thousands of people have been indiscriminately exposed to fallout from atmospheric testing and to unnecessary X-rays, and many of them have contracted cancer, largely because it was once believed that there were safe doses of radiation (see Shrader-Frechette 1983, 99–100, 109). In light of our past mistakes with alleged radiation thresholds, and because many pesticides, like radiation, have effects that are carcinogenic, mutagenic, persistent, and cumulative, one ought to proceed very carefully before suggesting that there is a threshold for chemical injury. If this belief is wrong, countless people could pay for the error with their lives, health, and genetic integrity.

In spite of the risk suggested by the threshold hypothesis, many scientists have proposed that such a threshold may exist, and have then supported an argument in favor of increased pesticide use by this hypothesis. Let us examine the ethical assumptions implicit in the argument and then determine whether the threshold hypothesis provides morally acceptable grounds for the use of pesticides.

Even though the existence of thresholds for chemical carcinogenesis has never been firmly established (Lowrance 1976, 84), let us assume with a number of scientists that such a threshold does exist for certain pesticides. If we grant this point for purposes of argument, are we thereby committed to accepting the ethical conclusion (TA) allegedly following from it?

The reason that establishing a threshold for pesticide poisoning does not make subthreshold doses ethically acceptable is that such doses are virtually impossible to assess for individual persons. As Rachel Carson explained in her famous work *Silent Spring*, although experimental situations are controlled, "in real life humans never know how much of a given pesticide they are receiving" (Carson 1962, 181–82). One person may eat five or ten times the "average" amount of a particular food and thereby ingest five or ten times the "normal" amount of a particular chemical, while others may be exposed to excessive amounts through crop dusting (see previous citations to Baker and Reese; see also Jukes 1973, 103–6; Reese 1972, 23; and Carson 1962, 155–72).

Synergistic effects also determine an individual's dose of a chemical. Although a particular dose may be below an alleged threshold, the combined doses of two or more pesticides, or a single pesticide dose plus some naturally occurring event, may together have far more serious consequences than merely the sum of their individual effects (see Baker 1972, 2–3). This means, practically speaking, that the synergistic effects of a subthreshold dose of a contaminant often cause far greater harm than theoretically predicted. As Rachel Carson puts it, "any supposedly safe dose" may be enough to tip the scales that are "already loaded" with allegedly safe doses of other chemicals (Carson 1962, 237). Temperature, for example, might increase the effects of certain pesticides. The metabolism of some aquatic organisms doubles for every ten degrees Celsius that temperature increases, and this metabolic increase renders any amount of pesticide much more toxic. As one Environmental Protection Agency scientist explained, synergistic effects of pesticides have not been completely investigated by anyone; therefore, he says, current "static bioassays" give results about chemical dosage that are "of little use in predicting the effect in natural systems" (Baker 1972, 191). Hence an alleged "threshold dose" is "a highly relative level which applies only for the precise experimental conditions generated" (Epp 1977, 56).

One practical condition, not considered in experimental tests of pesticide toxicity, is *biomagnification*, or heightened concentration, of these chemicals as they move higher in the food chain. Because of biomagnification, a person could easily ingest above-threshold amounts of a particular pesticide. In a California freshwater lake, for example, there were no traces of pesticide (in terms of ppb, parts per billion); however, birds and fish using the lake for their water supply had as much as 2500 ppm (parts per million) of this toxic substance (Harmer 1971, 62; Baker 1972, 2–3). Likewise, some crustaceans, exposed for 24 hours to 8 ppb of a chemical, concentrated it in their bodies at a level 23,000 times as great as the pesticide level present in their water (Reese 1972, 31–32). Eventually, this will constitute a health hazard to humans, via contaminated food and water (Baker 1972, 3). Besides food- chain concentrations, other factors could raise a pesticide dose to above-threshold levels: the delayed effect of toxic chemicals; transport of pesticides via vaporization, rainfall, runoff, dust, and wind (Baker 1972, 8, 127–28; Reese 1972, 13–24); their persistence in the environment (see Baker 1972, 104; Rudd 1964, 149–66 for example); and cumulative effects (Baker 1972, 174–75; Crawford and Donigian, 6; Reese 1972, 55–56, 73). All this suggests that nothing short of monitoring every person, obviously an impossible task, could guarantee accurate knowledge of whether an individual had received an above-threshold amount of a particular pesticide. But if this is so, then it is not clear that even alleged subthreshold exposure to pesticides is morally acceptable.

Admittedly, one could rely on statistical sampling procedures to obtain a rough idea of the pesticide dose ingested by a particular individual. But reliance on such procedures makes it likely that analyses of "acceptable" doses commit the fallacy of assuming that what is safe for the statistically average person is therefore safe for everyone. If similar assumptions were made in other areas of ethical reasoning, then disastrous consequences would follow.

For example, if it were assumed that legal rights to equal protection are awarded only on the basis of statistical or average characteristics, then it could be argued that handicapped people deserve no more protection than the average person. Obviously, however, such an argument would be erroneous; legal rights are accorded in part on the basis of individual characteristics and not merely because of the statistical properties of the group to which someone belongs. For instance, women on the average score lower than men on standardized tests (e.g., the Graduate Record Exam, the College Entrance Board) allegedly measuring mathematical ability. Even if it is presupposed that such tests do in fact measure real *ability*, which is doubtful, the results clearly do not warrant the assumption that all individual women have less mathematical aptitude than all individual men. Nor do they warrant the assumption that the right to a mathematics-related job is determined by gender rather than individual characteristics. But if rights are accorded on the basis of individual, as well as group, characteristics, then it is at least questionable whether the legal right to equal protection (from pesticides) can be determined on the basis of "average" limits below which there is no pesticidal injury. This is true because anyone with higher than "average" response to pesticidal injury (e.g., sedentary people, people with allergies, infants, children, women, the elderly) will not receive genuinely "equal" protection under the law (see Davis 1977, 27; Carson 1962, 194; Harmer 1971, 39, 49, 153; Graham 1970, 131–40; Headley and Lewis 1967, 89; and Jukes 1973, 102). Perhaps this is why acceptance of any threshold for pesticidal residues amounts to playing Russian roulette (Van den Bosch 1978, 34), making it quite difficult, even on classical utilitarian grounds, to justify use of RA. (See Shrader-Frechette 1981, 298–300, as well as previous references above to equal protection.)

Where We Go from Here

Although this essay has been too brief to settle most of the troubling ethical questions raised by use of pesticides, it does challenge two important avenues, the realism argument and the threshold argument, for evaluating public policy regarding pesticides. But, since "ought implies can," it is also important to establish that it is practically possible, not merely ethically desirable, to reduce our use of pesticides.

It can be established that there are workable alternatives to pesticides, making their use unnecessary, that use of these toxic chemicals is not needed to insure food and fiber production for human survival, and that the costs of using pesticides outweigh the benefits. It can be shown that biological forms of pest control and integrated pest management are viable alternatives to chemicals that do not destroy nontarget organisms, such as predators of the pest, and that help to maintain a certain balance of nature (see Shrader-Frechette 1981, 303–9). It can be further shown that a developed country, like the U.S., could reduce pesticide use by 50 percent without a substantial loss in either profits or crop production, in part because many food-crop uses of pesticides are for cosmetic reasons alone, and because most of the chemicals are not used on food crops in the first place (see Shrader-Frechette 1981, 309–12). Finally, it can be shown that use of pesticides is cost effective only if most of the social costs or externalities of this policy are ignored (see Shrader-Frechette 1981, 312–16).

Once all the arguments and counterarguments about pesticides are spelled out, it can be shown that present policy regarding these toxins must change. In attempting to use pesticides against insects, we have unwittingly used them against the earth, against ourselves, and against some of our most cherished ethical traditions.

References Cited

Baker, R. A. *Pesticide Usage and Its Impact on the Aquatic Environment in the Southeast.* Washington, D.C.: U.S. Environmental Protection Agency, 1972.

Bloom, S. C., and Degler, S. E. *Pesticides and Pollution.* Washington, D.C.: Bureau of National Affairs, 1969.

Carson, R. *Since Silent Spring.* Boston: Houghton Mifflin, 1962.

Cole, L. C. Quoted in N. De Nevers, *Technology and Society*. Reading, Mass.: Addison-Wesley, 1972.

Crawford, N. H., and Donigian, A. S. *Pesticide Transport and Runoff Model for Agricultural Lands*. EPA-660/2-74-013. Washington, D.C.: U.S. Government Printing Office, 1973.

Davis, J. E. *Pesticide Protection*. Washington, D.C.: U.S. Environmental Protection Agency, 1977.

Eichers, T. R., and Andrilenas, P. A. *Evaluation of Pesticide Supplies and Demand for 1978*. Agricultural Economics Report no. 399. Washington, D.C.: U.S. Department of Agriculture, 1978.

Epp, D. J., *et al. Identification and Specification of Inputs for Benefit-Cost Modeling of Pesticide Use*. EPA 600/5-77-012. Washington, D.C.: U.S. Environmental Protection Agency, 1977.

Furtick, W. R. "Uncontrolled Pests or Adequate Food," in *Pesticides and Human Welfare*, edited by Gunn and Stevens, 1976, pp. 12 ff. Glasser, R. F. "Pesticides: the Legal Environment," in *Pesticides and Human Welfare*, edited by Gunn and Stevens, 1976, pp. 228–39.

Graham, F. *Since Silent Spring*. Boston: Houghton Mifflin, 1970.

Gunn, D. L., and Stevens, J. G., eds. *Pesticides and Human Welfare*. Oxford: Oxford University Press, 1976.

Harmer, R. M. "Pesticides and Living Things," in *Unfit for Human Consumption*. Englewood Cliffs, N.J.: Prentice-Hall, 1970, pp. 56-71.

Headley, J. C. and Lewis, J. N. *The Pesticide Problem: An Economic Approach to Public Policy*. Baltimore: Johns Hopkins Press, 1967.

Irving, C. W. "Agricultural Pest Control and the Environment." *Science* 168: 1419-1424.

Jukes, T., *et al. Effects of DDT on Man and Other Mammals: I*. New York: MSS Information Corporation, 1973.

Kraybill, H. F. "Pesticide Toxicity and the Potential for Cancer." *Pest Control* 43, no. 12 (December 1975): 10–16.

Lashoff, *et al. Assessment of Technologies for Determining Cancer Risks from the Environment*. Washington, D.C.: Health and Life Sciences Division, U.S. Office of Technology Assessment, 1981, p. 3.

Lowrance, W. W. *Of Acceptable Risk*. Los Altos: William Kaufman, 1976.

Mathews, J. T. *World Resources 1986*. New York: Basic Books, 1986.

Repetto, R. *Paying the Price: Pesticide Subsidies in Developing Countries*. Research Report no. 2. Washington, D.C.: World Resources Institute, 1985 Reese, C. D., *et al. Pesticides in the Aquatic Environment*. Washington, D.C.: U.S. Environmental Protection Agency, 1972.

Rudd, R. I. *Pesticides and the Living Landscape*. Madison: University of Wisconsin Press, 1964.

Shrader-Frechette, Kristin. *Risk Analysis and Scientific Method*. Boston: Reidel, 1985.

———. *Science Policy, Ethics, and Economic Methodology*. Boston: Reidel, 1984.

———. *Nuclear Power and Public Policy*. 2d ed. Boston: Reidel, 1983.

———. *Environmental Ethics*. Pacific Grove, Calif.: Boxwood Press, 1981.

Van den Bosch, R. *The Pesticide Conspiracy*. Garden City, N.Y.: Doubleday, 1978.

———. "The Cost of Poisons." *Environment* 14 (September 1972): 18–31.

Pest Control For a Whole Earth

Sara Ebenreck

In 1986, a quarter century after the publication of Rachel Carson's classic warning about the dangers of pesticides, the U.S. Environmental Protection Agency (EPA) issued an emergency suspension of the commonly used farm pesticide dinoseb.[1] Even short-term continued use of the weed killer could have dire effects, EPA Administrator Lee M. Thomas said. Over 45,000 agricultural workers could be threatened by exposure to the product, which new tests showed caused developmental abnormalities in rabbits exposed to relatively low dosages. As many as thirty-one endangered or threatened wildlife species would also be in jeopardy.

The extent to which this pesticide had been used on farmlands was detailed in the notice: about 50 percent of the U.S. potato acreage, 33 percent of the green pea crop, and 20 percent of the snap bean crop—not to mention cotton, soybeans, grapes, almonds, and walnuts—had been managed with its aid. The withdrawal of dinoseb from the market would have economic impacts for farmers, EPA admitted, but the risks outweighed that cost.

Pesticide Risks

The case of dinoseb illustrates only a portion of many dangers posed to human and environmental health by the use of agricultural pesticides. Only minuscule amounts of that product were found in groundwater, for example, but other research is turning up increasing evidence of pesticide contamination of water sources. In 1985, the EPA reported seventeen pesticides detected in the groundwater of twenty-three states. Past monitoring had been minimal, EPA admitted, and most pesticides on the market in the 1980s were registered for use before testing related to groundwater impacts was required.[2]

Each year, about 750 million pounds of pesticides are used by

American farmers to control weeds, insects, and diseases. Cornell entomologist David Pimentel estimates that less than 1 percent of the amount applied actually reaches the target pests, while an unknown percentage of the products end up in soils, water, and nontarget organisms.[3] In a 1980 study cited by Pimentel, all soil samples taken from Oregon coastal mountains forty miles from the edge of the nearest farm region contained pesticide residues, probably blown through the air. Pesticides used on farm fields may run off with water and sediment, ending up in aquatic habitats. Chemicals taken up into plant tissue may be transferred to birds or other herbivores that eat the plant.

The impacts on human health are also potentially large. Overall, Pimentel places human poisonings from pesticides at 45,000 per year, including about 200-fatalities. In one of the few studies to look at the effects of modern farming practices on farmers, Nebraska's Center for Rural Affairs noted that people living in counties with high herbicide use were 60 percent more likely to die of leukemia than people who did not.[4] Pesticide residues in food remain a continuing health concern of a broad sector of consumers.[5]

Worldwide, less is known about the extent of risks than in the U.S., but the dangers are likely very real. Many pesticides not allowed in the United States are still manufactured and sold in other countries. In 1982, DDT concentrations in the atmosphere over the Arabian Sea and Indian Ocean were 25 to 40 times the level in the atmosphere over the North Atlantic Ocean offshore from the U.S.—where DDT has been banned since the early 1970s. A report from the Institute for Food and Development Policy in California cites multiple cases of U.S.-banned pesticides used in the third world—often on food, such as pineapples and bananas shipped back into the U.S.[6]

The Ethical Questions

Such facts raise basic ethical questions. Who is responsible and liable for damage to water, land, food, people, wildlife, and entire ecosystems? Scientists who develop the products? Companies that manufacture and sell them? Landowners or operators who use them? Public agencies that have approved the registration of the products (EPA) or recommended their use (federal and state departments of agriculture)? Who is responsible for taking action to provide less risky alternatives? Even more basic, in what philosophical assumptions and frameworks are approaches to pest control formulated? Are those approaches adequate?

The Rationale for Chemical Pest Control

The current use of agricultural pesticides is not the result of malicious intent. As one estimate has it, for every pound of human beings, there are twelve pounds of insects, and controls designed to protect food crops from those insects date back to early human history.[7] Roman farmers used camel urine and oil of leeks to control pests, for example. Our current dilemmas about pesticides are based in the peculiar mix of historical opportunities and philosophical approaches common to American agriculture in the post–World War II period.

In the first part of this century, pest control on North American croplands involved a mix of such cultural methods as rotations and the use of natural poisons like sulfur and arsenic. The development of DDT in the 1940s, followed by the pesticides toxaphene, chlordane, and parathion, led to spectacular first results in control of pests in farm fields. Washington State apple growers saw losses from codling moths drop from 15 to 5 percent as they switched from lead arsenate to DDT, for example.[8] The use of farm chemicals was quickly linked to images of success by a farm chemical industry eager for profits, and a scientific/farm-advisor community eager to advance new technologies. Modern farming to "feed the world," an ideal made possible by "sure" pest control and leaps in production levels, shaped the imaginations of a generation of farm producers and advisors.

Underlying the movement was an implicit philosophy about the nature of the relationship between humans and the natural world of the farm that was being manipulated. Rather in the model of "just-war" theory that justifies killing in self-defense (a model amply present in the American imagination in the immediate post–World War II period), the fact that crops were attacked by a pest seemed to imply the ethical right of the farmer to do away with the pest, completely if possible. To farmers and industry alike, farm fields clean of pests and weeds were seen as a sign of hard work and skill. For scientists involved in developing farm chemicals, other assumptions played critical roles: the supposition that the complexity of the natural world could be ignored as controls targeted on single pests were developed; and the idea that the use of pesticides was ethically analogous to such earlier management practices as plowing, since both simply manipulated the environment for human good.[9]

Such assumptions were not a matter of public or ethical debate. In part, that was because the image of modern American agriculture, built upon chemical pest control and fertility sources, was of overwhelming success. One farmer could now produce what a dozen had produced merely a few years earlier. But practical strategies based on dubious assumptions have a way of getting entangled in unexpected effects, and that is exactly the history of pesticides.

Side effects in the form of killing off of wildlife species and genetic defects in their offspring began to appear. Resistant insects gave another sign that all was not well with the strategy. A 1979 United Nations State of the World Environment Report cited the rising numbers of resistant pest species: 182 in 1965, 278 in 1968, and 304 in 1977. In 1986, the National Academy of Sciences estimated pesticide-resistant species at 447.[10] Farmers began to experience pest control as a treadmill in which they had to keep a constant eye out for new strains of seeds and new chemical controls to stay ahead of pests. Government responded to public concern about environmental and health effects by instituting registration requirements that included safety tests for products and limits on acceptable amounts of pesticide residues on food. EPA suspension of use for a product such as dinoseb could send shock waves through the farm economy as producers found themselves suddenly looking for alternative controls.

In the 1980s, as gluts in grain on the world market left the American farm economy in a widespread depression, U.S. farmers began eyeing the "input" costs of farm chemicals in a newly skeptical light. Revelations about contamination of their own and their neighbor's drinking water by farm fertilizers and pesticides provided a second stimulus for change.

An Alternate Approach

In what for the last four decades has been a minority position in American agriculture, a quite different approach to pest control has also existed. One distinctive mark of the alternative viewpoint is a strong sense of respect for the natural world and its complexity, accompanied by a desire to "work with" or "learn from" it in production methods. Growers working within this tradition have called themselves "organic," or "biological," or—more recently—"regenerative" or "alternative" farmers. Scientists have called themselves proponents of "integrated pest management," "biological" controls, or "low input" farming systems.

While a broad diversity exists among alternative practitioners, it can generally be said that from this viewpoint pest control proceeds best by understanding nature's methods of regulating pest populations and then maximizing the application of such biological controls. Parasitic wasps, for example, have been successfully used to control alfalfa weevils, and crop rotations to keep other pests in check. Indeed, seen from the viewpoint of appreciation for biological diversity, pests might be beneficial if their populations were kept to a reasonable number. On a California rice farm, a tadpole that was experienced as a "pest" in the conventional cycle of planting turned into a "beneficial insect" when delayed flooding of the rice fields allowed the tadpole to attack water weeds instead of rice seedlings.[11] Resilient, diverse, and flexible systems that can weather shifts in climate and market conditions are valued by alternative farmers.

In 1980, a landmark study by the U.S. Department of Agriculture found that with the use of such ecologically sound methods, a group of completely nonchemical farmers were able to achieve production levels that, on the average, were equal to those of their conventional chemical-using counterparts. Net incomes were often as high or higher than those of farmers using conventional methods.[12]

Despite such discoveries and despite strong support for alternatives from many individual scientists, farmers, and policymakers, the vast, complex, and loosely organized conventional "community" of farmers, research scientists, farm advisors, agribusiness corporations, government agencies, and farm media is only slowly moving from what might be called the "chemical pest eradication" model to the "alternative ecological control" model. One obstacle was cited by the 1980 USDA study: the lack of research and information on how to make the transition from chemical-intensive to alternative methods without loss of profitability. When shifts in pest control demand shifts in cropping patterns, marketing of different crops is involved, for example. A major industry with ownership investment by millions of individual operators making millions of individual decisions does not easily shift from the skills, habits, and philosophical assumptions learned over four decades of apparent success.

The Ethical Dimension

Yet the environmental and health effects of many pesticides combine with the existence of alternative methods to make a strong ethical argument for limiting their use. The imperative that we avoid actions that have high potential to harm others is a first ethical principle that applies to their use. As negative side effects of particular pesticides are shown, this principle points to the need to use—and for the research community to develop, when no such alternative is available—less harmful alternatives. Although it is arguable that avoiding all harm to others is an impossible ethical ideal, in any harm/benefit calculation the option of a safer alternative to a harmful product radically alters the ethical equation. If the use of field traps to monitor cutworm infestations can lead to cutting by a third the use of a potentially harmful chemical product (as it has in Iowa), this first principle would surely argue for that action.

Second is the principle enunciated by Aldo Leopold in his 1947 essay on the land ethic: that our action respect the "inner workings" of nature, and be directed so as to preserve the integrity, stability, and beauty of the biotic community.[13] This principle points to the human species as one member in a diverse, interconnected, and living community of the natural world, each of whose elements deserves respect. From this viewpoint, the "total eradication" of some one "pest" species is suspect because it is likely to have unintended effects on larger ecological systems. The use of toxic substances likely to have significant negative side effects on the biotic community is also questionable.

Neither of these principles argues against all use of agricultural pesticides. The risks of pesticides vary from product to product, and at least some products claim to be relatively benign in their environmental and health effects. In any case, rather than beginning from an absolute imperative such as "use no pesticides," ethical decision making in this area may better originate as a matter of practical wisdom, in which risks and benefits—including profits—are weighed in the light of the principles above. Use of a clearly harmful pesticide might be ethically supported if, for example, the crop produced was essential for human life and the economy of a region and if no alternative methods of control were available. But the principles would surely argue for all possible funding of an alternative direction.

Since so much destruction of the biotic community and risk to human health has already occurred as a result of the use of pesticides, a third ethical principle of "healing the wounds" applies: that responsible members of the human community do what is needed to restore the damaged portions of the ecosystem to a fuller integrity, and share in the burden of transition for the affected human community.

Who Should Act?

To say "responsible members of the human community" ought to accomplish this restoration, as well as the work of putting in place more ecologically responsible methods of pest control, raises the question of exactly what members or groups within the human community hold that responsibility. This designation is made especially important by the economic costs of carrying out these general ethical responsibilities. Water cleanup is not cheap, and undertaking new methods of crop production can be risky. Development of biologically sounder pest controls demands research funding, and testing of new products itself is expensive.

In fact, a broad sector of people are responsible. Farmers use the products on the land, but huge international agribusiness corporations and dealers as small as the local farm co-op have manufactured or sold the products. All of these have profited in some way from the use of farm chemicals. The federal Environmental Protection Agency has approved products for use that, like dinoseb, have later turned out to be hazardous. Federal and state departments of agriculture as well as land-grant universities, accepting EPA regulations, have conducted research ranging from plant breeding to soil conservation techniques with the use of pesticides, and then advised the application of such products in their work with farmers. Consumers have been more interested in foods free from blemish by insect or disease than in the means used to produce such "perfect" products.

The principle that persons with responsibility for a harmful situation and the capacity to remedy that harm should act argues that initiatives for a more sound pest control system should be undertaken by a broad sector of the human community, with specific allocations resting on the ways in which particular sectors interact with pesticide use. Scientists and research organizations funded by public monies, for example, ought to be clearly charged by government agencies with developing alternatives to hazardous pesticides. Farm industries and advisors can respond by selling ecologically sound pest management information, services, and products. Farmers ought to seek out alternatives, and consumers to support incentives for their use.

Policy Needs

Overall, consistent protection of environmental and human health is likely to demand public policy action, the one clear way in which "all of us" can act for a common good. In mid-1987, a significant portion of pesticide-related policies to achieve these ethical goals are already in place, but others need action.

Chief among protections in place is the Federal Insecticide, Fungicide, and Rodenticide Act (FIFRA). First enacted in 1947 as a way to protect farmers from dangerous or ineffective products, a series of strengthening amendments to FIFRA in the 1970s provided a mandate for the Environmental Protection Agency to develop a comprehensive pesticide regulation process aimed at protecting the public and the environment from pesticide use. Today, FIFRA requires extensive testing of pesticide products for human health and environmental impacts before they are registered and provides for designation of either general or restricted use for products judged relatively safe. Appropriate labeling, access to information, and setting of "acceptable" levels of residues in food products are also provided by FIFRA and other federal regulations.

Current protection policies are far from sufficient, however, Environmental groups have called for federal policies to protect groundwater from contamination by pesticides. Issues related to the detoxification and disposal of pesticide stocks and containers need attention. Funding is needed for research and demonstration of alternative agricultural methods that rely on biological and cultural controls for pests for which such controls are not now tested or known. Indeed, it is arguable that a fair response to the pesticide problems we face demands new, creative social solutions from all levels of government. State taxes on sales of pesticide products, perhaps in direct proportion to the hazards of use, could raise public funds for water cleanup and education while providing incentives to use safer alternatives. Disincentives could be put in place to discourage use of environmentally dangerous products: a demand that "sound pest management" plans be in place for farmers to participate in federal price support programs might work, for example. Government programs might assist individual producers in making the transition to less environmentally harmful methods by providing a form of temporary insurance for crop losses in combination with planning assistance.

Which Values for the Future?

Overall, the issues posed by the hazards of pesticides lead to basic value questions because the methods of food production reveal fundamental characteristics of a culture. In America, our fascination with abundance, efficiency, and "sure fixes" proposed by scientific and business experts has, for a time at least, led us to a highly productive but unsustainable food system. One insight derived from thinking about pest controls is that other values—long-term sustainability, health of humans and ecosystems, openness to learning from the natural world and living in some form of active harmony rather than dominance over it—are vital for our survival. These lessons, of course, carry import that goes far beyond concern with farm pests. They are likely keys to a future on earth that would replace environmental degradation with systems that help heal and promote life in the whole earth community.

Notes

1. Rachel Carson, *Silent Spring* (Boston: Houghton Mifflin Co., 1962). "Dinoseb: Intent to Cancel and Deny all Registrations for Pesticide Products Containing Dinoseb," in *Federal Register*, 51, no. 198 (October 14, 1986): 36650.

2. U.S. Environmental Protection Agency, *Pesticides in Ground Water: Background Document* (Washington, D.C.: U.S. EPA, 1986), pp. 6, 8.

3. D. Pimental and L. Levitan, "Pesticides: Amounts Applied and Amounts Reaching Pests," in *Bioscience*, 36, no. 2 (February, 1986): 86–91.

4. Center for Rural Affairs, *It's Not All Sunshine and Fresh Air: Chronic Health Effects of Modern Farming Practices* (Walthill, Nebraska: Center for Rural Affairs, 1984), p. 58 ff.

5. A federal report, *Need to Enhance FDA's Ability to Protect the Public from Illegal Residues* (Washington, D.C.: U.S. Government Printing Office, 1986) found that in 107 of 179 cases of residue-level violations, the federal Food and Drug Administration took no significant action.

6. David Weir and Mark Schapiro, *Circle of Poison: Pesticides and People in a Hungry World* (San Francisco: Institute for Food and Development Policy, 1981), ch. 1, 3.

7. Ross H. Hall, *A New Approach to Pest Control in Canada* (Ottawa: Canadian Environmental Advisory Council, 1981), p. 1.

8. John H. Perkins, "The Quest for Innovation in Agricultural Entomology, 1945–1978," in *Pest Control: Cultural and Environmental Aspects* (Boulder, Colo.: Westview Press, 1980), p. 27.

9. *Ibid.*, p. 49.

10. M. K. Tolba, *The State of the World Environment 1979: Report of the UN Environmental Programme* (New York: United Nations, 1979); National Academy of Sciences, *Pesticide Resistance: Strategies and Tactics for Management* (Washington, D.C.: National Academy Press, 1986).

11. Patrick Madden, "Case Studies of Farms in Transition," Staff Paper 56, (University Park: Pennsylvania State University Agricultural Economics and Rural Sociology Dept., 1983), pp. 26-33.

12. U.S. Dept. of Agriculture, *Report and Recommendations on Organic Farming* (Washington, D.C.: U.S. Department of Agriculture, 1980).

13. Aldo Leopold, *A Sand County Almanac*, (New York: Ballantine Books, 1977), p. 262.

III.B.
Animal Welfare, Animal Interests and the Proper Treatment of Animals in Agriculture

ANIMAL PRODUCTION RESEARCHERS HAVE BEEN CONCERNED with animal welfare for some time. Their attitude has been that animal well-being will serve the end of higher productivity, and high productivity means good animal husbandry. This approach has led to ethically indefensible excesses according to many opponents of both animal consumption and intensive animal production. Stanley E. Curtis, himself an animal production scientist, takes up this allegation and also the idea of the linkage between productivity and animal welfare. In "The Welfare of Agricultural Animals," Curtis proposes that we approach animal welfare through a Maslow-like hierarchy of physiological needs, the need for safety, and behavioral needs.

Since the physiological needs have a demonstrated connection with productivity, Curtis maintains that most producers will strive to meet them. After detailing how these needs have been approached, he moves on to the need for safety. According to Curtis, many dangers that threaten animal safety and production are less well attended to than physiological needs. But failure to fully understand and meet these is an ever greater source of difficulty to the producer and researcher. Curtis discusses one approach that identifies behavioral needs in terms of the stimuli or "releasers" of the behavior in question and that separates needs aroused by environmental stimuli from those released by some internal factor. Curtis defines "essential needs" and endorses meeting those internally cued essential needs that production animals demonstrate.

Curtis next discusses strategies for meeting behavioral needs and beneficial ways of simulating the natural environment in the production setting. The article concludes with a lengthy discussion of strategies for further research that is needed to assess the well-being of animals. Since mental suffering cannot be assessed with any confidence, we must use indirect indicators of the ways and extent to which animals needs and wants are not met, according to Curtis. Still, the objective should be to achieve, in any of a variety of ways, a production setting in which the animal is as free from suffering as possible.

Bernard E. Rollin, a major advocate and investigator of animal rights, takes a slightly different approach to understanding animal welfare. For Rollin, we can and must assign to animals a mental life complete with interests, conscious awareness, the capability of feeling pain, and many attendant psychological needs. He makes clear both the varied sources of evidence for this conclusion and their implications. Rollin argues that it is possible to identify the *telos* of an animal, that is, the species-specific sort of life best for the animal. If we can identify that, then we can identify the rights an animal has to satisfaction of the needs and interests contributing to that *telos*. Reasoning this way is, Rollin maintains, exactly parallel to reasoning that supports rights humans have because of their *telos*.

Modern production research has shown how the environment and animals themselves can be manipulated so that they can be raised in conditions unsuited to their *telos*, a practice bolstered by understanding welfare in terms of productivity. But morally, Rollin urges, this is wrong, and rearing practices must accommodate the animals' *telos* if we are to avoid deserving censure on moral grounds.

Rollin concludes with a review of how the rights of animals have come to be recognized and protected in recent U.S. legislation governing animal research. Legislation in Europe has gone even farther, regulating rearing conditions. Rollin urges that it would be a serious mistake for U.S. agricultural practice and regulation to not follow these leads.

Dana R. Flint, in his paper "Factory Farming and the Interests of Animals," considers the kind of approach to animal rights that Rollin takes—one that finds similarities between the mental lives of humans and production animals. He does this by first taking up R. G. Frey's claim that animals lack beliefs and desires, and so lack interests, which are the basis of rights. Flint guides us through some of the pertinent literature and arguments as he draws the conclusion that the most plausible explanation of certain behavior of many farm animals endows them with adequate mental abilities to make them possessors of interests and bearers of rights. The view that animals have a sense of self and future, endowing them with the rights of a moral patient as fully as any human, is moderated by Flint's belief that even if nonhuman animals have a sense of future and self, these are not embedded in a cultural matrix as they are for humans. This is ultimately important because as we try to understand "interests," Flint suggests, our account must be ethically loaded in terms appropriate to human life, *not* the life of any other animal. Indeed, the very notion of a *telos* that Rollin uses is, according to Flint, the idea of a good life as understood in cultural and other specifically human terms, such as the capacity to choose life pursuits and styles. Animals may have something analogous to the interests that form the basis of human rights, but the analogy is only that, and it strains to the breaking point when interests are understood as reflecting the choice of lifestyles and life pursuits.

If having rights means that valid claims can be made by or on behalf of an individual, then it might seem that animals can have rights, for they can be the object of claims. Again the appearance is misleading, according to Flint, for he seems to say that making a claim for a being yields a right for that being only if it already is a potential bearer of rights—a presupposition that cannot be made for nonhumans.

If Flint is right in all these arguments, the case for animal rights based on analogies with humans is weak. Flint himself thinks we would do better to leave aside talk of animal rights in favor of (instinctively based) animal interests as we assess the moral demands animal welfare places upon the producer.

Looked at this way, Flint claims in his conclusion, the ways of living for nonhuman animals are not as important, ethically, as are those of humans. Still, this does not justify the ways in which factory farms have, often cruelly, ignored the interests of animals.

The next selection explores the implicit question in Flint's conclusion. If nonhuman and human animals differ with respect to autonomy and cultural behavior, does that make the welfare of one less important than that of the other? The answer is in the title, "Why (Most) Humans are More Important than Other Animals," a position the author takes to be in the spirit of Immanuel Kant and to pivot on the concept of ethical standing. Following William K. Frankena, the author holds that ethical standing comes with manifesting whatever ultimately justifies our acts. Taking a pragmatic, but Kantian, approach to the question, he argues that those ultimate justifiers of action are the aims of individual human agents. The interests or well-being of nonhuman animals might be an object of those human aims and so have real importance, but this import would be derivative, not primary. The question the right treatment of animals in agricultural production thus turns out to be the question of what treatment of animals will maximally serve the (autonomous) aims of the humans affected by the action. The remainder of the discussion points out how complicated this last question is with respect to intensive production of veal, pork, eggs, poultry and beef. While certain practices seem clearly unjustifiable in the face of alternatives, which alternative is best is a complex empirical question that is not yet clearly answered for most meat production. The paper ends on the cautionary note that while animal welfare is not the same as nor so important ethically as human welfare, which animals may be raised for consumption, and how, remain complex interdisciplinary questions.

Thus, animal welfare and the ethical way, if there is one, to produce animal food and fiber can be approached in economic terms, in terms of the animal's characteristic interests, or the limited analogy between animal and human cognition, and in terms of who or what has ethical standing. To no one does the simple economic analysis seem adequate, but beyond this much, there is considerable disagreement. The issues of what animal welfare in a farm operation is and how it should ultimately be dealt with remain open questions that can be approached in several different ways.

Section III.C. covers two other production resources whose fate causes concern, genetic diversity and fossil fuels.

The Welfare of Agricultural Animals

Stanley E. Curtis

NOWADAYS THERE ARE QUESTIONS—based variously on humanitarian, economic, and scientific grounds—whether agricultural animals' limits of adaptability have been exceeded in certain intensive systems of production. Keeping hens in cages, sows in stalls, and calves in crates for all or part of their productive lives has been the topic of much of the debate. Are these animals distressed by certain commonly provided environments? Are they suffering? Is their overall well-being in jeopardy? What constitutes animal well-being must be defined before these questions can be answered. I will approach animal well-being through the concept of needs (Curtis 1985, 1987b).

Maslow's Hierarchy of Human Needs

A well-accepted theory of motivation in humans is that human needs are arranged in a hierarchy according to relative priority (Maslow 1970). More potent needs dominate an organism until they are satisfied, after which the less potent needs arise and become the motivating forces. A brief review of Maslow's hierarchy of human needs might supply a useful first approach to assessing the well-being of animals in various settings.

The most prepotent needs of humans are the physiological needs, including those for adequate food and a tolerable physical environment. Once these have been satisfied, the safety needs emerge, including security and freedom from fear and anxiety. Most humans develop additional needs in approximately the following order: love, esteem, the need for self-actualization, the desire to know and understand, and finally, aesthetic needs.

The physiological needs are considered the most basic (lowest) in this hierarchy; the aesthetic needs are considered the most complex (highest). Humans have the lower needs—physiological and safety—in common with subhuman animals, but they probably share the highest ones with no other species. Maslow (1970) made other observations, some germane to my discussion: (1) higher needs are less imperative for sheer survival, (2) gratification of higher needs can be postponed longer, (3) higher needs disappear permanently more easily, (4) higher needs require better environmental conditions if they are to emerge, (5) living at a higher need level results in greater biological efficiency, enhanced longevity, less disease, and better sleep and appetite, and (6) individuals gratified in both a higher and a lower need usually place more value on the higher one. Animal Needs Arranged Hierarchically

Application of Maslow's scheme to animals might result in a hierarchical organization of animal needs along the following lines (from lowest to highest): physiological needs, safety needs, and behavioral needs. What are these needs? What do they imply as to the well-being of agricultural animals?

Physiological Needs

A great deal is known about the physiological needs of agricultural animals and, as they are now understood, these needs are virtually being met. Animal responses to stressors are known to affect their productivity both directly and indirectly by (1) diverting nutrients from productive processes to maintenance, (2) altering functions involved both in productive and stress-response processes, (3) intentionally reducing the rates of productive processes, (4) increasing the individual variability in productive rates, and (5) altering resistance against infections (Curtis 1983). Thus, the most basic animal needs are generally not neglected.

Nutrition. Of all animal needs, the nutrient requirements are currently understood the best. The sophisticated dietary formulations used throughout the animal industries reflect this. Dietary recommendations have even been refined to account for hereditary and environmental influences. Much research continues on animal nutrition.

Environment. Direct and indirect climatic influences on the health, productivity, and survival of agricultural animals have been appreciated for decades. Studies of these and other animal-environmental relations in both extensive and intensive management systems have been expanded in recent years, and great effort is being made to provide agricultural animals with appropriate thermal, light, air, microbic, and social environments (Arnold and Dudzinski 1978, Curtis 1983, Fraser 1985, Maton et al. 1985).

Health. The health of agricultural animals has improved as their nutritional and environmental statuses have been upgraded and as disease management and veterinary care have evolved from arts to disciplines based more on scientific research. The recent ascendancy of diseases of multiple etiology—the so-called production or factorial diseases, which typically result in high morbidity and low mortality rates—has coincided with intensification of animal production. Clinical manifestations of certain infectious diseases clearly can be affected by the microenvironment. Changes both in microbic challenges to the animal and in the animal's defenses have been implicated (Curtis 1983). Environmental-management schemes are taking these relations into account as scientific knowledge increases.

Safety Needs

Safety needs are next in the hierarchy suggested for domestic animals. It is obvious that physical maltreatment of the animals by humans is not only inhumane but also anathema in efficient production. Furthermore, there is increasing scientific evidence that confirms conventional wisdom: agricultural animals respond positively in terms of health and productivity to supportive social contacts with humans (Gross and Siegel 1983, Hemsworth et al. 1980, Seabrook 1972). In practice the safety needs are tended to somewhat less rigorously than the physiological needs, even though laxity often results in physical injury or even death.

Weather accidents. Although animals are adaptable to a wide climatic range, many in natural environments are hurt or lose their lives in weather accidents. The number for agricultural animals would be much greater if elaborate steps had not been taken to protect them from severe weather. Occasionally, animals kept in closed houses succumb indirectly to stormy weather, as when a power outage leads to ventilation failure.

Predation. Predators kill many animals and seriously injure even more, despite the availability of effective and acceptable methods of control. Animals' chances of falling prey to coyotes and other wild carnivores ordinarily are decreased when they are shifted from extensive to intensive production systems.

Equipment and facilities. The design of equipment and facilities with respect to animal safety requires interdisciplinary collaboration (Curtis 1982a, 1987a). There is scope for improvement. Fortunately, problems of this sort are amenable to scientific inquiry and to the application of findings to the immediate benefit of the animals, as indicated by the following examples.

First, vast improvements in the hen's safety in terms of bodily entrapment and foot health have emerged during the past decade as a result of design changes in commercial laying cages, which resulted directly from carefully controlled comparative studies of special features of then-available commercial cages in a simulated production setting (Tauson 1980).

Second, a headgate is an essential piece of restraining equipment for beef cattle operations. Each of the four basic kinds of headgate was designed for a distinct purpose and has special advantages. Each also has drawbacks in terms of cattle safety—including tendencies to cause choking or head, shoulder, or leg injuries—when used for a purpose other than that intended (Grandin 1980).

Third, the floor surface in a dairy facility greatly affects the health of the cow's feet and legs; slipperiness frequently leads to falls and serious injuries (McDaniel et al. 1982). The ideal requirements for floors for hoofed animals—resiliency, a friction coefficient high enough to minimize the animal's chances of slipping, and low abrasiveness—are difficult to meet simultaneously and economically, but compromises are evolving (Nilsson 1981).

Behavioral Needs

Any instance of animal maltreatment caused by human action or inaction falls into one of three categories: abuse, neglect, or deprivation (Ewbank 1981). Abuse and neglect rarely occur in animal agricultural operations.

Deprivation, however, involves the denial of certain, often less vital, aspects of the environment. It is the form of maltreatment most difficult to assess (Kiley-Worthington 1977, Wood-Gush et al. 1975, Duncan and Dawkins 1983). Many of the needs under deprived conditions are behavioral and have not yet been ascertained, let alone characterized well enough to be useful in the design of animal quarters. These needs are signaled by demonstrations (often subtle) of frustration, fear, and discomfort. Whether agricultural animals experience well-being or suffering is most controversial in this area.

HUGHES'S UNITARY MODEL OF MOTIVATION. Hughes (1980) has proposed a unitary model of motivation that might be useful in the assessment of animal behavioral needs.

The model can be partitioned into three principles: (1) environmental stimuli of behavior are far more important than internal motivations near one end of this continuum, (2) internal and external factors both contribute significantly as behavioral triggers in the middle, and (3) internal factors are the chief releasers of behavior near the other end. Examples in the laying hen for these categories might be escape and agonistic behaviors, sexual crouch and dust-bathing, and pecking and nesting, respectively (Hughes 1980).

Hughes suggests that to ensure animal well-being, it is *desirable* to provide for some of the behavioral patterns in category two, and it is *essential* to provide for *all* of those in category three. The decision on whether a particular category-two behavior ought to be accommodated by environmental manipulation depends on the relative contributions of external and internal factors to the release of that behavior. Those behaviors that surface even without significant environmental stimulation should be accommodated. For example, a hen's sexual crouch depends on a distinct environmental releaser as well as an appropriate hormonal state; hence sexual crouching would not be considered a behavioral need. Phantom dust-bathing, on the other hand, occurs occasionally in many hens even in a relatively barren environment, such as a laying cage, where the normal external stimuli for this behavior are presumably weak. Thus, it would probably be desirable to provide hens the opportunity to dust-bathe, even though engagement in vacuum activities (such as phantom dust-bathing) does not necessarily mean that the hen is distressed. After all, she can perform the behavior in the barren environment. Likewise, animals sometimes are able to cope by performing displacement behaviors and in this way preserve their well-being for and by themselves.

For a behavior pattern to be considered an essential behavioral need (category three), Hughes would require clear evidence of either frustration (such as stereotyped pacing preceding oviposition in some caged hens) or distortion of the behavior pattern, which can be ascertained only if the behavior's normal limits are known.

Before any behavior can be designated a need, the animal must be subjected to careful, thorough behavioral analysis in the environments of interest. Moreover, to establish well-being, it is not necessary that an animal's behavior be the same in the environment of interest as in one arbitrarily set as the standard.

Consequences for environmental design and management. Baxter (1983) pointed out that sometimes productive processes and well-being can be accommodated without the animal's ever performing a certain behavior. With reference to nesting behavior in the prepartal sow, for instance, he suggested that its productive functions (protecting piglets from cold and from being crushed by the sow) could be replaced by appropriate husbandry techniques, whereas its welfare function (Postulated to be furnishing the sow's highly sensitive udder with a comfortable contact surface) might be achieved simply by providing a comfortable floor. Consequently the absence of nesting behavior in a sow would not necessarily mean the sow was suffering from behavioral deprivation; it might mean merely that the behavior is in category one or two of Hughes's model and that environmental manipulation had eliminated the releaser of the behavior (uncomfortable floor) as well as the behavior's usefulness (piglet protection and udder comfort).

This line of thinking can be taken a step further to embrace environmental richness. Sows characteristically wallow in mud to enhance evaporative heat loss during hot weather. In outdoor environments, however, the amount of wallowing behavior performed is related directly to environmental temperature, and sows do not wallow at all at air temperatures less than 12°C (Sambraus 1981). These observations could mean that a sow wallows primarily to achieve thermal comfort and that even at high environmental temperatures as long as the sow is made comfortable by some means, it is unlikely that she is either deprived or frustrated when her environment is devoid of a wallow.

Stolba (1981) took a different tack in designing an artificial environment for swine that would be minimally equivalent, in accommodating the animals' behavior, to an 11,000-square-meter natural setting outside Edinburgh, Scotland, arbitrarily designated as the standard. He carefully characterized behavior patterns—in terms of frequencies, sequences, orientations, contexts, and "clue factors," which provide releasing, orienting, and situational stimuli—and level of arousal of swine in (1) the standard natural setting described above, (2) cultural paddocks of varying environmental richness measuring either 1,000 or 300 square meters, and (3) a variety of pens, some relatively barren, others enriched in various ways.

These behavioral observations led to the development of several generations of artificial swine-rearing environments, which incorporated those elements of the standard natural setting that were deemed necessary to support standard behavior. Finally, an enriched housing system for matriarchal swine families was designed (Stolba 1981). It contains nesting, activity, and rooting areas as well as furniture, including partitions, feeding stalls, farrowing rails, a rubbing post, a straw rack, and a levering bar. A husbandry plan befitting the system was developed (Stolba 1983).

Stolba's approach is attractive because it exhaustively explores the relations between an animal's environment and its behavior (Duncan 1981). It presumes, however, that in any environment accepted as satisfying behavioral needs, the animals should behave as they do in some standard environment, a notion not held by all (Baxter 1983, Hughes 1980).

Animal Well-Being—Further Thoughts

The welfare of an agricultural animal might theoretically require fulfillment of all of the animal's physiological, safety, and behavioral needs (and some of its wants) most of the time. Strictly speaking, it is rare for any animal—in the wild or on a farm—to not be responding to several stressors at once (Curtis 1982b). Stress is the rule, not the exception, in an animal's life, and nature has endowed animals with a marvelous array of physiological, anatomical, immunological, and behavioral responses to these impingements. Indeed, the lack of stress usually leads to boredom, not necessarily to comfort. The challenge is to learn where stress that is usually natural and sometimes unavoidable ends, and, thus, where stress that is sometimes artifactual and usually avoidable begins. This is still a difficult task, simply because so many interrelated factors, several not very well understood, are involved. Following are brief discussions of a few.

Perception of Stress

The precise limits of experiences that give animals pleasure or displeasure, comfort or discomfort, pain or the absence thereof remain enigmas. The amount of stress an animal perceives apparently depends not only on the intensity and duration of the environmental impingement but also on the animal's psychological and physiological state (Curtis 1985). For example: —When the environment is more controllable or at least more predictable, animals tend to feel more comfortable, even when responding to stressors. On the other hand, when the environment is neither predictable nor controllable, animals sometimes become frightened or anxious, and eventually they might assume the state of learned helplessness and suffer its various consequences. —Alliesthesia, depending on internal bodily status, can markedly modify an animal's perception of its environment. —Environments sometimes contain features that give animals the opportunity to cope (alleviate stress) by engaging in adjunctive activities—e.g., nibbling on a chain—when they are frustrated, have unfulfilled expectations, or lack control of their environment. —Some animals able to control environmental temperature operantly inject a large variation into their daily cycle, suggesting, for example, that thermal surroundings found relatively comfortable by young pigs at midnight might feel uncomfortably cool to them at midday.

Influences such as these make it more difficult to identify the complex of environmental conditions that would ensure the well-being of a specific animal at a particular time.

Animal Preferences

How wise are animals? Their wants do not always correspond to their needs. In one study an adequate complete diet based on soybean meal and others offering five grains were made available to chicks in a choice situation (Kare and Scott 1962). The chicks strongly preferred corn- or milo-based diets by 3:1 over barley- or buckwheat-based diets and by 6:1 over rye-based diets. Nonetheless, when offered alone, all diets except the one based on rye supported normal performance, and the decrement on that diet was small.

What goes on in the minds of animals? Mental activities cannot be measured directly, but animals probably have at least some of the same features of consciousness as humans (Griffin 1976, 1984; van Rooijen 1981). However, it is doubtful that animals are consistently capable of making decisions based on conscious conceptions of the consequences (Duncan and Dawkins 1983, van Rooijen 1982). Therefore, results of choice tests, conducted as a means of letting animals identify their preferences (their wants, if not their needs) must be interpreted carefully. From choice-test experiences with domestic animals in the past decade, several critical points emerge. (1) Expressed preferences are relative among the choices available but give no idea as to the absolute properties of any of the choices. (2) Choice-test preferences are greatly affected by the animal's previous experiences. (3) The form of the choice test can markedly affect the results. (4) Animals do not choose rationally with respect to the choice's long-term consequences. (5) A choice made infrequently might nonetheless be very important to the well-being of the animal (Duncan and Dawkins 1983).

A practical means of fulfilling animal needs and wants is to give the animal operant control of important environmental features such as feed, temperature, and illumination (Baldwin and Ingram 1967, Baldwin and Meese 1977, Curtis and Morris 1982, Duncan and Hughes 1972, Kilgour et al. 1982). It can be presumed that such an approach increases the animal's sense of control in surroundings that fluctuate in both time and space, sometimes unpredictably and irrationally, and thus this approach probably has positive indirect consequences (Seligman 1975, Wiepkema 1987).

Assessing Well-Being

The assessment of well-being in agricultural animals cannot include an evaluation of any mental suffering that might be present, simply because scientists are unable to do the evaluation. But it must take into account all other available evidence (Duncan and Dawkins 1983). This includes all physiological, immunological, behavioral, and anatomical indicators of stress and distress, even though their interpretability still must be developed and refined. Recent good evidence shows that immunological indices might prove useful in this regard as well. Meanwhile, health and reproductive and productive traits continue to be the best indicators of fit between agricultural animals and their environments at the farm level (Curtis 1987b).

Welfare Plateau

It must be recognized that, in practice, achieving high levels of animal well-being is still a vague exercise and will most likely be so for several years. Duncan (1978) and Curtis (1987b) have put forth and expanded upon C. D. Hardwick's idea that satisfactory animal welfare exists over a range of conditions provided by various production systems. This plateau need not be exactly flat (some variation in welfare might well occur within it), but any point in it is acceptable. In other words, animal well-being is not achievable only in one ideal set of circumstances. With a welfare plateau, a relatively small environmental change might indeed subtly improve an animal's overall well-being; however, anywhere in this range the animal is as free from suffering as possible.

References Cited

Arnold, G. W., and M. L. Dudzinski. *Ethology of Free-Ranging Domestic Animals.* Amsterdam: Elsevier, 1978.

Baldwin, B. A., and D. L. Ingram. The effect of heating and cooling the hypothalamus on behavioural thermoregulation in the pig. *J. Physiol. London* 131 (1967): 370–92.

Baldwin, B. A., and G. B. Meese. Sensory reinforcement and illumination preference in the domestic pig. *Anim. Behav.* 25 (1977): 497–507.

Baxter, M. R. Ethology in environmental design for animal production. *Appl. Anim. Ethol.* 9 (1983): 207–20.

Curtis, S. E. Measurement of stress in animals. In *Proceedings of the Symposium on Management of Food Producing Animals, West Lafayette, Indiana, 1982*, edited by W. Woods. West Lafayette, Ind.: Purdue University, 1982b, p. 1–10.

Curtis, S. E. Livestock environment for the 1980s: animal science perspectives. In *Proceedings In. Livestock Environment Symposium, 2nd, Ames, Iowa, 1982*. St. Joseph, Mo.:

American Society of Agricultural Engineers, 1982a, p. 597–600.

Curtis, S. E. *Environmental Management in Animal Agriculture.* Ames: Iowa State University Press, 1983.

Curtis, S. E. What constitutes animal well-being? In *Animal Stress*, edited by G. P. Moberg. Philadelphia, Penn.: Williams & Wilkins, 1985, p. 1–14.

Curtis, S. E. Animal accommodations are not jigsaw puzzles. In *Latest Developments in Livestock Housing.* St. Joseph, Mo.: American Society of Agricultural Engineers, 1987a, p. 290–95.

Curtis, S. E. The case for intensive production of food animals. In *Animal Welfare Science 1986/87,* edited by M. W. Fox and L. D. Mickley. Boston, Mass.: Nijhoff, 1987b, p. 245–55.

Curtis, S. E., and G. L. Morris. Operant supplemental heat in swine nurseries. In *Proceedings of the 2nd International Livestock Environment Symposium, Ames, Iowa, 1982.* St. Joseph, Mo.: American Society of Agricultural Engineers, 1982, p. 295–97.

Duncan, I. J. H. An overall assessment of poultry welfare. In *Proceedings of the Danish Seminar on Poultry Welfare in Egglaying Cages, 1st Koge, Denmark, 1978*, edited by L. Y. Sørensen. Copenhagen: National Committee on Poultry and Eggs, 1978, p. 81–88.

Duncan, I. J. H. Animal rights—animal welfare: a scientist's assessment. *Poult. Sci.* 60 (1981): 489–99.

Duncan, I. J. H., and M. A. Dawkins. The problem of assessing "well-being" and "suffering" in farm animals. In *Indicators Relevant to Farm Animal Welfare,* edited by D. Smidt. Boston: Nijhoff, 1983, p. 13–24.

Duncan, I. J. H. and B. O. Hughes. Free and operant feeding in domestic fowls. *Anim. Behav.* 20 (1972): 775–77.

Ewbank, R. Alternatives: definitions and doubts. In *Alternatives to Intensive Husbandry Systems.* South Mimms, U.K.: Universities Federal Animal Welfare, 1981, p. 4–9.

Fraser, A. F. (editor). *Ethology of Farm Animals.* Amsterdam: Elsevier, 1985.

Grandin, T. Good cattle-restraining equipment is essential. *Vet. Med. Small Anim. Clin.* 75 (1980): 1291–95.

Griffin, D. R. *The Question of Animal Awareness.* New York: Rockefeller University Press, 1976.

Griffin, D. R. *Animal Thinking.* Cambridge, Mass.: Harvard University Press, 1984.

Gross, W. B., and P. B. Siegel. Socialization, the sequencing of environmental factors, and their effects on weight gain and disease resistance of chickens. *Poult. Sci.* 62 (1983): 592–98.

Hemsworth, P. H. A. Brand, and P. Willems. The behavioural response of sows to the presence of human beings and their productivity. *Livestock Proc. Sci.* 8 (1980): 67–74.

Hughes, B. O. The assessment of behavioural needs. In *The Laying Hen and Its Environment,* edited by R. Moss. Boston, Mass.: Nijhoff, 1980, p. 149–59.

Kare, M. R., and M. L. Scott. Nutritional value and feed acceptability. *Poult. Sci.* 41 (1962): 276–78.

Kiley-Worthington, M. *Behavioural Problems of Farm Animals,* Boston, Mass.: Oriel, 1977.

Kilgour, R. T. M. Foster, and W. Temple, Operant technology applied to solving farm animal problems. In *Proceedings of the Meeting of the New Zealand Psychological Society*, Hamilton, 1982.

Maslow, A. H. *Motivation and Personality.* New York: Harper & Row, 1970.

Maton, A., J. Daelemans, and J. Lambrecht. *Housing of Animals.* Amsterdam: Elsevier, 1985.

McDaniel, B. T., M. V. Hahn, and J. C. Wilk. Floor surfaces and effect upon feet and leg soundness. In *Proceedings of the Symposium of Management of Food Producing Animals, West Lafayette, Indiana, 1982*, edited by W. Woods. West Lafayette, Ind.: Purdue Univ. 1982, p. 816–33.

Nilsson, C. Floor coverings in standings and cubicles for dairy cows. In *Modeling, Design and Evaluation of Agricultural Buildings,* edited by J. A. D. MacCormack. Aberdeen, Scotland: Scottish Farm Builders Investment Unit, 1981, p. 309–17.

Sambraus, H. H. Das Suhlen von Sauen. *Dtsch. Tieraerztl.* 88 (1981): 65–67.

Seabrook, M. F. A study to determine the influence of the herdsman's personality on milk yield. *J. Agric. Labour Sci.* 1 (1972): 45–59.

Seligman, M. E. P. *Helplessness.* San Francisco, Calif.: Freeman, 1975.

Stolba, A. A family system in enriched pens as a novel method of pig housing. In *Alternatives to Intensive Husbandry Systems.* South Mimms, U.K.: Universities Federal Animal Welfare, 1981, p. 52–67.

Stolba, A. The pig park family system: housing designed according to the consistent patterns of pig behaviour and social structure (Abstract). In *Research, Management, Behavior and Well-Being of Farm Animals, Conf. Human-Animal Bond, Minneapolis, Minnesota, 1983*, p. 2.

Tauson, R. Cages: how could they be improved? In *The Laying Hen and Its Environment*, edited by R. Moss. Boston, Mass.: Nijhoff, 1980, p. 269–99.

Van Rooijen, J. Are feelings adaptations? The basis of modern applied animal ethology. *Appl. Anim. Ethol.* 7 (1981): 187–89.

Van Rooijen, J. The value of choice tests in assessing welfare of domestic animals. *Appl. Anim. Ethol.* 8 (1982): 295–99.

Wiepkema, P. R. Behavioral aspects of stress. In *Biology of Stress in Farm Animals: An Integrative Approach,* edited by P. R. Wiepkema and P. W. M. van Adrichem. Boston, Mass.: Nijhoff, 1987, p. 113–33.

Wood-Gush, D. G. M., I. J. H. Duncan, and D. Fraser. Social stress and welfare problems in agricultural animals. In *The Behaviour of Domestic Animals*, 3d ed., edited by E. S. E. Hafez. Baltimore, Md.: Williams & Wilkins, 1975, p. 182–200.

Social Ethics, Animal Rights, and Agriculture

Bernard E. Rollin

MANY OF THE PEOPLE IN AGRICULTURE, animal research, or other animal-using areas whose activities have been criticized on grounds designated as "animal rights" believe such criticism is irrational, misguided, misplaced, sentimental, or misanthropic. For this reason, the response by animal users to such attacks has often been to point out the patent benefits that accrue to human society by virtue of social adherence to the allegedly objectional practices. Thus, the biomedical community has pointed to medical advances achieved by invasive use of animals in medical research, and the agricultural community has called attention to the abundance of cheap, palatable, healthful food made available as a direct result of industrialized agriculture.

Sophisticated critics have in turn responded by raising questions about a biomedical science that stresses cure over prevention, or about the significant environmental costs of many agricultural practices. This discussion will focus on the more basic question of whether the claim that certain agricultural practices do violate the rights of animals is merely a sentimental prejudice, or whether it can be shown to rest in some sort of significant, rationally based moral argument that must be either acknowledged or refuted, not merely dismissed.

How does one demonstrate that a given social practice, widely accepted and demonstrably profitable or convenient—be it child labor, the barring of women from certain professions, or the raising of animals under intensive confinement—is morally problematic? One way to approach such a practice is by vigorous and forceful condemnation: "It was cruel to treat animals that way," "Only a monster would so exploit children," and so on. Unfortunately, such broadsides generally elicit simple denial or broadsides of their own: "You care more about animals than about people." What generally happens in such cases is a head-on collision—one set of moral convictions is run foursquare into its opponent, the moral equivalent of linemen clashing at line of scrimmage. Generally, as in football, power prevails.

In my view, philosophers and others who create moral systems de novo and set them in opposition to common moral practice are engaged in such a clash, one that resembles the grappling of sumo wrestlers. And given that their new ethic, however elegantly constructed and defended it may be, can rarely command the force required to dislodge the status quo, it ends up ejected from the arena, at best having shaken its opponent slightly, and caused him to plant his feet even more firmly.

Both recent and long-term histories of social moral evolution demonstrate that there exists a conceptual alternative to the clash of opposites, what one may call moral judo rather than moral sumo. Whereas in sumo, opponents pit their force against one another in a direct confrontation, in judo, they turn the opposing force to their own advantage. Precisely the same thing occurs in moral combat. Far more effective than head-on collision is the ability to demonstrate that the position one advocates is, in fact, grounded in the opponent's position, albeit implicitly.

Arguably, something of this sort occurred when (thinking) segregationists accepted integration, or when professions, such as veterinary medicine, that had traditionally barred women began to admit them. In both cases, presumably no change in moral principles was required. What was demanded was a realization that the moral commitment to equality of opportunity, justice, and fairness held by the segregationist or traditionalist entailed a change in practice. Such people had readily accepted democratic moral principles as applying to all persons, but they had ignored the fact that the class of "persons" was far greater than they had acknowledged and included blacks and women. It is this same broadening of accepted moral principles, rather than the adoption of new ones, that led to the steady augmentation of the class of rights-bearers defined in the U.S. Constitution beyond the original limited group of native-born white male adult property owners.

The point about moral judo can be found in Socrates' assertion that philosophers can not really teach, they can only remind, or help others to recall; that is, to draw out ignored or unnoticed implications of their own assumptions. This is not a simple or trivial task, since people's assumptions are often invisible to them, or highly protected from criticism, or self-contradictory. Nonetheless, it can be done, even in regard to the treatment of animals, an area in which common morality is virtually mute.

Although differences the ethical positions among diverse members of a society tend to be magnified, the similarities and agreement in ethical principles, intuitions, and theories that obtain in society far outweigh the differences. In American society, we are all brought up and steeped in the same Judaeo-Christian, democratic, individualistic heritage. We also live under the same set of laws, which encode much of that morality in ways guiding and shaping our theories and practices. And finally, it is fairly evident that we simply could not live and function together if we did not implicitly share a very significant set of moral guidelines. This simple fact is usually unnoticed precisely because it is always there and it is usually true. What is noted and remembered are the situations where it is not true and where we are greatly divided, over issues like capital punishment or, perhaps, abortion, although abortion, in my view, involves more of a metaphysical dispute than a moral one, since all parties would presumably acquiesce to the same moral principles governing taking human life; the debate seems to be over what counts as human life.

In any event, it appears that we do share something of a consensus ethical ideal for the treatment of human beings, which pervades our thinking and governs our laws and social policy. This ideal is easily outlined: In democratic societies, we accept the notion that individual humans are the basic objects of moral concern, rather than the state, the Reich, the Volk, or some other abstract entity. We act on this principle by generally making social decisions in light of benefit to the majority, or, in utilitarian terms, the greatest benefit to the greatest number. In such calculations, each individual is counted as one, and thus no one's interests are ignored. But such decision making presents the risk of riding roughshod over the minority in any given instance. So democratic societies have developed the notion of individual rights, protective fences built around the individual that guard him or her in certain ways from encroachment by the interests of the majority.

These rights are based upon plausible hypotheses about *human nature*, i.e., about the central interests and needs of human beings, needs that when unmet matter most to people (or, we feel, *ought* to matter most). So, for example, freedom of speech is protected, even when virtually no one wishes to hear the ideas of the speaker, a Nazi, for example. Similarly, the rights of assembly, of choosing one's own companions and beliefs are protected, as well as the individual's right not to be tortured even if it is in the general interest to torture, as in the case of a criminal who has stolen and hidden vast amounts of public money. And all of these rights are not simply abstract moral notions, but are built into the legal system. Thus, the notion of human nature is pivotal to our ethic—we feel obliged to protect the set of needs and desires that we hypothesize as being at the core of what it means to be human.

The obvious question that arises is, what does this have to do with animals? The answer is simple. If it can be shown that there are no rationally defensible grounds for differentiating animals from humans as candidates for moral concern, then, logically, the entire moral machinery used to deal with human questions must be brought to bear upon questions of animal treatment. And, as I have argued at length elsewhere,[1] it turns out that there are no rationally justifiable grounds for excluding animals from the moral arena, even as it has been shown that there are none for excluding such neglected humans as women, blacks, and children. None of the standard reasons offered up in the history of thought for excluding animals from the moral arena will stand up to rational scrutiny. Such allegedly relevant differences as animals lack immortal souls; do not reason; lack language; are inferior to humans in strength or intelligence; are evolutionarily inferior; are incapable of entering into contracts; turn out to be either false or lacking the moral relevance that would justify not considering them morally.

Equally important, not only are there no morally relevant differences for excluding animals from moral concern as we in society define it, there are in fact significant morally relevant similarities between animals and humans.

The same sorts of features that allow right and wrong actions toward people to be defined are also found in animals. The features that are common to people and to at least "higher" animals (and possibly "lower" ones as well) are *interests*—needs, desires, predilections, the fulfillment and thwarting of which matter to the person or animal in question. Cars have needs—for gas, oil, and so on—but they do not have interests, since we have absolutely no reason to believe that it matters to the car itself whether or not it gets its oil. That is why it is impossible to behave immorally towards cars—they are merely tools for human benefit. But animals with interests cannot be looked at as mere tools, for they have lives that matter to them.

There are, of course, categories of interests and interests that are common to all animals, including humans—food, reproduction, avoidance of pain. But even more significant are the unique variations on these general interests, and the particular interests, that arise in different species. Even as we talk of human nature, as defined by the particular set of interests constitutive of and fundamental to the human animal, we can also talk of animal natures as well—the "pigness" of the pig, the "dogness" of the dog. Following Aristotle, I describe the *telos* of different species of animals as the distinctive set of needs and interests, physical and behavioral, that determine the sort of life it is suited to live. This is not a mystical notion—it follows directly from modern biology and genetics, and is certainly obvious to anyone who is around animals and, indeed, to common sense: "fish gotta swim and birds gotta fly."

I have argued that the consensus ethic for humans protects certain aspects of human nature deemed to be essential to the human *telos*, shielding them from infringement by the majority and by the general welfare. If no morally relevant grounds can be found for excluding animals from the application of that ethic, and if animals too have a *telos*, it follows inexorably that animals too should have their fundamental interests encoded in and protected by rights that enjoy both a legal and moral status. Thus, it can be shown that the notion of animal rights is implicit (albeit unrecognized) in our consensus social ethics.[2]

The only possible way this conclusion can be avoided is to deny that animals are aware, enjoy mental lives, have consciousness, and feel pain and other modalities of suffering. However bizarre it may seem to ordinary people as well as farmers, scientists and philosophers since Descartes have denied that animals have feelings. In the twentieth century, this denial of animal mind, or at least of its knowability, became a mainstay of what I have termed the "common sense of science"; that is, the assumptions that are to science what common sense assumptions are to ordinary life.[3] This came about in part out of an effort to keep the unverifiable out of science and restrict its purview to the observable and operationally definable. Furthermore, the invasive use of animals was made far easier psychologically when pain and suffering were excluded from scientific legitimacy by methodological fiat.[4]

Happily, in recent years the pendulum has swung in the other direction, and the idea of consciousness in animals is again emerging. Some of this new thrust comes from burgeoning social concern about animal welfare—new laws governing animal research essentially mandate anthropomorphism regarding animal pain, by asserting that if something hurts a human, it should be presumed to hurt an animal.[5] Some of it comes from a growing realization, which Darwin and his contemporaries clearly had, that it is inconsistent to postulate evolutionary continuity on the morphological and physiological levels but deny it on the psychological level.[6] And some of it comes from an accumulation of neurophysiological and neurochemical data that stresses the similarity between humans and animals.[7] Finally, some of it comes from a realization that we simply cannot understand animal behavior unless we postulate mentation in animals.[8] To take one example relevant to agriculture: There is a body of literature that makes it patent that one cannot use the notion of stress as a purely physiological, mechanical, or behavioral response, but in fact must presuppose mentation to make it at all plausible.[9]

If we can therefore leave aside Cartesian skepticism as a way of forestalling the application of our social ethic to animals, we can now sketch its applicability to agriculture, recalling that it is an *ideal.* Obviously, for practical purposes, one must bracket the question of the animal's right to life, since much of animal agriculture consists in raising animals to be slaughtered. But the fundamental question of what *sort* of life agricultural animals are morally entitled to even if their ultimate fate is to be killed then becomes the key moral issue. And one surely cannot argue that since the animals are going to die anyway, it doesn't matter how we treat them—after all, we too are going to die anyway.

The basic issue of how agricultural animals lived their lives was not so acute before the advent of technological agriculture. After all, husbandry systems needed to fit the animals' *telos* fairly well; if they did not, the animals simply could not live and be productive—they would sicken, die, fail to produce, and fail to reproduce. In short, agricultural practice and agricultural animals had evolved a fit. To be sure, there were always practices that were morally questionable—hot-iron branding, castration without anesthesia, transport of livestock under harmful conditions—but the key point was that the basic conditions under which the animals lived had to be conditions for which their *telos* suited them.

With the advent of confinement agriculture, this naturally balanced process was undone. Confinement conditions, for example, that in the past would have inevitably led to decimation of animals by disease could now be imposed and their pernicious consequences avoided by antibiotics, vaccines, and other chemical means. This sort of tool paved the way for agricultural environments that were profitable, productive, and "efficient" (though often environmentally costly) without having to respect the animals' natures or modify them to fit these new environments. While sophisticated animal-preference studies of the sort pioneered by Dawkins[10] and others have given us additional evidence that animals would not usually prefer confinement, in a real sense such work merely gilds the lily. Anyone with a basic knowledge of a farm animal's nature would know that current intensive husbandry systems do not satisfy the set of needs constitutive of the *telos* of farm animals. It does not take an ethologist to realize that social animals need social environments, or that animals biologically built to move need space to do so. In fact, there is something odd and mischievous in persistent demands voiced by agribusiness and agricultural scientists that such claims be empirically verified.

The manifest behavioral pathologies occurring in confinement that are often treated symptomatically, for example, by surgical removal of beaks or tails, further support our point. Ironically, these pathologies—cannibalism in chickens, self-mutilation in a variety of animals, tail-biting in pigs, and many others—are termed "vices" by confinement agriculturalists, as if they were analogous to morally defective behavior in humans. The vice lies, if anywhere, in the systems that bring forth these behaviors. The roots of these behaviors can be found in animals under natural conditions, but under those conditions their pernicious consequences are avoidable—chickens, for example, flee from each other and establish a dominance hierarchy. In confinement, such behaviors are magnified and amplified, as are those other "vices" that seem to be occasioned by boredom or frustration of natural behavioral inclinations.

Technological agriculture tends to ignore many of the needs and interests constitutive of a farm animal's *telos*. Insofar as confinement agriculture has recognized animal nature at all, it has seen the animals as metabolic machines that need food, water, and shelter to eat, grow, produce, and reproduce. However, there is a great deal more to meeting a farm animal's interests than mere satisfaction of these most basic requirements. It follows that husbandry systems for farm animals should aim not merely at meeting the animals' physical needs, but at satisfying the basic physical *and* mental or behavioral interests that constitute the *telos*. Moral responsibility to either humans or animals is not fulfilled by simply attending to the physical needs alone. Well-nourished and physically healthy humans could be maintained in an aseptic environment on intravenous nutrients and electronic stimulation of the muscles, but to do so would not be to behave morally, because all the other parts of their *telos* would be disregarded. There is more to caring for humans and for animals than providing food, water, and shelter. Humans want to play, socialize, discuss, and travel as well as be nourished; there are analogous interests for animals.

I am suggesting that our *moral ideal* for farm animal husbandry ought to be the satisfaction of the complex set of mental and physical interests that make up the animal's nature or *telos*. It is reasonable to call such a state of satisfaction *happiness* for an animal, just as Aristotle long ago defined human happiness as the satisfaction of the human rational *telos*. In practical terms, satisfaction of farm animals' *telos* would mean that standards of farm animal husbandry, regardless of species, would be based on our knowledge of the animals' natures as determined in the environment to which they are biologically suited.

Adherents of technological agriculture will understandably be inclined to dismiss the above conclusion as unrealistic and utopian. It is therefore important to stress that these conclusions are not simply personal, but are logical consequences of widespread moral principles applied in society at large. How else can one explain the fact that, while scientific research on animals was essentially unregulated throughout its history in the United States, as of 1987 it is constrained by two new sets of laws, which require control of pain and suffering not essential to research, which mandate (as against the common sense of science) that animals feel pain under the same conditions people do, which require exercise for dogs used in research and environments for primates used in research that "enhance their psychological well-being." Surely this bespeaks some social concern about the rights of animals, as do vigorous efforts to adapt zoos to captive animals' natures. Most significant are new laws and regulations in Europe that constrain and even outlaw aspects of confinement agriculture taken for granted in the U.S. The most dramatic is, perhaps, the new Swedish law that ensures the right of cattle to graze. For U.S. agriculture to ignore these signs of growing moral awareness about animal rights would be both blind and ill-advised.

Obviously, there is something morally disquieting about pushing animals into environmental boxes where they fit only with great discomfort—the crated veal calf is both a literal and symbolic manifestation of this tendency. If we are to take animal lives for any sort of human benefit, itself a morally questionable presumption, we are at least obliged to ensure that those animals live happy lives consonant with their *telos.*

Notes

1. B. E. Rollin, *Animal Rights and Human Morality*. Buffalo, N.Y.: Prometheus Books, 1981.
2. *Ibid.*
3. Bernard E. Rollin, *The Unheeded Cry: Animal Consciousness, Animal Pain and Science* (New York: Oxford University Press, 1989).
4. B. E. Rollin, "Animal pain," in M. W. Fox and L. Mickley, eds., *Advances in Animal Welfare Science (1985–86)* (The Hague: Martinus Nijhoff, 1986) pp. 91–106. B. E. Rollin, "Animal pain, scientific ideology, and the reappropriation of common sense," *Journal of the American Veterinary Medical Association* 191 (1987): 1222–26.
5. B. E. Rollin, "Laws relevant to animal research in the United States," in A. A. Tuffery, ed., *Laboratory Animals* (London: John Wiley), pp. 323–33. See also *Panel Report on the Colloquium on Recognition and Alleviation of Animal Pain and Distress. Journal of the American Veterinary Medical Association* 191 (1987): 1186–91.
6. D. W. Griffin, *The Question of Animal Awareness* (New York: Rockefeller University Press, 1976). B. E. Rollin, *Animal Consciousness*, cited in note 3.
7. S. Walker, *Animal Thought* (London: Routledge and Kegan Paul, 1983).
8. B. E. Rollin, *Animal Consciousness*, cited in note 3.
9. B. E. Rollin, *Animal Consciousness*, cited in note 3. J. Weiss, "Psychological factors in stress and disease," *Scientific American* 226 (1987): 101–13. J. Mason, "A re-evaluation of the concept of 'non-specificiy' in stress theory," *Journal of Psychiatric Research* 8 (1971): 323–33. R. Danzer and P. Mormede, "Stress in farm animals: A need

for re-evaluation," *Journal of Animal Science* 57 (1983): 6–18.

10. M. S. Dawkins, *Animal Suffering: The Science of Animal Welfare* (London: Chapman and Hall, 1980).

Factory Farming and the Interests of Animals

Dana R. Flint

SOME PEOPLE ARGUE THAT FACTORY FARMING is morally objectionable because it violates the rights of farm animals. But is the appeal to animal rights a sound basis for such a claim? On one view, whether or not farm animals have rights depends on their level of mental capacity. It is argued that farm animals have mental capacities sufficiently similar to human beings to warrant extending rights to them. Opposed to this view are those who argue that farm animals have such limited mental capacities that the extension of rights to them is indefensible. If the question whether farm animals have rights depends on their level of mental capacity, then one controversy seems to replace another. Just what mental capacities do farm animals have? And what connections does that have with farm animals having rights? I will argue that it is unreasonable to deny that farm animals have cognitively qualified mental states—complexes of beliefs, desires, and emotions—but that there remains differences between animals and human beings that have a bearing on the question whether and to what extent farm animals have rights.

Prelinguistic Beliefs and Desires Are Possible

A good place to start is with the following argument: Animals have interests, beings with interests have rights, and so animals have rights.[1] R. G. Frey has rather provocatively objected to this argument, holding that animals do not have interests and so do not have rights. He interprets "interests" in the "traditional and most common analysis"[2] as having wants as desires, and argues that animals do not have interests because they lack the capacity to have wants as desires. Taking it a step further, Frey says having desires is dependent on having beliefs, and beliefs are dependent on possession of linguistic competence. To believe something, he suggests, is to believe that a certain *sentence* is true. Thus

> If what is believed is that a certain sentence is true, then no creature which lacks language can have beliefs; and without beliefs, a creature cannot have desires.[3]

Since animals lack linguistic competence, they do not have beliefs and desires. Lacking that level of mental capacity, they lack interests. So, for Frey, there is no basis for claiming they have rights.

But this argument is too strong. If the capacity for belief is language dependent, then no plausible explanation could be given of prelinguistic children and deaf-mutes who learn language. To learn to apply labels to objects, they would first have to perceptually discriminate those objects. But how could they perceptually discriminate such objects if they had no perceptual beliefs about them? A more plausible view is that they do have prelinguistic perceptual beliefs that enable them to learn to apply linguistic terms to objects. In fact deaf-mutes have reported having beliefs and thoughts before learning language, which suggests they have had prelinguistic beliefs.[4]

Explanatory Models for Understanding Farm Animals

This much suggests only that one cannot rule out the possibility of animals' having cognitively qualified mental states. It does not show that languageless animals actually do have the capacity for beliefs. Even if the above reply to Frey is accepted, Frey's metatheoretical model of animal mental capacities remains eligible as an explanation of animal behavior. On Frey's model, animal behavior is adequately explained by reference to instinctual behavioral cycles that do not require reference to any mental states. Rather, a deficiency with respect to a non-psychological need triggers a behavioral cycle guided by instinct, a kind of internal "program" that causes the behavioral patterns that in the animal's normal habitat fulfill its needs. When the need is satisfied, the behavior of the animal becomes quiescent.[5] On a second metatheoretical model, however, essential reference is made to cognitively qualified mental states—such as beliefs and desires—in explanations of the functional import of animal behavior. Because animals cannot report them, such mental states are theoretically postulated as *analogical approximations* to the real mental states of animals. The particular complex of beliefs and desires assigned to animals will, on this account, be constrained by a species-specific theory of their rational capacities.[6]

The idea is to shift the question to which explanatory model, the prelinguistic belief model or Frey's instinct model, best explains the behavioral evidence. As a matter of explanatory economy, it seems reasonable to propose that complexes of beliefs and desires should not be postulated unless explanations on an instinct model are inadequate. And this model does seem to provide inadequate behavioral explanations where the behavior involved exhibits sequential patterns of complicated and variable adjustments to the environment. A dog retrieving a ball or riding a surfboard exhibits just that sort of variable adjustment to its environment. The rigid behavior pattern of oysters does not. While the instinct model may be adequate for oysters, it is not adequate for dogs.

The best explanations of the behavior of higher animals most likely combine elements of these two models, as in Midgley's distinction of "open" and "closed" instincts. Midgley defines "open" instincts as instincts in which general patterns of behavior are fixed, but "gaps" exist that need to be filled by adjustments requiring learning and experience. "Closed" instincts are those which are rigid, with no apparent capacity for adjustment to changes in the environment.[7] If animals with closed instincts have any awareness, it would be incapable of reaching beyond immediate sensory experience. But as animal behavior patterns become more complicated and variable, postulation of open instincts that include cognitively qualified mental states becomes more reasonable. Otherwise, it is difficult to provide plausible explanations of the behavior of such "higher" animals.

If we look at farm animals from this perspective, then I think we will conclude that cows, chickens, and pigs have open instincts. Cows, for example, are able to learn that electric fences give an unpleasant jolt, and will seek to circumvent them. If so, then it cannot be argued that these farm animals lack interests because they lack cognitively qualified mental states. Their learning to adjust to novel environments would suggest that they have such mental states, and on Frey's definition of interests, they have interests. Frey's strategy of drawing a line between rights-holders and nonrights-holders on the basis of whether they have interests is plausible, but his assessment of the actual level of the mental capacities of higher animals is rather implausible. On the argument we started with, such farm animals would be possessors of rights.

Persons Have Culturally Qualified Abilities

Tom Regan has defended the view that animals are full-blown possessors of rights. He emphasizes that mammalian animals have "beliefs, desires, memory, a sense of the future, self-awareness, an emotional life, and act intentionally."[8] Animals that have these capacities are "subjects-of-a-life" and have inherent value.[9] They have lives that can be better or worse for them. As moral patients, such animals have equal inherent value to moral agents.[10] But Regan recognizes the need to draw the line between animals above and animals below that level of mental capacity. Those below include animals that are merely conscious but have no sense of future or memory of the past,[11] and single-cell animals that utterly lack consciousness.[12] Animals that fall below the level of subjects-of-a-life do not have such inherent value. Those above that level do have inherent value and the same right of respectful treatment as moral agents.[13]

If these characteristics (beliefs, desires, memory, a sense of the future, self-awareness, an emotional life, and intentional action) are intended to draw the line between those animals that have inherent value and those that do not, it is unclear just which species of animals get included in the former category. There is no evidence to suggest that night herons who travel in anonymous flocks recognize other members of their species as unique individuals.[14] And if they are incapable of recognizing other members of their species as unique individuals, then they are incapable of recognizing themselves as unique individuals. If so, then they could hardly be thought to have self-awareness. Nevertheless, they might still have desires associated with satisfying instinctual needs. They might still act so as to bring about the satisfaction of their desires, though not being aware that it is *their* desires they are acting to satisfy. Hence, they have some of the qualifying characteristics but not all. Do they get included or excluded according to the subject-of-a-life criterion?

In fact, Regan's account faces a dilemma. On the one hand, if all these characteristics are required for being subjects-of-a-life, then even some farm animals may not qualify. Capacities for having beliefs, desires, and an emotional life are less difficult to establish than the capacity for self-consciousness and a nontrivial sense of the future. Where adequate empirical evidence is lacking, the attribution of such capacities takes on the character of an unconvincing moral recommendation to look at these animals as if they had self-awareness and a sense of the future. On the other hand, if farm animals cannot be shown to have all of these characteristics, then the stress on their similarity to human beings loses force.

Since these characteristics are applied analogically to animals, it will be useful to consider what differences there are between their use for human beings and for animals. The differences are not only natural differences in the level of mental capacity. Margolis has persuasively defended the view that persons are culturally emergent entities belonging to a cultural realm which they have created. Human beings are distinguished more by their culturally emergent character than their species membership. Margolis says

> Persons, then, are in a sense not natural entities: they exist only in cultural contexts and are identifiable as such only by reference to their mastery of language and of whatever further abilities presuppose such mastery . . . Among those "further abilities" is, precisely, the ability to change the interests and direction of human activity for reasons of contingent and variable doctrinal conviction.[15]

On his view, persons are culturally emergent realities that have a whole range of further capacities dependent on linguistic mastery, capacities that languageless animals cannot have. So even if farm animals have capacities for belief, desires, a sense of the future, self-awareness, an emotional life, and intentional action, only culturally emergent persons have these capacities in this culturally qualified sense. Hence, only persons have a sense of the future that is framed in terms of culturally available options, significant forms of self-awareness such as self-respect and self-esteem, an emotional life with a moral character, and morally significant intentional action.

The Moral Significance of Culturally Qualified Capacities

These culturally qualified capacities make a significant difference when one considers the matter of welfare interests of persons and animals. According to Regan, "welfare-interests" are those interests possessed by animals that may have a well-being. The reason is that if an animal has a well-being, then it would be possible to benefit the animal, which is to provide conditions of that animal's living well. According to Regan, to live well is to have one's desires satisfied in an integrated an harmonious way "relative to one's capacities."[16] Thus the three conditions of living well for humans and animals are

> (1) they pursue and obtain what they prefer, (2) they take satisfaction in pursuing and getting what they prefer, and (3) what they pursue and obtain is in their interests.[17]

The first thing to notice about this is that it is circular, for while these three conditions are intended to define living well, condition three is defined in terms of living well. What is in the interests of animals, on this condition, is precisely what is conducive to their living well. Unless Regan could give some independent account of living well for both animals and humans, this condition is quite unhelpful.

Telfer characterizes living well in an Aristotlean fashion as *eudaemonia*, as living a life that is *fit* to live. Eudaemonia is to be distinguished from—but includes—subjective happiness because the latter concerns the kind of life the individual is actually satisfied with, while eudaemonia is attributed to a life in terms of some criteria of objective valuation.[18] She proposes that the life fit to live is a life composed of intrinsically worthwhile activities, including intellectual inquiry, understanding, aesthetic creation, aesthetic contemplation, the exercise of moral virtue, and the practice of friendship. The determinate forms these activities take and which of these gets emphasized in an individual life is what she characterizes as a *style* of eudaemonia.[19] Subjective happiness may consist in a harmonious and integrated satisfaction of one's desires, but to live well requires that the subjective happiness be shaped by desires that are fit to have. Mere subjective happiness is not sufficient for living well. To live well, then, one must live a life that is fit to live according to some objective standards of valuation.

If this view is correct, then to have one's desires fulfilled in an integrated and harmonious way relative to one's capacities is not sufficient for living well. Would the collective aggression of rats against other rats constitute living well? Such rats might fulfill Regan's conditions (1) and (2), but that is not enough. They might pursue what they prefer, and take satisfaction in pursuing and getting what they prefer, but that is not sufficient to show that they do what is fit to do. Condition (3) poses the problem. For if the interests of these animals is what provides conditions of their living well, we are still left with the question whether their species-specific activities constitute a mode of living well. Are these activities fit to do?

Now this may sound like it presumes that the only model of living well is the model for human beings. But that is not quite accurate. Rather, the *only* normative standards available to answer such a question are those drawn from the culture and traditions of human beings. There is no rat point of view to compare with corresponding viewpoints of human beings concerning what constitutes living well, nor is there any natural proper "telos" for rats. If rats do what they "prefer," then that is merely to say they do what they desire, and what they desire is not necessarily desirable. If there is a species-specific form of living well for rats, a "telos" for rats, then it has to be one that is formulated and defended in terms of the normative categories of human beings. Without such a defense, it is reasonable to suggest that there is little in the way of "interests" to protect by extending rights to rats.

One approach to such a defense would be to draw analogies between living well for human beings and for species of animals. For example, some analogies might be drawn between human friendship and animal bonding, such as is implicit in Lorenz's account of Ada, the greyleg goose. Lorenz says

> All the objectively observable characteristics of the goose's behavior on losing its mate are roughly identical with those accompanying human grief.[20]

Lorenz immediately discounts the scientific merits of this claim through the expression of a positivist bias against animals having subjective states. But if it were possible for animals of certain species to experience grief, and if that is indicative of a kind of bonding analogous to what occurs in human friendship and kinship relations, then perhaps some value ought to be attached to such animal bonding. It would be stretching the analogy too much to include those species of animal capable only of the anonymous bonding of flocks. And there are enormous differences insofar as (1) human friendship and kinship relations are culturally informed while animal bonding is not, and (2) animals lack the capacity for the remaining range of activities included in the idea of living well. But even though attenuated by the lack of culturally qualified capacities, the fact that greyleg geese can bond in this way provides some basis for arguing that they may in a limited sense live well. So at least some species of animals may, on Regan's definition, have welfare-interests.

The differences between human beings and animals are fundamental regarding autonomously choosing a style of eudaemonia. Even animals with "open" instincts still have the "ends" of their behavioral activities blindly fixed by survival-oriented instincts. Since the "ends" of human beings are culturally qualified, persons have the capacity to choose a style of living well. Only human beings have the capacity to engage in doctrinal debate and decisions concerning the proper ends of living, or the proper style of eudaemonia. This is one of those "further abilities" that animals never have. Perhaps "Martians" might have this culturally emergent capacity, but there is no other known species whose members do have that capacity. What this suggests is that while human beings have a spectrum of options for living well that are available only to beings with culturally qualified "further abilities," the lack of these "further abilities" makes it impossible for animals to have options. If rights are intended to guarantee "space" within which a being can autonomously choose its particular style of living well, then in the case of animals, what space needs to be guaranteed is significantly diminished. The only space that we might legitimately claim on behalf of animals is room for bonding and other animal activities to which *we* attach significant value.

The Question of Animal Rights

We need to take a closer look at the significance of this difference for the question whether farm animals possess rights. Regan agrees that there are no animal moral agents, which indicates just one of those "further abilities" animals do not have. Nevertheless, Regan thinks there are both human and animal moral patients. Unlike moral agents, moral patients cannot do what is right or wrong or make reasoned moral choices. They, however, can be the recipients of right and wrong actions. But we must ask whether animal and human moral patients are significantly different regarding the question of rights possession.

Feinberg argued that moral patients could be rights-holders even though claiming rights was one of the central points of the concept of rights and moral patients are incapable of claiming their rights. Moral patients were conceptually eligible as candidates for rights because proxies could claim rights on their behalf. Hence, the connection between claiming and rights would not be lost.[21] If so, then though rights are conceptually tied to the activity of claiming, it would not be conceptually absurd to attribute them to moral patients.

But when Feinberg considers the moral significance of claiming rights, he says

> Having rights makes claiming possible . . . but it is claiming that gives rights their special moral significance . . . Having rights enables us to "stand up like men," look others in the eye, and to feel in some fundamental way the equal of anyone.[22]

If the moral significance of rights is concerned with our asserting our fundamental equality with other people through claiming our rights, then animal moral patients can *never* enjoy that moral significance. There is no evidence to suggest that animals ever have the conceptual and cultural prerequisites necessary to claim their rights. Even if animals do possess rights, their possessing rights will lack this specially morally significant character.

But the situation is different for human moral patients. With very few exceptions, children may be groomed and trained to exercise their rights. Childhood itself is a phase in the development of human beings, including the development of the "further abilities" human beings possess. So if claiming rights is morally significant, then surely children ought to be groomed and trained to participate in such a morally significant activity. And this can only be done if children are already deemed possessors of rights. Looked at in the long view—which is appropriate for a cross-species comparison—it is part of the normal life of a person to develop the capacity to claim rights. So while humans may sometimes be merely moral patients and not moral agents, they are moral patients as part of a larger species life in which they exercise and claim their rights. Rights seem to be especially appropriate, then, for members of the human species.

This suggests that human moral patients are significantly different from animal moral patients. Animals will never be claimers of their rights, while it is a reasonable presumption that human moral patients will participate as claimers of their rights. Given this special moral significance of rights, it is reasonable to propose that "rights" be understood as attributed to animals only in a secondary and less morally significant sense than with human beings. This is not to say that some species of animals, including farm animals, are undeserving of consideration of what interests they do have. It is only to say that the language of rights may not be the best language within which to frame these concerns. In fact, it may be better to frame these questions in terms of the interests to animals rather than their rights. When we attribute interests to animals, we mean only that they want some things to which we attach significant value.

Implications for Factory Farming

It seems reasonable to propose that because of these differences, the rights of human moral agents and patients have greater weight than the interests of animals. While both farm animals and human beings can suffer and experience pain, the rights of persons not to suffer ought to weigh more heavily in our moral deliberations than the interests of animals. The reason is that the suffering and pain of human beings interferes with a far more significant form of life than the suffering and pain of animals. Animals can never enjoy that significance because they can never have the culturally qualified capacities that only human beings are known to have. Having said this, however, it is wrong to entirely ignore the interests of animals in our moral deliberations. Factory farming, unfortunately, has sometimes done just that. Putting chickens in cages that do not permit movement and that cause perpetual misery is cruel.

Factory farming is a collection of technologies and practices used to rear animals. Once such a technology is in place, it is typically fixed and rigid. Hence, the key point at which change is possible is in the design phase of farms, or in the choice of which farm design is to be used. With their narrow focus on designs that exclusively serve the ends of productivity and efficiency, designers of factory farms and farmers have ignored the interests of farm animals, such as the interests in not suffering and in engaging in "natural" activities.[23] A more holistic approach to designing farms, however, would take into account such items as the health of consumers, the way of life of farmers, and the interests of farm animals.[24] Presumably, as technology advances, the range of flexibility for designing farms should increase. It does seem that the "side effect" of the perpetual misery of farm animals might be avoided if the designers of factory farms would take such animal interests into account in their designs. If so, then designers, manufacturers, and owners of factory farms ought to adopt this more holistic approach.

Notes

1. R. G. Frey, *Interests and Rights: The Case Against Animals* (Oxford: Oxford University Press, 1980), pp. 5, 78–79.
2. Ibid., p. 78.
3. Ibid., p. 88–89.
4. Roger Trigg, "Thought and Language," *Proceedings of the Aristotlean Society* (1978): 69–71.
5. Frey, *Interests and Rights*, pp. 72–77.
6. Joseph Margolis, *Culture and Cultural Entities* (Boston: D. Reidel Publishing Co., 1984), pp. 42–59.
7. Mary Midgley, *Beast and Man* (New York: Cornell University Press, 1978), p. 53.
8. Tom Regan, *The Case for Animal Rights* (Berkeley: University of California Press, 1983), pp. 77, 243.
9. Ibid., p. 243.
10. Ibid., p. 244.
11. Ibid., p. 76.
12. Ibid., p. 77.
13. Ibid., p. 279.
14. Konrad Lorenz, *On Aggression* (New York: Bantam Books, 1963), pp. 133–43.
15. Joseph Margolis, *Persons and Minds* (Boston: D. Reidel Publishing Company, 1978), p. 245.

16. Regan, *The Case for Animal Rights*, cited in note 9, p. 89.
17. Ibid., p. 93.
18. Elizabeth Telfer, *Happiness* (New York: St. Martin's Press, 1980), pp. 37–38.
19. Ibid., pp. 77–80.
20. Lorenz, *On Aggression*, p. 201.
21. Joel Feinberg, *Rights, Justice, and the Bounds of Liberty* (Princeton: Princeton University Press, 1980), p. 163.
22. Ibid., p. 151.
23. James Mason and Peter Singer, *Animal Factories* (New York: Crown Publishers, Inc., 1980), pp. 122–27.
24. Stephen V. Monsma, ed., *Responsible Technology* (Michigan: William B. Eerdsmans Publishing Company, 1986), pp. 164–83.

Why (Most) Humans Are More Important Than Other Animals[1]

Charles V. Blatz

The Setting of the Problem

Animals are used both for the production and transportation of agricultural products, and also as sources of food and fiber. Many now question the justifiability of treating animals as consumable products. Critics challenge our beliefs that either nonhumans have no intrinsic ethical significance and deserve no serious attention on their own merits, or else that humans are more important than other animals.[2, 3]

This discussion will mainly address these two issues: the intrinsic and relative importance of human and nonhuman animals. I shall present a detailed defense of the view arguing that ethical standing is to be reserved for ethical agents, thus excluding nonhumans and even some humans. This leaves only a derivative importance for those who are not ethical agents. Later, I will examine the difficulties for assessing particular animal agricultural practices and veganism.

The Problem

Let me begin with the intrinsic importance of human and other animals. What is the basis of ethical standing or of a being's deserving consideration in itself? As William K. Frankena raises the question, it amounts to asking for the ultimate considerations in determining what is justifiable, and what beings manifest those features.[4] Every ethic begins somewhere, naming the objects of certain aims or certain pursuits are as justifiable in themselves and not because of their relation to some other justifiable aim or pursuit. The justification of an ethic begins here, at least, conflicts aside, with respect to what Ross called prima facie duty and what consequentialists might call a, but not necessarily the, right or optimific act.[5] Characterizing these beginning points would establish the most general norms of the ethic, those hypothetical claims that if an aim is of a certain sort, then, conflicts aside, it is justifiable. These norms, in turn, would justify other norms of the ethic (by what Paul Taylor calls "validation") and particular acts as well, either directly or derivatively (by the process Taylor calls "verification").[6] These ultimate considerations are "the seeds of justifiable conduct" in an ethic.

Different ethics identify different "seeds." Classical utilitarianism, for example, selects pleasure and the absence of pain as the basis of John Stuart Mill's "theory of life." Religiously oriented ethics, for another example, emphasize enlightenment or beatitude.

Once we know what the seeds of an ethic are, we can identify that which might manifest those seeds, and which will then have standing within that ethic. These will be conditions or beings whose presence, sustenance, and pursuits can be justified, conflicts aside, without reference to anything other than their manifesting (or perhaps being able to manifest) the seeds of justifiable conduct.

Questions of the justifiability of animal agriculture begin with the questions, what are the seeds of justifiable conduct and in what they are manifested? Are they found only in human beings, or in nonhumans as well? To assess animal agriculture, we first need to select among the various possible views of seeds and among the possibilities for assigning ethical standing.

How might we make this selection? Some have thought that this question amounts to asking how might we find what the *correct* ethic counts as seeds of justifiable conduct and the possessors of ethical standing.[7] That view of the matter, however, rests upon a fundamental confusion.

To select a method that will deliver the correct view of seeds (or to know that a method will fail to do so), we would have to have some way to attest to the reliability of the methods we select from. This in turn requires that we already have some grasp on what really are seeds in a correct ethic. Grasping the seeds of justifiable conduct, however, amounts to knowing the (basic) norms, and, consequently, the ethic we seek. Thus, to select a method to identify the *correct* ethic requires that we first have in hand the correct ethical theory. That, of course, is incoherent. Thus, it seems that nothing will satisfy getting at the correct ethic. But what is the alternative?

One suggestion comes from Rudolf Carnap's radical Kantian approach to the question, what exists?[8] Carnap recognizes that if we stand outside of all commitments to what kinds of things might exist, and so outside of all standards or tests of what does exist, we have moved outside all *correct* (or, as he put it, "theoretical") answers to questions of what there is. From such an *external* vantage point, questions about what kinds of things exist call for a decision, not a discovery. And for Carnap, this decision is a "practical" one based wholly on what answer will most effectively and efficiently serve the purposes of those asking what exists: purposes, for example, of constructing a theory of the foundations of mathematics or of empirical science.

Applied to our problem, this suggests the following. Without incoherence, we cannot give an internal view of what is justifiable and of who or what has intrinsic significance. We need a decision, not a discovery. And following Carnap's radical lead, we would make the decision on the basis of what could serve well the purposes for which we have ethical codes. We could ask, how would seed aims and ethical standing be specified in a code most appropriate to the aims of anyone embracing any ethic? This I shall call the *functionalist* approach to our problem.

Should we follow Carnap's functionalist lead in deciding upon an ethic to guide us in matters of animal agriculture? Yes. Otherwise, the ethic we select would be pointless, and thus unacceptable. To identify the point of an ethic is to single out what it is about the code that gives it some function for some being. An ethic's point is whatever allows it to have a real impact upon our lives. Without point, an ethic would make no impact upon anyone. There would be nothing about it that would make any difference to anyone and so might be counted in its favor or against it. Adopting it then (or not doing so, for that matter), would be arbitrary, and so the ethic would not be acceptable as opposed to unacceptable. Thus, if an ethic is acceptable, it has point.

This result limits what an acceptable ethic might say about seeds and standing. A minimally acceptable ethic will have features, including seeds, that allow it to function in some way such that it makes some difference to our lives or those of others. What might be the seeds of justifiable conduct and who or what might have standing in such a functional ethic? That is the problem we need to address.

The Answer to the Problem

My main contentions are, first, some ethics *do* have point, and in fact, there is one characterization that fits any point that any ethic might have. Second, having this common feature does place restrictions upon what aims and pursuits are acceptably counted as seeds. As it turns out, these restrictions deny ethical standing to nonhuman animals, indeed, to any but ethical agents.

To make good these contentions, we need to begin with an account of the point of any ethic. Kant, in the *Foundations of the Metaphysic of Morals*, reminds us that ethics always have their impact through influencing choice and behavior by appeals to reason bearing on the justifiability of our options.[9] The first main contention of my argument is this Kantian one: if there is any impact that is attributable to the operations of a code of ethics itself, then it is an impact that the code has by directing choice and behavior through the application of its norms to the options facing agents, through a directing influence upon the aims and pursuits of agents, an influence the code exerts by providing reasons pro and contra options open to the agent. Let me call that claim, "the functionalist's principle." According to this principle, then, the most general impact of ethics is to facilitate the choice and pursuit of options by providing reasons marking aims and pursuits open to us as justifiable or not.

This contention seems so fundamental to all of ethical theory that it is difficult to know just how to best argue for it. Ethics, as Frankena says, are action guides, and how else might they serve in this capacity but through providing reasons for or against the various options facing agents? It matters not *how* we see the operations of these reasons, for example, cognitively, as did Kant, or as emotively persuasive as sketched by C. L. Stevenson.[10] The conclusion is the same: ethics include, no matter what else, evaluations more or less general in scope,[11] evaluations that provide reasons pro or contra. And, if an ethic so understood is to have an impact, it must be the impact of the direction of reason upon an agent's aims and pursuits. The functionalist's principle records this point and, as such, seems uncontroversial.

Perhaps, however, it would be wise to note an intolerable consequence of rejecting the functionalist's principle. Ethics are thought to have no point for very young infants and for nonhuman animals, simply because their aims and pursuits are not open to the influence of justifying reasons. Even Tom Regan, that most thorough champion of animal rights, grants this (as do Peter Singer and Bernard Rollin, for example). He notes that nonhumans are not ethical agents and that the impact ethics would have on nonhumans must come through the influence of its justifying reasons upon ethical agents,[12] that is, the point of ethics is that they can influence choice and behavior only through such justifying reasons—the functionalist's principle.

To say that the point of ethics is lost on youngsters and nonhuman animals is not to say that how they are treated does not matter ethically. The next question, then, is, what are we to conclude from the functionalist's principle?

If an ethic is to influence choice and behavior through reasons, the influence will be exclusively on those whose choices and behavior can be directed by such reasons, namely, ethical agents. It will be the aims of *those agents* that are singled out as justifiable or not, acceptable or not. Otherwise, the normative guidance would fall on deaf ears.

Thus aims identified as seeds by the ethic's basic norms will *belong* to ethical agents. They might be *directed toward* the well-being of non-ethical agents, but the direction of an aim is irrelevant to whether there is any point to designating it justifiable or not. Whether there is any such point depends on whether those aims *belong* to ethical agents. The fact that seeds in an ethical code are the aims of ethical agents is what allows that code point, and makes it nonarbitrary and minimally acceptable. So, any ethic acceptable insofar as it has point will locate its seeds among the aims of ethical agents (those open to being guided by the justifying reasons it provides).[13] Let me call that the "rationalist's principle."

Now, the implication of the rationalist's principle is that the seeds of any ethic with point will be aims and pursuits of humans, as opposed to nonhumans. What significance nonhuman interests and well-being have in such an ethic is due to their being objects of the aims and pursuits of ethical agents. As objects of such aims, nonhuman animal welfare and freedom have a kind of fundamental importance stemming from the standing of those ethical agents who are their champions. Still, the ethical importance of nonhuman interests is derived from the ethical importance of humans, as opposed to nonhumans. This result I shall refer to as the "humanistic restriction of ethical standing."

Amplification of the Answer

Those with ethical standing are, then, humans. What is the significance of nonhumans as competitors in conflict with humans? What is the relative importance of humans and nonhumans?

The interests of nonhumans might end up more important than competing human interests in certain codes. This could happen in any ethic that allows nonhumanly directed aims as seeds and has a norm(s) of conflict resolution that allows such aims to win out over the competition. Do acceptable ethics operate this way?

The answer is "yes," but requires explanation about when ethical codes are acceptable. Adopting an ethic without point would be arbitrary, because there is nothing to say for or against adopting it, *as opposed to no ethic at all.* Choosing between two or more ethics, all of which have point but offer inconsistent guidance, will also be arbitrary if it is restricted, for no reason, the seeds of justifiable conduct and the aims that can win conflicts. Adopting such restrictions would be biased and would thus beg the question against those aims not counted or allowed to win conflicts. Only our minimal animal lovers' ethic is not arbitrary in this second way. No reasons can be given for saying that certain aims are or are not seeds of justifiable conduct. Thus, the animal interest advocate cannot be ignored as not having aims that count, ethically.[14] Aims calling for the protection of agricultural animals must be allowed to count. But how much do they count and what implications do their counting have for raising and consuming animals? That is a complex question!

Applications of the Answer

The major issue is just what treatment of nonhuman animals in agriculture will maximally serve the aims and pursuits of all who have standing and who count in conflicts over animal agriculture—namely, those ethical agents affected by the conflict's outcome. All I can do here is to try to make clear some of the complexity of the subissues.

Consider first some of the charges that have been leveled against the *procedures* used in animal agriculture. Perhaps the most notorious case is that of veal production. Veal calves are generally kept in quarters that virtually eliminate all but some head movement and the freedom to lie down. Social contact is essentially precluded. Their environment is often dark. Their lives are necessarily short. The object of all this is to produce quickly and economically a tender meat product for a limited but steady market. The animal is treated as a tissue factory, of concern to the producer only in how well and how fast it puts on flesh.

This sounds diabolical, but most producers of veal would not even raise the animals, regardless of procedures used, if the choice were up to them. Veal calves are mostly the male offspring of dairy cows, a progeny that is a problem to the dairy farmer. What is the farmer to do with such animals? Asking the farmers to raise and keep the animals would impose a serious financial burden on them. Without further subsidies wouldn't most farmers just cheat and destroy those unwanted calves?

Regulating the market so that only certifiable male dairy cow offspring could be sold for slaughter as calves, and requiring that they be sold by the animal, rather than per pound, for an amount equal to expenses, might well remove all current incentive for intensive techniques. Such a scheme would also have to require that the farmers keep the animals healthy so that selling calves by the animal would not lead to neglect. Regulations that would do all this would no doubt be intrusive and expensive to administer.

Perhaps, then, we should attempt to re-educate tastes, thereby undermining the market for veal? This, *if effective*, would eventually eliminate the unwanted intensive production, but the farmer will still have the animals to contend with.

What should we do, then, in the face of intensive veal production practices? These practices seem to put the animals in circumstances they would avoid if they could, and therefore seem harmful to the animals considered as sentient creatures with lives of their own. Avoiding this harm would impose monetary and gustatory losses, losses that are surely repairable and bearable, if we choose to repair and bear them. The protein of veal calves is not needed to maximally facilitate the aims and pursuits of all those in active conflict over the practices, let alone all those affected by the outcome of the conflict. What justification could be given for such practices if we appeal to an ethic that has point and is not question begging at the foundations? But, then, we just do not yet have all the facts, do we?

Although there are differences in the animals, the management practices, and the market size, some of the same sorts of points can be made about the treatment of brood sows. Unlike the veal calf, the brood sow is actively sought as a reproductive factory, and in this role can be subjected to considerable restraint in movement. Intensive hog raising practices, including sow restraint, mark a change from previous, more free-ranging, management techniques and were introduced to increase productivity and profit. Critics have urged that, at the least, these intensive practices are unjustifiable and ought to be eliminated. Some producers and production experts have defended them, often on a standard of animal welfare that measures only animal yield for profit.

Clearly, however, we lack the facts to decide the issue using a defensible ethic as outlined above. For example, what would be the impact on the industry structure if we were to remove the profit incentive supposedly fueling the engine of such practices? Would specialized producers be hurt the most and be driven to take their capital elsewhere? Or would a larger sector of the farming community be hurt, ultimately impairing a source of food going far beyond pork and important to all of us? Perhaps we could get along just fine with no more intensive hog production, letting those who want pork pay more? Do we know?

The question whether to make consumers pay for less intensive production techniques also looms large in intensive egg and poultry production. As the family farm has declined and the populations of

Western industrialized countries have become urbanized and suburbanized, intensified egg and poultry production has provided a stable and relatively inexpensive source of complete protein. What would be the cost of replacing those intensive management techniques in terms of the impairment of the aims and pursuits of the ethical agents touched by the conflict? Again, I think that we do not have a good idea of what to say.

That same question complicates the assessment of intensive beef production techniques. On the one hand, it would be most surprising if an acceptable ethic could justify the practice of grain-finishing cattle in intensive feedlot situations. As Lappé points out, the grain could be used elsewhere,[15] or the land used to produce it could support other products for human consumption. The food produced without this grain would be every bit as good a source of protein and, to some, every bit as palatable, as that produced with grain. Further, the beef produced nonintensively on open range in many areas of the United States and other countries, such as Australia, makes productive for the benefit of ethical agents land that would otherwise not be useful. (The same is true for what is even a better use of such arid range, namely, sheep production for wool, lamb, and mutton.) Here, then, it seems that nonintensive techniques avoid indefensible waste while at the same time being productive for the overall benefit of ethical agents.

On the other hand, however, if a world source of complete protein is the main issue, then intensive beef production, where economical and when conducted without the waste of grain finishing, is likely to turn out to be defensible. And, how could an assessment of animal agriculture ignore the fact that, in much of the world, human malnutrition is due to a lack of available complete protein?

Intensive beef production might also seem desirable in light of the social and environmental consequences of nonintensive beef production in areas of cheap lands and bipolar economies, such as those found in Central and South America. In those places, intensification of beef raising might be able to accompany land reform that would leave the peasant agriculturalists better off economically, and in some cases could provide the opportunity to reduce environmental depredation. Again, however, the point is that we just do not know.

The full weight of our ignorance and the complexity of the issues are made clear when we move from the criticism of animal food and fiber production techniques to the urging of veganism. A serious review of any move to veganism must assess the impact on the price and availability of vegetable protein sources, the balance of diets with respect to the amount of usable protein in them, the channels of public information that would be needed to convert people's diets, the livelihood of those now dependent on the production of animal food and fiber, and the international relations surrounding the production and distribution of animal food and fiber.

With a consortium of experts, no doubt we could carry out these assessments. But surely we are not yet in a position to apply an acceptable ethical theory to the question of veganism. Here, as elsewhere in the arena of animals and agriculture, we face questions calling for complex empirical inputs.

Conclusion

I have argued that our duties to animals are indirect. To deny this is to advocate an ethic without point or one that is question begging in its foundations. Let us not be so foolish or biased as to do either. And let us not act as though, operating alone, philosophers can settle questions requiring complex empirical inputs. In either event, we would be taking serious matters less than seriously.[16]

Notes

1. This paper originally appeared in *Between the Species: a journal of ethics* 1, no. 4 (Fall 1985). I want to thank the editors of *Between the Species* for permission to reprint this shortened version.

2. See, for example, Peter Singer, "All Animals Are Equal," *The New York Review of Books* 22 (1975), reprinted in James E. White, *Contemporary Moral Problems* (Saint Paul: West Publishing Co., 1985), pp. 266–78.

3. See, for example, Leslie Pickering Francis and Richard Norman, "Some Animals Are More Equal than Others," *Philosophy* 53 (1978): 527.

4. William K. Frankena, "Ethics and the Environment," in K. D. Goodpaster and K. M. Sayre, eds., *Ethics and Problems of the 21st Century* (Notre Dame: University of Notre Dame Press, 1979), p. 5.

5. See, for example, William David Ross, *The Right and the Good* (Oxford: The Clarendon Press, 1930) and William K. Frankena, *Ethics*, 2d ed. (Englewood Cliffs, N.J.: Prentice-Hall, 1973).

6. Paul W. Taylor, *Normative Discourse* (Englewood Cliffs, N.J.: Prentice-Hall, 1961), *passim*, but especially Chapter 9.

7. See, for example, Annette C. Baier, "Knowing Our Place in the Animal World," in Harlan B. Miller and William H. Williams, eds., *Ethics and Animals* (Clinton: Humana Press, 1983), pp. 62, 67.

8. Rudolf Carnap, "Empiricism, Semantics and Ontology," *Revue Internationale de Philosophie* II (1950), reprinted in Leonard Linsky, *Semantics and the Philosophy of Language* (Urbana: The University of Illinois Press, 1952), pp. 207–28. See especially pp. 31–32 (219–20). Also, see Immanuel Kant, *Critique of Pure Reason*, Norman Kemp Smith, trans. (London: Macmillan & Co., 1963).

9. Immanuel Kant, *Foundations of the Metaphysics of Morals*, Lewis White Beck, trans. (Indianapolis: The Bobbs-Merrill Co., 1959), p. 12.

10. Charles L. Stevenson, *Ethics and Language* (New Haven: Yale University Press, 1944), and *Facts and Values* (New Haven: Yale University Press, 1963).

11. I say "more or less" to include an extreme-act intuitionist like E. F. Carritt, *The Theory of Morals* (Oxford: The Clarendon Press, 1928).

12. See Tom Regan, *The Case for Animal Rights* (Berkeley: University of California Press, 1983), Chapter 5, and the preface, respectively.

13. Just who is open to such influence, and when? As others have suggested, we get some idea of the answer to this question by a study of moral and legal defenses. This source, however, has the danger of leading us in a circle. Therefore, we would do best to look more carefully at the potential of ethics to facilitate aims and pursuits in social arrangements, including practices of holding people to account. Where there is such potential, we have people open to the influence in question. (See Charlie Blatz, "Mad Bears and Innocent Hares: Remarks Toward a Theory of Diminished Responsibility," *Between the Species: a journal of ethics* 3, no. 1 (Winter 1987). Unclear or borderline cases will call, as usual, for decisions within the spirit of the project at hand, of maximally facilitating aims and pursuits by the guidance of reasons.

14. For a more complete account of the basics here, see my paper on the ethics of ranchland management and ownership, Chapter 11 in this volume.

15. Francis Moore Lappé, *Diet for a Small Planet* (New York: Ballantine Books, 1982).

16. I would like to thank Steve Sapontzis and Stan Dundon for their comments on an earlier draft of the original version of this paper.

III.C.
Consumption in Production

CONCERN ABOUT THE USE AND ABUSE of crop resources extends to genetic diversity in the field and in the wild, to energy for working the land or rearing animals, and to the relative efficiency of small-scale and large-scale production units. The articles in this section survey some of the pertinent facts and concerns about genetic resources, and the relative efficiency of production units.

Donald N. Duvick, in his article "Genetic Diversity and Plant Breeding," explains some of the difficulties connected with the diminishing genetic diversity of crop plants, primarily the increasing vulnerability to plant and animal pests, as well as extremes of weather. Local diversity, while producing a crop not entirely uniform in quality and yield, ensured some protection from pests to which specific stocks are vulnerable. Even the present genetic diversification, which comes from commercial breeding programs and characterizes present field diversity patterns, is no long-term guarantee of crop health and yield. The problem is that pests can diversify until a subspecies to which the crops are vulnerable comes along, and then new crops must be bred and planted to avoid devastation from the "new" pest.

There are several other difficulties attendant upon this need for new crop varieties. First, even affluent countries do not have a sufficiently robust breeding program; such programs are more inadequate in third world countries, where new varieties have been widely adopted. Second, even the largest breeding program requires a continuing source of genetic material as a source of new plant varieties. Some genetic material is preserved in seed banks, while wild or traditional seed stocks from other countries provide more sources of genetic diversity. Further problems concern equitable return for native seed sources and equitable worldwide allocation of genetic material. Duvick suggests that it is so difficult to trace the origin of genetic diversity that we should not hope to provide source countries with proper returns for their germ plasm.

Finally, Duvick discusses the worry that modern breeding programs place poor and underdeveloped countries at a disadvantage by developing seed stocks that perform well only with capital-consuming chemical inputs.

Hugh H. Iltis also discusses diminishing genetic diversity and related ethical issues in his paper "Tropical Deforestation and the Fallacies of Agricultural hope." As the title suggests, Iltis argues for preservation of the tropical rainforests. He describes the loss of forests from small-scale agriculture, hunting for food and pharmaceuticals, and logging and other enterprises. He details some of the vast wealth of diversity of flora and fauna that is being lost and reminds us of the short-term and especially the long-term importance of this diversity to industry, agriculture, and to other forest species. A particularly vivid example of the need to protect diversity in large undeveloped tracts of land is given by *Zea diploperennis*, a perennial relative of our annual corn.

Iltis also dispels the myth that short-term food production on cleared forest land offers an economic advantage over the potential profits of preserving the forests' genetic diversity. Even if Iltis's subtext of the great intrinsic worth of plants and animals of the rain forest is disregarded, he maintains that a utilitarian argument will favor preservation, not development. Consistent with this conclusion, Iltis offers a scheme to finance a worldwide system of tropical rain forest preserves.

Finally, Iltis argues, it is fallacious to believe that population growth can be matched by an increased food supply grown on tropical forest lands. We must decide to aggressively curb population growth through all forms of birth control. The alternative, according to Iltis and others, is massive biological collapse and the loss of the earth's ability to sustain future generations. In what seems like one last utilitarian appeal, Iltis urges agriculture in the temperate zone, preservation of the biologically diverse tropics, and worldwide limitation of human population growth as the only ecologically responsible way to meet the needs of those who will follow us.

Equally pressing, according to some, is the rapid depletion of another nonrenewable resource integral to present-day agriculture, namely, fossil fuels. This depletion is increased by heavy dependence upon mechanized and chemically supported large-scale farming. Is the cost of energy consumption, when added to attendant soil and water problems, a wise investment? Those who say "yes" claim that larger scale agriculture is much more efficient than smaller scale agriculture. Michael Perelman takes up this claim in "Energy and Agricultural Production." Perelman touches on the conservation of fossil fuels as he discusses the efficiency of large-scale versus small-scale farming in the United States. He leads into the topic by noting that efficiency will be understood as a (relatively) high return of output for input of land, labor, *and* purchased goods and services.

The efficiency of large-scale U.S. agriculture cannot be proven by its yields per acre of land used, nor can the claim of efficiency rest upon fuel use, consumption of topsoil, or distribution of labor. Perelman details a number of intuitively accessible and appealing calculations which show that, in the end, the present farm system of larger production units is not made more efficient by its consolidation of production.

What of small farms, then? Perelman argues that while collective alternatives might be even better, small farms are more efficient than larger ones, as shown by an analysis of recent USDA statistics. These figures also make clear that, for tax advantages, the largest farms fail to show a profit.

While the main text of Perelman's article concerns the relative efficiency of large- and small-scale farming, one subtext is that smaller scale agriculture is less energy consuming on the field and in the production of labor-saving amendments. If this is so, and if Perelman's general claims about the relative efficiency of larger and smaller units are correct, then the trade-offs we see in U.S. agriculture would not seem to be economically justified. But if this is so, then how can we support the consumption of soil, water, genetic diversity, and fossil fuels that seems endemic to that system?

The answer is not clear. But at the same time, it is also not clear that moving to the sustainable, smaller-scale agriculture now favored by the National Academy of Sciences is the answer either. Just as the questions raised thus far in this book are extremely complex, so too are the research, development and infrastructural questions concerning those agricultural alternatives that seem to be less ethically suspect. Much needs to be resolved about the shape tomorrow's agriculture can take—both ethically and technically. Section IV offers a vision of the agriculture of the future and how it might be molded in the U.S. and elsewhere, followed by a discussion of providing food for the world and assigning agriculture its proper place in world development.

Genetic Diversity and Plant Breeding

Donald N. Duvick

WHEN I WAS GROWING UP on a midwestern dairy farm, I would help with the annual harvest of our oat crop. Farmers used horses in those days, and oats were an essential feed for horses. A grain binder cut down the oat stalks and tied them into foot-thick bundles. My job was to arrange the bundles into miniature tepees called "shocks," which stood in orderly rows in the oat field until threshing day, when they were loaded onto hay racks—large flat-bed wagons—and carried to the threshing machine for separation of grain from straw.

In 1946, our oat harvest was unusually early—the oat plants had turned yellow and dry much sooner than normal—and as I shocked the oats, I noticed that the bundles were unnaturally light in weight. My father and the neighbor we cooperated with at oat harvest time talked about a "blight" that had affected the ripening crop. After threshing, our grain bin contained only one-fourth the usual amount of oats, and I noticed that they were strangely light in weight as I shoveled them from a wagon into the bin.

My father's oat crop was not the only one affected. All of our neighbors had the same problem, except for one dissenter who, for some reason, had used a variety of oats different from the single one used by all the other farmers in our neighborhood. His choice had not suffered from the "blight."

I did not know it at the time, but I had just been introduced to "genetic vulnerability," the consequence of excessive uniformity of crop plants. And our unique neighbor—the one with a different, healthier, oat variety—had also demonstrated the value of "genetic diversity," of planting more than one variety of a given crop.

Genetic diversity as a means of stabilizing the performance of crop plants has been used, consciously or not, by farmers throughout the world ever since farming began ten thousand years ago. But it is only in the past twenty or thirty years that scientists have evaluated the usefulness of genetic diversity, devised the best methods of applying it, and advocated its widespread use.

Genetic diversity is said to give protection against epidemic spread of disease or insect pests and also against yield loss due to weather-related stresses such as heat or drought, and soil-related stresses such as nutrient deficiency.

For reasons that are not entirely clear to plant pathologists, mixtures of genotypes in a field (such as mixtures of different varieties of a particular crop, or of several subtypes of a particular variety) can often slow down the rate at which variety-specific disease or insect pests multiply and spread. In contrast, large acreages of a single uniform crop variety tend to favor epidemic increase and spread of any disease or insect uniquely adapted for growth on that variety.

Before the advent of modern plant breeding, farmers generally grew several varieties of each crop, or more typically, they grew varieties that were extremely variable, genetically. Further, individual varieties usually were not planted on a large scale; they had highly specific requirements for particular soil types or for local microclimates, and performed poorly when taken out of their favorite habitat.

But during the past fifty years, scientific plant breeding has produced high-performance varieties that are genetically uniform, both to achieve maximum performance and to meet consumer and farmer demand for uniformity. Such varieties are also broadly adapted, performing well across entire countries, or even around the world.

Because farmers worldwide are increasingly producing their crop for sale, rather than for home consumption, they are strongly motivated to select and plant only those varieties that reliably produce the greatest yield; they select, therefore, the best of the modern varieties, the one or two top performers. And because modern varieties are broadly adapted, the one or two top varieties are chosen by many farmers.

The consequence has been that very broad expanses of farmland in the United States, Europe and Asia are now planted to a very small number of highly uniform varieties of the world's major field crops, such as rice, wheat, maize, soybeans, grain sorghum, and cotton. In the Philippines, for example, 90 percent of the land planted to rice in 1984 was planted to just two varieties. In the United States in 1980, 42 percent of the land planted to soybeans was planted to only 6 varieties.

Farmers are inadvertently exposing themselves to the danger of unexpected epidemics or specific weather stresses to which their favorite one or two varieties may be uniquely vulnerable. Farmers, in concert with plant breeders, have reduced genetic diversity and thereby increased genetic vulnerability.

It may seem strange that plant breeders would release varieties uniformly susceptible to a serious disease, insect pests, or weather stress, and even stranger for farmers to risk their livelihood by deliberately planting susceptible varieties.

Of course, neither plant breeders nor farmers knowingly take such risks. Plant breeders continually breed and select new varieties for resistance to all known diseases and to insect and nematode pests expected to occur where the variety is to be grown. And farmers pay attention to descriptions of pest resistance and tolerance to weather stress in the new varieties they may choose to grow; they pay even more attention to performance of those varieties on their own farms—or on their neighbors' farms—in previous years.

But disease, insect, and nematode pests are themselves highly variable, genetically. New pest biotypes with new kinds of virulence continually appear, some of them able to grow well on crop varieties that are highly resistant to other races of the same pest species. Once a new pest race is established in large plantings of a susceptible crop of uniform genotype, the stage is set for explosive multiplication of the new race—an epidemic.

This is precisely what happened, I now know, to my father's oat crop in 1946. A fine new variety, specifically selected for resistance to a troublesome leaf rust, had been released by university-based oat breeders. Acceptance of this high-yielding, rust-resistant variety was widespread; its new growers included my father and all his neighbors—except the one dissenter, who for some reason stayed with his older, rust-susceptible variety.

Unknown to the oat breeders (and certainly to our neighborhood farmers) was the fact that the gene conferring rust resistance carried with it a gene for susceptibility to a new species of leaf disease called *Helminthosporium victoriae*, or Victoria blight. When the new oat variety—carrying, simultaneously, resistance to the old leaf rust and susceptibility to the new leaf blight—became widely planted, a classic shift occurred: the rust disease became so scarce that the old rust-susceptible varieties were no longer infected, but the previously unknown leaf blight—Victoria blight—exploded into an epidemic. As a result, our oat bin was not refilled by the harvest of 1946.

It must be noted that disease and insect epidemics are not new phenomena; they didn't first appear when modern plant breeding got underway some eighty years ago. Famines following wheat rust epidemics were so common in ancient Rome that special sacrifices were made annually to the wheat god, Robigus, in hopes that he might be induced to spare the wheat crop from devastating rust.

In actuality, widespread loss of crops due to epidemics is perhaps less common now than in previous eras, even though the genetic diversity in crops on the farm is much less, worldwide, than it used to be. However, some serious epidemics have occurred in recent years, as, for example, when *type T* of southern corn leaf blight caused a 10 to 15 percent reduction in U.S. maize yields in 1970.

Two reasons probably account for the relatively good record in recent years: chemical protectants to prevent insect damage are available now, although they may not be in the future; and plant breeders have continually and rapidly brought out new improved varieties, genetically different from those they replaced.

Modern plant varieties are usually widely planted for only about a few years, seven, in the U.S., before they are replaced by new, improved varieties. Thus "genetic diversity in time" is achieved; disease or insect organisms self-selected for easy growth on a specific variety find, after a few years, that their favorite (and to them, essential) variety has disappeared. They therefore also disappear or diminish in importance, and the new crop variety has a few years of freedom before a new pest specific for it builds up to troublesome levels.

However, this new strategy—genetic diversity in time—also places a special responsibility on those who fund and carry out plant breeding. A country that depends on modern varieties for its crop production is on a never-ending treadmill—vigorous plant breeding programs must be continually supported. Those third world countries that have recently switched to large-scale planting of modern high-yield varieties are now in an especially dangerous position, because their national breeding programs tend to be poorly funded or managed, often due to political interference. Even in first world countries, however, support for plant breeding is now diminishing.

Sources of support for plant breeding are varied. National or local governments may support plant breeding with tax monies. Farmers may support it directly through cooperative breeding organizations, or indirectly, by purchasing seed from commercial breeding companies.

But whatever the means of support, plant breeding must be carried on vigorously in modern societies if they are to have abundant food supplies. And to sustain plant breeding, abundant sources of genetic variability must be available, as needs arise for new genes for pest resistance, for better tolerance to environmental stress, or for new chemical constituents in plant products.

Elite breeding pools—adapted high-performance lines used as parents of new varieties—contain large amounts of useful genetic variability. Breeders usually find the new genes required in these high-performance stocks. But sometimes a new disease or insect pest arises for which no useful resistance genes can be found in elite adapted materials. At that point breeders turn to the wealth of diversity available in *landraces*—varieties grown by traditional farmers—from countries in all parts of the globe.

Peasant farmers in third world countries are the chief source of landraces. Hundreds of thousands of landraces exist worldwide. But ironically the success of modern plant breeding—the popularity of modern varieties—has threatened the existence of landraces as a class. Peasant farmers abandon their landraces in favor of modern varieties. Unless seed of the old varieties is preserved, they become extinct.

Therefore, during the past twenty or thirty years farsighted plant breeders have vigorously urged that worldwide collecting expeditions gather seed samples of all possible landraces before they disappear and that the seed then be stored in environmentally controlled chambers (that will preserve the seeds' viability for many years) against the time when breeders may need it.

Their work has borne fruit in the worldwide establishment or enlargement of numerous seed storage institutions ("germ plasm banks," "seed banks") such as the National Seed Storage Laboratory at Ft. Collins, Colorado. An internationally funded body, the Rome-based International Board for Plant Genetic Resources (IBPGR), was formed in 1974 to provide coordination, training, and information to all germ plasm preservation centers. In its brief lifetime IBPGR has contributed greatly to germ plasm collection, storage, and characterization.

In recent years, certain politically and socially oriented individuals and organizations have also taken a deep interest in germ plasm diversity and preservation. They have especially emphasized the contributions to modern plant breeding of landraces from the third world countries; they have suggested that individual third world countries be paid royalties by the first world countries for use of genes originating in those third world countries. Conversely, these political action groups and individuals have also said that private industry—plant breeding companies—should no longer have the opportunity to earn royalties on their proprietary varieties developed through private initiative. Rather, industry is urged to donate its proprietary varieties and breeding stocks to public use, free of charge. The United Nations's Food and Agricultural Organization (FAO) has been a forum for furthering of the political activists' views.

It is now clear that modern plant varieties trace back to so many origins that to calculate an individual country's "landrace royalties" would be impossible. It is also clear that all countries—third world as well as first world—depend on germ plasm from elsewhere for successful plant breeding. And conversely, all countries—first world as well as third world—have valuable germ plasm resources needed by other countries. No country is totally germ-plasm-rich; no country is totally germ-plasm-poor; all are rich and poor simultaneously. The world thus needs to find efficient ways to exchange and share germ plasm for breeding purposes and then to multiply and distribute the new varieties developed via modern techniques.

Meanwhile, plant breeders find their contributions criticized from another quarter: the new varieties are said to be excessively tender and disease-prone, yielding well only when given luxury amounts of fertilizer, water, and pesticides.

In actuality, most new varieties are measurably sturdier than the old ones they have replaced; they are more, rather than less, tolerant of drought and low soil fertility, and more, rather than less, resistant to the currently troublesome diseases and insects. Indeed, this is why they are favored by farmers; farmer experience shows that the new varieties are more dependable, year in and year out, up hill and down dale.

Farmer experience also shows that the new varieties are capable of very high yields when inputs of water and fertilizer are optimum. Thus, farmers using the new varieties can choose the farming system they deem to be most profitable—they can utilize low, high, or intermediate levels of inputs—knowing that most modern varieties will do the best possible job with whichever system they choose.

Plant breeders have yet another challenge, and this one is not yet well answered by them. Too few of the new varieties have durable (long-lived) resistance to disease and insect pests. Durable resistance is usually governed by complex, hard-to-manipulate genetic systems; breeders in general don't have the time and skill needed to select varieties with durable resistance, thus they are apt to turn out varieties with short-lived (even though temporarily very good) resistance. (Short-lived resistance is usually governed by simple, single-gene systems.) Breeders are increasingly breeding for durable resistance, or developing methods for deploying single-gene resistant genotypes (in blends, for example) in ways that prolong the varieties' useful lifetimes. But more needs to be done, and soon.

In summary, genetic diversity, deployed in new ways by plant breeders and farmers, is a useful strategy for protection against pest epidemics and weather-caused stress. Today's farming and economic systems encourage farmers to reduce genetic diversity by planting only one or two of the most productive varieties in a region. But dynamic plant breeding programs, continually turning out genetically new varieties, provide rapid genetic turnover that gives useful and generally adequate "genetic diversity in time." Multilateral international exchanges of breeding material are essential to maintain and increase this new kind of genetic diversity. Modern high-performance varieties are more, not less, stable in the face of environmental stress and nutrient deficiencies than the old ones. They are therefore better adapted to low-input as well as high-input farming systems. Finally, plant breeders need to do a better job of breeding durable (long-lived) pest resistance into varieties of the future, to give further insurance against unexpected, rapid build-up of disease and insect pests.

Bibliography

Anderson, Edgar, and W. L. Brown. 1952. "Origin and significance of corn belt maize." In *Heterosis*, pp. 121–48. Ames, Iowa: Iowa State Univ. Press.

Dalrymple, D. G. 1986. Development and spread of high-yielding wheat varieties in developing countries. Washington, D.C.: Bureau for Science & Technology, Agency for International Development.

Duvick, D. N. 1984a. "Genetic contributions to yield gains of U.S. hybrid maize, 1930 to 1980." In *Genetic Contributions To Yield Gains Of Five Major Crop Plants* CSSA Special Publication no. 7, edited by W. R. Fehr, p. 15–47. Madison, Wisc.: Crop Science Society of America.

———. 1984b. Genetic diversity in major farm crops on the farm and in reserve. *Econ. Bot.* 38: 161–178.

———. 1986. Plant breeding: past achievements and expectations for the future. *Econ. Bot.* 40: 289–297.

Frankel, O. H. 1986. Genetic resources: The founding years. Part 3: the long road to the International Board. *Diversity* 9:30–33.

Mooney, P. R. 1983. The law of the seed, another development and plant genetic resources. *Development Dialogue*, no. 1-2. Uppsala: Dag Hammanskold Foundation.

National Academy of Sciences, Committee on Genetic Vulnerability Of Major Farm Crops. 1972. *Genetic vulnerability of major farm crops*. Washington, D.C.

United Nations Food and Agricultural Organization. 1983. "International Undertaking on Plant Genetic Resources." In *Report of Twenty-Second Session of the FAO Conference*, 5–23 November 1983. Rome.

Wilkes, G. 1987. Plant genetic resource: making a public good private is not a solution. *Diversity* 10:33–34.

Witt, S. C. 1985. Briefbook on biotechnology and genetic diversity. San Francisco: California Agricultural Lands Project, 227 Clayton Street, San Francisco, Calif. 94117.

Tropical Deforestation and the Fallacies of Agricultural Hope

Hugh H. Iltis

MUCH IS BEING WRITTEN THESE DAYS about deforestation and the extermination of biological diversity all over the globe, and, related to these, the genetic erosion of agricultural germ plasm (Duvick, this volume). These alarming problems affect everyone, and should be of immediate concern at all levels.[1]

Tropical Destruction—Ecological Genocide on a Grand Scale

It is in the tropics, particularly in the diverse but vulnerable rain forests and seasonally dry monsoon forests, that this biological genocide is now in full swing. Of the estimated five to thirty million species of plants and animals on Earth, over half live in the tropics. Here, even on a highly localized scale, biodiversity can be overwhelming. Thus, fully forty-one thousand species of insects, mostly beetles, have been identified in one hectare (2.47 acres) of Peruvian tropical forest![2] The destruction of tropical habitats, therefore, will inevitably cause the extermination of millions of plant and animal species, for most of which we do not have a description, a life history, an estimate of their ecological or economic importance, or even a name. As many as 20 percent of all species on Earth may become extinct within twenty years—at least a million species, but more likely many more. The utter devastation that human action wreaks in tropical ecosystems has to be seen to be believed.

In 1962 I stood on a primitive bridge suspended over a clear mountain stream and watched as troops of chattering spider monkeys, on branches a hundred feet off the ground, gracefully jumped from one tree to the next, eating the yellow-orange fruits from a gigantic plank-rooted fig tree. Here, near San Ramń in the eastern foothills of the

Peruvian Andes, in a valley overwhelming in its greenness and serenity, giant, brilliantly blue *Morpho* butterflies sailed erratically through a sun-flecked clearing to disappear again into the rain forest canopy. Iridescent hummingbirds hovered over the yellow flower clusters of a trumpet vine liana, while a pair of banana-billed toucans sat motionless on a branch, silently watching. To our small group of biologists, this was a scene straight out of a tropical Eden.

Not one of these living glories has survived. Later that year, an energetic, intelligent, but ecologically unaware young man from the capital city of Lima bought the whole valley with a development grant provided by the U.S.-sponsored "Alianza para el Progreso" and, even on slopes exceeding 45 degrees, cut down the forest to plant coffee and bananas. Such forest conversion, common throughout the Andes, has resulted not only in the extripation of species, but in massive soil erosion, siltation of rivers, and (locally at least) climatic change. The dramatic and unprecedented fluctuations in Amazonian water levels in recent decades are believed to be the unintended consequence of such land clearing.[3] Similarly, the continuing siltation of the Panama Canal is a direct result of deforestation on surrounding watersheds by small-scale agricultural development.

With such extensive forest destruction, countless species must disappear. It can't help but be so: if you use up one, you destroy the other. For example, more than half of the world's primates—the lemurs, monkeys, and apes, our closest evolutionary relatives—are facing imminent extinction. To complicate matters, these are all highly endemic and often very rare animals, each with its own geography, each with its own specific ecology, which only now animal ecologists are beginning to understand.[4] What must be done to preserve them? The most obvious first step, of course, is to preserve their forest habitat from destruction. But even here, the human need for protein—red meat—has hunted out the larger mammals (including primates), birds, and reptiles from vast areas of Amazonia, so that now many a forest, though superficially pristine, is in actuality a vertebrate desert.

Medical research needs have also, irresponsibly and wastefully, taken their toll: of the lovely cottontop tamarin, a tiny, white-maned monkey endemic to dry forests of northwestern Colombia, fully thirty thousand were imported to the U.S. for research in the 1960s alone. Then they were so cheap that, if you disposed of one, you could always get another. But now, not more than one thousand are left in the wild; and even these, surviving in a small nature reserve, are threatened by destruction of habitat, poaching for food, and capture for pets or zoos (A. Savage and T. C. Snowden, University of Wisconsin, personal communication). During recent field work in South America, I saw only one spider monkey, a pet on a silver chain in (of all places) a hotel lobby. What will we do when chimpanzees and tamarins are only colored pictures in children's books?

Not only the animals living within the forests, but the richly diverse forests themselves deserve protection. The lowland forests of the Pacific slope of western Ecuador, for example, are the home of many unique plant species. Sharply separated for millions of years from their relatives in the Amazon basin by the snowy peaks of the Andes, they evolved here in genetic isolation. Near Santo Domingo de los Colorados lies a small remnant of such a moist tropical forest, intensively studied by Calloway Dodson and Alwyn Gentry. As described in their *Flora of the Rio Palenque Science Center*,[5] this tract of only 167 hectares (420 acres) contains over eleven hundred species of plants, almost half of which are trees, shrubs, or lianas. They found nearly 6 percent of the species to be new to science (including some giant forest trees). Fully 4 percent were local *endemics*, that is, known only from here and nowhere else on earth. The small "sierra" at Centinelas, only six kilometers away, had a strikingly different, but equally endemic, flora, with close to one hundred new species discovered there. In fact, some one-hectare plots of Peruvian rain forest recently sampled by Gentry contained three hundred species of trees, making them the richest forests in the world in terms of species numbers.[6] To any temperate-zone botanist, such localized diversity is astounding. But all over the tropics—whether in Mexico or Madagascar, Brazil or Borneo—local floras (and even more so, faunas) are saturated with unique taxa: local endemism is the rule, widespread species are the exception!

Incredibly, the flora of Ecuador—a country no bigger than Minnesota—is estimated to have more than 20,000 different species of plants, over half of them endemic. Compare this to only 17,000 species in all of North America, and only 1,700 native species in all of Minnesota, which boasts only one endemic, an insignificant, semisterile dogtooth violet lily.

The ecological interrelations of most tropical species are still poorly known by scientists. We have yet to learn the most basic facts of life about even the largest of tropical animals, as a wonderful recent study of five species of Peruvian monkeys demonstrates.[7] Furthermore, nearly 10 percent of neotropical plant species and more than 90 percent of neotropical animal species (especially insects) are still scientifically undescribed. Many tropical plants have turned out to be useful in industry, medicine, agriculture, or horticulture, furnishing alkaloids, waxes, oils, gums, spices, and fruits. Others, especially some gigantic fruit-producing trees, have been shown to be ecological "keystone species," indispensable to the survival of whole suites of large animals, including parrots, Amazonian fish, and the Peruvian monkeys mentioned above. For these reasons (among others) we need to protect extensive areas of tropical forests from agriculture, ranching, and plantation forestry; even selective logging of key species pulls the rug out from under many other organisms, tightly evolved and totally dependent on them.

About half of the world's tropical forests have already been destroyed. The World Resources Institute estimates that an additional 7.3 million hectares (seventy-three thousand kilometers squared or eighteen million acres) of closed moist forest are now being destroyed annually, and another 4.4 million hectares (forty-four thousand kilometers squared) selectively logged,[8] a combined area equivalent to half of Wisconsin! Even at these deliberately conservative estimates, most tropical forests may be destroyed within the next *twenty years*. On the whole of the central Pacific slope of Ecuador, the Rio Palenque preserve is now the only surviving example of "moist tropical forest," a tiny island of unique natural complexity surrounded by a vast ocean of sterile cultivated uniformity: thousands of square kilometers of pesticide-sprayed sugar cane, African oil palm, and banana (mostly for export to the USA, USSR, and Europe) and, as in much of Central America, cattle pastures for the Hamburger Society.[9] Even though the Rio Palenque forest is protected, most of its larger primary forest animals, such as monkeys and tapirs, have long since become extinct, for it is much too small, has far too much "edge," and contains too small a "core" to sustain them.[10]

The urgency of restraining tropical deforestation is well illustrated here. Only thirty-five years ago, western Ecuador was covered with the most inaccessible of tropical forests, stretching uninterrupted for one hundred kilometers from Quevedo to Esmeraldas, an area from which almost no biological specimens (even of common forest trees) were then available for scientific study. But today, except for the Rio Palenque Science Center reserve, and an acre here and an *arroyo* there, this entire forest has been recklessly destroyed. Even the marvelous forest at Centinelas, mentioned above, was clear-cut in 1984. Today only an occasional plank-rooted forest giant, uncut because of its immense size, survives alone in a field of bananas, a silent witness to the tropical forest diversity that once was, and a pathetic and grim reminder that, from now on, no one shall ever again be able to see or study these ancient forests, nor shall the world ever know what unique botanical or zoological treasures these forests might have once contained. When a work of creation is gone, there is no way to bring it back. *Extinction is forever!*

The Sierra de Manantlán: A Mexican Biosphere Reserve Protected

More hopeful are the prospects for the cloud forests of the Sierra de Manantlan, a towering mountain range of Mexico's Sierra Madre del Sur southeast of Puerto Vallarta. Its preservation started in 1977 with the chance discovery of a species of wild grass, later named *Zea diploperennis*, a perennial relative of annual teosinte (and hence of maize, i.e., corn), which grows nowhere else in the world.[11] This rare weed may have enormous economic potential: it is immune to just about every maize virus in existence,[12] and readily hybridizes with maize, the world's second most important cereal crop, with a global harvest in 1985 of 449 million metric tons, from 133 million hectares, worth around fifty billion dollars.

Until five years ago, logging slowly but steadily devastated the forests of this biological treasurehouse. Trucks roared down the mountains every half-hour, hauling gigantic logs of oak, magnolia, and pine, to be made into lumber for building houses, into veneer for bedroom furniture, and into broomsticks for export to the U.S. to gain badly needed foreign exchange to pay off Mexico's staggering hundred-billion dollar debt. But because of the discovery of that remarkable teosinte, and through the efforts of many Mexican educators, scientists, and government officials (and with international moral support), lumbering was stopped in 1984. A year later, twelve hundred hectares of the habitat of the diploperennial teosinte, the *bosques mesifilos de la montana*, were bought by state funds for the Botany Institute of the Universidad de Guadalajara as a research station. Eventually, with the help of Mexico's National Science Foundation (CONACYT), and under the United Nation's UNESCO *Man in the Biosphere* (MAB) program, a 140,000 hectare (350,000 acre) *Reserva Biosfera de la Sierra de Manantlan* was dedicated in 1988 by Mexico's President, Miguel de la Madrid. Administered by the Universidad de Guadalajara, the whole mountain chain, with all its diverse ecosystems (home to rare mountain lions, ocelots, crested guans, and hummingbirds, as well as to the teosinte and other endemic plants), has, for now at least, been protected. It is sobering, nevertheless, to contemplate what would have happened had agricultural development reached the mountainous habitats of *Zea diploperennis*: a few cows in a month's time could have obliterated this species, and with it the possibility of man ever utilizing its enormous virus- and nematode-resistance, or of developing a perennial maize.[13]

The Bioclimatic Paradox

Almost without exception, economists, scientific advisors, and humanitarians of the United States and Europe have been misled by the overpowering luxuriance of tropical vegetation. How many times have well-meaning "experts" announced that the answer to world hunger lies in the increased agricultural development of the tropics. But their happy, deadly ignorance of ecology and geography, their unfailing optimism that the answer to the world's ills lies in growing more food and increasing development—leading to a desperately hoped-for but illusory "demographic transition"—have been fatal for human life and natural ecosystems, as recent famines in Africa and Asia, recent floods in Bangladesh, and the horrendous torching of Amazonia in 1988 have so clearly demonstrated.

There are botanical reasons for tropical famines that are not hard to find. As geographer J. Chang of the University of Hawaii has explained,[14] slender annual grasses such as wheat, rye, barley, or rice have relatively low agricultural productivity in tropical latitudes compared with their high productivity in the cooler temperate climates where they originally evolved. This lower productivity reflects a simple bioclimatic fact: during the long, warm tropical nights, respiration burns up most of the surplus carbohydrates produced by photosynthesis during the relatively short day. On the other hand, in my own state of Wisconsin (or in the wheat belts of Kansas or the USSR), the hot sixteen-hour summer days followed by cool eight-hour nights allow a much greater accumulation of storage photosynthate, and thus a bumper crop at harvest time. Furthermore, in most parts of the lowland tropics, no matter how lush the vegetation, high rainfall (interacting with high temperatures) tends to leach the already nutrient-poor soils to sterile sands or stone pavements, often useless for agriculture after only three or four years of cultivation. Finally, in the tropics, there are no bitter cold winter temperatures to knock back insect pests.[15]

Dreams of making breadbaskets out of the tropical regions thus quickly evaporate into the fantasies they really are, notwithstanding optimistic editorials in prominent newspapers and lead articles by experts in scientific journals. As the German playwright Berthold Brecht wryly observed, "An optimist is a man who hasn't yet heard the bad news." And Canada's Marshall McLuhan was not far behind when he quipped that "An expert is a man who doesn't make the slightest error on the road to the grand delusion," the grand delusion in this case being the unlimited agricultural potential of the tropics. Simply put, the environment of the tropics (and hence its agriculture) is fundamentally different from that of the temperate zones, and cannot be developed according to "northern" models without destroying it.

In summary, tropical ecosystems in general, and tropical forests in particular, present a climatically determined paradox. Biologically they are diverse and valuable beyond belief, but agriculturally (in the field-farming tradition) they are usually quite poor. That the biologically depauperate states of Kansas, Iowa, or South Dakota can never become Mexicos, Panamas, or Amazonian Brazils in terms of biological diversity is obvious. That, at the same time, these tropical countries can never become Kansas, Iowas, or South Dakotas in terms of agricultural productivity should by now be obvious as well. But fallacies of hope die hard for nationalistic dreamers of economic glory, foreign investors greedy for profit and power, religious leaders stubbornly determined to ignore demographic realities, and humanitarian do-gooders hungry to rearrange the world despite inviolate environmental limits.[16] Nevertheless, we must accept these fundamental ecological realities or the consequences, ecological and political, will be very unpleasant indeed.

The Problem of National Parks and Biosphere Reserves

There is, then, this great productivity-diversity-preservation paradox: the less-developed tropical countries are blessed with Earth's richest biota, hence to them falls the often unwanted, but unavoidable, responsibility to maintain in national parks or biosphere reserves their unique biological and ethnological wealth, not just for themselves, but *for the whole world.* Yet they are the very ones most desperately in need of money and personnel, and thus often much too poor to afford them. Statistics on park personnel show how critical a problem this is. Compared to the tropical nations, the overdeveloped industrialized countries spend ten times the money, and support ten times the staff, per unit area of park.[17] And parks without botanists and zoologists, without guards and interpreters, cannot long survive.

Thus, the very countries with the most biodiversity to preserve are able in their poverty to preserve only little, and scientifically study even less. It is a colossal problem in search of a solution.

Yet some tropical countries have managed to make nature preservation an important part of their national aims. Tanzania's Serengeti Park, at least, is still well-protected.

Shining Examples, Worthwhile Proposals

Costa Rica and its directors of National Parks, Alvaro Ugalde and M. A. Boza, deserve special praise in this connection. Smaller than West Virginia, but with five times the number of plant species (over nine thousand!), Costa Rica has a national system of twenty-eight well-administered parks, reserves, and *refugios* unrivaled by any other country in the Americas. Fully 8 percent of its total area is under national park protection, and its per capita financial commitment to parks is higher than that of the United States. In fact, including national forests, 20 percent of Costa Rica's lands are under some sort of nature protection. Most promising are the efforts, inspired by an American ecologist, Daniel Janzen, to establish Guanacaste National Park, which combines remaining seasonally dry tropical forest with adjoining worn-out grazing lands to restore the latter to their original forested state.[18]

Other significant advances have been made in Amazonian Bolivia, Brazil, Colombia, Ecuador, Peru, and Venezuela. During the past two decades, over twelve million hectares of forest have been placed under protection, and, hopefully, many more will be protected soon by the recently conceived instrument of swapping international debt for protection of nature.[19] It is grim reality, nevertheless, that many of these Amazonian preserves are "paper parks" now being invaded by squatters.

Shouldn't we, then, seriously consider a recent proposal for a global system of tropical preserves, supported internationally by taxing all countries whose people enjoy a per capita income greater than $1,500 a year?[20] If this sounds utopian and unfair, remember that we of the overdeveloped nations have an economic stake in the survival of tropical forests at least as great as that of the less-developed nations in which these forests grow.[21] And the cost would not be excessive: only one percent of the $300 billion 1989 U.S. defense budget would go a long way towards the establishment of one thousand preserves of six hundred thousand acres (240,000 hectares) each, thus insuring the preservation of 10 percent of the world's tropical forests (only 4 percent are now protected).

If we are to keep faith with our children's future and survival, we in the overdeveloped nations must learn, as an integral part of any "good neighbor" foreign policy, to approach the problem of tropical biotic extinctions seriously and responsibly. Ecologically enlightened U.S. foreign aid would give priority to the purchase of wild lands, and subsidize the staffing and upkeep of local preserves, and the building of local museums of natural history, throughout the tropics. It would help train local biological (and not just agricultural) expertise by providing fellowships for teachers of biology to our universities, or to theirs, and would make the world's biological literature available in the *local* language so that, finally, *local scientists themselves can become experts on their own biota.*[22] This calls for major international cooperation, which among biologists is already well-established, for the enormous complexity of tropical ecology and systematics cannot be mastered by the scientists of any one country alone. Only through a deep appreciation of their biological wealth can the less-developed nations protect their biota from opportunistic technocrats bent on development, be they American, European, or Japanese—or their own. The empowerment that comes with biological education and knowledge is what the developed nations could, and should, bequeath their tropical neighbors. In the final analysis, only by fully understanding—and loving—their own flora and fauna can tropical countries defend and preserve their irreplacable biological heritage.

The Population Bomb Is Still Ticking, Only Faster!

The world in just the last ten years has gained an additional 850 million people, some 85 million each year, some 260,000 every single day, some 12,000 each and every hour! All of them will need land and water, wood and fiber, food and housing, things even now in short supply. And population growth means more roads and dams, more cars and concrete, more corn and cows, more erosion and floods, more garbage pits and pollution, more acid rain and greenhouse effects, more dead elephants and dolphins, more hunger and starvation, more riots and refugees, more prisons and torture, more war, mayhem and disaster—and less and less nature. It need not be so!

Admitting that the overdeveloped countries must adopt more reasonable expectations for their standard of living, that tropical exploitation by their multinational banks and corporations must stop, that their massive commercial development schemes promoted in the third world are among the prime causes of deforestation, and that freedom, justice, and equality are indispensable to a well-ordered world, let all of us—liberals, humanists, socialists, communists, or conservatives—never forget that poverty, lack of education, and above all, overpopulation, *in and by themselves* are equally responsible for biological extinction—the chop-chop of a billion axes and machetes, the cravings of a billion hungry mouths all wanting to be fed. In fact, it is a poor excuse to blame the "population bomb" solely on capitalism or imperialism, or to absolve population growth of its increasingly crucial role in the world's ecological collapse. As necessary as political struggles against the injustices of oppressive social and economic systems are, they must always go hand in hand with actions to correct the grave and ever-increasing imbalance between human populations, resources, and the environment.[23]

Thus, although the poverty-stricken people of the tropics have to have food and firewood, they need birth control even more. By now, any knowledgeable observer of the world's scene must come to the conclusion that the food vs. population race can never be won by growing more food, but that it can only be won by decreasing the birth rate (and, eventually, the world's population), preferably through education and persuasion, and always with the ready availability of every possible method of contraception: from condom to diaphragm to pill, and, including as a last, and always personally difficult resort, state-supported and freely available, medically safe abortion. Let us be clear: to effectively facilitate the modification of human breeding behavior, to bring it into line with ecological realities, *all* methods of birth control must be made available. And, here also, the developed nations have a vital responsibility.

Preventing famine and disease are noble goals. Ending injustice and poverty are noble goals. But none of these will induce a "demographic transition" to lowered birthrates *in time* to prevent widespread biological collapse, a collapse that would not only intensify human miseries, but would further intensify the destruction of the environment. We simply cannot wait for the demographic transition to happen. We simply cannot allow the environment (which, after all, is the only environment humanity has) to deteriorate any further. In addition, none of these noble goals will be accomplished by furthering the immaculate misconception that raising more food by cutting down more tropical forests, draining more tropical wetlands, or breeding more bountiful crops will solve the demographic dilemma.[24] We are running out of wild nature, space, and water, as we are running out of nonrenewable resources. Meanwhile, the population bomb keeps on ticking, faster and faster.

The answer to the demographic dilemma is clear enough: we must abandon the fallacies of agricultural hope,[25] for it is not a question of raising more food, but of raising fewer people! If population growth is not curtailed voluntarily, the brutal powers of the state (as in China) or the brutal catastrophies of nature (as in Africa's Sahel) will surely do it for us.

Only an ecologically responsible people, sternly self-restrained in both resource use and human reproduction, can give this spaceship world of ours any realistic hope of bequeathing to its children a nature-rich, beautiful, and livable earth.[26]

Notes

1. G. O. Barney, *The Global 2000 Report to the President: Entering the Twenty-first Century* (Washington, D.C.: U.S. Government Printing Office, 1980); D.W. Ehrenfeld, *Conserving Life on Earth* (New York: Oxford University Press, 1972); P. and A. Ehrlich, *Extinction: the Causes and Consequences of the Disappearance of Species* (New York: Random House, 1981); A. Gomez-Pompa, C. Vasquez-Yanes and S. Guevara, "The tropical rain forest: A nonrenewable resource," *Science* 177(1972): 762–65; H. H. Iltis, "To the taxonomist and ecologist: Whose fight is the preservation of nature?" *BioScience* 17(1967): 886–90; N. Myers, *The Sinking Ark* (Oxford: Pergamon Press, 1979); N. Myers, *Conversion of Tropical Moist Forests* (Washington, D.C.: National Academy of Sciences Press, 1980); G. T. Prance and T. S. Elias, eds., *Extinction is Forever* (New York: New York Botanical Garden, 1977); P. H. Raven, "Tropical rain forests: A global responsibility," *Natural History* 90(1981):28–32; H. H. Iltis, "Tropical forests, what will be their fate?" *Environment* 25(1983):55–60; N. Guppy, "Tropical deforestation," *Foreign Affairs* (1984): 928–65; C. Caulfield, *In The Rain forest: Report from a Strange, Beautiful, Imperiled World* (Chicago: The University of Chicago Press, 1984); H. H. Iltis, "Los bosques tropicales y la extincion de la vida en la tierra," *Biocenosis* (San Jose, Costa Rica) 3(June 1987):27–35; E. C. Wolf, "Avoiding a mass extinction of species," in L. R. Brown et al., *State of the World 1988* (New York: W. W. Norton & Co., 1988), 101–17. Newspapers play a big role in both leading, and misleading, the public: For pro-development appraisals of Amazonian colonization, see T. Szulc, "Pioneers carve a new frontier. Will the next century belong to Brazil?" *Parade Magazine* (Sept. 4, 1983):4–6. This blindly economic justification and humanistic glorification of biological destruction reached perhaps thirty million unsuspecting American households. Equally myopic and optimistic is the editorial, "Rain forest of Amazonia," *Science* (Aug. 5, 1983): 507, by physicist P. H. Abelson, the long-time, influential but ecologically ill-informed editor of *Science*, who has written much nonsense about tropical development, e.g., "Energy from biomass" (editorial) *Science* 191(26 March 1976). Equally uncritical and amusing, were it not so pathetic, is the view of Amazonia by the prominent American businessman-diplomat, S. L. Linowitz: "The cause of this discouraging rate of development [of the Amazonian rain forest] is that the ground itself must first be cleared of jungle . . . and civilization itself introduced, before new farms can be laid out and made productive. . . . Whole new traditions and ways of life must be established. . . . Just to look at the geography is to see the formidable nature of the challenge. One huge belt of land . . . lies on the equator in the heart of the heat and fevers of the tropics. The Amazon River, unlike the Mississippi, flows through vast tracts of what are still sodden, malaria-ridden, impenetrable jungle wastelands, its waters patrolled by alligators and man-eating snakes. In contrast, the gentle, traffic-moving rivers of Europe . . . " ("The future of the Americas," *Science* 181[1973]: 916–20). Evidently, to this city-bred nature hater, wild unmanaged forests are the enemy that must be destroyed. That Europe's gentle rivers are heavily polluted, its few remaining forests without wild animals and dying of acid rain, and its wild nature is all but gone, would of course not interest this development-oriented capitalist, who only sees dollar signs in the Amazonian "jungle."

2. P. H. Raven and G. B. Johnson, *Biology* (St. Louis: Times Mirror/Mosby College

Publishing, 1986), 1190, an excellent reference. Estimates vary from a conservative five million species on Earth to thirty million, as predicted by Terry Erwin. See R. M. May, "How many species are there on Earth," *Science*, 16 Sept. 1988, 1441–49 for estimates ranging from five to fifty million species, only 1.4 million of which have been classified so far.

3. A. H. Gentry and J. Lopez-Parodi, "Deforestation and increased flooding of the upper Amazon," *Science* 210(1980): 1354–56; I. Friedman, "The Amazon Basin, another Sahel?" *Science* 197(1977): 7.

4. J. Terborgh, *Five New World Primates: A Study in Comparative Ecology* (Princeton, N.J.: Princeton University Press, 1983); D. Day, *The Doomsday Book of Animals* (New York: Viking Press, 1981); L. Roberts, "Beyond Noah's Ark: What do we need to know?" *Science* 242(2 Dec. 1988): 1247.

5. C. H. Dodson and A. H. Gentry, "Flora of the Rio Palenque Science Center," *Selbyana* 4(1978): 1–628.

6. A. H. Gentry, In *Proc. National Acad. Sci.*, January 1988, as quoted in *Environment* 30(1988): 22.

7. J. Terborgh, *Five New World Primates: A Study in Comparative Ecology* (Princeton, N.J.: Princeton University Press, 1983).

8. The World Resources Institute, *World Resources 1988-89* (New York: Basic Books, Inc.), 4. These figures are undoubtedly too conservative. See National Research Council, *Research Priorities in Tropical Biology* (Washington, D.C.: National Academy of Sciences Press, 1980), 29. See also P. M. Fearnside, "Deforestation in the Brazilian Amazon: how fast is it occurring?" *Interciencia* 7(1982): 82–88. The utilitarian, antipreservation opposition creates the erroneous impression [e.g., as in the Lugo and Brown critique of Norman Myers's book, *The Sinking Ark,* in *Intersciencia* 7(1982): 89–93] that there are no hard data on tropical deforestation, that environmentalists (such as Myers) exaggerate the extent of damage, and that, since there is nothing really to worry about, scientists and preservationists are misleading the public.

9. J. D. Nations and D. I. Komer, "Rain forests and the hamburger society," *Environment* 25(1983): 12–20; D. R. Shane, *Hoofprints on the Forest: Cattle Ranching and the Destruction of Latin America's Tropical Forests* (Philadelphia: Institute for the Study of Human Issues, 1986).

10. W. S. Alverson, D. M. Waller, and S. L. Solheim, "Forests too deer: Edge effects in northern Wisconsin," *Conservation Biology* 2(1988): 348–58 [note that "enclosure" on pages 348, 351, 352 (Figure 2), and 354 should read "exclosure"].

11. H. H. Iltis, J. F. Doebley, R. Guzman M., and B. Pazy, "*Zea diploperennis* (*Gramineae*): A new Teosinte from Mexico," *Science* 203(1979): 186–87; N. D. Vietmeyer, "A wild relative may give corn perennial genes," *Smithsonian* 10(1979): 68–75. Many articles have appeared about this plant and its home in the Sierra de Manantlán.

12. L. R. Nault, D. T. Gordon, V. D. Damsteegt, and H. H. Iltis, "Response of annual and perennial teosintes (*Zea*) to six maize viruses," *Plant Disease* 66(1982): 61–62; L. R. Nault and W. R. Findley, "*Zea diploperennis*: a primitive relative offers new traits to improve corn," *Desert Plants* 3(1982): 203–5.

13. *Ibid.*

14. J. Chang, "Potential photosynthesis and crop productivity," *Annals of the Assn. of Amer. Geographers* 60(1970): 92–101; D. M. Gates, "The flow of energy in the biosphere," *Scientific American* 224(1971): 88–100.

15. D. H. Janzen, "Tropical agroecosystems," *Science* 182(1973): 1212–19. An excellent article, showing how these habitats are misunderstood by the people of the temperate zones, and mismanaged by those of the tropics.

16. D. W. Ehrenfeld, *The Arrogance of Humanism* (New York: Oxford University Press, 1978).

17. G. B. Wetterberg, G. T. Prance, and T. E. Lovejoy, "Conservation progress in Amazonia: A structural review," *Parks* 6(1981): 5–10; A. Gentry, "Extinction and conservation of plant species in tropical America, a phytogeographical perspective," in I. Hedberg, ed., *Systematic Botany, Plant Utilization and Biosphere Conservation* (Stockholm: Almquist and Wiksell, 1979). See A. Ross-Sheriff et al., *Technologies to Sustain Tropical Forest Resources*, prepared for the U.S. Congress, Office of Technology Assessment, OTA-F-214, 1984, for a thorough, neutral treatment of deforestation problems, but not of root causes, slanted toward forestry development and reforestation, not preservation. Also see *Bioscience* 38 (March 1988), a whole issue devoted to tropical reserves and innovative ways to solve their problems. For a thorough discussion of the destructive influence on the tropics of the world's bank policies, see B. M. Rich, "The multilateral development banks, environment policy, and the United States," *Ecology Law Quarterly* 12(1985): 681–745; and Friends of the Earth, "Financing Ecological Destruction" (Washington, D.C. [218 D Street SE, 20003]: Friends of the Earth-USA, 1988).

18. D. H. Janzen, ed., *Costa Rican Natural History* (Chicago: University of Chicago Press, 1983); M. A. Boza and R. Mendoza, *The National Parks of Costa Rica* (Madrid: INCAFO, 1981); J. H. Janzen, "Tropical dry forests: the most endangered major tropical ecosystem" in E. O. Wilson, ed., *Biodiversity* (Washington, D.C.: National Academy Press, 1988), 130–37; M. Sun, "Costa Rica's campaign for conservation," *Science* 239(1988): 1366–69; W. H. Allen, "Biocultural restoration of a tropical forest," *Bioscience* 38(March 1988): 156–61. See also note 17 above.

19. See Wolf in *State of the World 1988*, cited in note 1, and *World Resources 1988–89*: 100–101, cited in note 8.

20. I. Rubinoff, "A strategy for preserving tropical rain forests," *Ambio* 12, no. 5(1983): 255–58; J. D. Nations and D. I. Komer, "Central America's tropical rainforests: positive steps for survival," *Ambio* 12, no. 5(1983): 232–38.

21. N. Myers, *A Wealth of Wild Species* (Boulder, Colo.: Westview Press 1983); G. Wilkes, "The world's crop plant germ plasm: An endangered resource," *Bulletin of the Atomic Scientists* 33(1977) 8–16; J. V. Neel, "Lessons from a primitive people," *Science* 170(1977): 815–22; H. H. Iltis, "Serendipity in the exploration of biodiversity. What good are weedy tomatoes?" in E. O. Wilson, ed., *Biodiversity* (Washington, D.C.: National Academy Press, 1988), 98–105. See also note 10 above.

22. H. H. Iltis and D. A. Kolterman, "Botanical translations: Needs and responsibilities," *BioScience* 33(1983): 613. A step in the right direction is a collection of ecological studies recently translated into Spanish: Georgina A. De Alba and Roberta W. Rubinoff, eds., *Evolucion en los Tropicos* (Panama: Smithsonian Tropical Research Institute, 1982).

23. This is a deliberate inversion of a statement by Gerardo Budowski, a Central American ecologist: "Action to correct the grave imbalances between human populations, resources and environment must go hand in hand with struggles against the injustices of social and economic systems." [Quoted in *Green Paper* no. 2, Central Amer-

ica: Roots of Environmental Destruction (Environmental Project on Central America, 1986)]. Nobody would disagree, but it is far easier to change political systems than agricultural systems or reproductive patterns.

24. "We have now squarely to face this paradox. . . . We have increased human hunger by feeding the hungry. We have increased human suffering by healing the sick. We have increased human want by giving to the needy. It is almost impossible for us to face the fact that this is so. The truth comes as a shocking discovery, for we have all been brought up in the Christian tradition in which caring for the least of our brethren has been counted the highest virtue." Rev. Duncan Howlett, All Souls Church, Washington, D.C., December 6, 1969. [Quoted in *The Other Side*, The Environmental Fund Newsletter, Washington, D.C., September, 1979].

25. K. Clark, "The Fallacies of Hope," in *Civilization: A Personal View* (New York: Harper and Row, 1968), 293–320.

26. The editorial help of Martha Cook is greatly appreciated.

Energy and Agricultural Production

Michael Perelman

Introduction

In this discussion, I demonstrate that American farming has not economized on its use of land, labor-power, and purchased inputs; and I compare the productive efficiencies of large and small farms, showing that redistribution of resources toward the small farm would increase output and reduce input requirements. Yet large farms are rapidly replacing small farms in the United States, demonstrating a further inefficiency at work.

Understanding the U.S. food system is an important political task. The myth of the efficiency of U.S. agriculture is blindly accepted around the world, yet that system would prove disastrous for developing nations. This article is intended to warn of the dangers by revealing the enormous economic costs associated with American agriculture.

Agricultural Efficiency

Efficiency is a nebulous concept requiring a common scale of measurement for the disparate inputs of agriculture. The usual assumptions, which allow the use of monetary values, are not very realistic. When a particular production process has a low ratio of output per unit of *every* class of input—when land, labor, and purchased inputs of nonlabor goods and services are relatively high compared to output—then it may be judged to be inefficient.

The Use of Land in American Agriculture

Begin with land: Yields per acre depend on factors such as climate, the availability of inputs, and price structure. Despite the common perception of success, agricultural yields on American farms are not particularly high. The extraordinary quality of American land is shown by the land left untilled that farmers of other countries would gladly cultivate. Since only the best lands in the United States are farmed, while the most marginal lands of many other countries are farmed, yields here should be considerably higher than elsewhere, yet they are surprisingly poor. For example, American wheat farms harvested an average of 2.2 metric tons per hectare in 1980. By contrast, the figure for the Netherlands was 6.2 metric tons per hectare. Even the mountainous lands of Austria and Switzerland had yields double that of the United States (U.S.D.A.). Some might be tempted to explain away such differences by the higher support prices for European grain or by climatic conditions.

Let us then take Eastern Europe as a benchmark. The German Democratic Republic and Czechoslovakia more than doubled the 1981 wheat yields of the United States. Hungary's yield rounds to 4.4 metric tons per hectare, exactly double the figure for the United States. Even Albania, often caricatured as the quintessence of backwardness, harvests more wheat per acre than the United States (U.S.D.A. 1981).

In yields of corn, a crop particularly well suited to the American climate, Italy, Austria, Greece, Switzerland, and the world leader, New Zealand, outperform the United States. As would be expected, Japan produces more rice per acre than the United States, but so do many other countries, including the People's Republic of Korea, Yugoslavia, Egypt, Spain, Greece, and Kenya (U.S.D.A. 1981).

Of course, yields in the United States are higher than in some societies where farmers have access to few inputs besides their own labor. These familiar examples are commonly used to portray U.S. agriculture in a favorable light.

Economic logic suggests that lower yields might be a rational response to the U.S. price structure. Suppose that the ratio of land prices to the prices of other inputs is lower here than elsewhere. Farmers might then rationally substitute land for other inputs. But, could this reasoning explain why land lies idle in the United States that would certainly be cultivated in other lands? And, if U.S. farmers are substituting land for other inputs, then the relatively low output per acre of land should be compensated for by a higher yield per unit of other inputs. In point of fact, measured in terms of output per unit of specific nonland input, yields in the United States are low. For example, the

Soviet Union produces almost 50 percent more food per tractor than the United States does (Durgin 1982).

The Use of Resources in U.S. Agriculture

Low agricultural yields are a telling rebuke to the U.S. food system, especially when seen in the context of the network of purchased inputs that contribute to farm production.

In the United States, most farm inputs are less expensive relative to land than they are in the rest of the world. Consider petroleum products: Since petroleum prices are considerably lower in the United States than in Europe, our agriculture has been adept in applying petroleum-intensive technologies. American agriculture consumes ten to fifteen calories of fossil fuel for each calorie of food purchased by final consumers (see Perelman 1977). Agriculture need not be such a large consumer of fossil energy; it even holds out the possibility of providing alternative fuel sources.

American farmers not only have access to low-cost farm inputs, they also have the advantage of natural resources that are treated as free goods. For instance, about twenty pounds of soil erosion are produced for each pound of food consumed in the United States (see Perelman 1977).

In short, the American agricultural system fails to economize on either land or purchased inputs. Thus, the case for its efficiency can only rest upon its economical use of labor.

Labor Efficiency in U.S. Agriculture

To argue that output per unit of labor is low in the United States seems to fly in the face of common sense. On what grounds can its labor-saving nature be doubted?

Isn't the massive exodus from the farms proof of the labor-saving nature of modern agriculture? The farm population stood at more than thirty-two million in 1932 (U.S. Department of Commerce 1970, 457). By 1980, it had fallen to six or seven million, depending on the definition used (U.S. Department of Commerce 1981, 657).

On the Social Division of Labor

To evaluate its extensive labor requirements properly, the U.S. food system must be placed within the context of the social division of labor. The term "social division of labor" can be defined as the partitioning of the economy into a network of businesses and industries (see Perelman 1987, ch. 4; and Perelman 1984, ch. 1). Within this arrangement, firms buy goods and services from other firms or labor-power from households. In turn, they sell goods and services to other purchasers, whether firms or households. To make such a statement may seem to belabor the obvious, but all too often agriculture is described as if it were a self-contained system in a universe of its own.

An understanding of agriculture within the context of the social division of labor is of the utmost importance. Consider how the labor requirements of American agriculture might be analyzed in terms of the social division of labor. Most new agricultural technologies are embodied in commodities or services purchased from a broad spectrum of nonfarm businesses. For example, farmers purchase tractors and trucks and, to a lesser extent, fertilizer to replace horse manure. Labor that was once used to care for horses on the farm disappears, while other labor demands arise in the farm input sector. Accordingly, we popularly speak of agribusiness as a complex, which encompasses farms as well as those who supply farm inputs and market farm products. While this perspective is a step forward, it remains far too narrow.

Make an inventory of all the indirect work that contributes to the creation of a tractor. Include the manufacture of paint and tires; also count the service of accountants and the communications industry. By this standard, the labor requirements for the U.S. food production system fell a mere 3 percent between 1958 and 1970 (Howe et al. 1976; see also Dovring 1967 and Gossling 1972). Taking into account that output increased during this period, the estimated labor requirements per unit of output fell only by 20 percent, an amount far below the savings usually attributed to the food system.

In fact, the estimate of 20 percent stands in need of correction. Even though the number of hours worked in the food system may have been more or less constant, the mix of labor has changed. There has been an enormous rise in the number of highly skilled workers whose efforts are embodied in food production. I need only allude to the modern complexes formulating agricultural chemicals or the robots now welding farm equipment.

Of course, in the long run, the more the economy can employ highly skilled labor, the more it will prosper. The U.S. economy, as it is presently constituted, is unable to employ all its unskilled labor, and much highly skilled labor is in short supply (Melman 1983). Thus, to the extent that agriculture has been substituting skilled for unskilled labor, the benefits of labor-saving methods will be overestimated.

If this point is accepted, more traditional agriculture deserves considerable credit for providing employment opportunities for those whose labor otherwise would have been wasted. For example, one survey of the Ozarks area of Arkansas, Missouri, and Oklahoma revealed that nearly 20 percent of the household heads on small farms were either totally or partially disabled (Long 1975). Even if this region were two times as reliant on such workers as other regions, these data imply a serious social cost resulting from the elimination of small farms in the United States.

In addition, of those who are working, many work only part time in farming. Thus, Patrick J. Madden suggests interpreting the small farm as a "producer not only of goods, but also of various services, such as custom work and of off-farm jobs" (Madden 1971, 21). Thus, we could argue that conventional measures seriously overstate the value of labor used on smaller farms.

Freeing up the labor of retired people, untrained farm workers, or the disabled is not an economic saving, unless those affected prefer unemployment. In many cases, eliminating the jobs of such people might not only fail to be a saving, it might actually be an outright cost to society. For example, the high Japanese price supports, which protect many tiny farms, function as a substitute for old age pensions (see Dore 1978, 109).

The estimate of a 20 percent saving in labor requirements calls for still another adjustment before it can be considered seriously. That figure excluded all labor not purchased as a commodity by agriculture and its suppliers. In reality, some of this excluded labor participates in the new organization of the food system.

For example, the reorganization of farming into units that rely heavily upon purchased inputs significantly contributed to the process of urbanization. Between 1920 and 1970, a net movement of more than thirty million people streamed from the farms to the cities (U.S. Department of Commerce 1970, 685). This shift of population from farms to concentrated urban areas created a multitude of economic costs that should be included when calculating the labor costs of modern agriculture. For example, the transfer of people to urbanized environments requires a far more complex infrastructural network than is required for rural life and work. Fire departments and sewage treatment plants represent obvious examples of the diseconomies of scale associated with urbanization. Such costs are not paid directly by the businesses, whose decisions change the social division of labor. Nor are they wholly reflected in the data that counted the changing agricultural labor requirements.

A precise estimate of the labor costs of U.S. agriculture, including the hidden costs to which I just referred, is impossible to make. I will roughly estimate the sort of costs that fall through the cracks of a standard input-output model. The Nobel Prize winner Simon Kuznets estimated that the "inflated costs of urban civilization . . . amounted to from 20 to 30 percent of all consumers' outlay in 1920 as estimated by the Department of Commerce" (Kuznets 1953, 195–96; see also Kuznets 1971, 76–90).

A number of later estimates seem to center around the figure of 20 percent. Irving Hoch calculates that wages in Standard Metropolitan Statistical Areas (S.M.S.A.) with populations of ten million must be deflated by about 18 percent to be equivalent to the buying power of residents in S.M.S.A.s with populations of one hundred thousand (Hoch 1972, 236). Urban families are estimated to require between 17 and 42 percent more income than rural families (President's National Advisory Committee on Rural Poverty 1958, 549). Koffsky estimated that in 1971 the cost of goods in the city, excluding rent, was from 14 to 30 percent higher than in rural areas, depending upon whether city or farm expenditure weights were used (Koffsky 1949, 170).

Now apply a very crude sort of adjustment. Taking the upper bound of Kuznets' figure of 30 percent, assume that each job transferred from the farm to the city between 1958 and 1960 was associated with a net increase in labor requirement of 0.3 other jobs not included in the measure of agriculture labor. The Bureau of Labor Statistics estimates a 60 percent reduction in hours of farm work between 1958 and 1970 (see Durost and Kirkley 1976, 133). Since the total labor requirement was more or less constant, we can assume that 60 percent of the farm labor force was moved from the farm to the city. If each of these hypothetical new city jobs entailed an extra 30 percent of a job, then the total labor requirements would increase by an additional 18 percent, an amount more or less equal to the increase in farm production.

In addition, recall that much of the labor supposedly saved was either unskilled or disabled. By conventional economic standards, it had a zero or, at least, a very low opportunity cost. Thus, the claim that modern agricultural technology has saved labor is doubtful, to say the least.

In conclusion, the farm sector seems to have a low output per unit of land, purchased inputs, and perhaps even labor. Since the U.S. food system fails on all three counts, American agriculture can be judged inefficient. This conclusion is reinforced by the enormous subsidies for water development and research and the awesome environmental costs of agriculture in the United States.

In charging the U.S. food system with inefficiency, I have deliberately limited my scope. Strictly speaking, any farming system should be judged by its ability to contribute to the quality of life in general. I have refrained from making a general analysis of capitalist society. Instead, I am merely attempting to show that, on strictly economic grounds, where the case for U.S. agriculture should be the strongest, it fails.

On the Relative Efficiency of Small Farms

The case against the capitalist agricultural system of the United States is made clearer through the use of a second methodology. I show that, contrary to popular belief, small farms are able to produce food with the least inputs, yet small farms are being systematically eliminated. Again, the food system seems to be moving in a less labor-saving direction.

In presenting my argument, I may seem to be making a case for small, undercapitalized, independent farming. Let me say at the outset that such an impression would be mistaken. I do not believe that such farms are absolutely efficient. Collective agriculture represents a preferable alternative to small farms, but I am convinced that small farms are more efficient than the seemingly progressive agribusiness-type operation.

Before beginning my analysis, let me point out that a small farm is not synonymous with poverty. Keep in mind that the labor of the small-farm operator is often combined with other employment. Nationwide, according to the 1969 Census of Agriculture, on farms with sales between $2,500 and $10,000, 40 percent of the farmers worked at least one hundred days off the farm. Of these workers, 60 percent worked at least two hundred days. The average number of days worked off the farm falls with increasing farm size. Farms with sales from $10,000 to $20,000 had farmers working an average of sixty-four days off the farm in 1974. The figures for farms with sales of $20,000 to $40,000 and with sales of $40,000 to $100,000 are thirty-one and twenty-four days, respectively (U.S. Department of Commerce 1978, xi, ch. 7, p. 9).

The decline of small farmers is, in fact, a decline in the numbers of those who entirely, or almost entirely, depend on agriculture for their incomes. Part-time farming seems to have been increasing (See Tweeten, Cilley, and Popoola 1980). Thus, when seen in conjunction with the returns from other employment opportunities, the family farm may well be able to provide a substantial return, in spite of the well-known disadvantages that the market heaps upon small farmers.

Despite the usual claim that large farms prosper because of economies of scale, the fall in the numbers of full-time small farmers can be attributed to a number of causes: inadequate credit, tax laws, a market structure geared to the needs of larger farms, and research and extension efforts that frequently overlook the needs of small farmers. I have published a more extensive list of such biases elsewhere (see Perelman 1977, pt. II).

On the Relative Efficiency of Large- and Small-Scale Farming Again

According to conventional economic theory, output is maximized when the marginal product of a dollar's worth of input is equal for every firm that uses that input. Presumably, such market behavior should also maximize the net income per dollar's worth of input for each firm in an industry.

This sort of reasoning must be taken with a grain of salt. It ignores externalities, increasing or decreasing returns, and a host of other problems. Nonetheless, I believe this approach sufficiently robust to apply as a crude rule of thumb for analyzing modern methods of agricultural production.

First of all, the Census Bureau does not classify farms according to their size or the modernity of their production methods, but by the value of their marketed output. Despite this deficiency, census data leads to striking results.

The first two columns in Table 1 list the percentage of total farm expenses and total farm revenue experienced by each class of farms, arranged according to level of gross sales. The third column, labeled "Efficiency Indicator," shows the net farm income per dollar's worth of purchased input for each class of farm. Notice that the class of smaller farms generally outperforms the class of larger ones.

Can Table 1 be taken to suggest that the optimal farm size would be one that results in sales under $2,500? Of course, the income from such operations would be inadequate; however, theoretically it could be coupled with outside employment of less than forty hours per week. For example, in the Orient, the combination of small farms and part-time farming was successful in promoting economic growth (see Smith 1970, 129, 211, and 216). The exact details of such an arrangement are beyond the scope of this paper.

Table 1 exaggerates the efficiency of large farms because unsuccessful farms tend to be classified as small farms. For example, according to the 1974 Census of Agriculture, 1,265 farms, each with more than two thousand acres, sold less than $2,500 worth of produce, and

TABLE I
Farm Size and Efficiency

	1	2	3	4	5
	Percent of Total United States				
Gross Sales ($ x 1,000)	*Production Expenses*	*Net Farm Income*	*Net Efficiency Indicator (Col.2/ Col.1)*	*Production Expenses Minus Wages*	*Adjusted Efficiency Indicator (Col. 2/ Col. 4)*
Less than 2.5	2.3	6.3	2.7	1.8	3.5
2.5-5	1.6	1.7	1.3	1.0	1.7
5-10	2.6	3.2	1.2	2.2	1.5
10-20	4.5	6.2	1.4	3.7	1.7
20-40	8.9	13.2	1.5	8.8	1.5
40-100	22.5	31.1	1.4	21.5	1.5
100-200	15.8	18.6	1.2	21.1	0.88
200 +	41.8	19.7	0.47	39.9	0.49

Source: U.S. Department of Agriculture 1979 and 1979a

another 1,768 sold between $2,500 and $5,000 worth (U.S. Department of Commerce 1978, xi, pt. 2, ch. 2, p. 7).

Presumably, other farms that use relatively little land or purchased inputs might be able to market a great deal of produce. Such farms will be classified as large because they are efficient, although the data might appear to suggest that they are efficient because they are large (see, for example, Hoch 1976). This identification problem increases the share of revenues and decreases the share of purchased inputs associated with large farms, if we fail to distinguish between small farms and those farms with relatively little gross income.

Furthermore, almost no emphasis is placed on research suited to the special requirements of small-scale farming. Instead, agricultural science typically identifies with the largest, most capital-intensive farms (see Perelman 1977, 88, 99, and 229–30). For example, in California's Imperial Valley, little study has been devoted to crops such as eggplant or squash, which are grown by small farmers (Madden 1977, p. 26). Had the smaller farms the benefit of the massive infusion of research devoted to the needs of the large farming operations, the ratios might have shown the small farm system in a still more favorable light. Moreover, the small farmer has difficulty obtaining credit to grow lucrative, but risky, specialty crops (Perelman 1977, 97). Some evidence suggests that even those areas of research that are allegedly equally applicable to large- and small-scale farmers may offer no apparent profit to the family-size farm (Klepper et al. 1976).

Admittedly, the measure of net income per unit of purchased input is far from a perfect indicator of efficiency, especially with respect to the farms with the smallest sales. The marginalized farmers within this group may be more likely to set aside land to produce food for home consumption. The importance of this phenomenon for agriculture as a whole has declined considerably since 1941, when aggregate homegrown food consumed on the farm was still equivalent to 12.5 percent of farm income (U.S. Department of Agriculture 1943, 409). By 1973, the average farm family was spending more than $2,000 for food purchases (Throp 1975). To the extent that the smaller farms are more likely to channel resources into personal use instead of the market, reported net farm income will be lower.

We might also add that the small farm is also more likely to skim off a higher proportion of its produce for home consumption. I make this conjecture on two grounds. First, farmers traditionally grew much of their own food. The small farm is more likely to adhere to traditional lifestyles. Second, if the owners of large and small farms both consumed equal amounts of homegrown food, the produce used by the small farm would represent a larger proportion of the total harvest.

In addition, personal expenditures are frequently reported as production expenses. For example, some sources allege that farmers claim gasoline burned on a pleasure trip as a farm expense (Anon. 1978). Such practices will lower the efficiency indicators of small farms much more than large ones. For the same reasons that produce consumed at home on a small farm reflects a larger proportion of total production, a gallon of gasoline burned on a pleasure trip to town will represent a larger share of total costs for a small farm than for a large one. Thus, we could expect that the typical small farmer would probably charge off a larger percentage of total farm costs than the larger ones.

This phenomenon may explain why the average gasoline use per acre for farms with less than 100 acres is reportedly three to four times as much as for farms with over 180 acres (U.S. Senate 1974, 80). For other types of fuel, the input per acre was not very different. By dividing farms into statewide groups, Buttel and Larsen have shown that large farms actually use more fuel per acre than small farms (Buttel and Larsen 1979).

These data suggest that a considerable amount of other farm inputs might actually be diverted for personal use. We have no way of knowing how extensive such practices are, but they seem to be rather widespread. Because of the tax advantages of writing off personal consumption on small farm operations, farming has become popular with some people whose interest in farming per se is limited. We get some indication of this trend from the fact that in 1977 average production expenses per farm claimed by those farms with sales between $2,500 and $5,000 were double those reported in 1970; for farms with sales less than $2,500, the figure rose by an astounding 279 percent during the same period (U.S. Department of Agriculture 1979, 55).

Keep in mind that inflation cannot be blamed for the cost increases. If all prices increased proportionally, small farms would move into a higher classification. Costs of production should not increase within any particular class of farms, unless such farms suddenly became less-efficient. What reason do we have to believe that small farms should have substantially less efficient production techniques than they did earlier? The likely answer is that more people are farming for tax advantages or as a lifestyle.

Taken together, the lack of research support, the price disadvantages, personal consumption of farm inputs and produce, and the confusion of cause and effect in determining the relationship between scale and efficiency all combine to make the data for small farms in Table 1 appear far more unfavorable than it would if the table measured the actual productivity of large and small farms.

Table 2 recasts the data in a slightly different fashion. It shows the net farm income for the average size farm in each class and the average production expenses, excluding the cost of wages. By calculating the differences between farm classes, we can see how much of an increment of net income is created by transferring one dollar's worth of farm inputs from one class of farm to another. Notice that the largest farms do very poorly by this measure. Farms with sales between $10,000 and $100,000 do quite well. Consequently, the least efficient strategy for maximizing income would be to transfer resources from one of the smaller classes of farms to the largest class.

Based on the crude sort of general equilibrium reasoning that I discussed earlier, breaking up larger farms into smaller operations would seem to be justified in terms of creating a larger pool of income available for society. I base this conclusion on the fact that the larger farms require more inputs to produce a unit of net income. This result holds in spite of all the biases that make the smaller size of farms appear to be less efficient than they really are.

What has been the fate of the smaller categories of farms? For example, farms with sales of $20,000 to $40,000 grew by 41 percent be-

TABLE 2

Per Farm Production Expenses and Net Farm Income, 1978

	Farms with Sales in Thousands of Dollars						
	$200+	*$100-$200*	*$40-$100*	*$20-$40*	*$10-$20*	*$5-$10*	*$2.5-$5*
Production Expenses	658,286	176,887	57,482	28,378	12,841	8,327	3,605
Farm	74,635	35,774	19,067	9,734	4,990	2,683	1,480
	Change in Income and Production Expense Required to Move to Next Highest Class						
Production Expenses	451,399	119,405	29,104	15,537	4,514	4,632	
Net Income	38,861	16,707	9,333	4,744	2,307	1,213	
Change in Net Income/ Change in Net Farm Income	0.09	0.14	0.32	0.31	0.51	0.26	

Source: U.S. Department of Agriculture 1979 and 1979a.

tween 1960 and 1977; however, a farm in this category in 1960 was a relatively larger operation than it would be today because of the impact of inflation, which has effectively doubled. If we compare farms with sales from $10,000 to $20,000 in 1960 with those with sales of $20,000 to $40,000 in 1977, we find a net decline of about 55 percent, which is significantly larger than the percentage reduction for all farms. In contrast, during the same period farms with sales over $100,000 have increased sevenfold, much more than could be explained by the effect of inflation (U.S. Department of Agriculture 1979, 53).

Yet, even with the advantages heaped on the large-scale farm, it is still a relatively unprofitable venture. The U.S. Department of Agriculture reports that "the typical farm corporation in 1970 had . . . business receipts of about $150,000 and showed a net loss after paying salaries to its officers" (U.S. Department of Agriculture 1976). In addition, the large farming operation is more likely to experience bankruptcy than the typical farm (see Lane and Moore 1972, Paarlberg 1971, and Melichar 1979). True, much data do imply a relatively steep decline in conventionally defined cost structures as farm size increases, but only up to very modest farm sizes. Thereafter, increases in farm size are associated with no apparent cost advantage (Hall and LeVeen 1978).

The argument thus far has suggested that the allegedly efficient large farm may not be efficient after all. I have used the small farm as a benchmark for making my point. As I said earlier, the small farm is hardly likely to be able to take advantage of all the production possibilities of agriculture, which would entail some combination of planning, cooperation, and delegation of authority to those who actually grow the food.

The Limits of the Analysis

The evolution of agricultural technology has been a very complex process. In spite of quantitative data that I have used, I do not pretend to be exact. I am convinced that the modern social division of labor, shaped by the quest for profits rather than social well-being, has been detrimental to both rural and urban life. Rural life is impoverished when the amenities of modern civilization are concentrated in the city. Urban life suffers when these amenities are accompanied by inadequate housing, pollution, and the other excesses of the city.

The data of the sort that I am using provide very imperfect indicators of this economic evolution. My purpose was only to show some of the strictly economic costs of the U.S. food system, to raise the suggestion that our imperfect measures give us reason to doubt that the labor requirements of agricultural production have fallen over the past few decades, and reason to believe that efficiency in U.S. agriculture may actually be declining.

The method employed here captures only some of these costs. For example, the corn growing in the fields today is very different than the corn harvested at the turn of the century. Not only is its chemical composition different, but it is designed to be harvested within an entirely different civilization (see Perelman 1977, ch. 6).

Nonetheless, the results of this study are troubling. The conditions of farm workers, the widespread use of toxic chemicals, and billion-dollar water projects are all justified in terms of the efficiency of large-scale capitalized agriculture. Yet our data seem to indicate that this system may not be efficient after all. People would be better served by taking more advantage of the sort of agriculture represented by the small-scale farm, or even more, by a planned agriculture developed in the interests of people rather than profit.

References Cited

Buttel, Frederick H., and Oscar W. Larsen, III. "Farm Size, Structure, and Energy Intensity: an Ecological Analysis of U.S. Agriculture." *Rural Sociology* 44, no. 3 (Fall 1979): 471–88.

Dore, Ronald. 1978. *Shinohata: A Portrait of a Japanese Village*. New York: Pantheon.

Dovring, Folke. 1967. *Productivity of Labor in Agricultural Production*. Urbana: University of Illinois Agricultural Experiment Station Bull. 726, September.

Durgin, Frank A. 1982. Soviet Agriculture: A Radical Analysis of Some Commonly Cited Facts and Conclusions Regarding its Performance. Paper presented at Allied Social Science Association Annual Meetings, Dec. 29, New York.

Durost, D. D. and J. E. 1976. Changes in the Food and Fiber System, 1958-1974," *Agricultural Economics Research* 28, no. 4 (October): 130–35.

Gossling, W. F. 1972. *Productivity Trends in a Sectoral Model: A Study in American Agriculture and Supporting Industries*. London: Input-Output Publishers.

Hall, Bruce F., and E. Phillip LeVeen. 1978. "Farm Size and Economic Efficiency: The Case of California," *American Journal of Agricultural Economics* 60, no. 4 (December): 589–600.

Hoch, Irving. 1976. "City Size Effects, Trends and Policies," *Science* 193, no. 4256 (September 3): 856–63.

———. 1972.

"Urban Scale and Environmental Quality," in Commission on Population Growth and the American Future, *Research Reports*, Vol. 3, *Population, Resources and the Environment*, edited by Ronald Ridker, pp. 235–84; reprinted as Resources for the Future, Reprint no. 110.

Howe, Eric C., Gerald E. Schluter, and Charles R. Handy. 1976. "Measuring Labor Productivity in Production of Food for Personal Consumption," *Agricultural Economics Research* 24, no. 4 (October): 123–29.

"Income Farmers Hide." *Business Week*, April 17, 1978.

Klepper, R., W. Lockeretz, B. Commoner, M. Gertler, S. Fast, D. O'Leary, and R. Blobaum. 1976. "Economic Performance and Energy Intensiveness on Organic and Conventional Farms in the Corn Belt: A Preliminary Comparison," *American Journal of Agricultural Economics* 59, no. 1 (February): 1–12.

Koffsky, Frank. 1949. "Farm and Urban Purchasing Power," *Conference on Research and Income and Wealth, Studies in Income and Wealth*, Vol. 2. New York: National Bureau of Economic Research.

Kuznets, Simon. 1971. *Economic Growth of Nations: Total Output and Production Structure*. Cambridge: Harvard University Press.

———. 1953. *Economic Change*. New York: W. W. Norton.

Lane, Sylvia, and Charles V. Moore. 1972. "Analysis of Attributes of Insolvent Farmers in San Joaquin Valley Study," *California Agriculture* 26, no. 2 (February): 6–7.

Long, Robert W. 1975. "Letter of Robert W. Long, Assistant Secretary of Agriculture, August 15, 1975," reprinted in General Accounting Office, *Report to the Congress by the Controller of the U.S.: Some Problems Impeding Economic Improvement of Small Farm*

Operations: What the Department of Agriculture Could Do.

Madden, Patrick J. 1971. *Economies of Size in Farming*, Agricultural Economics Report no. 107. Washington, D.C.: U.S. Department of Agriculture, Economic Research Service.

———. 1977. "Testimony and Cross Examination," U.S. Senate, Committee on the Judiciary, Subcommittee on Administrative Practice and Procedure, *Priorities in Agricultural Research of the U.S. Department of Agriculture*, 95th Congress, 1st Session (Washington, D.C.: U.S. Government Printing Office): pp. 13–27.

Melichar, Emanuel. 1979. "A Review of Selected Farm Financial Developments," 2d printing revised. First presented at Agricultural Outlook Conference, 7 November.

Melman, Seymour. 1983. *Profits without Production*. New York: Alfred A. Knopf.

Paarlberg, Don. 1971. "Future of the Family Farm." Speech before the 55th Annual Convention of the National Milk Producers. Bal Harbour, Fla. November 30.

Perelman, Michael. 1977. *Farming for Profit in a Hungry World: Capital and the Crisis in Agriculture*. Totowa, N.J.: Allenheld and Osmun.

———. 1987. *Karl Marx's Crisis Theory: Labor, Scarcity and Fictitious Capital*. New York: Praeger.

———. 1984. *Classical Political Economy, Primitive Accumulation, and the Social Division of Labor*. Totowa, N.J.: Rowman and Allanheld.

President's National Advisory Commission on Rural Poverty. 1968. *Rural Poverty in the U.S.* Washington, D.C.: U.S. Government Printing Office.

Smith, Thomas. 1970. *The Agrarian Origins of Modern Japan*. Stanford: Stanford University Press.

Throp, Fred C. 1975. "Family Expenditures: The Farm Living Survey," 1976 Agricultural Outlook Papers Presented at the National Outlook Conference Sponsored by the U.S. Department of Agriculture, Prepared for the Committee on Agriculture and Forestry. U.S. Senate, 94th Cong., 1st Sess.: pp. 312–18. Washington, D.C.

Tweeten, Luther, G. B. Cilley, and I. Popoola. 1980. "Typology and policy for small farms," *Southern Journal of Agricultural Economics* 12, no. 2: 77–85.

U.S. Department of Agriculture. 1981. *Agricultural Statistics*. Washington, D.C.: U.S. Government Printing Office.

———. 1981. *Economic Indicators of the Farm Sector: State Income and Balance Sheet Statistics*, ESCS Statistical Bulletin no. 661.

———. 1979. *Farm Income Statistics*, ESCS Statistical Bulletin no. 609. Washington, D.C.: U.S. Government Printing Office.

———. 1979a. *Farm Production Expenditures for 1978*. U.S. Dept. of Agriculture, Economics, Statistics, and Cooperative Services. Washington, D.C.: U.S. Government Printing Office.

———. 1976. *Fact Book of U.S. Agriculture*. Washington, D.C.: U.S. Government Printing Office.

———. 1943. *Agricultural Statistics*. Washington, D.C.: U.S. Government Printing Office.

U.S. Department of Commerce. 1981. *Statistical Abstract of the U.S.* Washington, D.C.: U.S. Government Printing Office.

———. 1978. *Census of Agriculture*.

———. 1970. *Historical Statistics of the U.S. from Colonial Times to 1970*, part 1.

Washington, D.C.: U.S. Government Printing Office.

U.S. Senate, 93d Cong., 2nd Sess. 1974. *The U.S. Food and Fiber Sector: Energy Look and Outlook: A Study of the Energy Needs of the Food Industry*, prepared by the Economic Research Service of the U.S. Department of Agriculture for the Subcommittee on Agricultural Credit and Rural Electrification of the Committee on Agriculture and Forestry, 20 September. Washington, D.C.: U.S. Government Printing Office.

IV.
Agriculture's Development

IV.A.
New Sources of Food for the World

IF PRESENT INDUSTRIALIZED METHODS OF FARMING are unsustainable, as many have argued, what are the alternatives for the future, both in the industrialized countries and in the developing areas of the world? The two articles in Section IV.A. provide visionary glimpses of alternatives now under development that go beyond those mentioned above. Wes Jackson, in his discussion "New Roots for American Agriculture," draws on the work of his Land Institute to suggest that we develop a perennial polyculture of seed-bearing plants in highly erodible areas. Jackson's five arguments for making this move are based upon the inadequacies of current alternatives and the market indifference to the environment. He shows that the evolved dietary needs of humans can be met by perennial food stocks. Further, such perennial food sources—subject to replanting no more frequently than every three years—would bring with them significant savings in fossil fuel consumption and costs. And, finally, such farming would allow for broader economic access to new (marginal) lands, while relieving pressure for irrigated farming that erodes soil and pollutes deep aquifers.

The three types of plants that Jackson identifies as potential perennial food sources could first be cultivated on marginal lands as a supplement to available food sources. This approach and the modification of available harvest machinery should make the cost of beginning to raise these perennials minimal. Furthermore, since perennial cultivation is not dependent upon great soil disturbance and pesticide application, it should be a much more sound solution to the problem of ecologically responsible food production.

One of the major questions, of course, is the extent to which such a source of food could satisfy our needs. In anticipation of that question, Jackson next surveys the yield potentials of perennial crop plants, comparing them favorably with presently popular cereal grains. Jackson concludes by discussing the three major obstacles to development of this alternative food source and how to deal with them.

Eugene B. Schultz, Wayne G. Bragg, Alejandro R. Martinez, and David W. Pluymers consider problems of new food sources in the international arena. The constraints on their thinking reveal their ethical agenda: First, food self-sufficiency for the third world must have priority over the exploitative production of cash crops for export. Second, only socioeconomically and environmentally sustainable crops and processing should be chosen. Crop processing must be kept low-tech and localized, both to decentralize new jobs and monetary return, and also to keep agricultural products inexpensive and locally available. Third, where goods are exported, value should be added in the country of origin with local capital. Finally, the development schemes followed should arise indigenously and be appropriate to the local society and environment. Schultz et al. explain the reasons underlying these principles in terms of the ethical cost of ignoring them.

In keeping with these ethical concerns, Schultz et al. present three examples of proper bio-resource strategic planning with respect to underutilized tree products suitable for the tropics. These three case studies cover *jïcaro* (a tropical dryland hickory), *pejibaye* (another tree, but of "the humid neotropics"), and *neem* (another tropical dryland tree). Jicaro is a source of food for both humans and animals, and a source of charcoal. Pejibaye can also feed humans and animals, but is a source of cooking and industrial oil as well. Neem provides an extremely effective insect-control substance. The authors outlined the details of appropriate development planning for these products.

Clearly, Schultz et al. are concerned with providing just treatment and a sustainable way of life to rural inhabitants of third world countries. The basic ethical concern of the authors could be a utilitarian one, but its emphasis upon individual justice and access to economic and agricultural self-sufficiency gives a strong impression of a rights-based or autonomy-driven set of ethical constraints upon their visions of new food sources. A similar remark might be made about Jackson's vision of new food sources. However, in Jackson's discussion one also can find hints of Leopold's land ethic at work. Several of the essays in the next section seem much more communitarian than individualistic in their initiating ethical orientation. Perhaps this is natural since the articles concern large-scale economic or political obstacles to the production and distribution of food for the world's hungry.

New Roots for American Agriculture[1]

Wes Jackson

SOIL CONSERVATION SERVICE (SCS) OFFICIALS recently set the annual average loss of soil on cropland nationwide at five tons per acre. A 1977 U. S. General Accounting Office report put the average annual loss at fifteen to sixteen tons per acre. An even earlier study, done at Iowa State University in 1972, estimated average annual soil loss to be about twelve tons per acre. Despite the disparity in these estimates, each makes one point clear: Soil loss continues at an unacceptable rate in nearly all of the areas tilled for agricultural purposes in the United States.

This failure on the part of conventional agriculture to develop a sustainable soil policy leads us to advocate development of a mixed-perennial grain-producing agriculture on sloping soils. Such an agriculture would more closely reflect natural ecosystems, substituting for soil-wasting, petroleum-intensive annual monocultures. While these perennial mixtures would be derived from plants possessing little promise now for meeting human needs, there is every reason to think the scientific community has the know-how to develop a sustainable agriculture of this sort simply because of the advances in biology over the past half-century.

There are at least five important reasons why this nation needs to pursue research into high-yielding mixtures of perennial grain crops that eventually augment annual monocultures:

1. The array of soil conservation measures used across this land is substantial, but the extra thought and effort necessary to make them effective has not been and probably will not be very compelling.

2. The doctrine of enlightened self-interest assumes that the economic system is sensitive to long-term considerations (beyond one person's lifetime), when in fact it is not.

3. Stewardship generally has failed.

4. Various forms of conservation tillage, particularly no-till, are chemical-dependent.

5. The economic system is almost totally insensitive to ecological necessity. Therefore, a reward-and-punishment system imposed on farmers would have to be sufficiently powerful to accommodate ecological necessity. This has not worked in the past and likely will not work in the future.

Toward an Ecological Agriculture

An ecological agriculture must consider human nature. Humans are primarily seed eaters, particularly grass seed eaters. Even when eating meat, humans are but one step away from grass seeds, for in developed countries livestock rely heavily on grains. Any compelling alternative to corn, wheat, and soybeans, therefore, cannot be a forage crop even if processed into pellets. If most of humanity is to stay with its evolutionary heritage, we must have grains.

If the nation were to resort to high-yielding perennials to save its soils, why not begin with the traditional annual crops and, through wide crosses and subsequent breeding, convert them into perennials? Gene splicing between conventional and perennial crops might also be investigated, but for now attention should probably focus on wild perennials.

Traditional annual crops (corn, wheat, soybeans) have been genetically narrowed, and most depend heavily on fossil fuel for fertility and protection from competitors. Grown in monoculture, they lack anything close to the water management system of the prairie. This is important when one considers that some of the nitrogen used by the prairie is supplied by rain. Finally, farmers have selectively bred conventional crops over the millennia to respond well in monoculture. Less difficulty is likely in breeding perennial mixtures than annual monocultures, even if the parent stock consists of plants that historically have been regarded as useless or nearly so. Specialized germ plasm would be selected from the wild plants bred for high yield to mature in synchrony. There would be one or two harvests each rear.

Three families of flowering plants would be involved in the perennial mixtures: grasses, legumes, and composites, particularly members of the sunflower tribe.

If one looks at the bottom line of yield alone, mixed perennial grain crops may be only marginally competitive, especially in the early stages of development. If, however, the nation were to allocate no more fossil fuel to conventional agriculture than to perennial polyculture, conventional agriculture probably could not compete.

Because the watchword is sustainability, mixed perennials will be less susceptible to environmental perturbations. The diversity of a polyculture, if it is like a natural ecosystem, will make the plants less vulnerable to insects and disease. The more efficient retention and use of soil moisture by perennial roots will make the ecosystem more resilient than that of a traditionally plowed field, with its high rate of soil runoff. This resiliency in turn contributes to yield because reduced soil loss means retained fertility even after severe rainstorms.

Most perennial polycultures presumably would be grown first on marginal land. The availability of such land is enormous, more than 100 million acres. These grain mixtures would be safely planted on most of this acreage. Though yields would be lower on this poorer quality land, the penalty to the farmer, to agribusiness itself, and to energy companies enjoying agricultural business would be much less in the initial stages than if these mixtures were planted on the currently cultivated landscape.

The economics of incorporating this biological approach to agriculture into what is fundamentally an industrial-style agriculture should not be prohibitive. The cost for seedbed preparation and planting should then be the same as pasture establishment now. If mixed grains grown on marginal land become grain sources for livestock, this amounts to an economic plus for farmers accustomed to feeding traditional grains.

All inputs would be greatly reduced in perennial mixtures, including fertilizers, pesticides, labor, and energy. These reductions, in turn, would reduce the farmer's capital investment and dependency on credit.

During the course of polyculture research and development, plant breeders at various institutions, particularly the land-grant universities, would be assisted by their colleagues in agricultural engineering in adapting conventional combines to harvest the experimental plots. In short, no fundamental technological innovation requiring huge capital investment seems necessary. Technological changes will likely be modest.

Annual polyculture was once common in underdeveloped countries. The classic corn-bean mixes are probably the best known. Perennial polyculture in which fruit seeds are harvested has been limited to woody vegetation (e.g., fruit and nut trees). Herbaceous perennial seed-producing mixtures in which seeds have matured at the same time would be harvested in a substantially different way than the polyculture of annuals or trees and shrubs. The latter do not lend themselves to machine harvest, but the herbaceous perennial polyculture does. Furthermore, some, if not most, of these perennial mixes would not have to be grown in rows.

In recent years there has been a steady increase in reduced tillage or no-till farming. A prime reason has been to reduce soil 1088. Perennial polycultures would have the same result. But from here on, the differences between the two methods nearly overshadow the similarities. No-till is pesticide-dependent. Perennial polyculture would be essentially independent of pesticides. No-till features annuals in monoculture. Perennial polycultures imitate natural ecosystems.

Yields of Select Perennials

The incentive to develop high seed yields in perennials has been small compared with the effort that has gone into development of high-yield annuals. Native seed merchants have probably had more reason than most to increase yield, but even for them a modest increase in germination has been more important than a yield increase. The SCS regional plant materials centers have likewise had reason to increase the yield of various perennials, and they have done 80 in several species. But they have little time to devote to such work. They are woefully understaffed, considering their mission of supplying seed for the nation's three thousand conservation districts. Range agronomists have understandably paid close attention to forage yield increases, devoting only minor effort to seed yield improvement. To date, there has been nothing close to what one might consider an aggressive national program for increasing herbaceous perennial seed yields.

Are herbaceous perennialism and high seed yield mutually exclusive? Woody perennials probably can produce high seed yields because of their greater height and exposure to light. But what about herbaceous species? Part of the answer depends upon what is meant by "high yield."

Winter wheat is regarded as a high-yielding crop. As an arbitrary standard, assume then a yield of 1,800 pounds of winter wheat per acre (thirty bushels at sixty pounds/bushel). Subsequent adjustments can be made for protein, carbohydrate, and oil yields on a per acre basis.

A survey of the literature on herbaceous perennial yields revealed the following: Buffalo grass (*Buchloe dactvloides*) that had been fertilized and irrigated yielded 1,727 pounds per acre. Although this yield included the burs, of which seeds are a small part, the yield represents fruit/seed material. Fertilized and irrigated Alta fescue (*Festuca arundinacea*) averaged 1,460 pounds per acre. A native stand of sand dropseed (*Sporobolus cryptandrus*) under dryland conditions at Hays, Kansas, yielded 900 pounds per acre.

Irrigated legume yields were also encouraging. A five-year average for Illinois bundleflower (*Desmanthus illionensis*) amounted to 1,189 pounds per acre. Fertilized cicer milkvetch (*Astragulus cicer*) yielded 1,000 pounds per acre, as did sanfoin (*Onobrychis viciaefolia*) that received seventy pounds of nitrogen.

Two species of sunflower produced exceptional yields when irrigated. The gray-headed coneflower (Ratibida Dinnata) yielded 1,600 pounds per acre. Maximillian sunflower (*Helianthus maximilianii*) yielded 1,300 pounds per acre.

While these high yields from relatively unselected plants are encouraging, these are cases in which yield may be somewhat less important than the quantity of protein per acre. Based on the per acre yield mentioned for Illinois bundleflower, cicer milkvetch, and sanfoin and their respective protein content, all have a protein yield of about 400 pounds per acre. This exceeds the protein from an acre of wheat yielding 31.6 bushels in which the protein, by weight, amounts to 228 pounds. It even compares favorably with 100-bushel-per-acre corn, which yields about 500 pounds of protein per acre.

As more data on perennial seed yields is collected, numerous perennials with high yield potential may be discovered. For example, almost all grass seed yields are from grasses ordinarily used for forage and hay. Such grasses have been selected to send much of their energy to the leaves rather than to the seed. Perhaps there are perennial grasses that are poor for forage but good for seed yield that have not been studied, such as the dropseed genus *Sporobolus*.

To be a good candidate for seed producer, a species should demonstrate high variation so the breeder has a basis for selection; show promise as a potentially high seed-yielder unless it serves another role, for example, a strong nitrogen-fixer or natural repellent of insects and pathogens for associated species; suggest some potential for determinate seed set, shatter resistance, and a favorable reproduction-to-vegetation-shoot ratio; promise a relatively high yield for a minimum of three years in order to accommodate itself in a three-year or more replant cycle; and exhibit meiotic stability, that is, the ability to display normal chromosome behavior during sex cell formation. For example, if the species is of polyploid or hybrid origin, the probability of regular meiosis should be very high or show some promise of high regularity. With perennials, meiosis need not be as regular as with annuals.

Benefits of Perennial Polycultures

An agriculture based on a perennial polyculture would produce a number of dramatic benefits for society and the nation's natural resource base. The resource-oriented benefits include the following:

1. Soil 1088 would be cut to zero, and then soil would begin to accumulate. The fossil energy savings in fertilizer to replace this lost soil would be significant.

2. The indirect consumption of fossil energy in agriculture would decline substantially. For example, the application of commercial fertilizer would drop greatly because, like a prairie, a perennial polyculture would use nitrogen more efficiently.

3. The efficiency of water use and water conservation by the perennial ecosystem would be near maximum, and springs, long since dry or short-lived during the year, would return. Irrigation would decline, reducing fossil energy use.

4. Commercial pesticides, especially those with no close chemical relatives in nature, would be abandoned or nearly so. In addition to the reduction in chemical contamination, a minor fossil-energy savings would result.

5. The direct consumption of fossil energy at the field level would be greatly reduced.

Among the social benefits of perennial polyculture would be the following:

1. Long before such an agriculture would be completely in place, its efficient use of water would render more manageable major policy questions surrounding irrigation projects that involve aquifer mining or water diversions that lead to soil salting and silting problems.

2. Policy considerations that include equitable land ownership rather than major corporate control of land would become more manageable due to the reduced need for high capitalization in machinery, energy, farm chemicals, irrigation, and seed.

3. More than one hundred million acres currently considered marginal land largely because of the serious erosion potential under current cropping systems could be brought into production, reducing the pressure for ever-increasing land prices. Stable land prices would increase the opportunity for people to have a farm as a place to promote and experience right livelihood rather than as a food factory.

Resource Savings

The primary purpose for developing such a radically new agriculture is to save soil from being eroded or chemically contaminated. What would be the effect on soil conservation if herbaceous perennials occupied the 316 million acres in the United States currently planted with the top ten crops? Results vary, of course, depending upon the estimate of soil loss chosen and the number of years between replantings. Let us assume that all 316 million acres, including the cotton and hay acreage, were planted to mixed perennials. If fields were replanted every five years, 253 million acres of the 316 million acres in any given year would remain unplowed. On the basis of a soil 1088 of five tons per acre, that would save 1.27 billion tons of soil. Given a twelve-ton-per-acre soil 1088, the savings would exceed three billion tons a year, an amount equal to the annual 1088 when SCS was established.

These estimates are conservative. They are not adjusted to account for the soil buildup during the years of no plowing, nor are they adjusted to reflect that plowed perennial fields, if they behave like plowed perennial pastures, would lose less soil the first year than a field that has experienced continuous annual plowing.

It is also possible to calculate the energy required to replace the nitrogen, phosphorus, and potassium in the eroded soil on these 316 million acres. If that loss is five tons per acre, the energy value is about 96.4 million wellhead barrels; at twelve tons, the energy value is 231 million barrels; and at fifteen tons, 289 million barrels.

The energy value of the nitrogen, phosphorus, and potassium lost through the harvest of 100 bushels of grain from an acre roughly equals the energy lost in nine tons of eroded soil on an acre—more than half a barrel of petroleum at the wellhead in each case. Assuming a five-year replant cycle, the savings could be equivalent to 80 million wellhead barrels if the loss is fifteen tons per acre.

Substantial energy savings are also possible as a result of reduced seedbed preparation and field work, pesticide and fertilizer use, and irrigation.

Prospects for Research and Development

Two constraints impinge on the prospect for development of perennial polycultures. The first constraint is that promoters of conventional agriculture believe the traditional methods of soil conservation—terracing, grass waterways, check dams, contour farming, stubble mulching, conservation tillage, and crop rotation—are adequate for the task. Many apologists for conventional agriculture believe that where these methods are not practiced it is the result of either a farmer's ignorance or his bad character. At the deepest level of contemplation, soil loss is regarded as a lack of exercise of stewardship. However, any exercise of stewardship that employs these traditional measures may be beyond the ethical stretch for *most* farmers. By this I mean that they may be unable to practice what they know to be correct behavior. Good practices require attention, care, small scale, intelligence, and economic solvency.

The second constraint is the consequence of the somewhat uncritical acceptance of conservation tillage, which is expensive and chemical-dependent, for growing traditional row crops, particularly corn. This acceptance indicates that most agriculturists believe a technical fix is already at hand to reduce soil loss significantly.

What can be expected of agribusiness and government in the way of research on perennial polycultures? Little help will likely come from private seed companies. Who can blame them for not producing a perennial or groups of perennials that could put them out of business? To leave them out of the action, however, may be unfortunate. These companies have important resources, particularly human power for extensive analysis, an absolute necessity if new crops are to be developed. But if these companies are to be involved, they will likely want in return patents on their products.

The agribusiness firms that sell fertilizers and pesticides would likewise appear to be poor candidates for promoting cropping systems that reduce the sales of their products. Involving them requires a stretch of the imagination. Perhaps instead of paying them for applying "medicine," some of which has harmful side effects, they might be paid for contributing to the maintenance of soil health and balance. Nutrients will have to be added, but why should the nutrient and pesticide bill be based on quantity alone? It is in the spirit of the recent emphasis on integrated pest management to recognize that a species mix is automatically a chemical mix, and if that chemical mix discourages insect and pathogen spread, the organizations and individuals responsible could be rewarded. The entire idea is somewhat like paying a doctor fee while the individual is healthy, with payments ceasing or slowing when an individual is sick. In our increasingly service-oriented economy, "package plans" are sold more and more.

This is not a promotion of agribusiness involvement. The burden of defining their role in the development of a sustainable agriculture should be on their shoulders, not on the shoulders of the rest of the people in a free market economy. But neither should private seed companies or other agribusiness firms be written off before they are given a chance to show how they can participate in developing a sustainable agriculture.

The USDA has the greatest potential of any institution for defining the mission of a sustainable agriculture. If it decided internally that such an agriculture were appropriate, the machinery exists within the department to give sustainable agriculture the necessary emphasis and financial support.

Private research agencies perform tasks very well when they are clearly defined. They could perform many of the biochemical studies and much of the cytogenetic screening.

Probably the most competent of all would be the national laboratories, though the nature of their work does not lend itself to the type of research considered here. The most ideal situation would be the establishment for sustainable agriculture of a mission-oriented agency comparable to the National Aeronautics and Space Administration.

Government traditionally has responded to the direct interests and needs of farmers so long as there is some indication of ever-increasing yields. Research has been oriented to high yield even when that has meant the demise of small farmers and the growth of corporate farms and agribusiness. When one considers that food exports are a major way of softening our mounting balance of payments deficit, it seems unlikely that the emphasis will change. In 1981, the United States sold about $45 billion worth of agricultural products, which pales in comparison to the $100 billion-plus bill for foreign oil. This history, in which the emphasis has been on the bottom line, is partly the consequence of the fact that the time frame of too many politicians has been "until the next election." One might hope, however, that leaders would see the long-term economic sense of a truly sustainable agriculture and allocate substantial funding to the development of perennial polycultures.

Notes

1. This article originally appeared as Wes Jackson and Marty Bender, "New roots for American agriculture," *Journal of Soil and Water Conservation* 36, no. 6 (November-December 1981): 320–24. It has also appeared as Wes Jackson, "New Roots for American Agriculture", in *Altars of Unhewn Stone* (San Francisco, North Point Press, 1987), pp. 106–18.

New Strategies for Bioresource Development in the Third World

Eugene B. Shultz, Jr., Wayne G. Bragg, Alejandro R. Martinez, and David W. Pluymers

Introduction

If the choice and introduction of new crops is properly managed, agricultural productivity of the third world can be significantly advanced. But we believe that this is unlikely if current agricultural strategies continue to be employed. The choice of species and processing methods for new agriculture and silviculture must be based on new strategies for development, and these strategies must be grounded in enlightened, ethical visions of development.

Ethical issues lie at the heart of current agricultural strategies and current economic arrangements between the poor agricultural countries, largely in the southern hemisphere, and the industrialized world. The poverty gap is expressed not only in low GNP, but also in malnourished children whose parents labor at low wages on export crops, soil erosion from poor farming practices, destruction of the environment by extensive cropping or deforestation, death and deformation by toxic pesticides, unemployment, and the rural exodus to overcrowded cities.

We propose an alternative strategy that uses bioresources for a more equitable agricultural system and a more viable rural way of life. Our research group, the Bioresources Development Group at Washington University in St. Louis, is actively involved in interdisciplinary studies of underutilized plants and trees for the third world. Our contribution to this volume is a strategic analysis of development of new economic crops for the third world, illustrated with three examples that we have been studying: *jicaro*, *pejibaye*, and *neem*. All three are promising tree crops for the tropical third world, in our opinion. The principles in light of which we make this assessment can best be seen in the context of third world issues they illuminate.

Issues and Principles

Self-Reliance

Export cropping dominates current practice. Instead, underutilized bioresources should first be developed for import substitution, and then, when it is clear that domestic needs will be met, the same bioresources might also be developed for export to generate foreign exchange. Domestic needs, especially for food, must have priority to avoid food dependency on the industrialized nations, and to avoid the exploitation of labor and environment that often is associated with nonfood cash-crop production in the third world.

In their zeal to expand their agricultural bases, third world leaders must avoid overcommitment to specialty and luxury export crops that tend to go through quick boom-and-bust cycles, and that compete with domestic production of food and other necessities. Such crops jeopardize the retention of domestic competence for growing food and other essentials for local consumption, and raise many other questions that fall collectively under the "flowers vs. food" issue. It is important for third world national governments to resist the considerable pressures that are exerted by, for example, the International Monetary Fund, to grow specialty export crops such as flowers instead of food and feed for domestic consumption.

Further, it must be more widely acknowledged that agriculture generally does not adapt well to crop switching in search of short-term profit maximization, the principal objective of much nonagricultural business enterprise. Farming skills are often difficult to transfer to unfamiliar crops, such as flowers or macadamia nuts, crop-processing infrastructure is often impossible to adapt, and short-term profit maximization often conflicts with environmental imperatives such as the need to conserve the soil for future generations.

Environmental and Socioeconomic Sustainability

It is essential that new species and techniques be chosen so that the new agriculture and the new processing will be indefinitely sustainable, both socioeconomically and environmentally. Favorable short-term economics without long-term sustainability must no longer be considered good business in third world agriculture. In addition to its obvious shortcomings from a humanitarian viewpoint, social exploitation for short-term profit causes poverty, which inevitably leads to political unrest and civil disturbance, disruption of production, destruction of invested capital, and loss of life.

Like social exploitation, environmental exploitation for short-term profit also leads to poverty, and the same chain of unfortunate social and political events, as well as the inability of the land to support subsequent generations. Sustainability criteria are often not met or even considered in the third world agricultural context, with well-known adverse effects.

Decentralization and Scale

It is strategically important for new crops to be processed at small scale in rural areas, so that decentralization can spread the benefits of new jobs and inexpensive food and other products as widely as possible, using labor-intensive and capital-conservative technologies. For many reasons the large agribusiness model, typical of the United States, is unlikely to be feasible in much of the third world. Therefore, decisions on underutilized bioresources in the third world should favor those bioresource species options and processing technology options that lend themselves to decentralization of production and processing by not requiring large-scale plantations or large-scale processing technology.

Decentralization includes avoiding both internal centralization of processing and the concentration of processing of third-world agricultural raw material in industrialized nations. For example, Latin American countries have been essentially city-states, each with a capital city absorbing the wealth of the rest of the country, thereby impoverishing the rural population. Internal migration to seek employment in centralized industries has created huge socioeconomic problems in the cities. This disparity between the cities and the rural areas in Latin America has contributed to external migration to the United States.

Value-Added Processing Before Export

In the case of export crops, it is strategically important to carry forward the decentralized processing as far as possible within the nation's borders before relinquishing semiprocessed products to a more industrialized nation for more capital-intensive finishing. As much value as is feasible must be added within each third world nation, utilizing local capital to the fullest extent possible.

Autochthonicity

Although some parts of the United States may be suitable for large-scale, capital-intensive and labor-conservative production and processing technologies, we challenge the notion that this management approach is appropriate for much of the third world. In most cases, technical and demographic considerations require the rejection or at least the questioning of the U.S. agrotechnology model. Instead, suitable models will derive in an autochthonous or indigenous manner from the local context and not from imported models. Autochthonous models originate from and are characteristic of the specific region involved, environmentally and socioeconomically.

Planning

Good planning, therefore, requires that new crops be selected with more than just a concern for short-term economic returns per hectare. Planning must begin with careful screening and identification of promising underutilized species and equally promising agricultural and agroprocessing techniques that are clearly appropriate for the climate, soil, topography, culture, and the socioeconomic characteristics of a specific region.

An enhanced, mature concept of what constitutes a viable economic enterprise, along with fresh views of third world development ethics, must be accepted by the business community and by government planners. Classical technical/economic feasibility analyses, market studies, and investment analyses, although still necessary, are no longer sufficient. Additional analyses must also be carried out to provide a more complete basis for intelligent decision making, or the exploitation is likely to continue, with adverse consequences for all, including business.

The technical aspects of import-substitution agroindustry will likely differ from those of export agroindustry, for example, in their different processing technologies. The socioeconomic aspects will almost certainly differ. These differences and their complexities require special technical, cultural, socioeconomic, political, and strategic analyses.

In more detail, we submit that a good general strategic planning process for new bioresources starts with identification of species from which valuable products are potentially available, and proceeds to choice of technologies for growing and harvesting, extracting, and further processing; technical/economic feasibility and market studies; analysis of technology transfer problems; environmental, cultural and socioeconomic impact analyses; strategies for commercialization and research and development; and analysis of government policy options for encouraging new crops. This interdisciplinary planning process is illustrated by the following three examples.

Jicaro

PRODUCTS AND USES. *Jicaro* or *morro*, *Crescentia alata* HBK, is a tropical dryland tree of Central America that abundantly produces large fruits containing much pulp and many seeds. The edible polyunsaturated seed oil is of high quality. The seed meal contains a high percentage of high-quality protein for animal feed, but with potential as an edible flour for human food. The pulp can be fermented to fuel alcohol, and the fermentation by-product (stillage) used as animal feed. The fragments of the woody hull can be carbonized, briquetted, and sold as charcoal fuel. These are all new uses for jicaro.[1]

GROWTH CHARACTERISTICS. The jicaro tree is useful for erosion control, reforestation, and agroforestry. Cattle can be grazed within jicaro orchards because the natural openness of the leaf canopy allows sufficient sunlight to penetrate for grass to grow. Cattle are more productive with shade than without. Jicaro can be grown from seed in poor, stony, arid soils. Its long taproot brings water and nutrients from deep in the ground. High yields of fruit are possible even without irrigation. Because the flowering of the jicaro is not seasonal, mature fruits can be available throughout the year; thus, harvesting will not seasonally overtax the labor force.

PRODUCTION AND PROCESSING. Research and development on the production and processing of jicaro fruit has been in progress since 1984 in northwest Nicaragua by a private enterprise, Jicaro, S.A. This company has accumulated the most experience, by far, in learning how to develop the potential of jicaro.[2] In their plan, small processing plants handling about five thousand tons of fruit annually would each service 125 acres of jicaro orchard.

The first plant of this size is under construction. Nearly all of the equipment to be used in the plant is being constructed by local mechanics, fitters, and practical welders, or manufactured by Central American enterprises. High technology is not required. Planting and harvesting requirements appear to be undemanding. No large or expensive machinery is needed for any production activity. Based on our on-site inspections, it seems likely that it will be feasible to carry out fruit production and processing in a small-scale, labor-intensive, capital-conservative mode with relatively simple technology. This evaluation only awaits the test of running the five thousand ton/year plant and its orchard.

STRATEGIC PLANNING. We also perceive that this enterprise is likely to relate effectively to the sociopolitical and economic situation in Nicaragua and neighboring nations, which requires a sharp break from the conventional agriculture based on a few export crops with inadequate domestic production of food and other commodities, and insufficient employment in rural areas.[3] Both the production and processing of jicaro seem to be amenable to organization as cooperatives or as private enterprises. In Nicaragua today, the government is encouraging the formation of cooperatives owned by local *campesinos* (small farmers), as well as productive private landholdings, large and small.

A Nicaraguan socioeconomic imperative has been the need to care for those people who have been displaced from their farmlands in the northern provinces that came under attack by the counterrevolutionary (contra) forces. These thousands of families have been relocated to *asentamientos* (centers), some of which are located in the dry Pacific coast where jicaro is a native tree of major importance. Housing is provided by the government and international relief agencies in these settlements, but unemployment is a serious problem. The agricultural skills of these campesinos might be well utilized in a jicaro project.

Neither fruit production nor processing would require concentration of land or capital, and both could be labor-intensive, so it should be feasible for either or both to be accessible to campesinos for employment and investment, if credit and training, as well as initial technical input, are provided. Nicaraguan government extension programs, which are well developed, would provide the necessary managerial and technical training. In addition, there are many international professional and technical volunteers in Nicaragua who provide such services.

This model would entail a combination of land tenure arrangements based on the actual situation in the region: first, the landless labor force in existing and future settlements can collect jicaro fruits from the wild and sell them to the processing plant under construction, and can plant jicaro seeds on a day-labor basis in the proposed orchards; second, the landless can obtain land through the agrarian reform laws for private ownership, or for a cooperative of jicaro and cattle producers; third, land can be leased or bought by an external donor agency for production of jicaro by campesino coops or individual families.

Similarly, the processing plant could be visualized in several ways as a cooperative or as a private enterprise. It would probably be advisable for the processing plant to evolve in stages as technical and managerial skills are developed; initial products might be limited to food oil, charcoal briquettes, and animal feed from the pulp and seed meal, since alcohol production requires a somewhat higher level of technical competence. Capital for this initial plant could be obtained from government credit programs or from international aid agencies, and could be repaid by the *maquila* principle of a percentage of the product remaining with the processing plant as a user fee.

Pejibaye

PRODUCTS AND USES. The *pejibaye* tree, *Bactris gasipaes* HBK, also known as *chontaduro* or *pupunha*, is an underutilized bioresource of the humid neotropics.[4] We have given special attention to pejibaye in Costa Rica.[5] Five possible new agroindustries based on the fruit of this lesser-known palm tree include food-grade flour, cooking oil, industrial oil (high in lauric acid), fuel alcohol, and animal feed.

The pejibaye is a prolific producer of fruits that contain starch, protein, and two different types of useful oils, one from the mesocarp (pulp) and one from the kernel. For years, pejibaye has been widely sold as a fruit with a short market life. It is also canned, for a small market. Currently, the fruit has no other commercial uses.

However, up to about 10 percent of the wheat flour in breads can be replaced by pejibaye flour without loss of function, demonstrated in experiments carried out by Tracy.[6] Tracy also reported that up to 50 percent of the corn in tortillas can be replaced by pejibaye flour. Most of the corn and essentially all of the wheat consumed in Costa Rica is imported, so replacement in part would be a desirable substitution for imported grain.

The oil from the mesocarp of pejibaye fruit is polyunsaturated, and can be of food quality after refining. Removal of the oil would improve the storage life of the flour. Pejibaye exhibits much genetic diversity that would allow development of varieties for specific purposes, e.g., for food oil production, and for flour production, but more genetic research and development would be needed.

As an alternative to flour production, the mesocarp starch could be fermented to fuel ethanol. Protein is also present in the mesocarp, and the starch, protein, and fiber of the dried mesocarp could, instead, be used in animal rations.

Intuitively, production of food rather than animal feed may seem to be the obvious strategy, because food generally commands a higher unit price in the marketplace. However, sometimes it is a better strategy to produce feed to nourish animals that supply products for human consumption. A potentially attractive example is production of feed for aquaculture of fish that produce high- quality food protein, with a high return on investment per unit area of pond, and little environmental disruption. Chickens, rabbits, pigs, and goats would also be able to similarly convert pejibaye, offering another economical use of the land.

Production and Processing. Value-added processing on a relatively small scale appears to be feasible, at least for the drying of the mesocarp, the separation of dried mesocarp from the kernel, and the production of 180-proof fuel ethanol. Those steps can be carried out in small plants in rural areas. But for technical reasons, other processing steps would have to take place in larger plants in central locations: solvent extraction of food oil, milling of the extracted mesocarp to make flour, and extraction of the industrial oil from the kernels. In no case, however, are the technology requirements so demanding that raw material need be shipped abroad for value-added processing.

Strategic Planning. Pejibaye can be a vehicle for development in poor rural communities where the tree flourishes under warm, humid conditions. In such locations, Mora[7] and colleagues at the University of Costa Rica propose formation of rural cooperatives for small-scale drying of pejibaye. The plan gives attention to the employment needs of women and the elderly.

Costa Rica needs to earn more from agriculture and related agroprocessing industries than it earns at present. Therefore, it may help Costa Rica to have new economic crops for import substitution, and for export to world markets. However, we do not support the argument that Costa Rica should choose nonfood luxury specialty crops, such as flowers, over the production of new food crops. We strongly favor the food side of the current "flowers vs. food" debate in Costa Rica. Flower crops grown in the tropical third world for air shipment to the large cities of the first world are likely to undergo volatile boom-and-bust cycles, as buyers learn to drive costs down by bargaining with many different tropical countries to get the best price.

Pejibaye might be utilized as a replacement crop for pineapple. Prevailing agronomic practices in pineapple plantations do not appear to be sustainable, so the land is typically abandoned when it is no longer productive. Pejibaye does not require such good land, so it could take over from pineapple and thus prevent the loss of rural employment. We examined one location in Costa Rica where the prospects for pejibaye to replace pineapple appear to be promising.

Another Costa Rican agroindustry that violates basic principles of sustainability is cattle ranching.[8] New agroindustries must not add to the long-term environmental and social problems being caused by this unfortunate industry. Its return on investment per hectare is very low, so large tracts of land have been despoiled, irreversibly, and many small farmers and ranchers have been displaced as ranches have greatly expanded in size. The many disadvantages of cattle ranching are creating serious difficulties for Costa Rica; therefore, cattle ranching serves as an antiparadigm for development of good agroindustry strategy. Its present value is not worth the future cost.

Neem

PRODUCTS AND USES. The *neem* tree (*Azadirachta indica* A. Juss.) is the principal resource of the botanical insect-control movement, which is gaining strength in its opposition to synthetic chemical insecticides. Neem thrives under tropical dryland conditions on all continents of the third world, producing high yields of a seed oil containing several compounds that control dozens of harmful insects with safety to farm workers, and apparently without inducing mutational resistance.[9]

This stands in marked contrast to the dismal record of the synthetic chemical insecticides, many of which are toxic to farm workers, expensive, and subject to rapid development of mutational resistance in insects that destroys their effectiveness. Although now wisely banned in the industrialized world where they are produced, sale and use of the more dangerous of these chemicals is not yet forbidden in most of the third world.

Therefore, the manufacturers still produce and sell these toxic materials, and may continue to do so until all third world nations ban their use. The most toxic dozen are DDT, 2,4,5-T, aldrin, camphechlor, chlordimeform, chlordane (heptachlor), DBCP, ethylene dibromide, lindane, parathion, paraquat, and pentachlorophenol. Eventually the most dangerous of the synthetics will probably be universally banned because of the many thousands of deaths and illnesses, annually, among farm workers. Therefore, alternatives to the synthetic chemical insecticides must eventually be developed.

The botanical insect-control agents seem to be the obvious alternative, and there seems to be no persuasive reason why the development of this option should be further delayed. Botanicals, which will be used as major elements of integrated pest management (IPM) systems, will greatly strengthen the ability of IPM to deal with insect pests, and perhaps even revolutionize the IPM field.

STRATEGIC PLANNING. In our neem example, we deal only with the need for safe and effective botanical insect-control agents from neem seeds; other uses for neem (there are many) will not be addressed. Two general approaches will be discussed, import substitution (domestic use) and production for export. In our opinion, these will require different means of processing seed oil, and technologies differing in sophistication.

Usually, no great effort is needed to convince entrepreneurs to develop a profitable new export crop. The problem, instead, will be to ensure that the needs of small-scale farmers in the third world are not overlooked in the process of rushing into a neem-based export project.[10]

Therefore, we need complementary strategies for bringing neem to two different insect-control marketplaces. One calls for low-cost appropriate technology for local application of crude but effective and cheap neem extracts, and the other involves a high-technology approach that will produce specialized products for use by the farmers of the industrialized world who can afford these more expensive insect-control agents. Fortunately, neem lends itself well to this developmental dualism.

It should be pointed out that the dual strategies for two markets means that some neem seeds will be sold at higher prices for production of relatively high-priced export products, and other neem seeds will be sold at lower prices for production of relatively low-priced crude extracts for local use. The viability of such a two-tier system would, of course, be threatened if insufficient seed were to be produced.

If this should happen, the export market would certainly outbid the domestic market for seeds, leaving the peasant in the position of working at low wages for an unjust economic system in which the insect-control needs of the industrialized world are being met with products that he cannot afford to buy. It is necessary, therefore, for enough neem to be planted to satisfy both markets. Fortunately, neem trees can be easily grown both in large export-bound plantation settings, and in smallholder settings for the domestic (import substitution) market.

Corresponding to the two strategies, there are two technical methods by which insect-control products may be prepared. The first employs simple but effective cold-water extraction of crushed neem kernels. This lends itself to smaller-scale production for local use. The second method begins with extraction of oil from dried seeds. The bioactive substances can then be extracted from the oil, separated from one another, and special preparations formulated by recombination. In this way, many proprietary mixtures, each with optimal bioactivity for a specific pest, can be offered to the world market.

Conclusions

It is likely that new crops can be developed in the third world for long-term socioeconomic and environmental sustainability, self-reliance, decentralization of production and processing, and stimulation of viable small- and medium-scale rural agroprocessing businesses. Jicaro, pejibaye, and neem are examples of this new approach to agricultural/silvicultural strategy; jicaro and neem are applicable in the semi-arid tropics, and pejibaye in the humid tropics.

Food, feed, fuel, and safe and effective insect-control substances can all be produced locally, without the need for sophisticated, expensive technologies. It is also possible to organize production so that domestic needs for these products are not subordinated to export demand. These findings suggest that our strategic approach may have general applicability, and that it may be possible to find other new agroindustries that conform in large part to the ethical principles for third world bioresource development presented in this paper.

These and other potential agroindustries will begin to address the disparities and injustices inherent in the current extractive agricultural system. When developed, they will allow rural people to use their resources for a more viable, just, and sustainable way of life for themselves and future generations.

Notes

1. Karsten Jochims, "Energia Renovable Reemplaza el Petroleo y Soluciona el Problema de Proteina en el Tropico" (Jicaro S.A., Apartado Postal 2389, Managua, Nicaragua, 1987, Mimeographed), 16 pages, 2 annexes; Alejandro R. Martinez, Eugene B. Shultz, Jr., and Wayne G. Bragg, "Foods and Fuels from the Central American Jicaro Tree," Proceedings of the 14th Annual Third World Conference, Chicago, April 7–9, 1988 (Third World Conference Foundation, P.O. Box 53110, Chicago, IL 60615).

2. *Ibid.*

3. Alejandro R. Martinez, Eugene B. Shultz, Jr., and Wayne G. Bragg, "Foods and Fuels from the Central American Jicaro Tree," Proceedings of the 14th Annual Third World Conference, Chicago, April 7–9, 1988 (Third World Conference Foundation, P.O. Box 53110, Chicago, IL 60615).

4. Jorge Mora Urpi, et al., *The Pejibaye Palm* (San Jose, Costa Rica: Banco Nacional de Costa Rica, 1984).

5. Eugene B. Shultz, Jr., and Wayne G. Bragg, "New Foods from the Pejibaye, an Underutilized Palm," Proceedings of the 14th Annual Third World Conference, Chicago, April 7–9, 1988 (Third World Conference Foundation, P.O. Box 53110, Chicago, IL 60615).

6. Mitchell D. Tracy, "The Pejibaye Fruit: Problems and Prospects for its Development in Costa Rica" (M.A. thesis, Dept. of Economics, University of Texas, Austin, 1985).

7. Interview with Prof. Jorge Mora Urpi, University of Costa Rica, San Jose, Costa Rica, October 1987.

8. P. M. Meehan and M. B. Whiteford, "Expansion of Commercial Cattle Production and its Effects on Stratification and Migration: A Costa Rican Case," chap. 10 in William Derman and Scott Whiteford, eds., *Social Impact Analysis and Development Planning in the Third World* (Boulder, Colo.: Westview Press, 1985).

9. Michael D. Benge, *Neem, The Cornucopia Tree* (Agency for International Development, Bureau for Science and Technology, Office of Forestry, Environment, and Natural Resources, Washington, D.C., 1986); David W. Pluymers, "Natural Insect Control Materials from the Neem Tree (*Azadirachta indica*)" (M.S. project report, Dept. of Engineering and Policy, Washington University, St. Louis, Mo., 1988); David W. Pluymers, Wayne G. Bragg, and Eugene B. Shultz, Jr., "Natural Insect Control Agents from the Neem Tree," Proceedings of the 14th Annual Third World Conference, Chicago, April 7–9, 1988 (Third World Conference Foundation, P.O. Box 53110, Chicago, IL 60615).

10. David W. Pluymers, Wayne G. Bragg, and Eugene B. Shultz, Jr., "Natural Insect Control Agents from the Neem Tree," Proceedings of the 14th Annual Third World Conference, Chicago, April 7–9, 1988 (Third World Conference Foundation, P.O. Box 53110, Chicago, IL 60615).

IV.B.
Obstacles to Food for the World

ONE OF THE GOALS OF AGRICULTURE discussed in Part I of this book is to provide nutritious, wholesome food for the people of the world. That this goal has not always been economically or politically foremost goes without saying. Some of the intricacies of the ethical problems behind inadequate food distribution may not be so clear, however. For clarification we turn to articles on the ethical dimensions of several obstacles to food for the world.

The first of these contributions is by a geographer, Kent Mathewson, who concerns himself here with issues falling under the title "Plantations and Dependencies: Notes on the 'Moral Geography' of Global Stimulant Production." What Mathewson means by a moral geography is a study of how large-scale production and consumption of certain stimulants has led to economic and ecological change and exploitation of local peoples in many parts of the world. Mathewson begins with a survey of the six largest stimulant crops and some remarks on the history of their adoption worldwide. The discussion is mainly devoted to a stimulant-by-stimulant synopsis of the pattern and local consequences of their development as world commodities.

Ultimately, the plantation propagation and worldwide consumption of stimulants, including a reintroduction of their use, often in a new mode, in their original areas, have marked the development of modernity. That such developments have often occurred at the expense of traditional cultures and have met with varied local resistance raises serious ethical questions, Mathewson believes. How, for example, can such agricultural development be justified in the face of widespread hunger? Shouldn't the resources and energies that go into stimulant production be placed instead in the services of food production? If stimulant production is tolerated or condoned, who should benefit, the cultivators who might grow a substance as part of a strategy to preserve their own way of life, or states that have often benefited from the export of stimulant items? Raising questions of the demands of reciprocity, Mathewson even wonders whether industrialized societies can blithely pick and choose the stimulants sent their way, when rather major economic players in those societies export to the third world pesticides that are equally harmful in their own ways. What sort of reciprocity can we justify and enlist in the service of ethical regulation of the conduct and development of agriculture in a hungry world? On this last point Mathewson's concerns are reminiscent of those raised by Scherer (above) over identifying and establishing ethically right reciprocities in water distribution and use. Like Scherer's paper, Mathewson's is more a plea for taking seriously ethical problems than an attempt to argue for a particular resolution of these problems. For Mathewson, however, the primary lesson in the impact of global stimulant production on whole peoples and cultural traditions is the need to see these issues in the context of an ethically sensitive historicogeographical study.

A similar point is the place of departure for the next two studies in this section. Both William Aiken and Paul Thompson take off from the political temptation to see food as a weapon. Aiken's paper, "Using Food as a Weapon," is devoted to a critique of "the intentional use of trade in food substances as a means of gaining political influence." The idea is to create a shortage as retribution or to manipulate another government by depriving its citizens of food. For the weapon to be effective, Aiken points out, there must be a shortage of food that cannot be met other than with the "weapon" food. Unfortunately, this shortage will fall most heavily upon the shoulders of the poor, possibly creating life-threatening hardships, while the real target, those powerful people in a position to respond to the threat, will be relatively unaffected by it.

Having analyzed the food weapon as he sees it, Aiken then assesses its use. The food weapon can be treated as a means justified by the ends it serves, but Aiken sets this aside to consider the propriety of using harm to one in order to manipulate another. Aiken feels confident that no matter whether one finds the rightness of acts in the actions themselves or in the social welfare of rules prescribing or proscribing them, it is unacceptable to mistreat the innocent in order to manipulate others. Things are less clear in the case of exploiting an existing scarcity, but even if such action could be justified by utilitarian sounding principles or even if we could justify creating a shortage to get at "the guilty" through the innocent, we have to make good the claim that the weapon will be effective. On this point, Aiken is skeptical. By considering several possible examples of the intentional manipulative use of the food weapon, Aiken makes clear why it is at best a foreign policy instrument of dubious effectiveness, concluding that its use in general is defenseless.

Unlike Aiken, Paul Thompson is concerned with the withholding of food as a way to destroy an enemy or deter an enemy from acting against the weapon wielder. Thus, he wishes to explore the strength of the analogy between the food weapon and tactical or strategic military weapons. As a tactical weapon, Thompson argues, food is unacceptable even in a just war, for it cannot be directed to its target, the military and political elite among the enemy. Indeed, as Aiken also argues, that elite can often direct the harm of withholding food where it will do least damage to the military and political establishment. The use of food as a strategic weapon does not hold up, either. Thompson again reminds us that the threat to withhold food can serve as a strategic weapon or as a deterrent only if the targeted government can find no replacement. A quick survey of past U.S. uses of the food weapon shows this has not been the case. But Thompson further argues that the threat of withholding food could be justified only insofar as what it seeks to prevent is extremely serious, as is the sure destruction of nuclear war. Thompson rests his case by arguing that such a precondition is simply not present to justify food as a strategic weapon.

Thompson concludes with an analysis of why the food weapon metaphor, although illusory, is still appealing to us. He rejects thinking of food as a weapon both on ethical grounds and in response to a mistaken concept of the use of a real strategic weapon. If Aiken and Thompson are right, as we move into a world more and more populated—especially in less developed countries where we might be tempted to use food as a weapon to curb population growth and for our political ends—using this "weapon" would be both unjustifiable and illogical.

If food is not to be thought of as a weapon, then how should it be distributed around the world? Much writing has focused on the claim that all humans have a fundamental right, moral or otherwise, to food and other basic needs. Richard P. Haynes in "Food and Justice: The Real Issues" does not want to reject that claim. Indeed, he takes it for granted, along with the claim that present distribution of food is unjust. But he does want to challenge us to review the role of moral theories in redressing this injustice and in helping to guide policy to meet people's basic food needs. Moral theory, Haynes urges, has kept us from grappling with the economic and political realities standing in the way of meeting food needs. Haynes' discussion attempts to provide a corrective lens enabling moral philosophy to deal with this myopia.

Haynes begins with a detailed discussion of social crisis theory, or the view that societies (and their individual members) are in crisis, as seen in unresolved conflicts between their various contingents. One prevailing explanation Haynes accepts and refines is that society is now characterized by conflicts of values, each remnants of different heritages. Since these conflicting values constitute the normative principles of moral codes, what we see in social crises is a set of conflicting moralities with no clear overarching standpoint to create a coherent social context and resolve the conflicts of individuals and groups. Worse yet, this systemic disharmony might be concealed because the moralities we appeal to *seem* to be based on a set of universal values, when those values are really equivocal; and, those moralities seem to be guiding agents actually empowered to act, when, in fact, those who are suffering and those in a position of power are not members of the idealized moral communities our codes implicitly postulate. Haynes uses recent philosophical reflection on world hunger to show the difficulty of making sense of moral discourse and reasoning in a postmodernist context of conflicting multiple values and incommensurate approaches to practical reasoning. Others (for example, Onora O'Neill—see bibliography) have discussed similar problems in terms of "accessibility" and concluded that the moral differences between people, states, corporations, and other agents are, in the end, resolvable. Haynes concludes on a more radical and pessimistic note, suggesting that perhaps the only legitimate role for moral philosophy is one of conducting a postmodern postmortem on the failures of individual moral theories. And even *that* mission Haynes is reluctant to leave up to professional academic philosophers. Others more alive to the real parameters of lived moral problems need to take part in, if not lead, the critique.

Thus Haynes's study, and those of Thompson, Aiken, and Mathewson, all urge greater sensitivity to the historical, geographical, economic, and political realities of the moral and other ethical problems of world hunger. All of these authors are aware that world hunger is a problem concerning millions of people, one which seems to demand a social welfare or other ethical approach suitable to a broad solution, yet they are more or less cautionary about such an approach.

Some of this section's underlying concern to individualize, personalize, or contextualize thinking about the role of agriculture in development and in meeting the needs of people around the globe can be seen in many of the articles in this final section of the book.

Plantations and Dependencies

Notes on the "Moral Geography" of Global Stimulant Production

Kent Mathewson

Introduction

At the global scale, study of plantation agriculture has generally focused on questions of historical diffusions, socio-structural regularities, and political-economic consequences.[1] Each of these themes or approaches has enjoyed a certain scholarly vogue in the order mentioned. In turn, each of these themes is closely associated with the largest of moral and ethical issues of the modern age: race-based slavery, socioeconomic class formation and conflict, and uneven and unequal generation and distribution of wealth among nations. At lesser geographic scales, especially with microlevel studies, emphasis has been on the social-historical, anthropological, ecological, and agronomic aspects of plantation life. New interest in plantation agriculture as a singular and precocious form of capitalist production has begun to raise questions concerning specific crops and the effects of their consumption at a variety of geographical scales. The focus on consumption as well as production of plantation commodities raises a number of ethical issues that deserve discussion and debate.

Here I can only outline the origins and development of plantation agriculture by focusing on crops that are *not* ones providing for basic human needs such as food, fuel, and fiber. I will indicate the provenance and local production context of substances that have served to metabolically stimulate not only the consumers, but also entire economies. Looking at the global nature of plantation agriculture in this way points out connections among etiologies, ecologies, and economies that are more than metaphorical. Rather, each of the major stimulants discussed has played a role, at times significant, in the formation of the modern world. One might speak, then, of a "moral geography" in which at one scale (usually local) consumption of a particular stimulant is grounded in and bounded by ritual and tradition, hence raising few, if any, ethical problems.[2] At larger, especially global scales, and within secular contexts, production and consumption of the same substance (or its derivatives) may raise major moral issues.

Stimulants Produced on Plantations

Eric Wolf, in his monumental study of capitalism's impact on non-European peoples, separates plantation crops into three general categories: foodstuffs (staples), industrial crops (fibers, oils, and exudates), and stimulants (energizers as well as depressants).[3] The major stimulant crops, strictly speaking, include coffee, tea, and kola, all consumed primarily as beverages; tobacco, as snuff, for chewing, or, more generally, for smoking; cacao (chocolate), for drinking or eating; and sugar, as an additive to all of the above, and a "drug food," in the words of Sidney Mintz,[4] massively eaten in countless preparations. Each of these substances, up until the sixteenth century, was restricted in use and distribution to cultural realms contiguous to their centers of origin and domestication. By the twentieth century, all had achieved global patterns of distribution.

Tobacco is the most widely distributed. It is grown commercially in all but a few nations. However, smallholders account for much of its production. Cane sugar is more limited by climate, but is still grown on all the arable continents. In contrast to tobacco production, the bulk of past and present sugar production has been on plantations. Cane sugar and tobacco were the two most precocious and rapidly expansive stimulant crops after A.D. 1500. Coffee and tea followed them in the eighteenth century and soon enjoyed global consumer acceptance. Tea can be grown beyond the tropics and subtropics, while coffee is restricted to these two zones. The manner of producing tea and coffee has varied; the plantation mode has been dominant at various times and places. Cacao and kola are the most recent to win global consumer allegiances. Cacao is grown pan-tropically, while kola is restricted to Africa. Like the other crops, they are not restricted to plantation cropping.

While these six are the most widely consumed stimulant crops, there are many other cultivated and collected plants that serve similar functions within various regions of the world. For example, coca, *yerba mate* and *guarana* in South America, *khat* in East Africa and Arabia, betel nut in Asia and Oceania, and kava-kava in Oceania all have large user populations within their respective realms. However, in contrast to the previous six, these plants do not have global consumption patterns and are not generally produced on plantations. Save for coca derivatives, an increasingly significant exception, their use and modes of consumption remain primarily embedded within traditional or local cultures. One might logically ask why a particular substance becomes adopted globally, whereas another having the same or similar chemical constituents and behavioral effects does not. Is it a question of historical contingency, or a matter of relative constraints that inhibit or facilitate cultural adoption and adaptation?

Questions Large and Small

The question of historical contingency and structures that produced the currently dominant ensemble of stimulant crops deserves a multivolume study. Here I can only suggest that this question should be a central theme in any narrative account of the making of our modern world. The question of constraints is somewhat more tractable. It seems that the mode of consumption does influence the extent to which distribution becomes cosmopolitan. For example, in traditional use coca, *khat*, betel nut, and kava-kava all involve mastication, often in ritual contexts. Sugar, tobacco, and kola are also chewed, though these practices are viewed as the least sophisticated means of consumption and are closely correlated with their zones of production. Initially, coffee was probably chewed, but as an infusion it diffused along with Islam. Stimulants prepared as beverages, especially when combined with sugar, have found ready acceptance beyond their source areas, whereas stimulants activated by chewing have not. Modes of consumption then, especially with stimulant substances, reflect forcefully what it means to be "modern."

This points out a second level at which these questions might be viewed. Historical as well as geographical contingency does seem to play an important role, particularly in the competing fortunes of coffee, tea, cacao, and kola in the arenas of consumption and production. *Yerba mate*, or Paraguayan tea, and *guarana*, an Amazonian vine, are both sources of caffeine and related chemicals. They are used as beverages, but with vastly smaller consumer populations than the four major beverage stimulants. Coffee, tea, cacao, and kola all had source and use areas in or adjacent to premodern states and empires. From there they flowed easily into the currents of European global commerce. In contrast, *yerba mate* and *guarana*, or some even lesser-known sources of caffeine quite likely would have been impressed into global service and would have become the focus of widespread plantation production.

Moral Geographies of Stimulant Production and Use?

Implicit in the idea of grand trajectory or historical progression are the questions of imperial growth and decline, and macroscale socioeconomic phenomena such as the emergence and dissolution of various modes of production. But these are master plots, for which single substances can hardly be held accountable. Viewed from the perspective of moral geographies, the history of particular substances can be grounded within smaller plots. Nations and regions, classes and clans, communities and even individuals become the actors at this level. Through the process of extracting stimulants from contexts of traditional use and making them commodities, particular political entities, social strata, and persons profit. Other groups or their members are impoverished. In the realm of consumption, related patterns occur, but with somewhat different configurations. For example, most if not all of the major stimulants entered European society as luxuries and over time filtered down to the lowest economic strata. At first markers of elite status, they ultimately became daily expectations for the laboring classes.

Plantations' Progress: A Sequential Outline

Sugar was the first stimulant crop to be produced on plantations, followed by tobacco, then coffee and tea, and, most recently, cacao and kola. It is tempting to think of these six firmly and finally embedded in the structure and practices of the modern world. However, the current controversies surrounding the deleterious and addictive character of tobacco call into question the stability of consumer populations. Despite greater consensus that coca derivatives are harmful and addictive, the recent explosion in their consumption suggests that patterns of modern stimulant use are indeed dynamic. Obscured by the attention focused on the consumption of coca and its derivatives is the opportunity to see the transformation of a traditional stimulant into a plantation commodity, a process that began with sugar and is being repeated a millennium later with coca.

Sugar

Among the substances classified as stimulants, cane sugar has had the most pervasive, powerful, and perhaps pernicious impact at the global scale. Starting in Mesopotamia around A.D. 1000, sugar production has transformed entire societies and regional landscapes. In the Late Middle Ages it stimulated nascent capitalist development and helped to revive chattel slavery within the Mediterranean world. In addition, sugar used as an additive allowed coffee, tea, chocolate, and kola to become both commodities for mass consumption and crops for plantation production. Sugar, unlike the other stimulants, offers high caloric value to the consumer. Up to the point of morbidity, it can be employed as a food staple and often has been. Along Brazil's sugar coast, slaves were sometimes provisioned with little else. Under such conditions, slaves seldom survived more than five years after arrival. Analogues can be found in the dietary practices of the English urban working classes. Sugar added to old and new food and drink become symbol and substance of the changes ushered in with industrialization. The same has happened in the wake of industrialization elsewhere, though not often to the same extent as in England.

Technically more a depressant than a stimulant, alcohol derived from sugar must also be counted as one of the midwives of the modern world. Rum helped fuel the famous triangular trade between the New World tropics, the North American urban centers, and West Africa. Rum was exchanged for slaves in Africa, and used to extract labor from precapitalist cultures elsewhere. Like other distilled spirits, cane-based alcohol has served as an agent for disrupting many aspects of premodern cultures. Individual alcohol dependency is only the most obvious.

Tobacco

Tobacco, a New World psychotoxin occurring as several consumable species, was used by the aboriginals more in ritual than habitual contexts. As tobacco was adopted and popularized in Europe, its traditional use pattern was reversed, both within and outside of its source regions. At times eliciting more opposition than sugar did, while replicating sugar's top-down or hierarchical diffusion pattern, tobacco still spread widely and quickly after its "discovery" in the early 1500s. The chief significance of tobacco in the development of plantation economies may have been its ability to be cultivated outside the tropics. The establishment of the plantation ethos in North American owes much to tobacco's early success in Virginia. Other crops were later grown on

North American plantations, but they, like imported African slaves, followed in the wake of this stimulant crop.

Coffee and Tea

Coffee and tea, as mild and almost universally accepted stimulant beverages, compete for consumer loyalties around the world. Best grown in upland tropical environments, they sometimes compete for habitat. Unlike tobacco, coffee and tea apparently become global commodities with little disruption of traditional use patterns. In terms of production, however, coffee and tea contributed to spreading plantations to upland tropical areas where they otherwise might not exist. Coffee in highland Guatemala and tea in highland Kenya are but two examples.

Coffee and tea have played different but discernible roles in promoting national identity in the face of international rivalries. It may seem excessive to credit the English devotion to tea drinking as an effective force in promoting nationalism, however, it is through such habitual practices that the rituals of nationhood are in part constructed. Intranational rivalries have been strongly affected by the production of coffee and tea, as illustrated by coffee cultivation in Latin America. Planters and exporters were able to gain effective control over the government in various coffee-producing countries during the late nineteenth century, sometimes precipitating civil wars.

Cacao and Kola

Cacao and kola can also be considered together. Today they are primarily consumed as snack food and drink. Moreover, unlike other stimulants—sugar excepted—they are vigorously marketed to all segments of society, particularly the young. Both were originally used as ceremonial and trade items in ancient tropical civilizations, cacao in Mesoamerica, kola in West Africa. Chocolate in beverage form was widely available outside tropical America soon after the European conquest, but not until the Swiss successfully combined it with sugar and milk products in the nineteenth century did it become a confection of universal acclaim. Kola, like the East African stimulants coffee and *khat*, was promoted as an alternative to alcohol under Islamic proscriptions. Trans-Saharan trade brought kola to new markets, but it remained a curiosity in the North Atlantic world until it was added as an ingredient in carbonated "soft drinks." Like cacao, kola has only become a global staple in the last century. Generally perceived as even more benign than coffee and tea in physiological effects, as plantation crops cacao and kola have had a no less severe impact on certain parts of the tropics.

Coca

Among the group of stimulants that are locally important but not cosmopolitan in distribution, coca, through its derivative forms coca paste and cocaine, appears to be the one whose traditional use and area of production are expanding most significantly.[5] Probably this has as much to do with the imagery associated with consumption as with its physiological effects. Like drinking carbonated kola beverages, it bespeaks modernity. Betel nut is far ahead of coca and its derivatives in sheer number of users. Estimates suggest that up to one-quarter of the world's population chews betel nut,[6] but its production and consumption are centered in southeastern Asia and Oceania. As a masticant composed of two separate plant species, betel nut seems unlikely to become cosmopolitan in range or practice.

Coca in the Andes, like betel nut in Asia, is chewed by large numbers of people in its source region. But like chocolate and kola, coca derivatives were popularized beyond this region at the end of the last century. Their use was suppressed in the first decades of this century. Only the patented soft drink Coca-Cola managed to perpetuate the legacy with "decocainized" coca leaf extracts. In this sense, select coca derivatives have been globally consumed stimulants for much of this century. In the last two decades there has been another boom in the consumption of coca derivatives in the North Atlantic world, but this time consumption is illicit. While smallholders have managed to retain control over much of the legal production, illicit plantations capitalized and controlled by processors and exporters are emerging in parts of South America and possibly elsewhere. In many ways, the booming commercialization of coca products beyond their traditional source regions is simply the latest chapter in the history of plantation stimulants.

Conclusions

Plantations and stimulants grown on them have contributed centrally to the rise of new economic patterns in the past five centuries, and consequently to the attendant conditions and realities that are termed "modernity." The geography of these transformations has been global; the resistance to these changes has been largely local. In this sense one can speak of "moral geographies" as the actual and symbolic terrain upon which traditional cultures are perpetuated or reduced. Resistance to modernity has taken myriad forms. From millenarian upheavals involving the populations of whole regions to barely noticeable personal gestures of defiance, "progress" has been simultaneously accommodated and contested. The role of stimulants appropriated from traditional cultures, produced on plantations, and then reintroduced to these cultures as part of the process of modernization raises compelling moral and ethical questions.

The student of ethics and agriculture will certainly want to consider some of the more obvious questions. In a world confronted with massive problems of hunger and malnutrition, should labor and resources be committed to the agricultural production of crops with little or no food value? Or should any and all producers be allowed in laissez faire fashion to provide these substances to the market regardless of consequences? Should only traditional cultivators be encouraged to grow such crops as a strategy for cultural preservation and local economic development? Or should stimulant production on state-controlled plantations—all these crops have been produced in this setting—continue to be promoted as a prime vehicle for economic development? Conversely, can industrialized societies—responsible for producing immense quantities of toxic pesticides and herbicides exported to the third world and often used without regulation—legitimately call for the control or suppression of traditional crops such as coca? The issues are complex and do not lend themselves to simple solutions, yet elaborating ethical and moral positions on many of the issues is clearly possible, beginning from an understanding of history and geography of global stimulant production.

From the composite history of plantation-produced stimulants, a convincing morality-morbidity play could be constructed that should illuminate important aspects of the nature of capitalism itself. Among the lessons implied would be the way in which capitalism has acted as both a stimulant and a depressant on cultural regions since its emergence during the past several centuries. Particularly instructive are the ways people have adapted themselves and their collectivities to its various demands. The issues should be considered from a historical and geographical perspective, but the questions raised are by no means retrospective ones, nor are they confined to particular places. Given the global scale of the use, production, and commerce of various drug crops, and the problems associated with them, especially tobacco products and coca derivatives, these issues can be expected to occupy a central place in debates over ethics and agriculture well into the next century.

Notes

1. There is a large literature, theoretical as well as empirical, on the plantation as an institution for generating wealth from agricultural activity. No simple or single definition suiting all scholars is likely to be agreed upon. A workable definition is Vera

Rubin's: "an agro-social institution whose main production is destined for export market rather than for subsistence or local use," in her introduction to *Plantation Systems of the World*, Social Science Monographs 7 (Washington, D.C.: Pan American Union, 1959), p. 2. This volume remains one of the most useful and insightful on the subject.

2. The notion of "moral geography" is borrowed from the concept of moral economy developed in the work of E. P. Thompson, James C. Scott, and others who have studied the responses made by traditional communities and their members to threatened or actual disruption of their customary way of life. Thus the moral economist might interpret bread riots in early industrial England or peasant revolt in Southeast Asia as the outcome of actual or perceived violation by outside authority of accustomed modes of subsistence, security, or welfare. By analogy, I use the term "moral geography" to refer to the actual and symbolic terrain upon which traditional societies elaborate their customary livelihood and belief systems, and the cognate spaces in which they defend these practices and perceptions. The recurrent campaigns of colonial and contemporary Andean states to suppress indigenous coca cultivation and use offers an example of the construction and contestation of moral geographies. For an alternative (though perhaps related) notion of "moral geography," see Simon Schama, *The Embarrassment of Riches: An Interpretation of Dutch Culture in the Golden Age* (New York: Alfred A. Knopf, 1987).

3. Eric R. Wolf, *Europe and the People Without History* (Berkeley: University of California Press, 1982).

4. Sydney W. Mintz, *Sweetness and Power: The Place of Sugar in Modern History* (New York: Viking Books), p. 61.

5. For a good source material on aspects of the moral geography of coca see Deborah Pacini and Christine Franquemont, eds., *Coca and Cocaine: Effects on People and Policy in Latin America*, Cultural Survival Report 23 (Cambridge, Mass.: Cultural Survival, Inc., 1986).

6. For an authoritative and useful volume on various drugs in traditional cultures in Oceania see Lamont Lindstrom, ed., *Drugs in Western Pacific Societies: Relations of Substance*, Association for Social Anthropology in Oceania Monograph no. 11 (New York: University Press of America, 1987).

USING FOOD AS A WEAPON[1]

WILLIAM AIKEN

AMERICAN AGRICULTURE IS DRASTICALLY OVERPRODUCTIVE and it has been for several decades. Since the 1930s diverse policies have evolved to alleviate the adverse economic effects of this overproduction: from price subsidies and governmental purchase, to land banking and, most recently, the Payment in Kind (PIK) program. The most effective way to deal with surplus, however, has been to expand into foreign markets either through "trade" or, when necessary, through concessionary "aid." The expansion into foreign markets has not only helped to eliminate surplusses, contain subsidy and storage costs, and stabilize domestic prices, it has also proven to be quite profitable for agribusiness. In the last decade there has been an additional impetus helping to promote this strategy—the need to substantially increase our exports in order to offset the unhealthy trade deficit that higher oil prices and Americans' preference for foreign consumer items has created. Hence the government has endorsed and complied with the expansion of food trade.

The Russian grain embargo dramatically called attention to the political aspects of food trade. By explicitly subordinating economic advantage to political objectives, President Carter inadvertently opened the public's eyes to the complexity of the food trade and the extent to which American agribusiness had become dependent on foreign markets. Throughout the 1960s the public had viewed United States' involvement in international food trade, especially the "aid" programs (called by fancy names like Food Aid, and, later, Food for Peace), almost entirely as "humanitarian" projects in which America, the "Breadbasket of the World," was benevolently "feeding the world's hungry." This image was promoted by agribusiness and even the U.S.D.A. even though the economic and political advantages were the prime factors in developing these programs. Food trade was being used as a political and economic tool of diplomacy even though the public was largely unaware of this. It wasn't until the Russian grain embargo that the public began to see and to ask questions about the propriety of using food as a weapon. The overt clash between the economic policy of expanding trade and the political objective of regulating trade to punish the Soviets began to awaken the public to an issue that had been seething for years—to what extent and for what purposes should food trade and aid be used to promote political objectives. The food weapon had been an issue for some time among environmentalists, Neo-malthusians, zero-population growth advocates, agribusiness interests, those critical of and those supportive of American involvement in IDC development, various factions in the U.S.D.A. and the Pentagon and C.I.A., the farm lobby, the relief organizations, and just about everyone else knowledgeable of the international food situation. But when it "hit" the public it caused confusion and fervor.

This issue is precisely the kind of social policy issue that exhibits deep and perhaps irreconcilable value conflicts. It is one that cannot be solved by seeking the popular consensus since there is none. It is not one for which a public opinion poll will be of much use since the public is often sorely uninformed on the issues involved. (I am reminded of a country and western song which came out not long after one of OPEC's embargoes that suggested "Food for Crude" as if Saudi Arabia could not buy grain elsewhere.) It is not very likely to be solved by the Washington experts since, depending on the department to which they are attached, they will differ on the varying importance which should be attached to the possible economic, strategic, and symbolic gains resulting from a specific wielding of the food weapon. Nor is it likely to be solved by a satisfactory compromise between varying interests since the divergence of objectives is too great (for example between the grain exporters and the Neo-malthusians). Thus, it is the kind of issue on which some philosophical analysis, reflection and guidance may prove to be instructive.

Furthermore, this is the time to do this reflection because even though the food weapon issue is on the back burner in Washington right now, due to President Reagan's preference for more "direct" weapons (such as the installation of missiles, the deployment of military advisors, and the giving of military aid) to achieve his objectives, it is likely to arise again, especially in our dealings in Central America since the Congress is increasingly blocking President Reagan's preferred methods. Even though the President is a general advocate of free trade, his attempt to block the Soviet gas pipeline by embargo demonstrates his willingness to use commodity weapons to achieve what he considers to be an advantage. So an effort to get a clear understanding of the "food weapon" now may at least help us to see what is involved in adopting such a policy and it may help to prevent the careless implementation of a misguided policy in the future.

How can food be used as a weapon? Of course food is not a weapon in the sense of being an implement of destruction. The expression "food weapon" is a metaphor for the intentional use of trade in food substances as a means of gaining political influence. It is a weapon only in the sense of being a tool for punishing, manipulating, exploiting, or influencing others for some political objective. Unlike "real" weapons which work by directly threatening or causing harm to persons or property, the food weapon works indirectly by frustrating the expectations, wants or needs of the victims. It is designed to cause, exacerbate, discontinue or fail to alleviate a shortage (real or felt) of food. In wielding this weapon one foresees and intends a hardship to result from the scarcity and this hardship is the "harm" that will either serve to punish the victim or render the victim vulnerable to the manipulation of his or her decisions and actions. But for this weapon to work, the hardship must be substantial. A commodity weapon can only work in conditions of scarcity since without scarcity there can be no leverage. The scarcity may be created (for example, by blockade), exacerbated (for example, by creating a trade dependency through "dumping" subsidized grain in order to undercut local production and then curtailing or withholding further shipments), or it may be found (as when a drought or a civil war or crop failure drastically reduces the available supply). In order for the scarcity to be substantial enough to make the weapon effective, there must be no other (easily available) source of the commodity. Thus for the food weapon to be a weapon, other dealers in foodstuffs must either cooperate with the wielder, or be charging prices that exceed the capability of the country suffering the shortage. It would be useless to try to manipulate a country by refusing to trade if others are willing to trade without similar conditions.

All of these features are common to commodity weapons in general, from the sale of oil, to arms, to pipeline equipment, to Coca Cola and blue jeans. Unless there is a politically motivated, intentional attempt to frustrate expectations of attaining a scarce good, there can be no "weapon." But the food weapon differs from other commodity weapons in one essential aspect; the scarcity level has very narrow limits of tolerability. Since food is necessary for life itself, a scarcity can cause severe hardship rather quickly. The standard ways of coping with a scarcity are substitution, abstinence, and conservation. But these don't work very well for food shortages. Unlike blue jeans, basic food stuffs are not substitutable and unlike Coca-Cola, they cannot be done without. Attempts at conservation are effective only if the general level of nutrition exceeds the basic minimum. Yet in virtually all countries vulnerable to the food weapon (those suffering substantial shortages) there is both a maldistribution of wealth and purchasing power and a significant portion of the population already surviving at or below the subsistence level. Even though the rich and well to do in any country will not go hungry no matter how hard times are, the most vulnerable (the poor, young and powerless) will feel the adverse effects of conservation efforts soonest and most severely. Even minor attempts at conservation (without redistribution) will drastically affect their well being. This special link between food and essential needs and the fact of the narrowness of the range of toleration of scarcity are what make the food weapon potentially a powerful tool for coercion and manipulation. However, it should be stressed that the "food weapon" used against impoverished nations does not have the same potential effect that the "oil weapon" has against oil-importing, industrialized nations since the hardship imposed is disproportionately borne by the poor and since this hardship is less likely to disrupt the entire economy (even though it may exact more lives).

In using the food weapon you are attempting to coerce or manipulate political leaders to abide your will by knowingly acting so as to indirectly cause (or at least permit) a scarcity level of food severe enough to threaten those who are most vulnerable to suffer from want of food. What this boils down to is: using the suffering of the innocent to manipulate the powerful. This point is important because much of the debate over the food weapon seems to confuse the victims with the ones you are trying to manipulate. The targets of the weapon (those who suffer the hardship) are not the same as those toward whom you are hostile (the political leaders). It is only by evoking a spurious notion of collective liability that these two can be equated. Knowing who the food weapon "hurts" is important if one is to properly evaluate the acceptability of this policy.

Is there anything wrong with this use of food trade as a weapon? There are two ways to assess the food weapon. First, one can treat it as a morally neutral means and judge the propriety of a particular use by assessing the merit of the end or objective being sought by its use. In addition to national interest objectives, there are broader international goals for which it could be used; for instance to enhance international economic stability or cooperation in solving global problems such as overpopulation, natural resource depletion, and environmental damage. Or it may be wielded for humanitarian goals such as to enhance quality of life, protect human rights, or spur reforms for more equitable distribution of wealth within the country against which it is wielded. Many of the conflicts in values that have arisen over the use of the food weapon stem from disagreement over the legitimacy of the goals pursued. Support for population control (no more food without birth control) ran high in the 1970s. Support for environmental protection runs high in the 1980s. And of course, winning friends and punishing enemies in the third world goes hand in hand with our military interests. Debate over the worthiness and advisability of these goals, though ultimately related to using the food weapon as a means to attain them, is a separate topic. But even granting that some of these goals are worthwhile does not settle the question as to whether the food weapon is an effective means for attaining them.

The second way to assess the use of food as a weapon is to address the propriety of the means itself. Is there anything wrong with using A's hardship to manipulate B to abide your will? The answer to this question depends very much upon the extent to which you caused the scarcity. Indirectly causing harm to innocent persons by intentionally causing a scarcity is wrong for the same reason that directly causing harm to innocent persons (for example, bombing a school) is wrong. If there are moral duties at all, the duty of non-malficence (which prohibits the intentional harming of innocent persons) is one, and it is considered the most stringent duty by virtually all moral theories. The purported justification for causing this harm in both the case of terrorism and intentionally causing life-threatening scarcity is that this harm is justified to the extent that it successfully coerces or manipulates others so as to attain some good goal. But this justification for overriding the *prima facie* duty of non-malficence falls prey to another moral criticism. Such action violates another moral duty which is staunchly upheld by both deontologists and rule-utilitarians, the duty to treat persons as ends in themselves. So both the aspects of "harming" and "using" cause moral problems, and when combined they make it difficult to justify using the food weapon in a way that causes the scarcity.

But typically, the scarcity which makes the food weapon possible is found, not created. Though one's actions may exacerbate it, one has not caused it. What is wrong with fanning the flames a little and then exploiting the situation for your advantage? Even though you know that your actions will result in increased suffering of innocents, still technically you are not causing harm by failing to alleviate hardship unless your terms are met. Is it permissible to use innocent persons' needs due to scarcity to manipulate others to abide your will? Kantian purists may still object that this is to use persons merely as means and thus is an unacceptable disregard for their autonomy. And many who oppose the food weapon in principle object to this playing of politics with persons' lives on grounds that such bargaining becomes shameful when the stakes for some are life or death. However, since the practice is so common it would be desirable to find a stronger argument than the ones that appeal to the vague notion of treating of persons as ends in themselves or merely point out the extremity of the costs to some.

The standard move here is to challenge the moral relevance of the omission-commission distinction and suggest that intentionally refusing to alleviate suffering is as morally wrong as intentionally causing suffering. Thus it is not merely the "use" aspect that makes it wrong, it is also the "cause" aspect reinterpreted to include "inaction" as a causal factor (which reintroduces the duty of non-malificence). Causing harm to manipulate, e.g., terrorism, would be on a par with failing to alleviate so as to manipulate, the food weapon. I happen to be one of those who find the omission-commission distinction to be of questionable moral relevance (or more accurately, I do not find that omissions are entirely permissible though perhaps not as wrongful as com missions). But for the sake of argument, I will grant that the exploiting of scarcity and the use of innocents' suffering to manipulate others is, in principle, permissible. This allows the food weapon when used as a means for exploiting scarcity to be considered morally permissible.

But the story is not over yet. We must link the means (permissible by hypothesis) to the end (worthy by hypothesis). We must demonstrate that the food weapon as a tool of diplomacy can deliver, can be an effective means for attaining a political objective. If the case can be made that this tool is not very likely to be an effective means of attaining one's objective (no matter how worthy) then the conflict over the various goals for which it is being used, and the conflict over the general permissibility of the means itself will become secondary, if not moot. The most severe conflicts surrounding the food weapon can be largely resolved by being rendered irrelevant if the food weapon can be shown to be (usually) an ineffective means to attain the goal.

First, some refinements on the various uses of the food weapon must be made. A symbolic use is one designed to make a political statement to other nations. It is a public relations action designed to stress a difference in ideology or to push a point of principle. (For example, refusing to sell grain to a country whose leader we refuse to acknowledge.) A retaliatory use is backward looking; it is designed to punish a nation for past action. (An example might be Stalin's starving of the Ukraine.) A manipulatory use is forward looking; it is designed to pressure an adversary into abiding your will. The manipulative use is by far the most common. Pure cases of the retaliatory use are rare. Even though the Russian grain embargo was officially retaliatory, its real function was symbolic (to make a statement to other nations) and manipulative (to influence future Soviet action). I will grant that the food weapon can be an effective means for attaining the political objectives of making an international symbolic statement, and that it may be an effective means of retaliation (if in fact a substantial hardship results—which was not the case with the Russian grain embargo). But since these uses are peripheral to the dominant manipulative use I do not think that this concession will weaken my case that the food weapon is generally an ineffective means of attaining your objective.

To see why the food weapon is not likely to be an effective means of manipulating political leaders to abide your will, consider the following two cases.

CASE 1: I offer to save a woman's child from a burning house only if she promises to have sexual intercourse with me.

CASE 2: The United States' government refuses to continue to sponsor the selling of grain at concessionary prices to an impoverished and import-dependent nation unless it permits the installation of United States' nuclear missiles on its soil.

In both cases the distress of the sufferers (child, citizens) is being used to manipulate another (mother, political leaders). In both cases the conditions demanded are not, we shall assume, judged to be in the best interests of the one being manipulated. What is the likelihood in each case of attaining the objective by manipulation?

The attempt to exploit the mother is likely to be successful because the special relationship to the child is usually strong enough to predict a sacrifice of self-interest. But what about the second case? Organic theories of state aside, few political leaders feel such a strong bond to their citizens. Governmental leaders even of highly affluent nations can and do tolerate the suffering of their poor (and powerless) people. There is no special familial bond, and the motives of genuine benevolence or empathetic concern cannot be counted on to motivate political leaders to sacrifice what they perceive to be in their rational interest. The mere fact that the poor are suffering (and stand to suffer even greater hardship) by itself is no reason for compliance.

What would motivate political leaders to "buckle under" to the manipulation? Perhaps if the scarcity threatened to provoke sufficient dissent and unrest so as to challenge the leaders' authority, power, or government itself, then they may be motivated to comply. Fear of food riots, a coup, or a revolution stemming from the scarcity might compel them to concede for the sake of retaining their power. Or they may (and this seems far more common) strengthen their security forces to suppress the dissent by force. Or, if they are clever, they can deflect the criticism onto the manipulating nation and call their people to a patriotic sacrifice to avoid being a puppet of "foreign imperialists." Political turmoil generated by food scarcity need not be (and historically has not often been) quieted by concessionary bargains with food supplying nations. Accurately predicting this response before wielding the food weapon (a requirement if the weapon is to be part of a rational policy) is dubious.

Alternatively, the leaders may "buckle under" because they (belatedly) acknowledge that the objective being foisted upon them is actually in the long term interest of their nation. Population control, military alliance, stronger economic ties, and even United States' missiles may serve the manipulated nation's interest. So the weapon in this case would be used in a somewhat paternalistic manner, to persuade the victim to realize that the conditions being demanded are actually beneficial to the manipulated as well as to the manipulator. Under these conditions political leaders would be foolish not to "buckle under" for by so doing they win doubly—their food scarcity problem is not exacerbated and additional long term advantages are obtained. Of course, if they are skilled, they will hold out for the maximum derivable advantage even at the cost of tolerating some adverse effects from the prolonged scarcity. It is not the fact of scarcity that motivates them, it is the potential advantage of the objective. So they are not "sacrificing" anything for those who suffer from the scarcity.

Or they may simply see the manipulation threat as a game of horse trading, of playing tit for tat: you obviously want something, we want the food, so let's make a deal—what do you have in mind? The conditions of the trade need not promote their nation's long term interests. Provided that the conditions do not substantially interfere with that interest and provided that they do prevent an increase of the scarcity problem, the leaders may choose to cooperate. But they can always choose not to, if the price seems too high or if the conditions begin to infringe on what they perceive to be in the interest of their nation. It is meaningful to talk about using the food weapon in this context only if we understand it as a somewhat hyperbolic expression for the advantage enjoyed by the supplier of a scarce commodity in a seller's market. But it should be noticed that there are limits to the price, beyond which the consumer won't go. The leverage is not what we would normally call coercive.

In all of these cases, the "effectiveness" of the food weapon is questionable. In the first case the outcome is highly unpredictable. In the second and third cases the coercive element has dropped out and we have a bargaining for mutual advantage. What compels the leaders in all of these cases to comply is not merely the suffering of their people due to scarcity. This they can tolerate. It is rather the possibility of a personal power loss or the prospect of benefit that motivates them to "buckle under." If this is (generally) the case then the food weapon is, at best, an unpredictable and not overly effective tool of coercion.

As a bargaining chip it might be used with influential effect if used well (so as to avoid evoking a reactionary refusal) and if the terms demanded are reasonable for the one being manipulated. But this certainly takes the cutting edge off of the food "weapon."

If these reflections are accurate, then the policy implications for any contemplated future use of the food weapon are two. First, it is unwise (because unpredictable) to attempt to use the food weapon to destabilize a leader or his or her government. Second, if it is to be used effectively, the objectives sought must be ones that the manipulated nation can find to be in its national interest. But since such cases will not (I would suggest) be frequent, then food trade will not be a very useful "weapon." Since it is not likely to be a very useful weapon, and since there may well be other moral reasons which seem to make it undesirable, and since there is a sharp conflict of values over the acceptability of this weapon and thus no popular consensus supporting its use, then this weapon should (except perhaps in rare cases) be removed from our arsenal.

Notes

1. This paper was originally published in Thomas Attig, Donald Callen, and R. G. Frey, eds., *Social Policy and Conflict Resolution*, Bowling Green Studies in Applied Philosophy, vol. 6 (1984): 49–58. It is reprinted with the kind permission of the author and the Department of Philosophy of Bowling Green State University, Bowling Green, Ohio.

Of Cabbages and Kings

An Analysis of the "Food as a Weapon" Metaphor

Paul B. Thompson

THE PHRASE "FOOD AS A WEAPON" is generally traced to Earl Butz, Secretary of Agriculture under President Nixon, but the concept it states could hardly have originated with him. When princes defended themselves from marauders by retreating into the fortress castles of the medieval era, the siege—starving them out—was one of the tactical options at the attacker's disposal. Butz's idea was that the United States might starve another nation into submission, not with a military blockade, but simply by refusing to sell (or give) them grain. The idea was more attractive in the mid-1970s when limits to growth were all the rage and the U.S. controlled up to 80 percent of the world market in some basic commodities. As the last decade of the century approaches, the world is awash with grain. Food surplus has been created by aggressive production subsidies for agriculture in many developed countries, including Canada, Australia, the European Economic Community, and the United States; but a policy-stimulated surplus can disappear as quickly as it is created. The phrase "food as a weapon" may not be gone for good.

Food trade (and aid) is inextricably a fundamental component of the U.S. bilateral relationship with other nations, their governments and their peoples. In some cases, the phrase "food as a weapon" is used euphemistically to refer to the way that aid or trade policy can be linked to other aspects of the bilateral relationship, such as emigration, capital investment, or cultural exchange. For example, even in a food surplus, food export policy might be used as a tool to express pleasure or displeasure at another country's actions, perhaps by "dumping" surplus food in a deliberate attempt to spoil someone else's market. Food is here a weapon only in the broadest of senses, whereby *any* component of a bilateral relationship might be construed as a "weapon" for influencing other components. While there are indeed ethical questions to be raised about the diplomatic use of food policy, they are different, subtler, than those raised when food trade is seriously posed as an option for achieving specifically military objectives.

Butz's intent in coining the phrase "food as a weapon" is not clear. He contrasted it to the "oil weapon" of the OPEC states, which suggests that he may have been speaking within the general context of bilateral relations (though oil, like food, is not without strategic significance). Nevertheless, subsequent authors have been quite clear in intending food trade to be analyzed on a par with tanks and missiles, as a component of the U.S. arsenal.[1] Under this interpretation, the food weapon raises ethical issues because the use of any weapon raises ethical issues. A weapon is an instrument for destroying one's enemy. An enemy is another being bent on destroying you. A weapon is useful primarily in war. There are, of course, other uses for weapons: for defense against the unlawful acts of others, for amusement in various sports and tests of skill, and for untold other minor uses too obscure (or too Freudian) to mention; these uses are not analogous to the food weapon's proposed use, hence irrelevant to the issue at hand. The relevant use is in the destruction of an enemy in time of war, or in the deterrence of an enemy's attempt to achieve ends contrary to the user's interest. The plausibility of a food weapon, thus, turns upon the analogy to military weapons. These weapons may be of two kinds: tactical and strategic. In order to make a moral evaluation of the food weapon, the strength and exact import of this analogy must be assessed.

Food as a Tactical Weapon

The first point to be established concerns the possible analogy between food and the traditional tools of war, referred to herein as "tactical weapons." Tactical weapons are weapons used in combat. Bayonets, barbed wire, bombs, bombers, pistols, machine guns, punji sticks, napalm, and torpedoes are tactical weapons. The traditional moral criteria for the use of tactical weapons have included injunctions against inflicting needless suffering and against unnecessary destruction of nonmilitary personnel and personal property. Therefore, two characteristics become important in determining the moral acceptability of tactical weapons: destructive power and the deliverability of that power.

Destructive power refers to the weapon's capacity to render the enemy harmless by killing, injuring, or, in some other way incapacitating them once a target has been struck. Assuming the destructive force of the weapon can be delivered, how likely is the weapon to be effective? In this connection, it becomes pertinent to inquire about the cruelty of a particular weapon. Weapons that destroy an enemy without undue pain and suffering are, all other things being the same, morally preferable. Weapons that have good success in destruction of enemies are tactically preferable. These are not necessarily exclusive categories.

Deliverability refers to the ability of a soldier to strike the intended target. How likely is the intended target (and only the intended target) to receive the destructive power of the weapon? The primary moral consideration is indicated by the qualification. A weapon capable of being precisely aimed at military targets is morally preferable to one that exposes innocent people and their property to the risk of destruction. Tactically speaking, the criterion is accuracy: will a weapon hit what it is aimed at? Again these considerations can and do conjoin in practice.

These are the considerations raised, for example, by Richard J. Krickus in his discussion of the morality of chemical and biological war. Krickus argues for a distinction between chemical and biological weapons based on the fact that chemical agents can be limited to battlefield use, while biological agents cannot be easily controlled. The nature of biological weapons makes discriminate use against military targets impossible. Krickus thus concludes, "From the viewpoint of the just war doctrine, then, chemical weapons can be justified, but biological weapons cannot."[2]

The analogy between food and conventional tactical weapons depends minimally upon an assessment of the proposed food policy in terms of destructive power and deliverability. The primary moral considerations arise in connection with deliverability. Following Krickus, the moral justifiability of a tactical weapon is partially a function of a user's capacity to control and direct its destructive force. Weapons that destroy indiscriminately, that cannot successfully be confined to a field of battle or to otherwise military targets are not morally acceptable according to the dictates of just war.

The telling point against the "food as a weapon" metaphor arises when purely tactical aspects of deliverability are addressed. Deliverability refers to the weapon's capacity to be aimed and strike a specific target with its destructive force. A weapon that cannot be aimed is worthless. The problem with food assistance programs, however, has been that gifts of food or the benefits of increased production are poorly distributed, never reaching their intended recipients. It is far easier to deliver five hundred tons of explosives on target than it is five hundred tons of rice. There is little reason to assume that food withheld would be taken from the mouths of the target population; in the absence of contrary evidence it is reasonable to assume that the effects of withholding aid will be as poorly distributed as the benefits of assistance programs. Certainly military and political targets will be among the last to experience the debilitating effects of a food weapon. The tactical effectiveness of food is limited by the fact that food aid or the lack thereof must be filtered through the various market and bureaucratic mechanisms of the distribution system of the targeted country. Economic and political forces are free to influence the trajectory of the weapon.[3] It is roughly like attacking an enemy with a bomb of significant destructive power, but leaving the final detonation point of the bomb up to the choice of the enemy. An enemy determined to resist our attack will simply direct the destructive force of the food weapon away from military and political installations and toward the sector of the population that is least critical to the preservation of military and political authority and power.

To conclude, food makes a lousy tactical weapon, not because it lacks destructive capability, and not because it affects the innocent, but because it cannot be controlled. The point of impact for a food policy initiative is determined in large degree by factors beyond the control of the agent using the weapon, and, indeed, to a significant degree by factors within the control of the parties the weapon has been directed against. Surely, once relations between two nations have escalated to the point of tactical warfare there can be little thought of trade in foodstuffs between the nations; but the basis for a wartime breakdown in food trade has more to do with the general bilateral relationship of warring nations than it does with food per se. There can be little point in discussing food as a weapon if there are no strong parallels between the use of weapons and the use of food policy as a leveraging mechanism. The analogy between food leveraging and tactical weapon use breaks down precisely on the point of deliverability. It makes no sense to talk of food as a weapon when precise targeting is relevant to effectiveness.

Food as a Strategic Weapon

If food cannot be successfully compared with tactical weapons, perhaps it may still be compared with strategic weapons. The purpose of a strategic weapon is expressed not in its use but in the threat of its use. Strategic weapons are intended to affect the policies and actions of a potential enemy; if such weapons were actually used against an enemy, we would say that their strategic function had failed. The rationale for increasing the power and effectiveness of nuclear weapons is to preclude their use by making the probable consequences of their use utterly unacceptable. Potential enemies will be deterred from attack when they know that the threat of utter annihilation awaits. As such, strategic weapons are intended to prevent wars, not to be used in war. They are intended to influence a rival's acts so as to make any thought of war impossible.

The idea of food as a policy leverage is clearly commensurate with the basic thrust of the deterrence argument. The talk of food as a weapon arises in Western culture at a time when Americans have become accustomed to the use of strategic weapons for deterrence. As such, we have grown used to the idea that the primary application of a weapon is, ironically, not its use, but its disuse, its being held in abeyance against the turn of events. Given the United States's preeminence as a food exporter, why not tie our food policy to the extraction of promises and behavioral conditions? Surely we could wreak havoc in the world's food markets if we so decided, so why not turn this power to our benefit? Why not deter other nations from policies we fail to approve just as we deter other nations from attack upon us with our nuclear arsenal?

Strategic weapons differ from tactical weapons in that their vast destructive power makes it impossible to draw a distinction between military and nonmilitary targets. It may appear, therefore, that the targeting problems associated with tactical application of food trade are not relevant to strategic concerns. Certainly the fact that harms can be shifted to civilian populations, preserving military strength, is less damaging to strategic considerations. The food weapon would require only two prerequisites in order to emerge as a strategic option: the United States would have to declare an intent to retaliate against unwanted actions by cutting off aid and trade in food commodities, and the threatened nation would have to be convinced that withdrawal of U.S. food would cause a significant (if not massive) disruption of their social order.

There is evidence that the second of these criteria is not likely to be fulfilled. When the United States cut off agricultural trade with the Soviet Union in 1979 following the invasion of Afghanistan, the Soviets were able to replace lost American grain shipments with contracts from other exporters. The pattern of world grain trade shifted, but there were no net losers from the embargo.[4] Indeed, critics of the Carter administration claimed that U.S. farmers had been hurt far more than the Soviets.[5] When longshoremen refused to load grain bound for Iran during the hostage crisis, their actions were even more futile.[6] In order to insure deterrent effectiveness, the United States would have to insure that alternative sources of food were unavailable to an enemy and that U.S. food sold to neutral parties would not find its way into enemy hands. In other words, the United States would have to control precisely that which it does not control: the international food distribution system.

Short of total control, one might argue, the United States might still be able to cause an opponent some inconvenience. An enemy would have to seek out new suppliers, possibly charging inflated prices. The enemy government might decide that the nuisance created by a food embargo is not worth it; the policy objective might be achieved. Perhaps; but such petty concerns will not deter a nation from policies it takes seriously. This limitation in scope is of philosophical importance, since the moral justification of deterrence appeals to the momentous importance of that which is deterred.

If strategic nuclear weapons can be countenanced morally at all, it is only because their extreme effectiveness is thought to deter the realization of a great harm altogether. Modern deterrence is therefore a strategy for avoiding war among nations capable of mutually assured destruction. Deterrence *may* thus be justified in light of the extreme consequences of nuclear war. A measure that promotes the avoidance of nuclear war may be morally justifiable even if that measure paradoxically entails an intention to commit the morally indefensible act of nuclear war itself.[7] Without the conditions of such extreme consequences, deterrence devolves into mere extortion, bullying, and adventurism.

But the issues related to food policy are not of such extreme consequence. The failure of U.S. policy in a third world nation might plausibly be described as a contributing event in a slide toward war, but in and of itself it would hardly be tantamount to the degree of harm required to justify strategic deterrence. One cannot allow the slippery slope in which any failure of policy is unacceptable; such an argument proves far too much and is too adaptable to changes in mood, style, and opinion. Policy objectives cannot be universally equated with national survival. Failure in policy should not be compared with the threat of annihilation posed by nuclear war.

Conclusion

The "food as a weapon" metaphor arises during an age of deterrence by no coincidence. In the cold-war world, deterrence is neither an act nor an event, but a strategy. The strategy of deterrence is predicated on the possession of weapons so devastating that an enemy will not dare to attack so long as there is even the vaguest hint that they might be used. Deterrence hinges upon the destructive power of the weapon, but the strategy of deterrence goes beyond destruction of the enemy forces. The deterrent capacity of nuclear weapons resides not in their effectiveness against military targets but in their capacity for the annihilation of an opponent's civilian population. This strategy of deterrence is thus a euphemism for a kind of extortion—an extortion that may be morally justified, perhaps, but is a use for a weapon which nonetheless goes beyond traditional bounds of wartime uses.

The arrival of strategic nuclear weapons is significant in the evolution of U.S. food policy because nuclear weapons have changed the way that we think about weapons. Nuclear weapons demand "thinking the unthinkable" or intending to do what must never be done. This has allowed us to become, perhaps, too accustomed to making threats that can never be carried out. In fact, the food/weapon metaphor cannot sensibly be grounded in any traditional (that is, preatomic) sense of weaponry; as such, it is only meaningful as an empty threat.

Extension of the "food as a weapon" metaphor is bankrupt from both the ethical and literary standpoints. It is bankrupt ethically because it comes down to bullying, and idle bullying, at that. What is more, it fails metaphorically because, far from revealing a deep similarity of form, when compared with other weapons, the food weapon attains verisimilitude only by exploiting a flaccid and obscurantist trend in contemporary political discourse. The food weapon is plausible only as a weapon of deterrence, but linking food policy with strategic aims devalues the meaning of "deterrence" by making it equivalent to the practice of bluffing in geopolitical poker. Such a result serves neither food policy nor nuclear strategy; "food as a weapon" should be forgotten.

Notes

1. See Lowell Ponte, "Food: America's Secret Weapon," *The Reader's Digest* (May 1982): 65–72; Susan George, *How the Other Half Dies* (Totowa, N.J.: Allanheld, Osmun, 1977).

2. Richard J. Krickus, "On the Morality of Chemical/Biological War," in M. M. Wakin, ed., *War, Morality and the Military Profession* (Boulder, Colo.: Westview Press, 1979), p. 494.

3. Emma Rothschild, "Food Politics," *Foreign Affairs* 54, no. 2 (January 1976): 285–302.

4. Economic Research Service, U.S. Department of Agriculture, *Embargoes, Surplus Disposal, and U.S. Agriculture*, Staff Report no. AGES860910 (Washington, D.C., November 1986).

5. Lindsey H. Clark, Jr., "Grain Embargo: Let's Declare Victory and Quit," *Wall Street Journal* (Feb. 10, 1981), p. 27; Robert L. Paarlberg, "Lessons of the Grain Embargo," *Foreign Affairs* 59, no. 1 (Fall 1980): 144–62.

6. Sandra S. Batie and Robert G. Healy, *The Future of American Agriculture as a Strategic Resource* (Washington, D.C.: The Conservation Foundation, 1980), pp. 3–7.

7. Gregory Kavka, "Some Paradoxes of Deterrence," in Wakin, *War, Morality and the Military*, cited in note 2, p. 509.

Food and Justice
The Real Issues

Richard P. Haynes

I have called this paper "food and justice: the real issues" not because I think I have some special insight into how food might be distributed more equitably, nor because I intend to identify any "issues" in the sense of contemporary social or moral issues. In fact, it is just the sense that some philosophers give to the notion of moral issues that I want to question in this paper, my goal is "taking issue with a certain way of doing moral philosophy." What follows will be, at best, merely the sketch of an argument.

Let me start by stating several propositions that I accept, but with qualifications. (1) Everyone has a basic right to the necessities of life, including food. (2) Current distributions of basic goods are grossly unjust. (3) Moral theories applied as deliberative aids frequently serve to mask structural defects. (4) Nevertheless, there is a legitimate role for critical moral philosophy. I will argue chiefly for (3) and use as my examples some applications of moral theories to food distribution issues. I want to argue that moral theorizing in the context of the academic discipline of philosophy can serve to distract us from understanding economic and political relationships (and hence the causal grounds for attributing responsibility). My ulterior motive is to alert the reader to the danger of conceptualizing social problems entirely within the boundaries of a narrowly conceived discipline.

Social Crisis Theory

Theories of social crisis try to explain the failure of social values to govern practices. The theories of Jurgen Habermas, Daniel Bell, and Alasdair MacIntyre are concerned with identifying defects in social structures that purport to integrate values and goals. Thus, the sociopolitical "legitimation crisis" in Habermas is the crisis that the advanced capitalist state faces in legitimating its authority over individuals who feel that they are powerless to control events placed before them.[1] For Bell, the cultural crisis we experience is a product of both ideological and material forces. The failure of liberalism to integrate the private and the public according to cultural standards reveals the basic structural defect of the liberal state in a capitalist society.[2] MacIntyre's account of the failure of moral theories to provide the integrating function that they purport to is analogous in many ways to the crisis theories of Habermas and Bell. MacIntyre's thesis is that moral reasoning fails to provide relief from moral disagreement, and this a symptom of cultural disunity.[3]

MacIntyre gives several examples of issues whose various sides are supportable by plausible arguments, arguments that, MacIntyre claims, are valid.[4] What is noticeable about them is that they invoke different sets of concepts that prove to be conceptually incommensurable—justice and innocence versus success and survival; rights versus universalizability; equality versus liberty. As arguments presented to support one side of an issue (abortion rights versus the right to life), they are presented publicly as impersonal efforts to win assent. Internally, they are also felt as equal claimants on our reason or moral sense. If we think the disagreements as disagreements are about values or how to rank them, then we have shifted the discourse to the new level of moral theorizing. The role of moral theory is to find a way of integrating moral values that appear to conflict.

The conceptual incommensurability of the values we appeal to, however, is a sign that these values are remnants from past cultures, values that were once integrated by the social systems from which they became separated. That these values are now incommensurable is a sign that the present social system does not provide a means for their integration. Our internal sense of that incommensurability when we debate these issues with ourselves is a sign of a crisis in our personal identity. The internalized crisis presents us with a skepticism about our ability to find our own essence, that is, any sense of who we are in relationship to some potential that we should realize in a social context. This leaves us with nothing but what we find ourselves wanting, preferring, or holding on to. Our social system, consequently, can only be conceived of as a system for regulating conflicts among persons who want whatever it is that they want. This leaves metaethical theory with two choices: emotivism or a managerial form of rationalism, since the sense of moral discourse must either be an *invitation* to share moral values or an appeal to the need for them. Emotivism conceives of values as individually held, that is, as feelings about things. Since they cannot be grounded in reason, because there is no true personal essence, they are idiosyncratic. When I make moral statements, then, I am expressing these feelings to entice you into feeling the same way. The alternative to emotivism is to find a way of showing that individuals should submit to moral regulation by a social authority, even when they don't want to, because it is rational to do so. But, since there is no basis for relating who the individual is to what the moral community is, moral reasoning turns into an appeal to settling conflicts of interest peacefully, even when there is no social basis for doing so. The project must fail, MacIntyre argues, just because there is no basis for identifying persons in their relationship to a moral community.[5]

At this point the role of moral theorizing becomes apparent. If I try to be a moral person in the capacity of my social roles, then the crisis in morality will be experienced as a moral dilemma. Moral dilemmas are felt against the background belief that the social values defining my roles are compatible—that there is a moral community, a community of interests. Yet I cannot find the solution to the conflicting demands on my moral person which I am experiencing in that role. One alternative in experiencing a moral dilemma is to cease to believe that the social system defining my public roles is capable of integrating the moral values that provide me with my moral dilemma. The other alternative is to turn in search of higher level principles that will provide the integration I am seeking. Utilitarianism, as a moral theory, provides a basic principle for this integration by introducing the concept of maximizing the social good, which is defined in terms of aggregates of individual goods. Aside from the various criticisms of utilitarianism as a deliberative aid in moral decision making (e.g., it is difficult to apply without middle-level principles), the theory does not adequately address the problem of identifying the social domain and its relationship to the values of individuals. It merely assumes that there is such a domain. And that is its legitimating function. Deontological theories also fail to integrate values for the same reason.

Many so-called moral dilemmas presuppose that the structures in which they are embedded can accomodate the values that create the dilemmas. For example, the principles "allocate scarce goods productively so that there will be more to allocate in the future" and "allocate scarce goods fairly so that all claimants can feel satisfied with their share" clearly come into conflict when they are embedded in structures that assume a community of interests where there is none. That is, conceptualizing moral issues presupposes that there is a moral solution within the structures that "authoritatively allocate values" when there may be none. So moral theorizing under those conditions may mask those structural defects. Let us take as our example a series of discussions primarily, though not exclusively, by moral philosophers, about the problem of moral obligation and world hunger.

These discussions, edited by William Aiken and Hugh La Follette,[6] are organized around the major theme "Do we have an obligation to help the hungry?" "We" is clarified to mean "affluent nations, or those people in them," and "the hungry" are described as "the starving masses." The philosophers included in this collection generally divide into liberals and libertarians, because the discussion has been conceptualized in terms of whether we have an obligation to help others in need or whether it would merely be charitable of us to do so. On the sidelines, some neo-Malthusians argue that we positively ought not to rescue some people because to do so would contribute to overpopulation. The philosophers involved in the discussion use "the moral problem" to introduce the reader to the various concepts of moral philosophy, and then proceed to argue about how these are to be conceived. Rights, obligations, and duties are the primary moral concepts in which the discussion is framed. Some argue that rights are merely "negative," that is, people only have the right to have others forbear from intervention into their affairs. Others argue that it makes good sense to insist that we have some positive rights as well. The owners of positive rights are entitled to make claims on others not just for forbearance but for help in certain circumstances or for the delivery of services.[7] The argument that we all have the positive moral right to adequate food is based on a consideration of the conditions that would make membership in a moral community acceptable. If a moral community will not consent to guarantee the wherewithal for survival, then it hardly has grounds for making other claims on its less fortunate members. A similar case can be made without the difficulties of expressing the distinction between negative and positive rights by arguing for the priority of subsistence *basic rights* to liberty *basic rights*.[8] What is objectionable about this way of formulating the moral issues concerned with food and hunger?

Nothing, if the moral issues are formulated with an understanding of why some people go hungry. But these issues are being raised by members of an affluent society in the context of a media-inspired awareness of famine in some third world countries, accompanied by appeals from private organizations for donations, and public discussions about whether the U.S. should provide aid.[9] The question whether the haves should help the have-nots can be phrased more generally as "what type of moral relationship or moral community exists between nations, or between People in one nation and people in another nation?" But even so, most of the discussants do not make a significant distinction between person-to-person moral relationships, group-to-group moral relationships, or person-to-other-group relationships.[10] Some argue that the have-nots have got themselves into their desperate situation by failing to control their population. Without population control, helping them will only hurt their chances for future survival, and it will also hurt others who are managing their affairs properly. This is the lifeboat analogy.[11] Others argue that we should simply help anyone in trouble, just as we should rescue a child who has wandered into the pond and will drown without our help.[12] Still others argue that there is no obligation to the unfortunate, although something like Christian charity is clearly a virtue. That is, we are not bad if we don't help, but we are better if we do.[13]

All of these ways of conceptualizing the moral problems involved in hunger cover up the real issues and our ignorance about economic relationships by assuming moral relationships that do not exist, because the actual relationships between the affluent and the hungry are not apparent to the discussants. Part of the problem is a misidentification of the actors in the moral drama. Rarely can the hungry be classified as a group that makes choices, even ignorant ones. They are not identical with "third world nations," nor with parts of third world nations that the affluent nations are trying or not trying to help. These third world nations are neither floundering, drowning, nor struggling to improve themselves. They are neither responsible for their current state of affairs nor are they acting irresponsibly in failing to help their poor or to curtail increasing populations. Although the so-called developing nations are regarded by international law as autonomous political systems, many of these systems fail to coincide with the social systems they are said to have authority over and represent.[14]

The social systems of developing nations do not constitute a moral community or a community of interests but a vast network of patron-client relationships that direct resources from the bottom to the top.[15] Those at the bottom—many of whom are precisely those we are talking about, the hungry—were at some time part of a social system that did represent a community of interests and did, for the most part, provide reasonably good services for its members.[16] The introduction of commerce to these systems changed the direction of the flow of resources. So, on this account, many precommercial social systems did an adequate job of taking care of their members. It is not the poor that are responsible for failing to take care of themselves, but the restructuring of the social system into client-patron relationships that direct resources to the top. And it is the structure of the world market that enables these patron-client relationships to develop.[17] By almost any criterion of justice, these systems are unjust, viewed as distribution systems and compared with the systems they replaced. Part of the problem with viewing them in this way is that the existing social systems have forced members of smaller social systems into them. The former systems had the characteristics of moral communities and distribution within them was reasonably just. But the newer social systems lack the integrity of moral communities, for they are not communities of interests, so it is difficult to evaluate them as distribution systems. However, those at the bottom, the poor, are worse off in the present social systems than they were previously.

So the way that the philosophers have conceptualized the moral issues reveals and reinforces their mistaken view of the nature of these systems. The proposal to give aid that they are evaluating is also, for the most part, beside the point, since most aid, at best, cannot reach those for whom it is intended, and, at worst, strengthens the patron-client network.

There are two important ways in which the moral problem has been misconceptualized:

Nations are treated as moral persons and judged responsible or irresponsible, deserving or undeserving. But many third world nations, conceived of as political systems, simply do not have that sort of power. Those individuals who are responsible, those who benefit the most from the system of patron-client relationships, are not affected by changes in the political system, although they would be affected by trade sanctions.[18]

The conceptualization autonomizes the actors in the moral relationships that are portrayed. Most of the analogies presuppose that there are no economic causal relationships between the actors—between the affluent in developed countries and the poor in third world countries. But this is surely wrong. We only need to think about the relationship between the standard of living of the affluent in developed countries and their relationship to world markets—and the role that world markets play in the relationship between the poor and the affluent in third world countries—to see that there are causal relationships that are beneficial to the affluent and detrimental to the poor.[19]

Even though moral theorizing of the sort described above serves illegitimate purposes, there still remains a role for critical moral philosophy in identifying the flaws in moral theories or arguments that function to legitimate structural defects or to rationalize inequalities. I am skeptical that it can be done entirely within the context of academic disciplines as they are presently constituted, however. Whether philosophers with traditional (post 1950) graduate training have an edge in critical philosophy skills is worth debating.[20] The project of reconstituting this training within the current organizational structure of the university may be as doomed to failure as the Enlightenment project that MacIntyre discusses.

Notes

1. See, for example, Jurgen Habermas, *Legitimation Crisis*, T. McCarty, trans. (Boston: Beacon Press, 1975).

2. Daniel Bell, *The Cultural Contradictions of Capitalism* (New York: Basic Books, 1976).

3. Alasdair MacIntyre, *After Virtue*, 2d ed. (Notre Dame, Ind.: University of Notre Dame Press, 1984), especially chapter 2.

4. Ibid., p.8.

5. This is what I take MacIntyre to mean by "the culture of bureaucratic individualism."

6. William Aiken and Hugh La Follette, eds., *World Hunger and Moral Obligation* (Englewood Cliffs, N.J.: Prentice-Hall, 1977).

7. See, for example, William Aiken, "The Right to Be saved from Starvation," in Aiken and La Follette, *World Hunger*, cited in note 6.

8. See, for example, Henry Shue, *Basic Rights: Subsistence, Affluence, and U.S. Foreign Policy* (Princeton, N.J.: Princeton University Press, 1980).

9. For a classic justification of food aid, see the report of The Presidential Commission on World Hunger (Washington, D.C.: U.S. Government Printing Office, 1980).

10. In the introduction to Aiken and La Follette, *World Hunger*, cited in note 6, the editors claim that they will be noncommittal about whether the duties that they will discuss are duties of individuals or of nations (p. 3).

11. See, for example, G. Hardin, "Lifeboat Ethics: The Case Against Helping the Poor," in Aiken and La Follette, *World Hunger*, cited in note 6.

12. See, for example, Peter Singer, "Famine, Affluence, and Morality," especially p. 24, and John Arthur, "Rights and the Duty to Bring Aid," pp. 43–46, both in Aiken and La Follette, *World Hunger*, cited in note 6.

13. For example, John Arthur, "Rights and Duty," cited in note 12.

14. This claim is made, for example, by Robert E. Gamer, *The Developing Nations: A Comparative Perspective*, 2d ed. (Boston: Allyn and Bacon, 1982).

15. Ibid., chapter 4.

16. Ibid., chapter 2.

17. Ibid., see especially chapters 4 and 8.

18. Ibid., chapter 8.

19. Ibid.

20. MacIntyre seems to make a similar point in *After Virtue*, p. 61, cited in note 3. For one articulation of this view of the role of moral philosophy, see Robert K. Fullinwider, "Philosophers in the Public Conversation, *Report from the Center for Philosophy and Public Policy* 7, no. 1 (Winter, 1987): 2–3.

IV.C.
Agriculture in Development

AGRICULTURE PLAYS A MAJOR ROLE in development schemes, a primary concern of which is how to improve the material quality of life of people in the developing country, through providing them with the food they need to survive and the opportunity to play a productive role in the planned development. Agriculture also often promises a source of income that a nation can apply toward the debts it incurs in industrial development and employment diversification. These two potential benefits of agriculture in development often conflict, for export agriculture is often developed at the expense of food crops for local consumption and the land use patterns of traditional lifestyles. Although new cultivars and farming methods have been introduced in the hope that developing countries could move toward food self-sufficiency while becoming net food exporters, this attempt to harmonize the two promises of agriculture in development has proven to be quite controversial. Many argue that the new technology is size- or wealth-biased, inappropriate to the social or physical ecology of the developing country, and ethically unjustifiable in its modification of the rural-urban distribution of the workforce. Some would even ask whether improvement of the material quality of living is true development if it puts at risk the cultural or environmental quality of life of the indigenous people. The articles in this section discuss these and other ethical problems of agriculture and development.

The first two articles are concerned with the ethically justifiable goals of development. Jerome Segal, in "Basic Needs, Income, and Development," argues that the primary aim of development schemes should be to realize human potential, not increased material output or other signs of economic well-being. Focusing on human and societal development, Segal distinguishes the "trickle down," "equitable growth," and "basic needs" approaches to development. The first two aim at higher levels of income, with the equitable growth model requiring that income growth be distributed fairly. The basic needs approach focuses on how completely the development scheme satisfies the food, health care, educational, and other basic needs of the developing people. Segal then argues that development approaches that target income, unlike those that target basic needs, do not have an essential link to human development.

Having argued for that connection, Segal next takes a closer look at the link between income and development, arguing in support of the widely held view that ever-increasing income devoted to consumption of goods and services can trap people in a cycle of "earn and consume." Development schemes must support whatever affords people the income to satisfy basic needs and the leisure to pursue individual growth and activities having intrinsic worth. The present systems of value and reward do not serve such ends; still, this should be our concern in both materially less developed countries and the most affluent industrialized countries.

It remains unclear whether Segal wishes to rest his ethical case on the presumption that development is justified and on his conceptual claims about the link between basic needs and human beings, or whether his ultimate normative basis is social welfare or autonomy. What is quite clear, however, is Segal's belief in the close connection between human development, the personal growth toward intrinsically valuable activities and associations that must accompany it, and the satisfaction of basic human needs that must precede it.

The next selection, Charlie Blatz's paper "Risk-Takers' Stewardship, Agriculture, and the Aims of Development," argues that ethically justifiable development is based on autonomy and urges that serving autonomy in agricultural development schemes will require putting the stewardship of agricultural resources in the hands of small-scale producers themselves. Along the way, the author outlines several principles that should be followed in development activities aimed at the autonomy of those in the developing country. These principles are then extended into a set of general guidelines for defensible development. After defining autonomy, he identifies methodological points common to all those looking for a defensible development ethic, particularly the point that basic normative principles to guide development must not be biased against the aims of any individual, either in assigning them initial ethical significance or in resolving a conflict between them.

From these methodological constraints on the basic principles of development, the author argues that all autonomously chosen aims should be treated as worthwhile, and conflicts should be resolved to facilitate the maximal pursuit of all the autonomous aims in conflict, two principles that engender five general guidelines for ethically defensible development. These guidelines speak against the potential bias of any established government or economic system, of either new or entrenched societal or cultural traditions, of time, which might favor present or short-term gains and discount future generations, and of resource control falling outside the management of those at risk in the use and development of those resources.

He concludes by pointing out the tendency of the principles and guidelines to support a strong constructivist ethic of specific development policies and plans. (Strong constructivism is discussed in the general introduction, above.)

Thus, both the satisfaction of basic needs and the pursuit of autonomously chosen individual aims are candidates for defensible development, in addition to aims oriented toward increasing income. These themes are evident in the remaining articles as they give specific attention to ethical problems of agriculture in development.

Susan D. Russell and Robert A. Zerwekh, in their study "Social Justice and Moral Responsibility: Ethical Reflections on Agribusiness in the Philippines," identify several ethically troubled features of Philippine agricultural development and try to assign responsibility while offering some recommendations for righting the wrongs described.

The first problem is socioeconomic inequality perpetuated or produced by the introduction of new agricultural technology and techniques. The technology itself, in being capital-intensive, not labor-intensive, is available only to the economic elite favored by credit policy and tax breaks. New wealth developed in a "trickle down" approach was consumed by the elite instead of redistributed, or multiplied to the benefit of the poor. Infrastructural benefits went to the elite, as did the political influence needed to change the distribution of wealth and opportunity connected to the agricultural development schemes.

The second problem area is paternalism, since the new technology entangles small farmers and rural communities in a net of expertise and regulation thrown by agribusiness and government. Russell and Zerwekh argue that the paternalism that goes along with that net is objectionable because of the limits it imposes upon the autonomy of those small farmers and their communities. Morally, this limitation is objectionable for the lack of respect it shows for the affected individuals as rational and self-determined.

Russell and Zerwekh endorse and develop the argument that moral responsibility can be assigned to the corporations participating in and profiting from the agricultural development, since corporations have a contract with society to abide by certain moral principles in the conduct of their business. The authors further argue that this assignment of responsibility is appropriate even if the deleterious effects of the new technology were unanticipated. Corporations do not stand alone in their moral guilt, however. Because of the government's role in development planning and the favorable conditions under which it welcomed in the agribusiness concerns that undertook the development, the Marcos government must share in the responsibility for the resulting injustices and loss of autonomy. The paper concludes with a more detailed separation of corporate and governmental responsibilities. The authors believe there are further lessons and challenges here for the Aquino government, and in this regard the paper is perhaps as timely as when it was first written.

Rachel M. McCleary's paper "Justice as a Kind of Proportionate: the Case of Rice Agricultural Policies in Costa Rica" brings up the impact on development strategies of the staggering debt incurred in the development process. McCleary's approach is concerned with equitable growth in development and assesses the Costa Rican rice production program of the mid-1970s from the standpoint of achieving equity through a proportionate distribution of program opportunities and benefits among the various socioeconomic groups. Looked at from the equitable growth perspective, while the rice production program served Costa Rica's need for food self-sufficiency, it was unfair to the smaller producers who could not qualify for program credit to adopt the new technology without purchasing additional lands beyond their reach. Outlining the traditional distinction of special obligations to particular rightsholders, and general obligations to others lacking such rights, McCleary explains why a country might have special obligations to provide an equitable share of benefits to all of its citizens. She argues that morally demanded equity cannot be understood fully in terms of rights to participate in decisions and other procedural opportunities and treatments. Furthermore, McCleary argues, equity requires that everyone be treated equally in the distribution of goods and opportunities, to prevent anyone from suffering from a failure to meet basic needs imposed by the majority. The assistance called for would be both individual service to ensure the meeting of basic needs, and appropriate infrastructural service to ensure that the least advantaged have a real share of the opportunities of the country. The amount of service would be proportionate to the scale of production and individual needs of the producers concerned.

In reviewing the Costa Rican rice program, McCleary points out that while the reasons for its ultimately hurting the country's finances were beyond the control of the development planners, its character was in their control. Had equity been a guiding concern, McCleary suggests, despite external factors, the rice program would have helped the economy and the poor. McCleary's judgment is not against the introduction of industrial high-tech strategies in agricultural development; rather, she urges a moral guidance system to steer that technology toward equitable benefit for all.

Vernon W. Ruttan and Yujiro Hayami offer somewhat the same message in their study "Green Revolution Controversies: A Retrospective Assessment," demonstrating that it is not new agricultural technology and new cultivars themselves that hamper defensible development. Rather, ethical problems arise because of the sociopolitical and economic contexts into which new agricultural technology is introduced.

The authors begin with a review of the allegations brought against agricultural development based upon the introduction of new high-yielding cultivars. Again, the issues identified are largely those of equity, in access to the new technology, the consolidation of farms into larger units, or the displacement of rural laborers and the attendant loss of employment and income for smallholders or tenant farmers.

Pertinent economic data indicate that smallholders adopt new technology as widely and as quickly as did larger landholders, even though they adopted mechanization at a far slower pace. In India and Pakistan at least, large and small producers made equally efficient use of the new technology, partly because the smaller-scale producers were able to make higher investments of labor. Perhaps, the authors suggest, precisely because of the higher labor costs of small-scale production and the need for labor elsewhere in the economy, countries still seem to favor larger producers in their agricultural development. Further analysis indicates that new high-yielding varieties did not necessarily usher in greater mechanization at the cost of cultivation-related jobs for the poor; in fact, the need for manual weeding associated with the high fertilization of new rice varieties offered more employment. The authors do make clear that mechanization and labor-reducing management has been favored through government credit polices and strategies to minimize the management time of large producers, but these are not problems with the new varieties or their growing requirements.

The adoption of green revolution technology can foster equitable growth if certain social, political, and economic requirements are met. The key is wide diffusion of the new technology, requiring research targeted on small-scale producers, the elimination of size-biased government favoritism, and land reform or other changes to empower small-scale producers. Because of the polarization of wealth in many developing countries, the authors are skeptical of such reforms getting a toehold, leading them to consider whether green revolution technology should have figured in those countries' development plans at all.

The authors cautiously conclude that such technology may offer the best chance for equitable growth benefiting people at all economic levels, if it is environmentally appropriate and if the distribution of wealth and power is not highly polarized. These concerns might make it tempting to answer the authors' question by suggesting that many developing countries are not good sites for the ethical introduction of the new agricultural technology. Still, if the authors are right, any ethically defensible development will include green revolution technology along with needed social, political, and economic reform.

But who should do the research and provide the financial assistance to make that new technology available to developing countries? Some have replied that the United States should not provide such aid, for this only hurts U.S. producers, and, while we have a strict duty to look out for U.S. producers and consumers, there is only a weaker general obligation to look out for those in other countries. As Paul Thompson pointed out above in "Aid and Trade," this line of reasoning assumes that aiding others to become food self-sufficient or capable of food export is against the interests of U.S. producers and consumers. The final article, Earl D. Kellogg's "Agricultural Development in Developing Countries and Changes in U.S. Agricultural Exports," considers this assumption.

Kellogg first explains the reasons for recent concerns and then examines specific issues, beginning with the question whether increased production in developing countries has caused a decline in U.S. exports. The statistics indicate that the decline in U.S. agricultural exports to developing countries is due to a loss of market share to competing countries, not to a reduction in the volume of food imported by the developing countries. Furthermore, the U.S. is exporting less food to developed countries as well, a loss accounting for a greater percentage of the overall decline than the loss in exports to less developed countries. The strength of the U.S. dollar, crop price supports that drive up world prices, greater export competition from developed countries, and an actual increase of percentage of total U.S. farm exports to developing countries all contribute to the decline is U.S. exports.

Kellogg next shows that economic growth in less developed countries leads to an overall increase in food consumption. The implication is clear: Since a large percentage of the population in less developed countries is engaged in agriculture, U.S.-assisted agricultural development that benefits those people seems likely to benefit U.S. producers as well.

Despite possible exceptions to this conclusion, Kellogg's contention remains that U.S. producers stand to gain, not lose, by continued assistance to developing countries. Agriculture's role in development is promising both economically and morally, and also complex in the ethical, environmental, social, political, and economic constraints under which that promise can be realized. However, in this regard, agriculture in development is no different from any other dimension of agriculture examined earlier in this book.

The discussion of these complex issues by scholars and policymakers in all fields is obviously well under way. One further concern with respect to agriculture in both developing and developed countries is that this discussion should inform and be informed by as many people as possible. However, that concern takes us beyond these writings to the actual workings of our educational systems and political processes, around the globe.

Basic Needs, Income and Development[1]

Jerome Segal

The term "development" and terms such as "less developed," "undeveloped," and "underdeveloped" are universally used in talking and thinking about change in the Third World. There are journals of development economics, textbooks on the process of development, organizations devoted to development. It is therefore striking that for all that has been written about development and how to achieve it, relatively little attention has been given to the basic question: What is development?

The notion of development suggests something of a natural process that an entity goes through. Thus we might speak of the development of an acorn, or of a child, but not the development of a stone or of a bookshelf. Moreover, the process envisaged is not a matter merely of change, but involves the working out of the *potential* of the entity. When an acorn develops into an oak tree, the change that takes place is coming from within; outside elements serve only as an environment within which the oak can develop into itself and in so doing fulfill its potential. The notion of development, then, carries within it the complementary notions of actualization, growth, maturity, fullness of being.

Given these particular features of the concept of development, it is striking that we speak of nations, economies, and societies as developed and undeveloped. Just what we mean by "potential," "maturity," or "fullness of being" when discussing economies and societies is elusive. Thus, economists, planners, and decision-makers typically turn to some notion that can be more easily articulated and more readily used as a guide to policy choices. The notion of economic growth is appealing in this way. An economy has grown if and only if the pile of goods and services produced by that economy (the total or per capita output) in a given time period is larger than the pile it produced in the previous time period.

But we cannot equate development with growth. Simply growing larger carries with it no notion of maturity. In principle, a mature elephant could get larger and larger, yet we would not say that the giant elephant was more advanced or had more fully realized its potential than had normal-sized elephants. Similarly, economic growth does not necessarily imply that the society is becoming more developed, or even that the economy is becoming more developed.

Economic *development*—as an ideal Third World countries are supposed to be striving toward—must depend on something broader. An economy is more developed, not if it produces an ever-larger pile of goods and services, but if it more fully contributes to the development of the society as a whole. And a society is developed insofar as it makes possible the development of the human beings within it. It is the notion of human development that is our central concept.

Income versus Basic Needs

How is one to link an appraisal of societies to judgments about the kind of human beings they give rise to? Almost all modern thought about development is egalitarian in the sense that there is concern with the *breadth* of human development rather than the *depth*. It does not measure development by the heights of human greatness achieved in a given society, but by the general level of human well-being. But within a general egalitarian framework, the distinction is made between three broad approaches to economic development that go under the rubrics: "trickle down," "equitable growth," and "basic needs." These three views adopt different understandings of what counts as development progress, of what it is for an economy or a society to *be* developed. They also differ with respect to *how* to achieve development—but that is not our immediate issue.

For both the equitable-growth and trickle-down conceptions the central good to be attained is higher income. Moreover, while it is clear that equitable-development advocates care about the distribution of income, the trickle-down conception is also concerned with distribution. The point of arguing that higher levels of overall GNP *will* trickle down through the society is to attempt to show that aggregate economic growth benefits *everyone*.

The two views have a fundamental difference with respect to the goals of development, however. The claim that economic benefits trickle down contains an implicit suggestion that so long as everyone, or almost everyone, ends up benefiting, all is well. The question of *how much* trickles down to *how many* is generally not raised by trickle-down advocates. It is sufficient that most people have higher incomes, whether or not there may have been some broad increase in inequality.

On the equitable-growth orientation, an increase in most people's—or even everyone's—income does not automatically constitute progress. Whether or not progress has occurred is a matter of the balance between the gains in income and the loss of equality. If there is a broad increase in inequality of income then the growth in income for the poorer classes would have to be significant; not any increase is adequate.

Now let us compare these income-based orientations to the basic-needs approach. The basic-needs theorist makes two observations. First, having more income is not a good in itself; what is important is satisfying basic needs. And second, we cannot assume that needs are better satisfied at higher income levels. A great deal depends on the composition of output, on the quantities and prices of the goods and services that are available for purchase with private income, and on the extent and quality of a wide variety of goods and services that are typically provided by the government (health services, education, water quality).

Both the trickle-down orientation and the equitable-growth orientation are prepared to accept income and its distribution as adequate indicators of developmental progress. They argue that income allows people to satisfy their preferences, and that there is no valid basis for giving priority to some other pattern of consumption than that actually chosen by the individual (and the public sector to which he is subject). The basic-needs orientation is unwilling to take income as an index of developmental progress. It insists on looking at the extent to which basic needs have actually been met, at the extent to which problems such as hunger, malnutrition, illiteracy, infant mortality, and disease have actually been overcome.

Earlier I maintained that a concept of societal development rests on something more fundamental, on a notion of human development. What basis is there for going from the claim that people have a higher level of income or basic-needs satisfaction to the claim that they have achieved a higher level of development?

Orientations that view income as ultimately significant regardless of the extent to which it results in need satisfaction will be hard pressed to establish the connection. But there is a logical link between the notion of needs and the notion of development. To see this, consider how it is that we distinguish between something that someone *needs* and something he *wants*. People want all sorts of things; there are only a limited set of things that they need. Moreover, they need these things whether or not they want them. Basic needs are no mystery, consisting essentially of food, shelter, clothing, health care, and education. To call something a basic need is to say that in its absence the most basic physical and intellectual development of the individual will be blocked. Thus, a basic-needs conception of development understands by developmental progress the elimination of conditions of mass deprivation that prevent the fuller development of the individual. Income approaches to development can make this connection only insofar as income is taken to be a reliable indicator of basic-needs satisfaction, and this, of course, is a highly questionable assumption.

The Case Against Getting Richer

Once basic needs have been taken care of, however, what is the relationship between human development and increasing wealth? One school of thought is that beyond a certain point the relationship is antithetical: accumulation leads to greater taste for accumulation, appetite merely begets further appetite, and in the end human development suffers as we become further engaged in the processes of accumulation and consumption. Few of us in the rich societies have not, at least for some brief moment, paused to wonder if in fact our involvement with "things" hadn't gone too far, hadn't in some ways taken us away from some undefined pursuit that is more important.

The case that can be made for economic progress well beyond the level of pure subsistence does not have to do with the value of things, but with the value of time. The greater value of higher levels of productivity is not that they make possible higher levels of consumption, but that they make possible lower levels of labor. The impoverished are forced to spend an enormous amount of time in activities that are ultimately destructive of their human potential. What the rich have, at least potentially, is the time to devote themselves to those things that are worth doing for their own sake. Their time—that is, their life—is no longer a means to the attainment of the means of staying alive.

If someone spends a major part of his waking hours engaged in activity that fails to serve as a vehicle for personal expression, does not embody his values, does not provide for him either the esteem of others or his self-esteem, and is not a vehicle for his personal growth, then his participation in economic life is destructive of his development, except insofar as it provides him with the resources and leisure time to pursue that development in other spheres of life.

Put in different terms, there are two possible notions of a developed economy. In both, a developed economy is one that contributes to the development of the human beings who participate in it. The distinction is between extrinsic and intrinsic impacts on human development. The primary extrinsic impact on human development is the provision of income and financial security. The intrinsic impacts have to do with the wide range of direct effects economic activity has on psychological, intellectual, and moral development.

Human health is precarious—activity that is not intrinsically healthful cannot be undertaken for long before it harms the individual. A developed economy which rests primarily on the extrinsic contribution of economic activity is possible only if work time is reduced to a relatively minor portion of a person's time. An extrinsically developed economy would provide the economic resources and financial security that allow individuals to pursue that which is worthwhile in itself with only, say, ten hours of work a week. The wealthiest economies today have this potential. In fact, however, these economies operate within a broader social life that does not permit individuals to avail themselves of this potential. The central dynamic is that at the income and consumption levels that would correspond to ten hours of work a week, the individual can rarely achieve self-esteem or the esteem of others. A person who works ten hours a week and lives on the average income that ten hours provides would be a misfit in our society. Periodically certain subcultures attempt to free themselves from material attachments—to develop an alterative shared understanding of the bases of personal and social esteem. But without cultural change that redefines the meaning of income and consumption, only isolated individuals can take advantage of the potential for extrinsic economic development that wealthy societies provide.

The other notion of a developed economy is one that provides for human development intrinsically, through forms of work and organization that are inherently enriching and thus promote rather than stunt human development. On a mass basis no such forms have yet emerged. Indeed, many have argued that we have moved toward forms of economic life that are intrinsically destructive of human development.

In general, over the last fifty years, Americans have taken most of the increase in labor productivity in the form of higher income rather than in the form of less labor time or more self-developing forms of labor. *Our economic life is neither extrinsically nor intrinsically developed.* And just as we have been undone by the rising level of income and consumption all around us, which has changed the social meaning of lower levels of income, so today the world is being enmeshed in our consumption styles. There is no Third World country today in which the life style of the rich countries is not known, and in which the tastes of the poor are not shifting toward appetites for what they do not have and will never attain. The implications of this are horrifying. The following table shows the number of years it will take various developing nations, at current growth rates, to catch up to the income levels of the rich countries.

What we need is an egalitarian concept of development that will function to advance the genuine development of the poorer nations. The notion of equitable growth will not do this. Even at rapid rates of equitable growth, the vast mass of mankind will be engaged indefinitely in pursuit of the income levels of the rich countries. We need a type of development that will allow the masses of mankind quickly to overcome the most debilitating aspects of their poverty and then to avoid transforming themselves into a mere means for the advancement of their incomes. In short, we need a notion of development that will permit the overcoming of the worst poverty-induced obstacles to human development and at the same time will articulate what it is to have a developed society and to be a developed human being at low levels of income. I have argued that a basic-needs conception of development is a central part of this notion. Basic needs can be satisfied at relatively low levels of income, but only if a society deliberately seeks a development path that will do so.

It may be objected that this is all very nice for those in rich countries to espouse because it leaves them at the top and tells the rest of mankind to settle for less. This objection misses the point. The prescription of low incomes and high leisure levels is not offered merely to the poor. It also represents the direction that we in the rich countries should go in, if we are to become not just rich, but truly and fully developed.

TABLE I
The GNP Race

Country	*$GNP per Capita 1983**	*Annual Growth Rate GNP/Capita 1965–1983**	*Number of Years Until Gap Closes if 1965–83 rates continue*
Industrial Market Economies	11,060	2.5	
Korea, Rep. of	2,010	6.7	42
Brazil	1,880	5.0	73
Syria	1,760	4.9	79
Yemen Arab Rep.	550	5.7	98
Ecuador	1,420	4.6	101
Indonesia	560	5.0	124
Egypt	200	4.2	167
China	300	4.4	196
Phillipines	760	2.9	687.5
Morocco	760	2.9	687
Sri Lanka	330	2.9	902
Cameroon	820	2.7	1334.7
Costa Rica	1,020	2.1	Never
Kenya	340	2.3	Never
India	260	1.5	Never
46 other developing countries (e.g, Bangladesh, Zaire Burma, Tanzania, Haiti Pakistan, Bolivia, Peru)			Never

*Source: The World Bank, World Development Report, 1985 gap calculations by author.

Notes

1. This article originally appeared as a *Report from the Center for Philosophy and Public Policy*, vol. 5, no. 4 (College Park, Md.: University of Maryland, 1985). It is reprinted with the kind permission of the author and the Center.

Risk-Takers' Stewardship, Agriculture, and the Aims of Development[1]

Charles V. Blatz

ALL DEVELOPMENT MOVES THROUGH CHANGE toward some condition that we regard favorably or unfavorably, a condition to be nurtured, maintained, destroyed, or avoided. And although the movement need not be deliberate, in this discussion we are concerned only with deliberate changes wrought with some particular outcome in mind. All such development is subject to ethical appraisal. In adopting a direction to pursue, deliberate developers will make several choices impinging on the present and future well-being of many. They will decide whose aims or possible ends deserve consideration in the planning process, and which of these to facilitate in their long or short-range planning. These decisions might be made without the guidance of ethical principles; however, they will be open to challenge and subject to defense by reference to the standards of ethics. Their impact on human lives, if nothing else, puts them squarely within the purview of normative assessment.

What follows is a consideration of basic ethical standards that might defensibly direct the acts and policies in deliberate development. Transnational ethical principles would be supportable and so hold good across national (or other community) division lines. Nationalistic or other relativistic principles would be supportable and hold good relative to conditions found only in certain spheres of development. We first shall see that deliberate development can and should be informed by ethical principles that are clearly transnational in character. These center on and are concerned for the autonomy of people in the developing communities.[2] By "autonomy" I mean being in control and responsible for one's own life: creating and acting out one's own life-plan, in social settings or communities chosen after reflecting upon the alternatives, and in a clear and vivid recognition of the cost of such pursuits—including the costs of being accountable for one's selection among those alternatives. Once I have set out transnational principles of autonomy for development I explore their normative implications by identifying a number of highly general guidelines for defensible development. This discussion does nothing more than begin to present the concerns of autonomy in defensible development. In fact, we will end with a call to assess development with reference to the changing aims and plans of individual people. Thus, our general principles of serving autonomy in development will not take us far toward specific policy recommendations, but will complement and balance the concern more familiar to development ethics, the concern with basic needs.[3]

Towards Defensible Development

What might be the beginning points of defensible development? Are they transnational principles? We might be tempted to search all the commonalities humans share and to find in them the needs basic to a decent and productive life, and which might be regarded as the transnational starting points of defensible development. I will take a different approach. One of my first contentions is that there are methodological points common to those in search of a defensible development ethic, and, more importantly, that these have significant ethical implications. The ethical implications I will argue for will turn out to be the transnational, autonomy-centered principles we seek.

If we take seriously the task of finding an ethic to guide development planning and practice, we are seeking a guide to action that is defensible through the use of reason. To seek an ethic that will guide us in development is to move toward a reliance upon reason instead of whim, caprice, or the force needed to make our caprice prevail. It is to seek ethical principles that provide the most general rules for separating the justifiable from the unjustifiable, and thereby guide our conduct or assessments of conduct. But what of the selection of the ethic itself? Adopting an ethic is taking up a set of reasons for action. If this were itself a matter of caprice, then we could pick any set of principles at any time to guide our development. Tolerating whim or caprice in selecting an ethic would amount to tolerating it in the principles we appeal to in particular assessments of development plans and practice. Thus the ethic itself must be selected by reason.

This first methodological presupposition leads immediately to a specific rule of reasoning, a rule that emerges from the process of forming beliefs through the use of reasons such as those provided in ethical principles. Put negatively, this is the logical injunction against begging the question. When choosing between two competing views—or ethical principles—it is unacceptable to merely assume one of the competitors to be correct or acceptable, or, what I take to amount to the same thing, to merely take up one or the other of the competing standards without any justifying reason for doing so. For those who undertake to follow reason, this is simply an injunction against inconstancy.[4]

The second common methodological presupposition is an outgrowth of the first. What we are after is an ethic that will provide a defensible foundation for making development policy. Development schemes, considered from one perspective, are plans for managing resources and opportunities to achieve certain opportunities for people to pursue their aims. These opportunities will differ depending upon the development plan, so development plans will choose between alternative competing aims. Thus, the second presupposition is that we are searching for an ethic that includes a (non-question-begging) method of recognizing alternative aims to choose between and of resolving conflicts between such aims.

With this much said, it should be clear that these two presuppositions bring with them substantial ethical constraints on development. The ethical principles we seek must do two jobs for us. First, they must tell us which aims—whose aims, and aims with which objects—are justifiable to pursue, aside from conflicts and without further justification. Such aims I have called "seeds" of justifiable conduct.[5] For capitalistic models of development, the seeds are instances of profit taking from the production or consumption of goods and services. Some thoroughgoing socialist models of development would seem to count self-realization as a member of the human community as the only seed of justifiable conduct.

Second, the ethics of development must resolve conflicts between the various aims whose pursuit can be facilitated or blocked by the development plan. In doing so, they can restrict or not restrict aims to be favored in a conflict resolution. The principle of conflict resolution might explicitly favor only certain seeds, disallowing any real consideration of others. Thus, a capitalistic developer might allow that self-realization as a member of a community is a seed of justifiable conduct but urge that capitalistic aims always take precedence. Alternatively, a principle of conflict resolution might explicitly rule against favoring certain seeds while being somewhat vague about what it does favor. Thus, it might urge that development always maximize human happiness as long as it does not take a socialist form. Contrary to these procedures and operating in a nonrestrictive way, conflicts can be resolved by urging the pursuit of something common to all seeds. No seeds would be ruled against in adopting the principle of such conflict resolutions. With such a principle, all, not just some, of the seed aims in conflict would be what I call "candidates" to win the conflict.

An ethic of development thus must identify seeds of justifiable conduct and, restrictively or nonrestrictively, it must identify candidates to win the conflicts it must settle. Further, adopting an ethic to serve these two ends must avoid begging the question. What would such an ethic look like? A little reflection will show that its basic principles must be nonrestrictive—giving ethical standing as seeds and candidates to the aims of any person, no matter the end sought. Principles restricting seeds or candidates to the aims of only a certain elite or to aims with only certain objects will have no support that is not question begging.

After all, to identify any goals as seeds or candidates of justifiable conduct is to make them the beginning points, the very foundations of any judgments about which aims are justifiable to pursue, without and with conflicts. Because of this, there are no more basic norms for what is justifiable, against which to check our selections of seeds and candidates. Thus, as I have argued elsewhere, we could never have good reason for making any particular restriction in our basic principles. And so, from the standpoint of persons with aims that are not given seeds or candidate status, adopting those principles would be question begging. Nonrestrictive principles alone will avoid that problem.[6]

Basic Principles of Defensible Development

So we must treat everyone's aims, regardless of object, as seeds and candidates. The first consequence of this is that the aims that are counted as seeds and candidates must really be the aims of some individual, not just ones imposed upon that person by circumstance, force, or guile. They must be aims that result from reflecting upon pursuits and their costs. Any aims other than those thus "belonging" to an agent could be externally imposed. To suit our development ethic to imposed rather than chosen aims would amount to begging the question in favor of those strong or clever enough to impose their will upon others. Similarly, seeds and candidates must include aims understood independently of the particular forms of government, type of economic systems, and resource allocation schemes that are featured in particular development plans. Otherwise, we would have assumed features of those plans in articulating the very ethical principles by which we are to assess those plans. In these ways, our nonrestrictive principles of development will favor a life of autonomous aim pursuits of every individual agent.

Thus, our first basic principle of development can be stated as follows:

The aim of any individual, regardless of its goal, will be considered in itself justifiable to pursue, conflicts aside, as long as the individual adopts it after reflection on the options he or she has, and does so in the face of a vivid recognition of the costs of pursuing that option. An individual's options are to be understood as not restricted by her or his present governmental, economic, or resource allocation system.

Our second basic principle, a principle of conflict resolution will assign candidate status to all aims that are seeds of justifiable conduct. Its point is to provide us a way of resolving conflicts without begging the question. To hold that all aims are candidates is to hold that they have equal claim to being favored in the conflict resolution. That is, nothing about any conflicting aim constitutes reason to prefer it over others, and short of having to pick between incompatible aims we can justifiably pursue every aim. With this in mind we should resolve conflicts in ways that facilitate a maximum number of autonomous aim pursuits.[7] Thus, our second principle is the following:

In conflicts between autonomous aims, the justifiable course of action is one that maximizes the autonomous aim pursuits affected.

For example, suppose that sacrificing one generation while capitalism raises the standard of living for all (as in the so-called Brazilian development model) will maximize autonomous aim pursuits for all affected now and into the future. That would then be the scheme to adopt for that region. Here the way to resolve conflicts would be by adopting policies that move toward (the pluralism and harmony of) the greatest possible autonomy for all people affected by the policy. Some would have less for now so that most or all can have more autonomy later, or so the justification might go, in accord with our second principle.

Generalities of Defensible Development

These two principles can be further specified by noting several of their corollaries. *Corollary 1*: By the above principles, forms of government, types of economies, and particular resource allocation schemes are justifiable to the extent that, and because, they are efficient means to the ends of maximizing autonomous aim pursuits for all affected.[8] This in, turn, has two important consequences. Thus, *Corollary 1a*: A defensible ethic of development will rest on ethical considerations that transcend the particular conditions in any individual nation. Thus *Corollary 1b*: Questions of developmental policy concerned with the justifiable distribution of goods and allocation of resources are not questions of how to distribute benefits and opportunities within and across existing political boundaries and economic systems. Short of reinventing the wheel, of course, we probably shall avail ourselves of existing institutions, political alignments, and economic opportunities when carrying out any development policy. But there is nothing ethically fixed about those alignments and arrangements. International organizations, with or without political alignment, that are integrative in academic discipline, technology, geography, and the cultures of the peoples affected, are ethically viable.[9]

Corollary 2: The general goal of ethically defensible development policies—to facilitate the autonomous aim pursuits of all affected—cuts across the boundaries between developed and underdeveloped nations. It is certainly not a goal guaranteed by industrialization, a certain level of gross national product or per capita income, or the availability of diverse high-quality consumer goods priced within the reach of most of a nation's citizenry. The most technologically well-off citizenry might be underdeveloped by the standards of ethically defensible development policies. Per capita income levels and availability of certain forms of consumer technology will give some indication of the means available to individuals to pursue certain—probably the most autonomous—aims. But not all autonomously selected goals are reached through such means—and autonomy itself is not found exclusively in having and pursuing such aims.

Thus, *Corollary 2a*: The focus of ethically defensible development is not materialistic accumulation or consumption. In fact, if we were to urge that development serve the greater production of goal objects, this would bias policy against the process of simply living certain ways according to spiritual, ecological, or other ideals. Further, we would bias policy against counting as seeds and candidates the autonomous aims of those who stand every good chance of failing to reach the goal object they aim at, yet choose to pursue it anyway, seeking the process of the pursuit as much as the end. For example, in the United States, more and more small-scale family agriculturalists are succumbing to overwhelming economic difficulties. Were development policies to justifiably serve only greater production and satisfaction of aims, rather than the processes of autonomous living, the demise of small-scale family agriculture would be a further step in defensible development.[10] Instead, by the standards of our two ethical principles, it is an indication of the absence or else the failure of defensible development policies. Thus, *Corollary 2b*: Defensible development policies will be focused on facilitating the process of autonomous aim pursuits, not the outcome in terms of some product.

But doesn't championing a life of autonomous aim pursuits smack of the sort of individualistic, acquisitive striving characteristic of the market economist's view of agency? Doesn't this separate the focus of defensible development from community life, which is and would be so central to the direction of the preferences of most in underdeveloped and developing nations? Can those outside of industrialized centers even be autonomous in the way spoken about here?[11] If not, isn't this view unforgivably biased? Put in terms provided by Peter L. Berger, do the principles I have offered afford those they would affect a "right to meaning"? Berger explains:

> Consequently, a 'right to meaning' has almost opposite implications within the two societal types: *In a modern society it implies the right of the individual to choose his own meanings. In pre-modern societies it implies his right to abide by tradition.*
>
> Much of the discussion of "human rights" when applied to the Third World is plagued by an incomprehension of this difference.[12]

We must recognize the difference Berger speaks of.[13] The point is that the preference a person holds after reflection might rest on a narrowly focused vision of the options, a focus attributable either to the power of the traditions in which he or she was raised or to a set of fears that sanction the traditional life goals. Does calling for development to facilitate autonomous aim pursuits deny ethical standing to such aims?

No. It should be clear that it accommodates the radical freedom of those who would choose their aims in order to give meaning to their life, and the reassuring freedom of those who under the wing of tradition, affirm a meaning given to them. Thus, *Corollary 3*: The autonomous aims that are the seeds and candidates of justifiable development are those held after reflection, regardless of the individual's community traditions and cultural perspectives, as well as those formed from the standpoint of the individual's community traditions or culture. (Similar remarks would hold good for understanding the requirements of vivid recognition of the cost of pursuing one's aims. This recognition, too, must be allowed to be tradition and culture free *or* bound.)

It also should be remembered that among the individual's options must be changes in tradition or cultural pattern insofar as these might be affected by development policies, as expressed by *Corollary 3a*: Defensible development will maximally facilitate autonomous aim pursuits within a community of the agent's own choosing, regardless of whether that community lies outside of or within the borders of the person's tradition and culture.

What of those who as yet have no clear aims at all? This is a matter I have discussed briefly elsewhere.[14] Basically the defensible view seems to be this: Since we don't know about the content or objects of possible and future aims, the best we can do is resolve present conflicts in ways that cut off as few as possible of the aim pursuits others might have later. Thus, *Corollary 4*: A defensible development ethic will not be biased against children and others (present and reasonably expected to follow) who lack autonomous aims. Its policy decisions will seek to minimize opportunity costs for those affected as one part of maximizing autonomous aim pursuits.[15]

Corollary 4 will require from developers good stewardship of resources, including arable land, water, and energy. Resource stewardship can fail to be defensible in two ways. In the first (and most problematic) way, resources and their attendant opportunities of aim pursuits might be allocated and consumed without regard to the basic concern of facilitating autonomy. Suppose a nation's land and minerals are put into the service of industrialized agriculture that produces export commodities, the income from which is then poured into the industrial sector, leading to increased food costs, loss of jobs, and resulting misery for most of the nation's formerly agrarian agents. This once was alleged to be a danger, in Mexico, for example.[16] Or suppose that nationalization of lands and industries, even when carried out in the name of greater equity, serves to lower production and opportunity for autonomous aim pursuits. This might be because there is simply less food available, as well as fewer jobs for those not on the land, a failing of socialist development schemes according to some.[17] In such cases, resource stewardship is not properly directed in development.

Things can go sour in another way. Those who control the resources needed for aim pursuits, the raw materials and means of working them, control the opportunities for those pursuits. The controllers then decide when the agents will pursue their aims and, to some extent, the costs of those pursuits. Unless the resource managers make the opportunities available at a time and at a cost most attractive to the agents, they would be adversely controlling the individual's aims pursuits as well as the resources. They would be deciding, for example, when and what the people in question would plant or harvest, regardless of whether this fits with the plans of those people.[18] But deciding how and when to use resources to pursue one's aims is part of the process of working out reflectively held preferences of pursuits and part of taking up those pursuits. Fostering autonomous aim pursuits requires, then, vesting resource management control in the hands of the individual agents who are the risk takers with respect to the management of those resources.[19]

This is not to say, however, that there should be no constraints upon the resource user. Constraints there must be to assure that the resource is used to its full carrying capacity for maximizing autonomous aim pursuits. That is, defensible development policies would determine the maximum of sustained autonomous aim pursuits that a given resource, such as land, reasonably could be expected to support. Defensible development would then allocate control to users in order to maximally facilitate all affected autonomous pursuits. Of course, any one of many resource management styles will be called for in various settings, depending upon such things as resource type and characteristics, available and ethically appropriate technology, and the demands placed on the resource for the ends of autonomous pursuits. Consider, for example, the variety of management styles that might be part of facilitating development of *agricultural resources* in the United States, Central America, and Africa.[20]

Thus, *Corollary 5*: Ethically defensible development will practice risk-takers' stewardship of the resources to be used.[21] In light of the deference to tradition paid by defensible development, we can also conclude that *Corollary 5a*, risk-takers' stewardship will often call for support of traditional patterns of agricultural resource management. This will be so especially in areas where, for reasons of sustainability or equity, high-input green revolution agricultural technology are inappropriate substitutes for traditional agricultural patterns.

Conclusions

In rough outlines, a defensible development policy starts with common methodological presuppositions that support two basic ethical principles specifying the seeds and candidates of justifiable conduct. From these are derived several corollaries for ethical constraints on development policy. These all favor autonomy while explicitly recognizing that it cannot exclude a concern for basic needs. The principles and their middle-level general corollaries ultimately tend away from universal rules for the specifics of defensible development, and toward a much more site-specific determination of the pieces of an acceptable development plan. The concern is universally for autonomy (and basic needs it requires), although specific concerns cannot be spelled out except by looking at the aims, capacities, and limitations of the people who would live the lives shaped by the development scheme.

In the end, a defensible development policy will give stewardship of the resources used to those whose autonomy is at risk. And thus, in the end, the specifics of defensible directions in development will be spelled out by the decisions and consensuses of risk-takers stewarding the opportunities of development. It must be left to other discussions—both academic and action-oriented—to determine just where this approach will take a developing community. And even then, the direction always will be tentative and open to revision in light of the responses, the changing pursuits, the accommodations, and the evolving plans of those whose autonomy is at risk. Here, however, such specifics were not our target. Instead, we intended only the more modest task of beginning to understand the constant and transnational bases of defensible development.[22]

Notes

1. This paper is a revised version of the first part of "Risk Takers' Stewardship and Transnational Ethics: Articulating Without Bias the Means and Ends of Development," in Luis Garita, ed., *Los Futuros De La Paz: Perspectivas Culturales*, World Future Studies Federation, Eighth World Conference (San Jose, Costa Rica, 1984), pp. 194–226.

2. Further related discussions of autonomy and development can be found in, for example, Charlie Blatz, "Agricultura, Desarrollo Y Autonomia" (trans. by Julio Baena), *Revista De Filosofia De La Universidad De Costa Rica* vol. 27, no. 66, Diciembre 1989, 339–48; and Susan D. Russell and Robert A. Zerwekh, "Social Justice and Moral Responsibility: Ethical Reflection on Agribusiness in the Philippines," in this volume, below.

3. See, for example, Jerome Segal, "Basic Needs, Income and Development" appearing in this volume, above.

4. This point and the general line of argument to follow I have pursued elsewhere, for example, in "The Ethics of Public and Private Ranch Land Management," in this volume, above.

5. Ibid.

6. Cf. Blatz, "Ranch Land" (cited in note 4) and "Conflicts Facing Western Agriculture," in manuscript.

7. Ibid.

8. Cf. Blatz, "Ranch Land," (cited in note 4).

9. See John E. Forbes, "A Framework for Considering the Future of International Organizations" (Discussion paper for the Eighth World Conference of the World Future Studies Federation, San Jose, Costa Rica, 1984); and in Luis Garita, ed., *Los Futuros De La Paz: Perspectivas Culturales*, cited in note 1.

10. See Wendell Berry, "Living in the Future: The 'Modern' Agricultural Ideal," in Wendell Berry, *The Unsettling of America: Culture and Agriculture* (New York: Avon Books, 1977).

11. Cf. Blatz, "Autonomy, Development and Agriculture," (cited in note 2).

12. Peter L. Berger, *Pyramids of Sacrifice: Political Ethics and Social Change* (New York: Basic Books, Inc., Publishers, 1974), esp. chap. 2 and 3.

13. Whether we should share his enthusiasm for its ability to accurately divide much of the world into two camps is another matter. Perhaps, for example, it is a distinction holding more and more between generations or between those with differing educational experiences.

14. For example, "Conflicts Facing Western Agriculture," in manuscript, cited in note 6, and "Ranch Land," cited in note 4.

15. Ibid.

16. See Denis Goulet's recommendations for development in Mexico in his *Mexico: Development Strategies for the Future* (Notre Dame, Ind.: University of Notre Dame Press, 1983), esp. chap. 4. A related but second-generation danger in Mexico seems to be the legacy of heavy debt service, which is taking the form of a need to streamline expanded industries, cutting jobs so that further loans can be secured. This and the debt-service-related closure of industry facilities, combined with less government assistance to agriculturalists, has cost Mexico many jobs originally secured through development efforts. For a recent synthesis of the problem see, for example, "Mexico's Money Squeeze," *The Christian Science Monitor*, April 19, 1989, pp. 1–2.

17. See Berger, *Pyramids of Sacrifice*, cited in note 12, esp. chap. 3.

18. Cf. Blatz, "Autonomy, Development and Agriculture," cited in note 2.

19. A specific proposal for how this authority might be vested in the case of United States federal range land is discussed in Blatz, "Ranch Land," cited in note 4.

20. A suggestion of that variety emerges from, for example, Wes Jackson, *New Roots for Agriculture* (San Francisco: Friends of the Earth, in cooperation with The Land Institute, Salina, Kansas, 1980); E. G. Vallianatos, *Fear in the Countryside: The Control of Agricultural Resources in the Poor Countries by Nonpeasant Elites* (Cambridge, Mass.: Ballinger Publishing Company, 1976); Goulet, *Mexico*, cited in note 16; Michael F. Lofchie and Stephen K. Commins, "Food Deficits and Agricultural Policies in Sub-Saharan Africa," *The Hunger Project Papers* no. 2, Sept. 1984 (San Francisco: The Hunger Project, 1984); Norman Myers, *The Primary Source: Tropical Forests and Our Future* (New York: W.W. Norton & Company, Inc., 1984; copyright 1984 by Synergisms Ltd.); Miguel A. Alteri, *Agroecology: The Scientific Basis of Alternative Agriculture* (Boulder, Colo.: Westview Press, 1987); and Gene C. Wilken, *Good Farmers: Traditional Agricultural Resource Management in Mexico and Central America* (Berkeley: University of California Press, 1987). See also Eugene B. Shultz et al., "New Strategies for Bioresource Development in the Third World," appearing above in this volume.

21. Cf. Blatz, "Ranch Land," cited in note 4.

22. On the need for attention to site-specific values of generally relevant variables and site-specifically relevant variables, see, for example, Onora O'Neill, *Faces of Hunger: An Essay on Poverty, Justice and Development* (London: Allen & Unwin Publishers Ltd., 1986; copyright by Onora O'Neill, 1986); and Charlie Blatz, "Ecology, Ethics and Development," in manuscript.

Social Justice and Moral Responsibility

Agribusiness in the Philippines

Susan D. Russell and Robert A. Zerwekh

ONE REASON FOR THE FAILURE of previous development programs in the Philippines to lessen socioeconomic inequalities was that the technology associated with agribusiness farming methods in general appeared better suited for certain sectors of the population than for others—e.g., those who already had large supplies of capital, irrigated land, and easy access to credit. It is a truism by now that technology transfers are never neutral: there are always social costs. This phenomenon can be explained in one of two ways, although the practical consequences of technology transfer remain the same in either case. One view, expressed by Edwin Levy (1982, 281), holds that the technology itself is not neutral, that it carries with it the values and goals of the scientists and researchers responsible for its invention:

> Although technology *can* be viewed as having a socio-political neutral core—as the neutralist argues—in fact much more than a technological core is transferred. The additional components of the transfer are, at the least, values which suggest how requirements generated by the core technology are to be met and, at the most, actual social, political, economic, and technological strategems [*sic*] for meeting those requirements.

In the Philippines, what was transferred signified much more than mere seeds. The proper use of those seeds to achieve the goal of higher yields carried with it the scientists' priorities and technological approaches, all of which had been shaped by their involvement in Western agriculture.

A second account of why technology transfers are not neutral contends that while the technology itself is socially and politically neutral, it is placed into an inappropriate social and political context (Anderson 1982). Capital-intensive Western technology, for instance, aims for greater productivity with fewer labor-hours. If such technology is placed into a context where labor is an overabundant resource, however, the increase in the labor force leads to more unemployment and lower wages. The declining real wages of agricultural laborers in the Philippines since 1950 (Hill and Jayasuriya 1984) partly reflects this disadvantageous consequence. Moreover, government agencies in charge of development planning formerly distributed basic resources in a pattern that favored the elite. The rural elite had an easier time getting favorable loans because they either owned large tracts of land or possessed capital reserves that could be used as collateral. They usually received favored treatment from the government and had close connections with those who ran the rural banks. The situation is entirely different for the rural poor. Many of them live far from rural banks, have marginally valuable land to use as collateral, experience difficulty in filling out complicated applications, and are unable to afford the time and expense of making several trips back and forth to receive a loan.

It is not only in the area of credit extension where basic resource distribution plays favorites. Agribusiness corporations involved in the production and marketing of cash crops got liberal tax breaks during the Marcos years. The independent grower did not. Capital investment by agribusinesses for infrastructure development (e.g., roads, factories, irrigation systems) tended to be concentrated in areas where the biggest and most secure producers had already established a viable commercial sector. The marginal areas that desperately needed infrastructure support were too often ignored.

The pattern of resource distribution formerly employed in Philippine development strategy reflected the usual supply-side philosophy of modernizing the elite and middle-peasantry classes in the hope that benefits would later trickle down to the poor. Benefits for the poor were supposed to take the form of higher wages or a later redistribution of goods once the society had begun a self-sustaining development impulse. Unfortunately for the Philippines, neither happened. Not only did the share of national income going to the poorest sector of the society decline (International Labor Office: 1974), but the "grow now, trickle later" orientation also suffered from the same defect that plagues policies of resource distribution in the first place. As resources for development initially went to the elite, this class acquired additional power and political leverage. They were then in a position to channel future resources according to their own preferences or else oppose any later plans for redistribution or popular participation in development processes. This policy of modernizing the elite ahead of others overlooked the fact that . . .

> income becomes embodied in goods—Mercedeses, luxury apartments, college educations—which cannot be redistributed. There is no way to turn a Mercedes into bicycles or a luxury apartment into public housing. Thus income becomes a stock which cannot be redistributed (Wilber and Jameson 1979, 14).

The outcomes cited above are hardly unique to the Philippines. This again raises the issue of introducing technology into an inappropriate social and political context. Popular participation in governmental decision making was greatly circumscribed in the Philippines during the Marcos martial-law regime. Throughout much of the latter part of Marcos's rule the government was neither willing nor capable of enforcing effective policies for redistributing resources from elite supporters to the rural poor majority, even for the common good (De Dios 1984; Magno 1983).

According to Dougherty, economic power was intensively concentrated among a limited number of wealthy families, many of whom enjoyed favored treatment from the Marcos regime; these family groups had interlocking directorates in top commercial and industrial enterprises, often with excessive profitability ratios. The resulting tight financial circle limited the competitive entry of entrepreneurs who were politically out of favor. In such a context it was unreasonable to assume that an economic philosophy workable in a democratic, developed country would be equally workable under a dictatorial regime in a developing country.

Paternalism

The second issue that constitutes a fundamental moral problem of previous Philippine development strategy consists of a systematic and pervasive kind of paternalism directed at the farming base.[1] Agricultural modernization necessarily involves intervention into the life of a rural community, presumably accompanied by good intentions. At the same time, government policies and agribusiness programs are supposed to integrate the previously isolated small farmer and his community into a larger and alien economic structure complete with bureaucratic characteristics, capital requirements, and new agricultural technology. A consequence of this is a paternalistic or dependent relationship between the small farmer and the rural community and the larger economic structure that sets all the rules.

This is a logical outcome of a system in which fundamental and important decisions remain in private hands. In spite of the fact that the corporate agribusiness presence and other modernizing programs have a tremendous socializing nature (by integrating former "outsiders" into a larger global system) and their activities touch so many lives with far-reaching consequences, the system remains private in its decision making, planning, and distribution of basic resources. A widening of the income gap, growing insurgency, and a general failure to achieve the socially desirable ends of development can result from denial of popular participation. The utilitarian and pragmatic arguments that urge developing participatory structures of some form or another are well known but certainly deserve a brief mention (Cook and Morgan 1971).

Popular participation in development planning may lead to improved services by providing important feedback from the recipients of development programs. In addition to serving as an effective way to gather information about various institutional and ecological constraints posed to rural farmers, participation is also a useful forum for adapting general solutions or plans to local conditions or needs. Most of the pragmatic arguments in favor of participation share an endorsement of decentralization. By themselves, however, decentralization arguments in principle are not totally persuasive since they may also increase the efficiency of immoral practices.

There are important moral reasons, however, that argue against the kinds of paternalistic relationships fostered by centralized development planning and in favor of greater local participation. To appreciate the significance and importance of these moral arguments, we must divest ourselves of thinking about development solely in terms of a means/end relationship—e.g., what are the most efficient means to achieve an increase in overall gross national product or a better balance of trade? Instead, we must begin to appreciate the ramifications of a local community member's involvement in decision making. Why, after all, might it be important or desirable to allow local communities to share in the decision making process? How does participating or not participating affect their moral responsibilities, their autonomy, and their dignity (see Ladd 1975)?

A key concept that surfaces when thinking about these questions is moral responsibility. Participation in decision making both arises from and leads to moral responsibility; sharing in decision making is an act of assuming responsibility. The need for local communities to become involved in planning development strategies is a moral response to ensure that they remain accountable for their own decisions. Keeping this in mind, it becomes clear that government planners' and project implementors' preferences (for not allowing local communities a voice in decision making) reflect a paternalistic perception that rural communities are either not responsible or are thoroughly irresponsible. This denial of responsibility (or, more precisely, the ability to account for one's actions) is also an implicit denial of moral autonomy. Responsibility and autonomy are intertwined. Refusal to recognize a community's capacity to take responsibility for certain decisions is a denial of that community's autonomy. It is, in essence, a challenge to the dignity of the community and the validity of its values.

This argument for allowing greater participation by local communities in the development process does not state that local communities should necessarily have a great effect *on* the process. It is simply an argument that local communities should be allowed to be active rather than passive participants *in* the process (Goodell 1985). Such an argument states that people should be allowed to develop rather than be developed by others. At this point the detractor may pose a question. Particularly if the following two hypotheses are true, why shouldn't people be developed? First, people in local communities typically do want the benefits promised to them by development programs. Who would not want to be rid of poverty, hunger, unemployment, and illness? Second, to achieve these socially desirable ends communities will need help from banks, government offices, and agribusinesses. If such benefits can be provided, and if the recipients are better off than they were before, is paternalism such a high price to pay?

One response to this argument is to acknowledge that assistance by others is most definitely required. This acknowledgement, however, does not weaken the argument for allowing greater participation in decision making by the local communities. Being accountable and responsible for one's decisions has nothing to do with the causal efficacy of such decisions, so the argument for participation is not affected by the fact that assistance and advice by others is required. The second response points out the fallacy in the question, "Aren't they better off with what we can offer than without it?" (Ladd 1975). From the point of view of what responsibility means for the individual, the question is not about the most effective means to achieve the end. The real question is: Who is to make the decisions? The classic argument against allowing others to decide for oneself is contained in the writings of John Stuart Mill (1859). Mill points out that the individuals who make decisions for others are themselves fallible and subject to error. Moreover, they usually lack the kind of total involvement in the outcome that is forced on the recipients of the decision. It is not irrational to suppose that decision makers should have some kind of personal moral stake in what is eventually decided. It follows that the recipients of development programs, therefore, ought themselves to be decision makers or to have some part in the decision making process. Not only will this ensure a more moral result, it also preserves the autonomy of the local communities and shows proper respect for their free and rational choices.

Corporate Responsibility

Although this analysis of agribusiness activity as part of the Philippines' former strategy for development has identified two fundamental moral problems, a more basic question remains. Should agribusiness firms be held morally responsible for such consequences? Can we really blame agribusinesses for perpetuating socioeconomic inequalities and for promoting paternalistic relationships? One view of corporate responsibility is that "the business of business is business." Supporters of this view would point out that the responsibilities of an agribusiness are twofold. On the one hand, the corporation has obligations to its stockholders to make a profit, ensure its fiscal integrity, and develop new markets for its services. It also has obligations to those with whom it has contracts; it must, for example, provide pesticides to farmers or canned pineapple to Japan. Any concerns outside this circumscribed area of responsibility fall beyond that for which it is responsible. The larger social consequences that result from carrying out specific tasks unique to an agribusiness are not seen to be legitimately within its scope.[2]

Although this view of the responsibility of corporations or businesses has had a long history and still receives support from some quarters, much recent work has criticized it as naive and inadequate (Goodpastor and Matthews 1983, DeGeorge 1981, French 1972, Feinburg 1970). Most of these criticisms observe that if a corporation's activities have harmful consequences for those affected by its activities, then such consequences must function as a constraining influence on the corporations' deliberations and activities. This requirement that consequences to others must have moral relevance holds whether or not it is true that the corporation has a special set of responsibilities to its stockholders. The fact that some business operation may have a unique set of responsibilities to its investors is not sufficient to isolate it from the larger social and institutional network in which it operates. Indeed, it is accurate to speak of a corporation as having a "contract" with society that holds the corporation accountable for observing accepted principles of morality such as justice, nonmaleficence, and respect for the autonomy of others (Bowie 1983). These background norms that provide the moral content of a contract between society and a corporation then function as a broader platform from which the special responsibilities of a corporation can be criticized or justified.

A broader view of the responsibilities of agribusiness corporations, then, understands their activities as bound and constrained by the accepted principles of morality and the ordinary criteria of moral responsibility for actions. These criteria make reference to notions such as use of foresight and circumspection in performance of tasks, absence of negligence, and presence of a causal connection between act and outcome (Hart 1968). From this broader perspective agribusiness firms are understood to be accountable for the full range of their actions and morally liable for any untoward consequences resulting from such actions, including the perpetuation of social injustice and the promotion of paternalistic, dependent relationships. An agribusiness that acquires and consolidates large tracts of land that tenants formerly cultivated, for instance, may be held morally liable if these tenants' quality of life is lower than it might have been had the agribusiness not invested there. It constitutes negligence to fail to consider what might happen to these individuals once their traditional means of livelihood have been removed. If their quality of life should deteriorate because of this action, then the agribusiness corporation can be held responsible even if there was no intent to cause harm. This observation brings to light the importance of the requirement to exercise foresight about immediate and long-term harmful consequences of actions. Since agribusiness firms, for example, rely extensively on products of scientific and technological innovation for increasing food yields, the failure to evaluate the goals, purposes, and consequences of such technology before introducing it to a rural community constitutes a serious neglect of basic precautions. Since we now know about technology (originally intended to produce only good results) that has brought about harmful, albeit unintended, consequences, to ignore this historical lesson without even considering the possibility of its happening again is a serious lapse of judgment.

Conclusions

Agribusinesses are thus partly responsible for the socially harmful consequences resulting from their activities, even if such consequences are unintentional; yet there is nothing in this analysis indicating that agribusinesses are solely responsible for these harmful consequences. Indeed, in the Philippines the presence of an active governmental hand in the planning and policy making of development strategy indicates that some of the responsibility for these consequences must rest on the government's shoulders. This point assumes even greater plausibility when one considers that agribusinesses are in the Philippines primarily because of the former government's policy to modernize the agricultural sector through the use of modern farming methods. Add to this observation the Marcos's government's creation of a very favorable economic atmosphere for agribusiness investment, and it begins to look as if we have a framework for holding the government primarily responsible for harmful social consequences. However, since both the former government's policies of resource distribution and the consolidation of lands by agribusinesses contributed to strengthening socioeconomic inequalities and establishing paternalistic relationships, one can argue that such corporations and the current government have a proportional obligation to rectify these situations. The identification of responsible parties implies that they should meet their obligations to repair the damage they have done. Since assuming power, the Aquino government's actions indicate the intention to abide by monetary and political agreements established during the Marcos years. One can argue, therefore, that this government is obliged to change the patterns of resource development that were generated during the Marcos years.

There are some areas of concern where the government would appear to be in a better position than agribusinesses in effecting substantial change in current policies. Ineffective land reform programs and biased credit extension relate to resource distribution for which the government appears to be morally responsible. The existing system of advantages and incentives, insofar as it is a direct consequence of previous governmental policies, ought to be changed to accord wider access opportunities. An agribusiness may rightly claim it has no direct control over such issues. There are other unjust social consequences, however, that are more closely related to the activities of agribusinesses than to governmental policies. The consolidation of lands and the welfare of contract growers and displaced farmers are only some of the problematic consequences of activities for which they can be held morally liable.

While policy choices between equity and growth clearly present imperfect trade-offs, public participation in decision making and monitoring are essential to achievement of the former goals (Gunatilleke 1983, De Dios 1984). As Goulet (1983, 611) has queried: "What kind of development is good for an abstraction known as the national economy, but bad for the flesh-and-blood people that economy is meant to serve?" To resolve this issue and provide the political stability necessary for equitable growth, both agribusinesses and government planners must accept that the interests, priorities, and needs of rural communities are morally significant parameters that demand a reshaping of former development policy.

The Aquino administration agrees in principle on the need for greater equity in its approach to agrarian development, but the usual dilemma of how to balance equity needs with growth and efficiency remains unresolved. This dilemma partly underlies the difficulty in producing a coherent set of development policies for agriculture, especially in regard to land reform and rural credit. Given the recent changes in high-level government personnel and the tight fiscal situation in the country, perhaps these delays are understandable. For a government that holds such a powerful moral mandate with the Filipino people, however, many of the aforementioned issues regarding obstacles to development are surprisingly underestimated. The current emphasis on improving irrigation, roads, access to agricultural credit, and rural employment opportunities are well taken, but they languish in an uneasy truce with the continued emphasis on centralized planning and the encouragement of agribusiness exports. Although the commodity monopolies that the elite enjoyed under Marcos are slowly being dismantled, the skewed social and economic class structure remains largely intact. If the Aquino government's current responsiveness and rhetoric about improving the lives of the rural poor is to translate into effective action, then a more radical restructuring of priorities and policy-making processes is required. While such restructuring is a heavy burden for a young government, the political will, need, and potential support for the task have never before coincided in a more opportune manner.[3]

Notes

1. For our purposes *paternalism* can be defined as "... the interference with a person's liberty of action justified by reasons referring exclusively to the welfare, good, happiness, needs, interests, or values of the person being coerced" (Dworkin 1976, 185). Dworkin's definition of paternalism has been criticized as being too narrow, since certain kinds of paternalistic behavior do not interfere with another's liberty of action—e.g., a paternalistic lie—(Culver and Gert 1982, 128). Although we believe these criticisms to have substantial merit, the type of paternalism that is fostered by development programs and the agribusiness presence in the Philippines does involve interfering with another's liberty of action and choice, and this is almost universally acknowledged as paternalistic behavior. See also Buchanan (1978) and Childress (1979).

2. Milton Friedman (1962, 1970) discusses this narrow view of corporate responsibility. For a good account of the logical reasons that lie behind this distinction between corporate responsibility and the concerns of ordinary morality, see John Ladd (1970).

3. This is a modified version of a paper originally published in *Asian Affairs: An American Review* vol. 13, no. 4 (1986–87): 22–40. We are grateful for the opportunity to print it here.

References Cited

Anderson, James N. "Rapid Rural 'Development': Performance and Consequences in the Philippines." In *Too Rapid Rural Development: Perceptions and Perspectives from Southeast Asia*, pp. 122–71. Edited by Colin MacAndrews and Chia Lin Sien. Athens: Ohio University Press., 1982.

Beckford, G. L. "The Economics of Agricultural Resource Use and Development in Plantation Economies." In *Underdevelopment and Development*, pp. 115–51. Edited by Henry Bernstein. Hammondsworth, England: Penguin., 1973.

Bello, Walden; Kinley, David; and Elison, Elaine. *Development Debacle: the World Bank in the Philippines*. San Francisco: Institute for Food and Development Policy, 1982.

Bowie, Norman. "Changing the Rules." In *Ethical Theory and Business*, pp. 103–6. Edited by T. L. Beauchamp and N. Bowie, 2d ed. Englewood Cliffs, N.J.: Princeton University Press., 1983.

Buchanan, Allen. "Medical Paternalism." *Philosophy and Public Affairs* 7 (1978): 370–90.

Callahan, Daniel. "Ethical Responsibility in the Face of Uncertain Consequences." In *Ethical and Scientific Issues Posed by Human Uses of Molecular Genetics*, pp. 1–27. Edited by M. Lappé and R. S. Morison. Annals of the New York Academy of Sciences 265, 1976.

Childress, James. "Paternalism and Health Care." In *Medical Responsibility*, pp. 15–27. Edited by Wade Robinson and Michael Pritchard. Clifton, N.J.: Humana, 1979.

Cook, Terrence E., and Morgan, Patrick M. *Participatory Democracy*. San Francisco: Canfield Press, 1971.

Culver, Charles, and Gert, Bernard. *Philosophy in Medicine*. New York: Oxford University Press, 1982.

David, Cristina. "Economic Policies and Philippine Agriculture." Philippine Institute of Development Studies Working Paper 83-02, 1983.

David, Cristina, and Balisacan, A. M. "An Analysis of Fertilizer Policies in the Philippines." *Journal of Philippine Development* 8 (1981): 21–37.

David, Randolf S.; Rivera, Temario C.; Abinales, P. N.; and Teves, Oliver G. "Transnational Corporations and the Philippine Banana Export Industry." In *Political Economy of Philippine Commodities*, pp. 1–133. Edited by Third World Studies Center. Quezon City: Third World Studies Center, University of the Philippines, 1983.

De Dios, Emmanuel S., ed. *An Analysis of the Philippine Economic Crisis*. Quezon City: University of the Philippines Press, 1984.

DeGeorge, Richard T. "Can Corporations Have Moral Responsibility?" In "Collective Responsibility in the Professions," Edited by Michael A. Payne. *University of Dayton Review* 5, no. 2 (Winter 1981–82): 3–15.

Dougherty, John S. "Who Controls the Philippine Economy: Some Need Not Try As Hard As Others." In *Cronies and Enemies: the Current Philippine Scene*, Edited by Belina Aquino. Philippine Studies Occasional Paper No. 5. Honolulu: University of Hawaii, 1982.

Dworkin, Gerald. "Paternalism." In *Moral Problems in Medicine*, pp. 185–200. Edited by Samuel Gorovitz *et al.*, Englewood Cliffs, N.J.: Prentice-Hall, Inc., 1976.

Feinburg, Joel. "Collective Responsibility." In *Doing and Deserving: Essays in the Theory of Responsibility*, pp. 222–51. Edited by Joel Feinburg. Princeton, N.J.: Princeton University Press, 1970.

French, Peter, ed. *Individual and Collective Responsibility: The Massacre at My Lai.* Cambridge: Schenkman Publishing Company, 1972.

Friedman, Milton. *Capitalism and Freedom.* Chicago: University of Chicago Press, 1962.

———. "The Social Responsibility of Business is to Increase its Profits." *New York Times Magazine*, September 13, 1970, pp. 32–33.

Goodell, Grace E. "Bugs, Bunds, Banks, and Bottlenecks: Organizational Contradictions in the New Rice Technology." *Economic Development and Cultural Change* 33, no. 1 (1984): 23–41.

———. "Paternalism, Patronage, and Potlatch: The Dynamics of Giving and Being Given To." *Current Anthropology* 26, no. 2, (1985): 247–57.

Goodpastor, Kenneth E., and Matthews, John B. Jr. "Can a Corporation Have a Conscience?" In *Ethical Theory and Business*, pp. 68–81. Edited by T. L. Beauchamp and N. Bowie, 2d ed. Englewood Cliffs, N.J.: Prentice-Hall, Inc., 1983.

Goulet, Denis. "Obstacles to World Development: An Ethical Reflection." *World Development* 11, no. 7 (1983): 609–24.

Gunnatilleke, Godfrey. "The Ethics of Order and Change: An Analytic Framework." In *Ethical Dilemmas of Development in Asia*, pp. 1–39. Edited by Godfrey Gunatilleke, Neelan Tiruchelvam, and Radhika Coomaraswamy, Lexington, Mass.: D. C. Heath and Company, 1983.

Hart, H. L. A., and Honore, A. M. *Causation in the Law.* Oxford: Oxford University Press, 1959.

Hawes, Gary. "Agribusiness in the Philippines." *Southeast Asia Business* no. 4 (Winter 1985): 28–32.

Hayami, Yujiro. "Asian Village Economy at the Crossroads: Reply." *Developing Economies* 20, no. 3 (1983): 344–51.

Hayami, Yujiro, and Kikuchi, Masao. *Asian Village Economy at the Crossroads.* Baltimore, Md.: Johns Hopkins University Press, 1981.

Hickey, Gerald C., and Flammang, Robert A. "The Rural Poor Majority in the Philippines; their Present and Future Status as Beneficiaries of AID Programs." Report to the U.S. A.I.D. Asia Bureau Research Committee, 1977.

Hill, Hal, and Jayasuriya, Sisira. "Philippine Economic Performance in Regional Perspective." *Contemporary Southeast Asia* 6, no. 2 (1984): 135–58.

Jose, Vivencio, ed. *Mortgaging the Future: the World Bank and the IMF in the Philippines.* Quezon City: Foundation for Nationalist Studies 1982.

Ladd, John. "Morality and the Idea of Rationality in Formal Organizations." *The Monist* 54 (1970): 488–516.

———. "The Ethics of Participation." In *Participation in Politics: Nomos XVI*, pp. 98–125. Edited by J. Roland Pennock and John W. Chapman. New York: Lieber-Atherton, 1975.

Lappé, Frances M., and Mc Callie, Eleanor. "Agribusiness in Mindanao—Multinationals in Control." *Ang Katipunan* (Nov. 1977): 5; (Dec. 1977): 5.

Ledesma, Antonio J. *Landless Workers and Rice Farmers: Peasant Subclasses Under Agrarian Reform in Two Philippine Villages.* Los Banos: International Rice Research Institute, 1982.

Levy, Edwin. "The Responsibility of the Scientific and Technological Enterprise in

Technology Transfers." In *Science, Politics, and the Agricultural Revolution in Asia*, pp. 277–97. Edited by Robert S. Anderson, Paul R. Brass, Edwin Levy, and Barrie M. Morrison. Boulder, Colo.: Westview Press, 1982.

Lichauco, Alejandro. *The Lichauco Papers: Imperialism in the Philippines*. New York: Monthly Review Press, 1973.

Magno, Alexander R. "Technocratic Authoritarianism and the Dilemmas of Dependent Development." In *Ethical Dilemmas of Development in Asia*, pp. 179–203. Edited by Godfrey Gunatilleke, Neelan Tiruchelvam, and Radhike Coomaraswamy. Lexington, Mass.: D. C. Heath and Company, 1983.

Mill, John Stuart. *On Liberty*. 1859. Edited by Currin V. Shields. Indianapolis: Bobbs-Merrill Company, Inc., 1956.

Ofreneo, Rene E. *Capitalism in Philippine Agriculture*. Quezon City: Foundation for Nationalist Studies, 1980.

Oshima, Harry T. "Sector Sources of Philippine Postwar Economic Growth: the Overall Record in Comparative Perspective." *Journal of Philippine Development* 10, no. 1 (1983): 1–44.

———. "The Transition to an Industrial Economy in Monsoon Asia." Manila: Asian Development Bank Economic Staff Paper no. 20, 1983.

Rocamora, Joel. "Agribusiness, Dams, and Counter-Insurgency." *Southeast Asia Chronicle* 67 (1979): 2–10.

Rosenberg, Jean G., and Rosenberg, David A. *Landless Peasants and Rural Poverty in Indonesia and the Philippines*. Ithaca, N.Y.: Center for International Studies, Cornell University, 1980.

Ruttan, Vernon W. "The Green Revolution: Seven Generalizations." *International Development Review* 19 (August 1977): 16–23.

Turner, Mark. "The Political Economy of the Philippines: Critical Perspectives." *Pacific Affairs* 57, no. 3 (1984): 462–70.

Umehara, Hiromitsu. "Review of *Asian Village Economy at the Crossroads*." *Developing Economies* 20, no. 3 (1982): 344–51.

———. "Asian Village Economy at the Crossroads: Rejoinder." *Developing Economies* 21, no. 1 (1983): 79–82.

Villegas, Edberto M. *Studies in Philippine Political Economy*. Manila: Silangan Publishers, 1983.

Wilber, Charles K., and Jameson, Kenneth P. "Paradigms of Economic Development and Beyond." In *Directions in Economic Development*, pp. 1–41. Edited by Kenneth Jameson and Charles Wilber. Notre Dame, Ind.: University of Notre Dame Press, 1979.

World Bank. *The Philippines: Priorities and Prospects for Development*. Manila: National Economic Development Authority, 1976.

Wurfel, David. "Philippine Agrarian Policy Today: Implementation and Political Impact." Singapore: Institute of Southeast Asian Studies Occasional Paper no. 46, 1977.

Justice as a Kind of Proportionate
The Case of Rice Agricultural Policies in Costa Rica

Rachel M. McCleary

IN THE EARLY 1970S THE WORLD BANK, under the leadership of Robert McNamara, began to focus its institutional efforts on poverty alleviation.[1] The majority of the world's poor were then, and remain today, tenant and small farmers. To orient itself towards these people, the World Bank consequently devoted an increasing proportion of its funds and expertise to agricultural and rural development. Its activities concentrated on projects designed to raise the productivity of farmers and provide the rural poor with access to public services. Project lending was geographically defined, concentrating resources on selected objectives and targeting specific population groups.

In the 1980s, with the advent of the global debt crisis, many development problems were perceived to be structural ones, requiring action beyond project lending. In response, the World Bank began shifting its focus away from project lending toward policy-based lending. Policy-based lending seeks to stimulate growth at the national level by emphasizing major reforms in a country's policies and institutions. Although policy-based lending does not inherently overlook poverty alleviation, the World Bank began to show less concern for the poor in its attempts to deal with the enormous external debts of developing countries.

The argument of this paper is that development strategies implemented to deal with current debt servicing need to be guided by justice as a kind of proportionate if growth is to occur with equity. Justice as a kind of proportionate is the idea that each party (be it an individual or a group) receives a portion of society's goods according to his or her merits. The merits of one party are relative to that of another. For example, a large agricultural rice producer merits more credit, different machinery, and less technical advice than the small farmer who requires less credit, more technical assistance and different machinery for his or her smaller acreage. By weighing the merits of each party in relation to one another, the portion due to each is determined. Although justice is fundamental to equitable practices, the poor will benefit along with the rest when society recognizes the necessity for policies and institutions that are equitable.

Each member of a society does not, in relation to other members, have equal access to opportunities such as education, employment, medical care, or adequate housing. Although each member of society may have equal voting rights, policies are often instituted that provide some members greater access to certain opportunities and scarce resources. In 1973 Costa Rica instituted a Basic Grains Program for domestic grain production, particularly for rice.[2] By implementing policies that guaranteed minimum prices for domestic producers, access to credit and technical assistance, and a crop insurance program that protected both the banks and farmers from crop failure, the Costa Rican government hoped to foster increased productivity as well as to save foreign currency.

The credit policy of the incentives program was tied to a technological package that required mechanization of production, aerial seeding, fertilization, and pesticide spraying. These modern farming techniques were seen not only as more efficient for growing rice than manual labor, but necessary for farming marginal lands. The technological condition necessary for obtaining credit meant that a farmer had to be in a financial position to borrow heavily and have access to larger tracts of land. The small farmer, who did not have the capital to go heavily into debt and who farmed on small tracts of land, was unable to obtain credit from the government. This credit policy, even though it favored large producers, did achieve one of its intended results: to make Costa Rica more self-sufficient in rice production. However, increasing the productivity of the land through technological opportunities further increased the inequalities between large producers and small farmers, landless or not, in two ways. First, the tenant or small farmers could not take advantage of the increasing productivity because of lack of access to credit or technology. Second, the drop in net income due to price decreases and the rise in rent forced some farmers to be evicted or dispossessed of their land. Thus, the Costa Rican incentives program demonstrated that the availability of increased technological opportunities to populations with unequal abilities to respond to them exacerbated existing inequities between large and small farmers.

Two social justice issues are raised by this case. First, why does a society like Costa Rica need to concern itself with equitable policies? Second, how does a society institute equitable policies if it is dealing with unequal parties, namely, large agricultural rice producers on the one hand and small farmers on the other?

To understand the basis for equitable policies in society, a distinction is often made in traditional morality between special and general duties.[3] Special obligations are those we have to particular persons and, correspondingly, the recipients have a right to our performing the action. For example, we have a duty not to harm others and they have a right to stop us from doing so. Special duties can also be voluntarily entered into, for example, when we contract to perform services. Failing to perform the services would constitute a case of unjust action. General responsibilities are owed to no one in particular and do not generate a corresponding right to our performing the action. For example, being charitable is a moral duty we have, but to no one in particular. To which charitable institution we contribute, and when, is considered a matter of personal discretion. And, should we choose not to donate, no one has a right to demand we contribute to their charity. Based on this distinction, it is commonly believed that we have a special obligation to the poor and hungry of our own society but only a general duty to the less advantaged elsewhere. This belief is justified by an appeal to national loyalty. As members of a state, we have obligations to our compatriots that override any similar obligations we might have to the less fortunate abroad.

The underlying premise for claiming that national boundaries legitimately allow us to aid the domestic poor at the expense of the less fortunate in other countries is that we are finite creatures living in a finite world with finite resources. Nations, the Hobbesian view states, are instituted to ensure that those of us who enter into a contractual arrangement have our needs met to some minimal degree and our liberties protected. The state protects our lives and guarantees us access to some portion of the world's moderately scarce resources.

Within a society, citizens have a special duty to assist the most disadvantaged, knowing that if we should find ourselves in a similar position, others would have a special duty to assist us in overcoming our poverty and hunger. This notion of mutual aid assumes some societal understanding of reciprocity: that I am just as worthy of your assistance as you are worthy of mine. "Indeed," says John Rawls, "it is only necessary to imagine what a society would be like if it were publicly known that this duty was rejected."[4] However, to have a reciprocal special duty does not entail having equal membership within a society. While it is a necessary condition of equal membership that society guarantee each person the opportunity to voice equal opinion in the running of the government (which Costa Rica constitutionally provides), equal membership as a procedural practice does not require the elimination of inequalities within society. Inequalities are not "evidence of poverty" and cannot therefore be, in and of themselves, morally or legally wrong.

A procedural notion of equal membership does not abolish inequalities. Rather, it requires the existence of political institutions and practices to balance competing legitimate claims arising out of acting on our liberties. Political institutions, however, can only ensure equal consideration of everyone's liberties by being grounded in some fundamental conception of equity. For a society to consider all members equal, it must be guided by some conception of equity that serves governments in weighing the priorities and consequences of various policies and projects, identifying who will benefit most and who will lose the most, and ensuring that the poor are not harmed or discriminated against.

However, the concept of procedural membership does not address the more fundamental problem of the poorest of society: those who live in abject poverty and lack the basic human needs—food, health, clothing, housing, education—that are prerequisites for participation or "enfranchisement" in society. The reason it does not is that the majority can institute policies that may produce results contrary to the common good, but at the moment are thought to meet the interests of everyone. An instantiation of this is what is popularly referred to as the "trickle down effect." The majority implements economic growth policies that are perceived to immediately benefit the majority and which, they believe, will eventually come to be of benefit to everyone in society in the form of an increase in real income. However, oftentimes this belief is never realized. The notion of procedural equality does not adequately capture what is meant by equity in that the better-off majority can be egotistically motivated to assist the poorest of the poor and fail to properly weigh the interests of various groups against the common good.

Equity is more than having equal membership. It is being treated equally. A landless farmer, just like the large producer, needs fertilizer, irrigation ditches, access to water, roads, improved seed and, more importantly, credit. The least advantaged in society, who are not nourished, clothed, and educated, cannot fully participate in the opportunities provided to them, and they need societal assistance to be capable of becoming productive and self-sufficient. The special duty of mutual aid, as the foundation for equity, needs to be supplemented with a concept of justice that delimits what it means to act in a way so as to treat every member equally.

Justice as a kind of proportionate obtains "in any kind of action in which there is a more and a less."[5] The just action is the intermediate between a greater and a lesser thing. It is relative to the people who own the greater and lesser things. The large producers and small farmers in Costa Rican rice production each have greater and lesser production needs. The large producer requires more fertilizer, seeds, different types of machinery. The small farmer requires more technical assistance, less seed and machinery. Justice as a kind of proportionate determines the equal treatment of the farmers by giving assistance each according to his or her due. Thus, the small farmer proportionately receives the same amount of assistance as the large prodcuer.

The goals of the Costa Rican grains incentives program were admirable: to increase individual productivity, reduce the risk to large farmers, and to supply inexpensive food to its urban populace. The program, however, exacerbated Costa Rica's national debt and failed to provide inexpensive food for its domestic consumers. The factors contributing to its failure were multiple. First, by obtaining machinery, fertilizer, and pesticides on cheap foreign credit, Costa Rican farmers could mechanize production and yield larger harvests both for domestic consumption and for export. Second, the prevailing price of rice, having risen at the inception of the program, began to drop. Third, oil prices dramatically rose and remained high, escalating the cost of mechanically producing rice and other grains.

Internal policies and institutional practices established in light of the aforementioned factors served to compound the failure of the program. At the time that the incentives program was implemented, the policies made good sense as they were meant to ensure that Costa Rica became self-sufficient in rice production. The policy of fixed purchase price for rice was instituted to encourage farmers to go into rice production, the negative interest rate credit for technology was meant to encourage farmers to increase their yield through mechanization, research and agricultural extension services primarily assisted the large mechanized producer, and an inflated exchange rate made imports less costly.

Although the domestic rice production increased fivefold between 1966 and 1986, the drop in the world price of rice coupled with an inability to adjust internal policies accordingly gave Costa Rica a surplus of rice that sold on the international market at a price almost twice below the cost of production. The effects were a drastic rise in external debt and lowered overall productivity due to the displacement of tenant and small farmers from the land.[6]

What would have happened if the prevailing price of rice had remained the same throughout the lifetime of the program? Would the neglect of the tenant and small farmer be justified? It would not, since the same disproportionate inequity would have obtained between the small farmer and the large producer. The small farmer would not have had access to technology, physical infrastructures, fertilizers, or improved seeds. The small and tenant farmers would have failed to qualify for credit, and the price of rice would have been driven down by large producers forcing the smaller farmers out of business. Small farmers, having been evicted or dispossessed of their land, would be unemployed, thereby adding to rural poverty.[7]

The introduction and use of technology in third world agricultural production is inevitable, yet, the displacement brought about by the introduction of mechanization is not per se a negative phenomenon. The employment policies of a country, transportation that allows migration to urban areas, and access to a primary education significantly determine whether or not rural poor will obtain employment in the higher-income industries in urban areas. These are the kinds of policies that can make displacement a negative or positive factor in a country's overall growth.

Economic growth, which is currently the major concern of development experts, needs to be guided by a notion of justice if everyone in society is to benefit. Two scenarios bring about inequity: The better-off majority gets wealthier while the poor become poorer, or the poor become wealthier and the better-off majority become less well off. Instituting practices and establishing institutions that stimulate growth at the national level while at the same time raising the productivity of the poor can avoid the two inequitable scenarios. In the case of Costa Rican rice production at least, the concept of justice as each according to his or her due would have balanced the interests of the majority with the needs of the poor and implemented policies geared toward the common good. With an incentives program based on justice as a kind of proportionate the production of rice, regardless of the fluctuating world price, would have improved the rate of domestic economic growth while alleviating poverty.

Notes

1. Paul Streeten with Shahid Javed Burki, Mabbub Ul Haq, Norman Hicks, and Frances Stewart, *First things First: Meeting Basic Human Needs in Developing Countries* (Oxford: published for the World Bank by Oxford University Press, 1981); *Focus on Poverty: A Report by a Task Force of the World Bank* (Washington, D.C.: The World Bank, February 1983); Sheldon Annis, "The Shifting Grounds of Poverty Lending at the World Bank," in *Between Two Wrolds: The World Bank's Next Decade* (New Brunswick, N.J.: Transaction Books, 1986), pp. 87–109.

2. See Sheldon Annis, "Costa Rica's Dual Debt: A Story About a Little Country That Did Things Right," a manuscript provided by the author.

3. For contemporary treatments of this distinction see Robert E. Goodin, *Protecting the Vulnerable: A Reanalysis of Our Social Responsibilities* (Chicago: University of Chicago Press, 1985); Onora O'Neill, *Faces of Hunger: An Essay on Poverty, Justice and Development* (London: Allen and Unwin, 1986); Onora O'Neill, "The Moral Perplexities of Famine and World Hunger," in *Matters of Life and Death*, Tom Reagan, ed., 2d ed. (New York: Random House, 1986), pp. 294–337.

4. John Rawls, *A Theory of Justice* (Cambridge: Belknap Press of Harvard University, 1971), pp. 338–39.

5. Aristotle, *Nicomachean Ethics* 1131a3–1131b20.

6. Sheldon Annis, "Costa Rica's Dual Debt," cited in note 2, p. 77.

7. This would not occur, according to Irma Adelman if "the increase in the demand for hired labor is sufficiently large to overcome the fall in net income from farming that arises from the price decreases and rent increases that accompany the rise in productivity on large farms." See her "A Poverty-Focused Approach to Development Policy," in *Development Strategies Reconsidered*, John P. Lewis and Valeriana Kallab, eds. (New Brunswick, N.J.: Transaction Books, 1986), p. 55.

Green Revolution Controversies
A Retrospective Assessment

Vernon W. Ruttan and Yujiro Hayami

THE DEVELOPMENT OF BIOLOGICAL-CHEMICAL TECHNOLOGY designed to increase agricultural output per unit of land area is a critical factor in offsetting tendencies toward a worsening of income distribution in the rural sector of developing nations. The modern high-yielding varieties (MVs) and their technology promise such a result. Yet, since its introduction, often heralded as the "green revolution," the MV technology has often been viewed as the source of great inequities in income distribution and as a source of polarization in rural communities.

The critics of the green revolution have argued that the new technology tends to be monopolized by large farmers and landlords who have better access to new information and better financial capacity, that small farmers are unable to use MVs efficiently because credit constraint makes it difficult for them to purchase cash inputs such as fertilizers and chemicals, that monopoly of the new technology by large farmers enables them to use their profits to enlarge their operational holdings by consolidating farmers' holdings, and that as farm size increases it becomes profitable to purchase large-scale machinery and reduce the cost of labor management. It is argued that the effect is to reduce employment opportunities and lower wage rates for the growing number of landless workers.[1]

Some Questions

How valid is the suggested sequence? Has the adoption of MV technology, in fact, tended to be dominated by large holders? Does the technology make large-scale operations relatively more efficient and profitable? Does the MV technology induce mechanization and reduce employment and earnings? Those are the issues that must be examined with empirical data.

Was MV Technology Monopolized by Large Farmers?

The available evidence indicates that neither farm size nor tenure has been a serious constraint to the MV adoption. The data on adoption of modern wheat varieties from Pakistan, presented in Table 1, are fairly typical of the data available from other areas where MVs are technically well adapted. Essentially, similar results have been reported for wheat in India; rice in India, Indonesia, Malaysia and the Philippines; and maize in Kenya.[2]

This is not to deny that small farmers have sometimes lagged significantly behind large farmers in the MV adoption. One example was found in a rice village in Andhra Pradesh, India, covered by an international project coordinated by IRRI to study the changes of rice farming in selected areas of Asia [37]. This village was characterized by extremely skewed farm-size distribution and, for that account, may be taken as evidence in support of the hypothesis that the introduction of MV technology into a community in which resources are distributed in a highly inequitable manner tends to reinforce the existing inequality.

However, this village is an exception rather than a norm. It was the only village of the thirty-six villages studied by the project where a significant differential in the MV adoption among farm-size classes was observed. On the average, small farmers adopted the MV technology even more rapidly than large farmers (see Figure 1, top). The pattern of MV diffusion contrasts sharply with the pattern in the diffusion of tractors in which large farmers achieved a distinctly faster and higher rate of adoption (Figure 1, bottom).

Did the MV Technology Make Large Farms Relatively More Efficient?

There is now a large body of evidence that suggests that small farms make more efficient use of available land than large farms.[3] Small farms apply higher levels of labor input, particularly family labor, per unit of land, and they are generally characterized by higher levels of livestock intensity than large farms. Among the more carefully conducted studies is Surjit Sidhu's [42] study of the adoption of modern wheat varieties in the Indian Punjab. He shows that the MV wheat represented a neutral technological change with respect to farm scale—both small and large farms achieved approximately equal gains in efficiency.[4]

A study by Azam [1, p. 418] in Pakistan interprets the data from the Pakistan Punjab to indicate "that, while the smaller farmers do face relatively more severe constraints of irrigation water and credit, the difference in the severity of these constraints is not serious enough to

TABLE 1

Mexican-type wheat acreage as percentage of all wheat acreage, by size and tenure of holdings: 1969/70 post monsoon season in Lyallpur, Sahiwal, and Sheikhupura Districts Pakistan

Number of Acres in Holding	*Owner Holdings*	*Owner-cum-Tenants*	*Tenant Holdings*	*All Holdings*
Less than 12½	71.0	30.4	66.7	72.5
12½ to 25	63.3	71.7	69.2	63.0
25 to 50	71.9	92.7	81.9	52.0
50	73.2	37.3	57.3	78.8
All sizes	69.4	30.5	30.0	73.4

Source: K. M. Azam, "The Future of the Green Revolution in West Pakistan: A Coice of Strategy," *International Journal of Agrarian Affairs* 5, no.6 (Marhc 1973): 403. Original source: Government of the Punjab, Planning and Development Department, Statistical Survey Unit, *Fertilizer and Mexican Wheat Survey Report* (Lahore, 1970), p.38.

---

have caused any significant differences in the yields obtained by the small farmers as compared with the large farmers."[5] Similar results have been reported for rice from the Philippines by Mangahas et al. [34], and from Indonesia by Soejono [44].

Again, there are cases in which differential productivities were recorded. However, they seem to be the exception. For example, among the 32 villages throughout Asia covered by the IRRI-coordinated project, significant differences in rice yields per hectare between large and small farmers were recorded in only eight villages [24, p. 96].

A major puzzle is why, in view of the evidence, do planners and officials in developing countries and officials in national and international development assistance agencies remain skeptical about the efficiency of small farms? One reason may be that as a country develops and the opportunity cost of labor rises, the special efficiency advantage of small farms tends to disappear. It thus becomes natural to associate large farms with a highly developed national economy.

Did the MV Technology Promote Mechanization?

The popular perception that the MV technology stimulates the introduction of labor-displacing machinery has not been borne out by careful analysis. The data in Figure 1 indicate that increases in the adoption of tractors by large farmers began earlier than the introduction of MVs. Nor was there any indication that tractor adoption was accelerated by the dramatic diffusion of MVs from the late 1960s to the early 1970s.

Much of the growth in the use of tractors in South and Southeast Asia can be attributed to distortions in the price of capital by such means as overvalued exchange rates and concessional credits from national governments and international lending agencies [4,32,14]. Also, the ease of supervising the operation of one tractor-cum-operator relative to that of supervising a large number of laborers and bullock teams seems to have worked as a strong inducement to tractorization on large farms [7]. This factor should have been especially serious when regulation of land rent and tenure arrangements depressed the incentive of large landowners to rent out their holdings in small operational units.

Did the MV Technology Reduce Labor Employment and Earnings?

An extensive review of the literature by Bartsch [5] indicates that the introduction of MVs into traditional wheat and rice production systems has typically resulted in substantial increases in annual labor utilization per unit of cropped area, and, in some cases, in higher cropping intensity.[6] Similarly, data assembled by Barker and Cordova [3] from various areas in Asia show that labor input per hectare of rice cropped area were higher for MVs than for traditional varieties on the order of 10 to 50 percent.

Sidhu's [41] econometric investigation indicates a very substantial shift to the right of the labor demand function on wheat farms in Indian Punjab as a result of the introduction of MVs. Similar results were obtained by both Rao and Staub [38,46].

Increases in labor use associated with MVs were often realized despite the concurrent progress in mechanization. The data on labor use in rice production from Laguna province in the Philippines, as presented in Table 2, are typical of this process. This province experienced rapid diffusion of both modern rice varieties and tractors. Labor application for land preparation was reduced by tractorization, but the reduction was more than compensated for by increases in labor use for weeding and other crop care.

How do we interpret the critical assessments of the income distribution effects of the green revolution in view of recent findings? First, it is apparent that many of the critical assessments that were made dur-

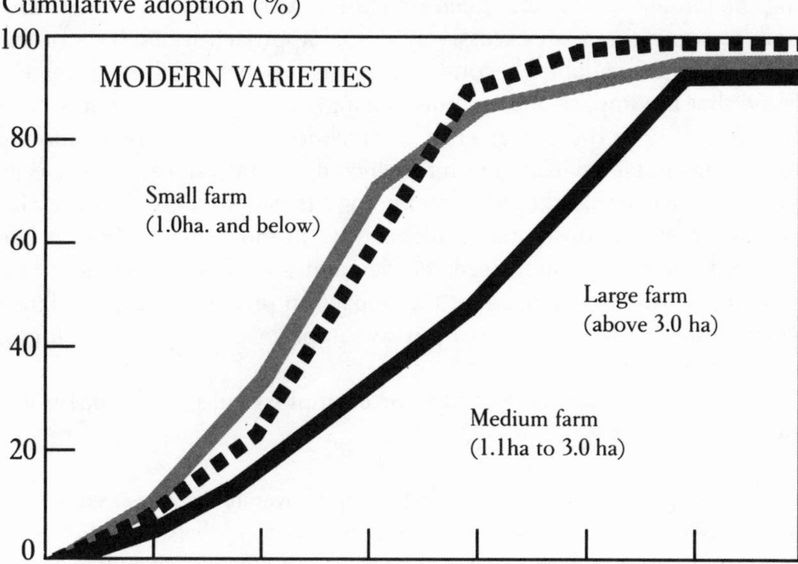

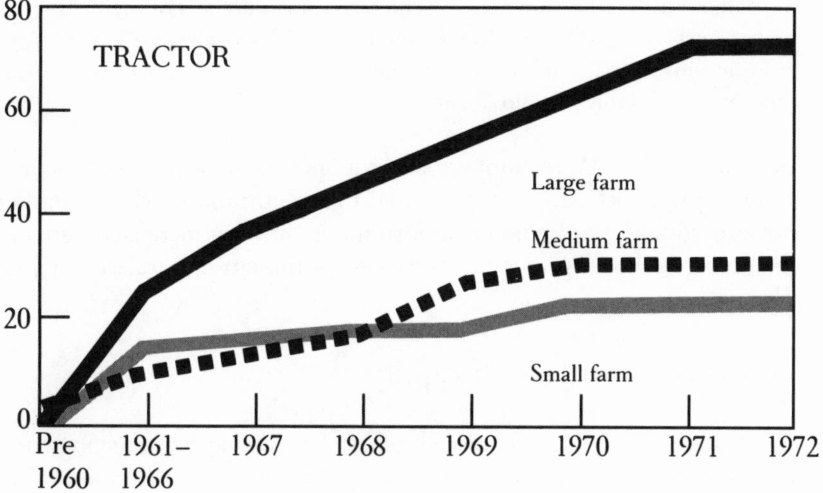

FIG. I Cumulative percentage of farms in three size classes adopting modern varieties and tractor in 30 villages in Asia.

Source: IRRI, *Interpretive Analysis of Selected Papers from Cahnges in Rice Farming in Selected Areas of Asia* Los Baños, Phillipines, 1978, p. 91.

ing the initial years of the green revolution were based on limited data and, in some cases, an excessively casual approach to analysis of the data that was available. Second, there was a general failure to understand that the impact of a technical change on income distribution is a function of both the character of the technology and of the economic and institutional environment into which it was introduced. There is as yet no evidence that the HYV technology is heavily biased against labor and there is substantial evidence that in most areas where it has been adopted it has increased the demand for labor.[7] And there is a growing body of evidence that the impact on production and on labor demand has spilled over into a positive impact on the quality of life in rural villages.

In his Punjab village study, for example, Leaf [30, p. 268] notes that farmers now

> grow more per hectare . . . and more per capita overall. As measured by food, medical care, educational facilities, and housing, there have been substantial improvements in general welfare. . . . the gains have gone at least as much to the poorer villages as to the wealthier. . . . the poorer families are remaining in the village and finding work and improving living conditions. . . . they are able to send increasing numbers of their children to school. . . . The wealthier families who have already invested more in education . . . are sending members out. . . . to white-collar and other types of service employment. . . .[8]

In addition, the MV technology and the increased agricultural income resulting from its adoption have had the important effect of creating nonagricultural employment opportunities through increased demand for nonagricultural goods and services by the agricultural sector [35, 31].

Towards Growth with Equity

Our examination of the relationship between technological change and income distribution suggests that the commonly assumed trade-off between growth and equity appears to be more relevant as an issue for ideological debate than as a description of contemporary development experience. The development and diffusion of new technology that is consistent with factor endowments is a necessary condition for agricultural output and productivity growth. The new technologies that meet the test of efficiency and productivity are also the technologies most likely to advance equity objectives.

In the agriculture of developing countries, in which land is be-

TABLE 2

Percents of farms adopting MV and tractors and use of labour mandays per-hectare for rice production in Laguna, Phillipines, 1966–75 wet seasons.

	1966	*1970*	*1975*
MV adopters (% of farms)*	0	76	94
Tractor adopters (% of farms)*	26	71	90
Average paddy-yield (t/ha)	2.5	3.4	3.5
Labour input (labourdays/ha):			
Land preparation	18.7	11.1	9.0
Transplanting	10.2	10.2	10.9
Weeding	13.8	17.8	31.3
Other preharvest operations	9.4	14.8	20.2
Harvesting and threshing	31.6	33.6	31.6
Postharvest operations	4.4	5.4	3.4
Total	88.1	92.9	106.4

* Averages for wet and dry seasons.

source: R. Barker and V.G. Cordova, "Labour Utilization in Rice Production" in International Rice Research Institute, *Economic Consequences of the New Rice Technology in Asia* (Los Baños, Phillipines, 1979), pp. 120 and 127.

---

coming increasingly scarce and expensive relative to labor as population pressure increases against land resources, the development of biological and chemical technologies is the most efficient way to promote agricultural growth. Technological progress of this type tends to make small-scale operations relatively more efficient. It thereby induces an agrarian structure characterized by a unimodal distribution of small family farms rather than a bimodal distribution consisting of large commercial farmers and large numbers of landless or near-landless laborers. Moreover, because such technological progress tends to be generally biased, or at least neutral, toward labor use, it helps counteract the effect of population pressure on land rent and wages.

Technological progress, by definition, results in a downward shift in the cost curve and a shift to the right in the product supply curve. In developed market economies where producers sell a large share of their output in the market, the shift to the right in supply, when confronted with the inelastic demand, causes a disproportionately large fall in product prices. The effect is to transfer the gains from technical change from producers to consumers. However, when technological progress occurs in a semisubsistence economy where producers consume a large fraction of their produce, a significant portion of the consumers' surplus remains with producers. The consumers' surplus gain may more than compensate for the loss in producers' surplus. The producers' gain, in the form of consumers' surplus, is proportionately larger for small farmers who consume a larger share of their production than large farmers. Thus, while large commercial farmers may lose from the decline in product prices, small subsistence farmers are more likely to share the benefit from technological progress.

The development of more productive biological and chemical technologies capable of offsetting the effect of growing population pressure appears to be a necessary condition for the simultaneous achievement of both growth and equity in developing countries today. If developing countries fail to achieve sufficiently rapid technological progress, greater poverty and greater inequity in rural areas will be the inevitable result. As the growth of population presses against limited land resources under existing technology, the cultivation frontier is forced onto more marginal land. More labor must be applied per unit of cultivated land with the result that the cost of food production increases and food prices rise. The long-run effect will be the reduction of wages to a subsistence level with the small surpluses that are available captured by landlords in the form of land rent.

It is clear that a necessary condition for escape from this Ricardian trap is land-saving and labor-using technical change. However, even if such technology is developed, its contributions to growth and equity will be small if it does not achieve rapid diffusion. If it is confined to a few regions or if adoption is limited to a few large farmers in each village, the aggregate product supply and the aggregate labor demand will not shift appreciably. There will be only a limited impact on product prices and wage rates. The adopters will continue to enjoy innovators' excess profits, or bid the profits into higher land prices, but the landless population will not be able to share in the benefits of technological progress in the form of higher wages and lower food prices.

The MV technology, enthusiastically heralded as the "green revolution," has often been regarded as a source of inequity in rural incomes. This view is generally inconsistent with the green revolution experience. The MV technology diffused rapidly among farmers irrespective of farm size and land tenure in the areas where the technology was superior to traditional technology. There are, however, numerous cases where adoption by small or poor farmers lagged significantly behind the large or wealthy farmers in the adoption of MV and related inputs. Such cases are largely a reflection of institutional rather than technical bias. In such situations institutional reforms are necessary to equitably partition the new income streams generated by an appropriate technology.

Grabowski [22, pp. 180–81] has listed the necessary reforms: "Research activities must be directed at developing new seeds for the majority of farmers who lack irrigation.

> Research activities need to be oriented toward improving cultivation practices and irrigation techniques in order to increase cropping intensity. Credit must be made available to allow farmers with small farms to irrigate their land and thus increase their cropping intensities. . . . Larger farmers' privileged access to machinery must be eliminated. . . . All of these require an increase in the power and influence of farmers with small farms, relative to those with large farms, on government decisions concerning agricultural research and credit priorities. This could possibly be accomplished through land reforms or, a less radical solution, the organization of small farmers into groups which could put pressure on government agencies to recognize and respond to the interest of small farmers.

These reforms are clearly desirable. But what are the conditions that make them economically and politically viable? It is a common observation that, in a society characterized by extreme bias in economic and political resources, it is difficult to design institutional reforms that are biased against those who possess substantial economic and political resources. A disproportionate share of institutional credit and subsidized inputs will, in such situations, be directed into the hands of the larger farmers. Land reform programs are likely to lead to eviction of tenants and conversion of land use from labor- intensive crops such as rice to extensive crops such as coconuts. It is exceedingly difficult to design institutions that are neutral or biased toward the poor in a society characterized by extreme inequality in economic resources and political power.

A relevant question, given the extreme inequality in wealth and power in many developing countries, is whether the development of the green revolution technology should have been withheld because of its possible adverse effect on income distribution. Even the most severe critics of the green revolution technology have seldom been willing to advocate such a policy. MV technology has been diffusing in Asia with sufficient speed to shift the product demand and the labor supply significantly. There have been substantial gains to both producers and consumers. In the absence of the new technology many developing countries would have moved several steps closer to the

Ricardian trap of economic stagnation and greater stress over the distribution of income. The conclusion that should be drawn from this experience is not that growth has been making conditions miserable for those in question, but that stagnation has [43].

A further reason for encouraging the development and diffusion of new biological and chemical technologies, even in societies characterized by inequitable distribution of economic and political resources, is that the new income streams generated by technical change represent a powerful source of demand for institutional change. In a society in which marketable surpluses are small and technology is static, there are few gains, either to producers or consumers, from the reform of market institutions. But when rapid growth of production, and of productivity, becomes possible, the gains become larger and the incentives that act to induce institutional reforms become more powerful.

We do not argue, of course, that the dialectical interaction between technical and institutional innovation always functions to enhance both growth and equity. Kuznets and others have documented the tendency for income distribution to worsen during the initial stages of development [28,2]. The potential gains from technical change set in motion both private and bureaucratic efforts to capture the gains from technical change in the form of institutional rents rather than allowing the market to partition the gains among factory owners and consumers. The possibilities for bias in institutional innovations are greatest in societies in which the distribution of economic and political resources is highly unequal.

These institutional biases may in turn induce further bias in the direction of technical change. In such situations the research system may respond to the demand of the larger farmers by producing technologies biased toward a labor-saving and capital-using direction even if a socially optimum direction of technological change may be labor using and land and capital saving. Those technologies, in turn, may strengthen the existing social system by making large-scale farms relatively more efficient.[9]

We emphasize, at this point, the limited impact that even the most appropriate technical changes have on the growth and distribution of income in rural areas when unaccompanied by effective development efforts in other sectors. If the rate of productivity growth in agriculture exceeds the rate of growth of the agricultural labor force it creates an opportunity for growth in per capita income in rural areas. And if the direction of technical change is consistent with resource endowments, and if the distribution of economic and political resources is not too badly skewed, the benefits of productivity growth may be broadly diffused within rural communities and between the rural and urban sectors. But rapid growth in rural incomes and in returns to labor is also dependent on rapid growth in nonagricultural employment opportunities and on effective intersector labor markets. We do not, therefore, argue that the rapid and appropriate growth in agricultural productivity represents a solution to either the income level or income distribution problem in rural areas. We do insist that it is a necessary condition.[10]

Notes

1. These concerns were expressed in Wharton [47], Johnston and Cownie [25], Falcon [17], Palmer [36] and Ruttan [39]. More radical views were expressed in Frankel [19], Cleaver [12], Fatemi [18], Griffin [23], and Lappe' and Collins [29]. For the debate on the impact the green revolution on income distribution in Pakistan see Khan [26], Chaudhry [10], Khan [27], and Chaudhry [11].

2. See Sen [40, pp. 32-54], Mangahas, et al. [34, pp. 23-43], Mangahas [33], Soejono [44;45], Gerhart [20], and Goldman and Squire [21]. For a more complete review of literature on the income distribution effects of the MV technology in South Asia see Singh [43].

3. The literature on the relationship between farm size and productivity has been reviewed by Berry and Cline [6].

4. Sidhu [42, p. 746] concludes, "(1) that small and large wheat producing farms have equal relative economic efficiency and equal relative price efficiency and (2) that tractor-operated and non-tractor operated wheat producing farms have equal relative *economic efficiency* and equal relative *price efficiency*. . . . This implies that these farms also have equal *technical efficiency*."

5. For a more recent assessment see Chaudhry [9], and also the exchange between Chaudhry and Khan referred to in footnote 1.

6. The Bartsch analysis [5] indicates that in wheat production, under a wide range of technologies ranging from primary dependence on human labor to fully mechanized production, the shift from traditional varieties to high-yielding MVs led to increased labor inputs per hectare. When this shift to MV technology was accompanied by a simultaneous shift to a fully mechanized technology, labor input per hectare declined. In all cases output per unit of labor input rose.

7. A limitation of most of the studies presently available is that they tend to employ a microeconomic partial equilibrium analysis. A series of sector level general equilibrium econometric studies is now under way which should provide more definitive results than are now available. For a preliminary report see Evanson [15;16].

8. See also Blyn [8].

9. See the Argentine example discussed in the work of Alain de Janvry [13].

10. This paper has been adapted from Vernon W. Ruttan and Yujiro Hayami, "The Green Revolution: Inducement and Distribution," *The Pakistan Development Review* 23 (Spring, 1984): 37–63.

References Cited

1. Azam, K. M. "The Future of the Green Revolution in West Pakistan: A Choice of Strategy." *International Journal of Agrarian Affairs* 5 (1973): 404–29.

2. Bacha, E. L. "The Kuznets Curve and Beyond: Growth and Changes in Inequalities." In *Economic Growth and Resources*, vol. 1, pp. 52–71, edited by E. Malinvaud. New York: St. Martin's Press, 1979.
3. Barker, R., and V. G. Cordova. "Labor Utilization in Rice Production." In *Economic Consequences of the New Rice Technology*, pp. 113–36, edited by R. Barker and Y. Hayami. Los Banos, Philippines: International Rice Research Institute, 1978.
4. Barker, R., W. H. Meyers, C. Cristostomo, and B. Duff. "Employment and Technological Change in Philippine Agriculture." *International Labour Review* 106 (1972): 111–39.
5. Bartsch, W. H. *Employment and Technology Choice in Asian Agriculture*. New York: Praeger Publishers, 1977.
6. Barry, R. A., and W. R. Cline. *Agrarian Structure and Productivity in Developing Countries*. Baltimore: Johns Hopkins University Press, 1979.
7. Binswanger, H. P. *The Economics of Tractors in South Asia*. New York: Agricultural Development Council; and Hyderabad, India: International Crops Research Institute for the Semi-Arid Tropics, 1978.
8. Blyn, G. "The Green Revolution Revisited." *Economic Development and Cultural Change* 31 (1983): 705–25.
9. Chaudhry, M. G. "The Green Revolution and Income Inequality: Some Empirical Evidence from Rural Pakistan." Ph.D. diss., University of Wisconsin, Madison, 1980.
10. Chaudhry, M. G. "Green Revolution and the Redistribution of Rural Incomes: Pakistan's Experience." *The Pakistan Development Review* 21 (1982): 173–205.
11. Chaudhry, M. G. "Green Revolution and Redistribution of Rural Incomes: Pakistan's Experience—A Reply." *The Pakistan Development Review* 22 (1983): 117–24.
12. Cleaver, H. "The Contradictions of the Green Revolution." *American Economic Review* 62 (1972): 177–88.
13. de Janvry, A. "A Socioeconomic Model in Induced Innovation for Argentine Agricultural Development." *Quarterly Journal of Economics* 87 (1973): 410–35.
14. Duff, B. "Mechanization and Use of Modern Varieties." In *Economic Consequences of the New Rice Technology*, pp. 145–64, edited by R. Barker and Y. Hayami. Los Banos, Philippines: International Rice Research Institute, 1978.
15. Evenson, R. E. "Economics of Agricultural Growth: The Case of Northern India." In *Issues in Third World Development*, pp. 145–91, edited by K. C. Nobe and R. K. Sampath. Boulder, Colo.: Westview Press, 1983.
16. Evenson, R. E. "Population Growth and Agricultural Development in North India." Paper presented at Conference on Recent Population Trends in Southwest Asia, New Delhi, Feb. 2–8, 1983.
17. Falcon, W. P. "The Green Revolution: Generations of Problems." *American Journal of Agricultural Economics* 52 (1970): 698–710.
18. Fatemi, A. M. S. "The Green Revolution: An Appraisal." *Monthly Review* 24 (1972): 112–20.
19. Frankel, F. R. *India's Green Revolution: Economic Gains and Political Costs*. Princeton, N.J.: Princeton University Press, 1971.
20. Gerhart, J. *The Diffusion of Hybrid Maize in Western Kenya*. Mexico, D.F.: Centro International de Mejoramiento de Maiz y Trigo, 1975.
21. Goldman, R. H., and L. Squire. "Technical Change, Labor Use, and Income Distri-

bution in the Muda Irrigation Project." *Economic Development and Cultural Change* 30 (1982): 753–75.

22. Grabowski, R. "Induced Innovation, Green Revolution, and Income Distribution: Reply." *Economic Development and Cultural Change* 30 (1981): 177–81.
23. Griffin, K. *The Political Economy of Agrarian Change: An Essay on the Green Revolution*, 2d ed. London: Macmillan Co., 1979.
24. International Rice Research Institute (IRRI). *Interpretive Analysis of Selected Papers from Changes in Rice Farming in Selected Areas of Asia*. Los Banos, Philippines: IRRI, 1978.
25. Johnston, B. F., and J. Cownie. "The Seed-Fertilizer Revolution and Labor Force Absorption." *American Economic Review* 59 (1969): 569–82.
26. Khan, M. H. *The Economics of the Green Revolution in Pakistan*. New York: Praeger Publishers, 1975.
27. Khan, M. H. "Green Revolution and Redistribution of Rural Incomes: Pakistan's Experience—A Comment." *The Pakistan Development Review* 22 (1983): 47–56.
28. Kuznets, S. "Economic Growth and Income Inequality." *The American Economic Review* 45 (1955): 1–28.
29. Lappé, F. M., and J. Collins. *Food First: Beyond the Myth of Scarcity*, rev. ed., pp. 121–68. New York: Ballantine, 1979.
30. Leaf, M. J. "The Green Revolution and Cultural Change in a Punjab Village, 1965-1978." *Economic Development and Cultural Change* 31 (1983): 227–70.
31. Lele, U., and J. W. Mellor. "Technological Change, Distributive Bias and Labor Transfer in a Two Sector Economy", *Oxford Economic Papers* 33 (1981): 426–41.
32. McInerney, J. P., and G. F. Donaldson. *The Consequences of Farm Tractors in Pakistan*. World Bank Staff Working Paper no. 210. Washington, D.C., 1974.
33. Mangahas, M. "Economic Aspects of Agrarian Reform Under the New Society." *The Philippine Review of Business and Economics* 11 (1974): 175–87.
34. Mangahas, M., V. A. Miralao, R. P. de los Reyes, with N. de Leon. *Tenants, Lessees, Owners: Welfare Implications of Tenure Change*. Quezon City: Ateneo de Manila University Press, 1976.
35. Mellor, J. W., and U. J. Lele. "Growth Linkages with the New Foodgrain Technologies." *Indian Journal of Agricultural Economics* 28 (1973): 35–55.
36. Palmer, I. *The New Rice in Asia: Conclusions from Four Country Studies*. Geneva: United Nations Research Institute for Social Development, 1976.
37. Parthasarathy, G. "West Godavari, Andhra Pradesh." In *Changes in Rice Farming in Selected Areas of Asia*, pp. 43–70. Los Banos, Philippines: IRRI, 1974.
38. Rao, C. H. H. *Technological Change and Distribution of Gains in Indian Agriculture*. Delhi: Macmillan Company of India, 1975.
39. Ruttan, V. W. "The Green Revolution: Seven Generalizations." *International Development Review* 19, (1977): 16–23.
40. Sen, B. *The Green Revolution in India: A Perspective*. New Delhi: Wiley Eastern, 1974.
41. Sidhu, S. S. "Economics of Technical Change in Wheat Production in the Indian Punjab." *American Journal of Agricultural Economics* 56 (1974): 217–26.
42. Sidhu, S. S. "Relative Efficiency in Wheat Production in the Indian Punjab." *The American Economic Review* 64 (1974): 742–51.
43. Singh, I. "The Landless Poor in South Asia." In *Growth and Equity in Agricultural Development*, edited by A. Maunder and K. Ohkawa, pp. 379–400. Proceedings, Eighteenth International Conference of Agricultural Economists, Jakarta, Indone-

sia, Aug. 24–Sept. 2, 1982. Aldershot, Hampshire, England: Gower Publishing Co., Ltd., 1983.

44. Soejono, I. "Growth and Distributional Changes of Paddy Farm Income in Central Java, 1968-1974." Ph.D. diss., Iowa State University, Ames, Iowa, 1976.
45. Soejono, I. "Growth and Distributional Changes in Paddy Farm Income in Central Java." *Prisma (Indonesian Journal of Social and Economic Affairs)* 3 (1976): 26–32.
46. Staub, W. *Agricultural Development and Farm Employment in India*. U.S. Dept. of Agriculture, Economic Research Service, Foreign Agricultural Economic Report No. 84. Washington, D.C., 1973.
47. Wharton, C. R. "The Green Revolution: Cornucopia or Pandora's Box?" *Foreign Affairs* 47 (1969): 464–76.

Agricultural Development in Developing Countries and Changes in U.S. Agricultural Exports

Earl D. Kellogg

An important question to emerge in the United States over the past few years is whether providing agricultural development assistance to developing countries around the world is in the best interests of American agriculture. The concern is that increasing agricultural production in these countries has contributed substantially to the decline in U.S. agricultural exports since 1981. This paper considers the basis for this recent concern and briefly examines the evidence and data relevant to it. In addition, it discusses why U.S. agricultural exports have declined over the past five years, examines more closely the relationship between increasing agricultural production in developing countries and those countries' demands for agricultural imports, and concludes with a few comments about the future.

Why Agricultural Assistance to Developing Countries Has Recently Become an Issue

Although the possible inconsistency between supporting agricultural development in poor countries and increasing U.S. agricultural exports has been potentially troublesome since agricultural development assistance began several decades ago, it has only recently become a big issue. Generally speaking, three reasons can account for this.

First, international and foreign phenomena are having increasing influence on U.S. agriculture.[1] For example, large international capital flows affect U.S. interest rates and exchange rates and help finance U.S. budget deficits. All these variables affect U.S. agriculture. The floating exchange rate of the U.S. dollar alone frequently changes prices of U.S. agricultural exports and imports. Also, substantial increases in the value of U.S. agricultural exports and imports between 1960 and 1985 (by 575 percent and 392 percent, respectively) have in turn increased the influence of global phenomena on our country (see Table 1). Finally, the proportion of U.S. agricultural exports going to developed versus developing countries has changed. In FY 1976, 30.5 percent of all U.S. agricultural exports went to less-developed countries (LDCs) while 69.5 percent went to developed countries. The same variables in FY 1985 were 41.4 percent and 58.6 percent, respectively.

A second reason lies with the growing visibility of U.S. universities (and other institutions supported by U.S. funds) in implementing projects designed to improve agricultural production in developing countries. Legislation in Title XII of the Foreign Assistance Act created a distinct mandate for U.S. universities to be involved in these projects, giving rise to small, but identifiable international sections in many institutions, and state clientele are raising questions about such international activities.

And third, U.S. farm problems affecting farmer net income and net worth positions have become more severe in the past four to five years. Many farmers are facing declining asset values, heavy debt burdens, high interest rates, low product prices, and reduced export sales (see Table 2).

Has Increased Agricultural Production in Developing Countries Caused U.S. Agricultural Exports to Decline?

If increased agricultural production in developing countries has been the reason for the decline in U.S. agricultural exports, one or more of the following conditions would also have to exist:

—Significant increases in total and per capita agricultural production in LDCs since U.S. agricultural exports began to decline in 1980-81;
—Increases in agricultural exports of LDCs
—Significant reductions in total agricultural imports by LDCs

Regarding the first point, from 1980-81 to 1984-85, total agricultural production in LDCs increased only 2.7 percent annually.[2] Further, per capita agricultural production in these countries has remained essentially constant since 1973-74; only in east Asian LDCs had it increased substantially in the past decade. Thus, since LDC regions in

TABLE 1

Value of U.S. Agricultural Exports and Imports, by Fiscal Year

	1960 ($ mil)	*1970 ($ mil)*	*1985 ($ mil)*	*1960–85 Increase (percent)*
U.S. Agricultural Exports	4,628	6,958	31,190	575
U.S. Agricultural Exports	4,010	5,686	19,716	392

Source ERS/USDSA, *U.S. Foreign Agricultural Trade Statistical Report* (various years).

TABLE 2

U.S. Agricultural Exports for Fiscal Years 1974–85

Year	*Developing Countries*[a] *($ bil)*	*To Developed Countries*[b] *($ bil)*	*Total ($ bil)*	*Share to Developing Countries (percent)*	*Share to Developed Countries (percent)*
1974	7.61	13.95	21.56	35.3	64.7
1975	8.27	13.55	21.82	37.9	62.1
1976	6.93	15.81	22.74	30.5	69.5
1977	8.46	15.51	23.97	35.3	64.7
1978	9.24	18.05	27.29	33.9	66.1
1979	11.04	20.94	31.98	34.5	65.5
1980	15.67	24.81	40.48	38.7	61.3
1981	18.24	25.54	43.78	41.7	58.3
1982	15.30	23.80	39.10	39.1	60.9
1983	14.45	20.32	34.77	41.6	58.4
1984	15.59	22.44	38.01	41.0	59.0
1985	12.92	18.27	31.19	41.4	58.6

Notes: [a] Includes all Latin American countries; all countries in Asia except Israel and Japan; and all countries in Africa except South Africa.
[b] Includes all countries except developing countries.
Source: ERS/USDA. U.S. *Foreign Agricultural Trade Statistical Report* (various years); ERS/USDA, *Foreign Agricultural Trade Statistics of the U.S.*, FY 1985 supplement.

general have shown little or no improvement in per capita agricultural production in the mid-1980s versus the early 1980s, they have apparently undergone no widespread boom in agricultural production to have caused the volume of their agricultural imports to decline.

As to possible increases in agricultural exports of LDCs, from 1965 to 1967 developing countries accounted for 35 percent of the world's agricultural exports, whereas in 1982-84 the value declined to 30 percent.[3] Overall, agricultural exports by LDCs during the 1980s have been steady to declining. Therefore, developing countries in general have not been taking away U.S. agricultural export markets. On the contrary, LDCs are losing agricultural export market shares, not increasing them.

Finally, far from being reduced, the value of developing countries' agricultural imports from 1974 to 1984 in fact increased by 141 percent. For the last four years of that period, however, their value declined by 8.9 percent. Moreover, if measured from 1982 to 1984, the value of those imports decreased by only 3 percent.[4] In addition, from 1980-81 to 1984-85, when their value was falling, the *volume* of agricultural imports by developing countries actually increased by 7.1 percent.[5]

Apart from these points, it should be noted that from 1968 to 1983 the developed world, excluding the United States, increased its market share of LDC agricultural imports from 27 percent to 37 percent. The U.S. market share during the same period, however, decreased from 32 percent to 27 percent.[6] Therefore, the United States has lost some of its share of the LDC agricultural import market to other developed countries.

In summary, then, there has been no major increase in per capita agricultural production in LDCs in the 1980s; the share of world agricultural exports accounted for by LDCs is declining, not increasing; and although their agricultural imports have been declining slightly in value in the 1980s, they have been increasing in volume, and other developed countries have been able to increase their share of the LDC agricultural import market much faster than has the United States. Therefore, based on the data, it is illogical to maintain the notion that increased agricultural production in developing countries has been a major factor causing U.S. agricultural exports to decline over the past five years.

Why U.S. Agricultural Export Values Have Declined since 1981

If decreases in U.S. agricultural exports cannot be blamed on increases in agricultural production in developing countries, why *have* U.S. agricultural exports declined from $43.8 billion in 1981 to $31.2 billion in 1985?

Significantly, the United States is the only major exporting country to experience an absolute decline in export volume in the 1980s, and that was due entirely to a loss of market share in world agriculture exports. World export volume, on the other hand, increased by 5.8 percent from 1980-81 to 1984-85. Therefore, it is not fair to say that the world agricultural export market has collapsed. It has grown, but the U.S. share has declined.

One study shows that since 1981, the volume of U.S. agricultural exports has decreased far less than their value (20 percent versus 35 percent).[7] About 60 percent of the decline in value of U.S. agricultural exports can be attributed to declines in exports to developed countries, and 40 percent rests with declines in exports to LDCs. Thus, the bulk of the problem is with U.S. exports to the *developed* world. Therefore, it is not logical to blame LDCs for buying fewer U.S. agricultural exports when LDC total agricultural imports have not fallen by very much. The problem is that the United States is not keeping pace with other countries for the LDC agricultural import market.

Why, then, has the value of U.S. agricultural exports declined over the past five years?

The first is that from 1980 to late 1984, the U.S. dollar increased in value against many currencies. This raised prices for all exports from the United States, and a recent USDA study has estimated that the resultant decline in volume of U.S. agricultural exports amounted to $6 billion between 1981 and 1983.[8] Although the value of the U.S. dollar has been falling since early 1985 relative to some currencies (e.g., Japanese yen and German mark), this decline has not been as substantial against many other important currencies. From February 1985 to August 1986, the U.S. dollar declined only 4 percent against seventeen currencies of important U.S. buyers and competitors.[9] It has actually risen against the currencies of several nations, including Canada and Mexico. Further, because some currencies are "pegged" to the U.S. dollar, it is difficult to devalue the dollar against these currencies. Given these situations, it will take longer to reduce U.S. agricultural export prices through U.S. dollar declines than might be expected.

Second, other developed countries have *increased* their agricultural exports, thus increasing their share of the world agricultural export market from 39 percent in 1965-67 to 45 percent in 1982-84, while the U.S. share has remained relatively constant.[10] For example, the U.S. share of world wheat exports declined from 45 percent in 1978-79 to about 28 percent in 1985-86.[11] The countries that were increasing their shares during this time were Canada, Australia, Argentina, and those in western Europe, none of whom have received agricultural development assistance from the U.S. for decades.

Third, developing countries have reduced their growth in the value of agricultural imports. This can be partly attributed to decreasing availability of foreign exchange in these countries. From 1970 to 1984, the percent of GNP that was debt service among LDCs increased 114 percent in low-income countries, 219 percent in lower middle-income countries, and 221 percent in upper middle-income countries.[12] During this same time, exports of LDCs generally decreased: the annual decline from the mid-1970s to 1983 was 0.8 percent for low-income countries and 0.4 percent for lower middle-income countries, although upper middle-income countries saw an annual increase of 0.5 percent. Out of 76 developing countries with data listed in the 1986 World Bank *World Development Report*, only nine (12 percent) had positive current account trade balances. Thus, foreign exchange in developing countries for agricultural imports is becoming more scarce. Yet even with all their economic difficulties in the 1980s, developing countries have been growing in importance as markets for U.S. agricultural exports, as shown in Table 3.

Reduced growth in agricultural imports among developing countries can also be attributed to their slower economic growth. One study reports that annual GNP growth among LDCs, which averaged a strong 6 percent during the 1970s, fell to 1.4 percent in 1981, to 0.9 percent in 1982, and to a dismal 0.4 percent in 1983.[14] Further, GNP per capita in many developing countries has declined in the 1980s.

A fourth reason for the declining value of U.S. agricultural exports since 1981 lies with U.S. policies of supporting agricultural prices. These policies have tended to increase world prices above what they would have been otherwise, thus encouraging other countries to increase agricultural production and exports. Additionally, U.S. restrictions of agricultural exports to several countries in the 1970s and at other times to the Soviet Union may have also made it attractive for other countries to enter the agricultural export business.

And fifth, the countries with centrally planned economies have decreased their agricultural imports since 1980. At that time, they accounted for 11 percent of the world's agricultural imports; in 1983, they accounted for only 8 percent.[15]

Not one of these reasons for the decline in U.S. agricultural export values since 1981 has much to do with increasing agricultural production in developing countries. Moreover, many researchers feel that the total volume of U.S. agricultural exports, which rose more than 10 percent annually during the 1970s, will return to a more normal long-term growth rate of 2 to 3 percent annually between the early 1980s and the year 2000. The mid-to-late 1970s was an extraordinary period, and the conditions that defined it may not be repeated for some time.

TABLE 3
Share of the U.S. Farm Exports That Went to Developing Countries

	1980	*1983*
Food Grain	55%	67%
Coarse Grain	29%	42%
Oil Seeds	15%	19%
Cotton	42%	44%

Source: R.L. Paarlberg, "U.S. Agriculture and the Developing World," in *U.S. Agricultural and the Developing World* (Boulder, Colo.: Lynne Reiner, 1987).

Relationship between Agricultural Production and Imports in Developing Countries

Does increased agricultural production in developing countries necessarily mean they will decrease their agricultural imports? Before this question can be answered, four important characteristics of developing countries must be acknowledged:

—Agriculture accounts for a significant proportion of their total economic activity.
—As incomes increase, significantly more is spent on both more food and diet diversification; food expenditures may increase 5 to 6 percent for a 10 percent increase in income. In many LDCs, 40 to 60 percent of income is spent on agricultural products, and as incomes rise, more is spent on meat and dairy products, which in turn increases the indirect demand for feed grains. Primarily for this reason, per-capita grain consumption in developed countries is typically two-and-a-half to four times that in developing countries.
—In general, people who work in agriculture have lower incomes than those who do not. Therefore, an increase in income for agricultural workers will create a higher demand for food than the same increase would cause in the nonagricultural sector.
—Population growth rates in developing countries, while declining slightly, are still relatively high and will remain higher than those in developed countries for many decades.

These characteristics indicate there may be strong possibilities for relatively high growth rates in the demand for agricultural products in developing countries and that to support and increase economic development, many developing countries will have to increase their domestic agricultural production.

Is there any solid evidence that such a positive relationship exists in developing countries between increased agricultural production and changes in agricultural imports? One study has shown that the sixteen developing countries with the most rapid growth rates in staple food production between 1961 and 1976 also increased their net staple food imports by 133 percent during this period.[16] In another study, the group of eighteen developing countries with the most rapid growth rates in per capita food production between 1970 and 1982 also increased total agricultural, corn, and soybean and soybean product imports at respective rates of 34 percent, 97 percent, and 257 percent faster than the group of thirteen developing countries with the slowest growth in per capita food production.[17]

Further, even developing countries that have become net exporters of agricultural products can also be expanding markets for certain agricultural imports. For example, Malaysia, a consistent net exporter of agricultural products, increased its imports of food, feed grains, and oil seeds from a wheat equivalent basis of about 1 million metric tons to almost 2.4 million metric tons from 1967 to 1983.[18] In addition, from 1970-72 to 1980-82, Brazil, a country that competes with us in soybean product exports, increased its imports of wheat and wheat products and corn and corn products from the United States by 27 percent and 86 percent, respectively. In addition, between 1970 and 1984, a time when Brazil was rapidly increasing its own agricultural production, the quantity of U.S. agricultural exports to Brazil increased by 8.7 percent per year while the value of those exports grew by 16.3 percent per year.[19] Finally, while the United States is acknowledged as a large net exporter of agricultural commodities, not so well recognized is its growth as an importer of agricultural products. As these examples show, increasing agricultural production along specialized comparative advantage lines in developing countries can complement increasing agricultural exports to them.

In a recent analysis of sixty-five developing countries from 1970 to 1982, for those LDCs experiencing growth in per capita agricultural production, a positive and significant correlation was found not only between such production and per capita agricultural imports, but also between such production and per capita income.[20] In this study, there was no evidence that increasing agricultural production in developing countries had a significant negative effect on agricultural imports. A similar study found a significant positive relationship between developing countries' agricultural productivity per worker and per capita gross domestic product (GDP). In addition, a strong positive relationship was found between per capita GDP and agricultural imports of developing countries.[21]

This evidence indicates that for LDCs, increases in agricultural production are necessary for widespread income growth that leads to increases in agricultural imports. Because of this, LDCs with the faster-growing agricultural sectors were the faster-growing markets for U.S. agricultural exports. Thus, American agriculture has nothing to gain and much to lose from slowing down agricultural development in developing countries.

Regardless of one's position on the issue of how agricultural development assistance in LDCs affects American agriculture, it is clear that U.S. government expenditures on such assistance in developing countries are relatively small. U.S. domestic agricultural commodity price and farm income support expenditures in 1983 (not even counting the payment in kind, or PIK, program) were twenty-five times larger than were U.S. expenditures on agricultural, rural development, and nutrition assistance programs for LDCs. Or, to put it another way, what we spent on agricultural development assistance was only 4 percent of what we spent in support of domestic agricultural programs.[22]

There are exceptions to this general proposition that agricultural development boosts broad-based income growth and thus the demand for imported agricultural products. For example, some countries have adopted policies to reduce imports and increase exports of agricultural products regardless of the current situation they face. In other countries, unequal income distributions, poverty, and poor performance in the nonagricultural sector can substantially constrain any demand increases resulting from increased agricultural production.

The Likely Scenario for the Future

Looking ahead to the future, the gap in developing countries between food production and demand will probably increase moderately over the next two decades. A recent study by the International Food Policy Research Institute has indicated that the overall net food deficit, which was fifty million metric tons in 1980, will be about seventy million metric tons by the year 2000.[23]

In addition, many developing countries that have had difficult economic times in the past few years will need to improve their foreign exchange positions and income growth records to continue as growing markets for agricultural imports. To accomplish these goals, agricultural development must be an important part of their plans.

At the same time, while LDCs will probably not be the growth market for the next twenty years that they were for agricultural imports from 1973 to 1981, they *can* be the most important growth market for agricultural exporters. Whether the United States can effectively compete with other developed countries for these developing country markets is another question.

Finally, macroeconomic forces such as interest rates, foreign lending, currency values, export performance of LDCs, trade barriers to LDC exports, oil prices, and other variables will have major impacts on the ability of developing countries to import agricultural products. In addition, the trade and domestic policies adopted by developed and developing countries will greatly influence the size and composition of agricultural imports by developing countries in the future. If LDCs are forced to turn inward by a lack of export opportunities and foreign assistance, and if they adopt import substitution and self-sufficiency policies, they may increase their agricultural imports only slowly. If this happens, it will probably be because of unfavorable macroeconomic forces and poor agricultural development performance rather than because agricultural production grew faster than the demand for many agricultural commodities.

Generally speaking, LDCs are the best hope for expanded markets for the world's agricultural exporters. For this hope to be realized, however, these countries will have to generate employment opportunities and achieve income increases for the billions of low-income people they contain, and this will require their successful agricultural development. Effective development assistance in agriculture that improves employment and income in developing countries can benefit vast numbers of poor people *as well as* American agriculture. Thus, the broader picture is one of mutual benefit for both American agriculture and agricultural development in poor countries.

Notes

1. G. E. Schuh, "Future Directions for Food and Agricultural Trade Policy," *American Journal of Agricultural Economics* 66 (1984): 242–47.

2. ERS/USDA, *World Indices of Agricultural and Food Production, 1975-84*, Statistical Bulletin no. 730 (Washington, D.C.).

3. T. K. White, G. E. Overton, and G. A. Mathia, "Global Trends in Agricultural Production and Trade," in R. Purcell and E. Morrison, eds., *U.S. Agriculture and Third World Development: The Critical Linkage* (Boulder, Colo.: Lynne Reinner, 1987), pp. 9–39

4. Food and Agriculture Organization (FAO), *Trade Yearbooks* (Rome, various years).

5. Ibid.

6. White, Mathia, and Overton, "Global Trends," cited in note 3.

7. F. H. Sanderson, "Long-Term Prospects for U.S. Agricultural Exports" (Statement Before the U.S. Senate Subcommittee on Foreign Agriculture, 3 June 1986, in manuscript).

8. J. Longmire and A. Mory, *Strong Dollar Dampens Demand for U.S. Exports*, Foreign Agriculture Economic Report no. 193 (Washington, D.C.: ERS/USDA, December 1983).

9. P. Coy, "Cheaper Dollar is Little Help," *Arizona Daily Star*, 5 October 1986.

10. White, Mathia, and Overton, "Global Trends," cited in note 3.

11. U.S. General Accounting Office (GAO), *Agricultural Overview: U.S. Food/Agriculture in a Volatile World Economy* (Briefing report to the Congress, Washington, D.C., November 1985); Sanderson, "Long-Term Prospects," cited in note 7.

12. World Bank, *World Development Report 1986* (New York: Oxford University Press, 1986).

13. R. L. Paarlberg, "U.S. Agriculture and the Developing World: Partners or Competitors?" In R. Purcell and E. Morrison, eds., *U.S. Agriculture and Third World Development: The Critical Linkage* (Boulder, Colo.: Lynne Reinner, 1987), pp. 221–41.

14. Ibid.

15. White, Mathia, and Overton, "Global Trends," cited in note 3.

16. K. L. Bachman and L. A. Paulino, *Rapid Food Production Growth in Selected Developing Countries: A Comparative Analysis of Underlying Trends: 1971-76*, Research Report no. 11 (Washington, D.C.: International Food Policy Research Institute [IFPRI], October 1979).

17. E. D. Kellogg, "University Involvement in International Agricultural Development Activities: Important Issues for Public Education," *Proceedings of the Association of U.S. University Directors of International Agricultural Programs* (Annual meeting, Athens, Georgia, 29-31 May 1985), pp. 121–36.

18. J. Lee and M. Shane, "U.S. Agricultural Interests and Growth in Developing Economies: The Critical Linkage" (Washington, D.C.: ERS/USDA, June 1985).

19. Kellogg, "University Involvement," cited in note 17.

20. E. D. Kellogg, R. Kodl, and P. Garcia, "The Effects of Agricultural Growth on Agricultural Imports in Developing Countries," *American Journal of Agricultural Economics* 68, no. 5 (December 1986): 1347–52.

21. J. P. Houck, "A Note on the Link Between Agricultural Development and Agricultural Imports," Staff Paper 86-26, Department of Agricultural and Applied Economics (St. Paul: University of Minnesota, July 1986).

22. U.S. GAO, *Agricultural Overview*, cited in note 11.

23. L. A. Paulino, *Food in the Third World: Past Trends and Projection to 2000*, Research Report no. 52 (Washington, D.C.: IFPRI, June 1986).

Select Bibliography

Aiken, William and Hugh LaFollette, eds., *World Hunger and Moral Obligation*. Englewood Cliffs, N.J.: Prentice-Hall, Inc., 1977.

Arrandale, Tom. *The Battle for Natural Resources*. Washington, D.C.: Congressional Quarterly, Inc., 1983.

Berry, Wendell. *Standing by Words*. San Francisco: North Point Press, 1983.

———. *Home Economics*. San Francisco: North Point Press, 1987.

———. *Openings*. San Diego: Harcourt Brace Jovanovich, 1980.

———. *A Place on Earth*. Revised. San Francisco: North Point Press, 1983.

———. *The Long-Legged House*. New York: Ballantine Books, 1971.

———. *Farming: A Hand Book*. San Diego: Harcourt Brace Jovanovich, 1970.

———. *Clearing*. New York: Harcourt Brace Jovanovich, 1977.

———. *The Unsettling of America: Culture & Agriculture*. New York: Avon Books, 1978.

———. *The Wild Birds: Six Stories of the Port William Membership*. San Francisco: North Point Press, 1985.

Blackstone, William T., ed., *Philosophy and Environmental Crisis*. Athens: University of Georgia Press, 1974.

Blanpied, Nancy A., ed., *Farm Policy: The Politics of Soil, Surpluses, and Subsidies*. Washington, D.C.: Congressional Quarterly, Inc., 1984.

Bowie, Norman E., ed., *Ethical Theory in the Last Quarter of the Twentieth Century*. Indianapolis: Hackett, 1983.

Brown, Lester R., et al. *State of the World 1988: A World Watch Institute Report on Progress Toward a Sustainable Society*. New York: W. W. Norton and Company, 1988.

Brown, Lester R., et al. *State of the World 1987: A World Watch Institute Report on Progress Toward a Sustainable Society*. New York: W. W. Norton and Company, 1987.

Brown, Lester R., et al. *State of the World 1986: A World Watch Institute Report on Progress Toward a Sustainable Society*. New York: W. W. Norton and Company, 1986.

Brown, Lester R., et al. *State of the World 1985: A World Watch Institute Report on Progress Toward a Sustainable Society*. New York: W. W. Norton and Company, 1985.

Browne, William P., *Private Interests, Public Policy and American Agriculture*. Lawrence: University Press of Kansas, 1988.

Brownell, Baker, *The Human Community: Its Philosophy and Practice for a Time of Crisis*. New York: Harper & Brothers Publishers, 1950.

Carson, Rachel, *Silent Spring*. Boston: Houghton Mifflin Co., 1962.

Charter, S.P.R., *Man on Earth: A Preliminary Evaluation of the Ecology of Man*. Sausalito, Ca.: Angel Island Publications, Inc., 1962.

Clarke, Robin and Geoffrey Hindley, *The Challenge of the Primitives*. New York: McGraw-Hill Book Co., 1975.

Clawson, Marion, *The Federal Lands Revisited*. Washington, D.C.: Resources for the Future, 1983.

Commoner, Barry, *The Closing Circle: Nature, Man & Technology*. New York: Bantam Books, 1974.

Comstock, Gary, ed., *Is There a Moral Obligation to Save the Family Farm?* Ames: Iowa State University Press, 1987.

Cronon, William, *Changes in the Land: Indians, Colonists, and the Ecology of New England*. New York: Hill and Wang, 1983.

Crowley, John J., ed., *Research for Tomorrow: 1986 Yearbook of Agriculture*. Washington, D.C.: U. S. Government Printing Office, 1986.

Dahlberg, Kenneth A., ed., *New Directions for Agriculture and Agricultural Research: Neglected Dimensions and Emerging Alternatives*. Totowa, N.J.: Rowman & Allanheld Publishers, 1986.

Dahlberg, Kenneth A., *Beyond the Green Revolution: The Ecology and Politics of Global Agricultural Development*. New York and London: Plenum, 1979.

Dalton, George, ed., *Economic Development and Social Change: The Modernization of Village Communities*. America Museum Sourcebooks in Anthropology. Garden City: The Natural History Press, 1971.

Daniels, Norman, ed., *Reading Rawls: Critical Studies of 'A Theory of Justice'*. New York: Basic Books, Inc., 1974.

Devereaux, James A., S.J., ed., *The Moral Dimensions of International Conduct: The Jesuit Community Lectures: 1982*. Washington, D.C.: Georgetown University Press, 1983.

Dillman, Don A., and Daryl J. Hobbs, eds., *Rural Society in the U.S.: Issues for the 1980s*. Rural Studies Series. Boulder, Colo.: Western Press, 1982.

Eckholm, Erik P. *Losing Ground, Environmental Stress and World Food Prospects*. New York: W. W. Norton & Co., 1976.

Ekins, Paul, ed., *The Living Economy: A New Economics in the Making*. London: Routledge Kegan Paul, 1986.

Elliot, Robert, and Arran Gore, eds., *Environmental Philosophy*. University Park: The Pennsylvania State University Press, 1983.

Englebert, Ernest A., with Scheuring, Ann Feley, eds., *Water Scarcity: Impacts on Western Agriculture*. Berkeley: University of California Press, 1984.

Faulkner, Edward H., *Plowman's Folly*. Norman: University of Oklahoma Press, 1943.

Fite, Gilbert C., *American Farmers: The New Minority*. Bloomington: Indiana University Press, 1984.

Ford, Thomas R., *Rural U.S.A.: Persistence and Change*. Ames: Iowa State University Press, 1978.

Garita, Luis, ed., *The Futures of Peace: Cultural Perspectives*. San Jose, Costa Rica: University of Costa Rica, 1986.

George, Susan, *Feeding the Few: Corporate Control of Food*. Third printing. Washington, D.C.: Institute for Policy Studies, 1985.

George, Susan, *How the Other Half Dies: The Real Reasons for World Hunger*. Totowa, N.J.: Rowman & Allanheld, 1983.

Goodpaster, K. E. and K. M. Sayre, eds., *Ethics and Problems of the 21st Century*. Notre Dame: University of Notre Dame Press, 1979.

Hadwiger, Dan F. and Ross B. Talbot, eds., *Food Policy and Farm Programs*. New York: The Academy of Political Science, 1982.

Halpern, Daniel, ed., *On Nature: Nature, Landscape, and Natural History*. San Francisco: North Point Press, 1987.

Hardin, Garrett, *Exploring New Ethics for Survival: The Voyage of the Spaceship Beagle*. New York: Penguin Books, 1968.

Hart, E. Richard, ed., *The Future of Agriculture in the Rocky Mountains*. Salt Lake City: West Water Press, Inc., 1980.

Hartmann, Hudson T., William J. Flocker, and Anton M. Kofranek, *Plant Science: Growth Development, and Utilization of Cultivated Plants*. Englewood Cliffs, N.J.: Prentice-Hall, Inc., 1981.

Haynes, Richard, and Ray Lanier, eds., *Agriculture, Change and Human Values: Proceedings of a Multidisciplinary Conference*, October 18-21, 1982. Vols. 1 and 2. Gainesville: Humanities and Agriculture Program, University of Florida, 1982.

Hennell, Thomas, *The Old Farm*. Salem, N.H.: Salem House, 1984.

Hewes, Thomas, *Decentralize for Liberty*. New York: E. P. Dutton & Co., Inc., 1947.

Jackson, Wes, *Man and the Environment*. 3rd ed. Dubuque, Ia.: William C. Brown Co. Publishers, 1980.

Jackson, Wes, *New Roots for Agriculture*. San Francisco: Friends of the Earth, 1980.

Jackson, Wes, Wendell Berry, and Bruce Coleman, eds., *Meeting the Expectations of the Land: Essays in Sustainable Agriculture and Stewardship*. San Francisco: North Point Press, 1984.

Kaplan, Sylvan J. and Evelyn Kivy-Rosenberg, eds., *Ecology and the Quality of Life*. Springfield, Ill.: Charles C. Thomas Publisher, 1973.

Kavtsky, John H., *Political Change in Underdeveloped Countrie: Nationalism and Communism*. N.Y.: John Wiley and Sons, Inc., 1964.

Kipnis, Kenneth and Diana T. Meyers, eds., *Economic Justice: Private Rights and Public Resposibilities*. Totowa, N.J.: Rowman & Allanheld, 1985.

Klayes, K.H.W., *Ecological Crop Geography*. New York: The MacMillan Co., 1942.

Lappé, Francis Moore, and Joseph Collins, *Food First: Beyond the Myth of Scar-*

city. Boston: Houghton Mifflin Company, 1977.

Leopold, Aldo, *A Sand County Almanac* with essays on conservation from *Round River*. New York: Ballantine Books, 1966.

Lipset, S. M, *Agrarian Socialism: The Cooperative Commonwealth Federation in Saskatchewan: A Study in Political Sociology*. Revised ed. Berkeley: University of Calif. Press, 1971.

Maclean, Douglas, ed., *Values at Risk*. Totowa, N.J.: Rowman & Allanheld, 1986.

Manson, Ronald, ed., *Man and Nature: Philosophical Issues in Biology*. New York: Dell Publishing Co., Inc., 1971.

Marx, Wesley, *The Frail Ocean*. New York: Ballantine Books, 1967.

McPhee, John, *Encounters with the Archdruid*. New York: Farrar, Straus and Giroux, 1971.

Meadows, Donella H., Dennis L. Meadows, Jorgen Randers, and William W. Behrens III, *The Limits to Growth: A Report for the Club of Rome's Project on the Predicament of Mankind*, 2nd ed. New York: New American Library, Inc., 1975.

Merrill, Richard, *Radical Agriculture*. New York: Harper & Row Publishers, 1976.

Meyers, Norman, *The Primary Source: Tropical Forests and Our Future*. New York: W. W. Norton & Company, 1985.

Nearing, Helen, and Scott, *Living the Good Life: How to Live Sanely and Simply in a Troubled World*. New York: Schocken Books, 1970.

Nickel, James W. *Making Sense of Human Rights*. Berkeley: University of California Press, 1987.

O'Neill, Onora, *Faces of Hunger: An Essay on Poverty, Justice and Development*. London: Allen & Unwin, 1986.

Paul, Sherman, ed., *Walden/Civil Disobedience* by Henry David Thoreau. Boston: Houghton Mifflin Co., 1960.

Perelman, Michael, *Farming for Profit in a Hungry World: Capital and the Crisis in Agriculture*. Totowa, N.J.: Allanheld, Osmon & Co. Publishers, Inc., 1977.

Powledge, Fred, *Water: The Nature, Uses, and Future of Our Most Precious and Abused Resource*. New York: Farrar Straus Giroux, 1983.

Radnitzky, Gerard and Peter Bernholz, eds., *Economic Imperialism: The Economic Method Applied Outside the Field of Economics*. New York: Paragan House Publishers, 1987.

Regan, Tom and Peter Singer, eds., *Animal Rights and Human Obligations*. Englewood Cliffs, N.J.: Prentice-Hall, Inc., 1976.

Regan, Tom, ed., *Earthbound: New Introductory Essays in Environmental Ethics*. New York: Random House, 1984.

Regan, Tom, ed., *Just Business: New Introductory Essays in Business Ethics*. New York: Random House, 1984.

Repetto, Robert, ed., *The Global Possible: Resources, Development, and the New Century*. New Haven: Yale University Press, 1985.

Rescher, Nicholas, *Risk: A Philosophical Introduction to the Theory of Risk Evaluation and Management*. Lanham, Md.: University Press of America, Inc., 1983.

Richards, Peter, and Wilbert Gooneratne, *Basic Needs, Poverty and Government Policies in Sri Lanka*. Serial edition. Geneva: International Labor Office, 1981.

Rienow, Robert, and Leona Train Rienow, *Moment in the Sun: A Report on the Deteriorating Quality of the American Environment*. New York: Ballantine Books 1967.

Sams, Henry W., ed., *Autobiography of Brook Farm*. Englewood Cliffs, N.J.: Prentice-Hall, Inc., 1958.

Schell, Orville, *Modern Meat: Antibiotics, Hormones, and the Pharmaceutical Farm*. New York: Vintage Books, 1985.

Scherer, Donald and Thomas Attig, eds., *Ethics and the Environment*. Englewood Cliffs, N.J.: Prentice-Hall, Inc., 1983.

Schumacher, E. F., *Small is Beautiful: Economics as if People Mattered*. New York: Harper & Row Publishers, 1973.

Science Action Coalition, with Albert J. Fritsch, *Environmental Ethics: Choices for Concerned Citizens*. Garden City: Anchor Press, 1980.

Sen, Amartya, and Bernard Williams, eds., *Utilitarianism and Beyond*. Cambridge: Cambridge University Press, 1982.

Shanks, Bernard, *This Land is Your Land: The Struggle to Save America's Public Lands*. San Francisco: Sierra Club Books, 1984.

Sheahan, John, *Patterns of Development in Latin America: Poverty, Repression, and Economic Strategy*. Princeton, N.J.: Princeton University Press, 1987.

Shue, Henry, *Basic Rights: Subsistence, Affluence and U. S. Foreign Policy*. Princeton, N.J.: Princeton University Press, 1980.

Simon, Arthur, *Bread for the World*. New York: Paulist Press, 1975.

Sinclair, Upton, *The Jungle*. New York: The New American Library, 1906.

Singer, Peter, ed., *Applied Ethics*. Oxford: Oxford University Press, 1986.

Smits, James H., ed., *Privatizing the Public Lands: Issues Involved in Transferring Federal Lands to Private Owners*. Proceedings of the Seminar, Reno, Nevada, Sept. 20, 1982. Washington, D.C.: Public Lands Council, 1983.

Staten, Jay, *The Embattled Farmer*. Golden, Colo.: Fulcrum, Inc., 1987.

Tong, Rosemarie, *Ethics in Policy Analysis*. Prentice-Hall Series in Occupational Ethics. Englewood Cliffs, N.J.: Prentice-Hall, Inc., 1986.

Truluck, Phillip N., ed., *Private Rights & Public Lands*. Washington, D.C.: The Heritage Foundation, 1983.

Van der Bosch, Robert, *The Pesticide Conspiracy*. Garden City: Anchor Press, 1980.

Vogeler, Ingolf and Anthony DeSouza, *Dialectics of Third World Development*. Totowa, N.J.: Rowman & Allanheld Publishers, 1980.

Volkman, Arthur G. (compiler), *Thoreau on Man and Nature*. Mt. Vernon: Peter Pauper Press, 1960.

Welsh, Frank, *How to Create a Water Crisis*. Boulder, Colo.: Johnson Books, 1985.

Westing, Arthur H., ed., *Herbicides in War: The Long-term Ecological and Human Consequences*. London: Stockholm International Peace Research Institute, 1984.

Wilber, Charles K., ed., *The Political Economy of Development and Underdevelopment*, 4th ed. New York: Random House, 1988.

Will, George F. and George E. Hyde, *Corn Among the Indians at the Upper Missouri*. Lincoln: University of Nebraska Press, 1964.

Wilson, Edward O., *Biophilia*. Cambridge, Mass.: Harvard University Press, 1984.

Worster, Donald, *Dust Bowl: The Southern Plains in the 1930s*. Oxford: Oxford University Press, 1982.

Contributors

William Aiken is associate professor of philosophy at Chatham College in Pittsburgh. His areas of specialization are ethics, and social and political philosophy. He is a contributor to and coeditor of *World Hunger and Moral Obligation*, with Hugh LaFollette (Prentice-Hall, 1977).

Terry L. Anderson is professor of economics at Montana State University and codirector of research as well as senior associate at the Political Economy Research Center (PERC) in Bozeman, Montana. He is the author of *Water Crisis: Ending the Policy Drought* (Cato Institute, 1983).

Wendell Berry lives in Henry County, Kentucky and teaches at the University of Kentucky. His latest books, *Remembering* and *The Wild Birds*, are published by North Point Press.

Charles V. Blatz is associate professor and chair of the department of philosophy at The University of Toledo. In addition to his work in agricultural ethics, he teaches and writes in ethical theory as well as critical thinking. He has worked extensively on and in programs concerned with critical thinking in the K-12 and college setting.

Wayne G. Bragg is affiliate professor of technology and international development and associate director of the Bioresources Development Group, Washington University in St. Louis. He is active in Third World rural development studies.

Harold F. Breimyer is professor emeritus of agricultural economics at the University of Missouri-Columbia. He is the author of various bulletins, articles, and speeches, and of three books, *Individual Freedom and the Economic Organization of Agriculture* (1965), *Economics of the Product Markets of Agriculture* (1976) and *Farm Policy: 13 Essays* (1977). A fellow of the American Agricultural Economics Association, he has given extensive government, international, and professional consulting service.

Jeffrey Burkhardt is associate professor of philosophy and director of the ethics and policy studies program at the Institute of Food and Agricultural Sciences at the University of Florida, Gainesville. He is also secretary of the Society for Agriculture, Food and Human Values.

Sam M. Cordes is professor and head, agricultural economics, University of Nebraska, Lincoln. He has published extensively on the topic of rural health.

He has also held a number of leadership positions in the rural health movement, and was one of the initial appointees to Secretary Sullivan's National Advisory Committee on Rural Health.

STANLEY E. CURTIS is professor of animal science in the college of agriculture at the University of Illinois. He has written and spoken extensively on issues in animal production and animal science.

STANISLAUS J. DUNDON is professor of philosophy at California Polytechnic State University, San Luis Obispo. He is the author of works in agricultural ethics, the ethics of nuclear disarmament, and philosophy of science. He is a former congressional research scholar in agricultural issues.

DONALD DUVICK is the former vice president for research for Pioneer Hi-Bred International, Inc., with oversight responsibilities for programs in plant breeding and microbial manipulation. His major fields of research are in maize genetics and physiology. He is active in promotion of genetic diversity for farm crops and in elucidating evolutionary changes in the products of plant breeding.

SARA EBENRECK is a writer in environmental ethics and conservation issues; she is also a visiting assistant professor in philosophy at St. Mary's College of Maryland.

SAMUEL R. EDWARDS is chief financial officer of a fifth generation family farm, director of a vertically-integrated agricultural company, director of an agriculture-oriented bank, and a physician.

DANA FLINT is associate professor of philosophy and former director of the honors program at Lincoln University in Pennsylvania.

CORNELIA BUTLER FLORA is University Distinguished Professor of Sociology at Kansas State University. Her research interests focus on social change in the United States and developing countries.

MARY GORE FORRESTER is author of *Moral Language* (The University of Wisconsin Press, 1982). Her graduate work in philosophy led to a degree from Johns Hopkins University. She has taught a range of courses in philosophy at the university level, including agricultural ethics. Currently she is pursuing a career in health care as a nurse practitioner.

CHRISTINE H. GLADWIN is associate professor in the federal resource economics department and an affiliate professor in the anthropology department at the University of Florida. She has published widely on small-scale farmer and entrepreneur decision making.

WALTER GOLDSCHMIDT is professor emeritus of anthropology and psychiatry at UCLA. He is a past president of the American Anthropological Association and former editor of the *American Anthropologist*. His latest book is a theoretical treatise entitled *The Human Career*.

JOHN HART was the director of the Heartland Project and is the author of *The Spirit of the Earth — A Theology of the Land*. He is professor of theology at Carroll College, Helena, Montana, and has been a delegate for the International Indian Treaty Council to the United Nations International Human Rights Commission, Geneva, Switzerland.

YUJIRO HAYAMI is professor of economics, School of International Politics, Economics, and Business, Aoyama Gakuin University, Tokyo.

RICHARD HAYNES teaches philosophy at the University of Florida. He is also director of the humanities and agriculture program and editor of *Agriculture and Human Values*.

HUGH H. ILTIS, University of Wisconsin-Madison botanist and herbarium director, specializes in the evolution of corn and its relatives, plant geography, Wisconsin and neotropical flora, and the psychological relationship of human evolution to nature and natural beauty. He was involved in the discovery of *Zea diploperennis*, a primitive relative of maize, and in the establishment of the 140,000 hectare Reserva Biosfera de la Sierra de Manantlan, in Jalisco, Mexico, where it grows. Supported by N.S.F. grants, and the U.W. Herbarium's E.K. and O.N. Allen Herbarium Fund.

HELEN INGRAM has had a continuing interest in water politics ever since publishing a monograph on New Mexico's role in the Colorado River Basin Bill. She is coauthor of *A Policy Approach to Political Representation: Lessons from the Four Corners States*. She is a professor of political science and acting director of the Udall Center for Studies in Public Policy at the University of Arizona.

WES JACKSON is founder and director of The Land Institute in Salina, Kansas. A geneticist interested in sustainable agriculture, he is the author of *New Roots for Agriculture* (Friends of the Earth, 1980), and *Altars of Unknown Stone* (North Point Press, 1987).

EARL D. KELLOGG is executive director of the Consortium for International Development (CID) and research professor at the University of Arizona. CID is composed of ten Western U.S. universities. An agricultural economist, he has twenty years experience in international development teaching, research, and management.

AL KURKI is the executive director of the Alternative Energy Resources Organization, a Montana-based citizen group. Kurki has worked for grassroots public interest organizations for over ten years.

DONALD R. LEAL is a research associate at PERC and conducts extensive research in environmental areas.

ALDO LEOPOLD was a noted author, conservationist, forester, and the founder of the field of game management.

CHARLES E. LITTLE is a Washington-based writer on environment, natural resources, and rural affairs. His most recent book is *Louis Bromfield at Malabar*, published by Johns Hopkins University Press in 1988. Previous books have been published by Island Press, Pergamon, Sierra Club, and Simon & Schuster-Pocketbooks. A study of the federal rural clean water program will be published by the USDA early in 1989. He is also a columnist and the author of many influential public policy monographs.

RACHEL M. MCCLEARY is assistant professor in the department of politics at Princeton University. Her research and writing has been concerned with ethical issues in international development. In addition to philosophical writings this research has led to the development of educational case-study materials.

J. PATRICK MADDEN was formerly professor of agricultural economics at the Pennsylvania State University. He now has his own consulting company, Madden Associates Sustainable Agriculture, in Glendale, California. He has written extensively on questions of agricultural policy, economics, and ethics.

ALEJANDRO R. MARTINEZ is a candidate for the Master of Science degree in engineering and policy at Washington University in St. Louis, carrying out thesis research in Nicaragua on the jicaro tree as a new agroforestry crop.

NANCY MATHESON is sustainable agriculture project coordinator for the Alternative Energy Resources Organization, a Montana-based citizen group. Matheson's background is in resource geography and public policy. She was born and raised on a Montana wheat farm.

KENT MATHEWSON is assistant professor, department of geography and anthropology at Louisiana State University, Baton Rouge. He is the author of *Irrigation Horticulture in Highland Guatemala* and articles on traditional intensive and prehistoric agriculture.

JAMES MONTMARQUET is assistant professor of philosophy a Tennessee State University. He is the author of *The Idea of Agrarianism: From Hunter-Gatherer to Agrarian Radical in Western Culture* (University of Idaho Press, 1989).

DAVID OIEN operates the family farm in north central Montana where he produces a variety of certified organic crop and livestock products. Oien founded the Sustainable Agriculture Task Force of the Alternative Energy Resources Organization, a Montana-based citizen group.

MICHAEL PERELMAN is professor of economics at California State University at Chico. He is the author of *Farming for Profit in a Hungry World: Capital and the Crisis in Agriculture* (Allanheld, Osmun Publishers, 1977).

DAVID W. PLUYMERS received his Master of Science degree in technology and human affairs from Washington University in St. Louis in 1988. His thesis dealt with the neem tree as a new crop for production of safe insect-control agents.

BERNARD E. ROLLIN is professor of philosophy, professor of physiology and biophysics, and director of bioethical planning at Colorado State University. He is the author of *The Unheeded Cry: Animal Consciousness, Animal Pain and Science* (Oxford University Press, 1989), and *Animal Rights and Human Morality* (Prometheus Books, 1981). His papers have appeared in many scientific and philosophical journals. He is a principal architect of recent federal legislation governing the treatment of laboratory animals.

SUSAN RUSSELL is assistant professor of anthropology and faculty associate of the Center for Southeast Asian Studies at Northern Illinois University. She conducted research in the Philippines in 1978-80, 1983-85, and 1986.

VERNON W. RUTTAN is regents professor in the department of agricultural and applied economics and in the department of economics, University of Minnesota, St. Paul.

LAWRENCE A. SCAFF teaches political science at the University of Arizona. His major field is political theory, and he has written particularly in the area of political participation. He received a Fulbright award for research in social theory in Germany.

DONALD SCHERER is professor of philosophy at Bowling Green State University, and writes in environmental ethics. He is a contributor to and coeditor of *Ethics and the Environment* (Prentice-Hall, 1983).

JEROME M. SEGAL is a research scholar at the Institute for Philosophy and Public Policy, University of Maryland. Previously he was senior advisor for agency planning, Agency for International Development.

PHIL SHEPARD is professor of philosophy, Lyman Briggs School and department of philosophy, Michigan State University, where he teaches philosophy of technology and coordinates the Briggs' science and technology studies component.

KRISTIN SHRADER-FRECHETTE has written six books and numerous articles on philosophy of science, environmental ethics, and science/technology policy. She edits the Oxford University Press series on environmental ethics and science policy and is graduate professor of philosophy at the University of South Florida.

EUGENE B. SHULTZ, JR. is professor of engineering and applied science and director of the Bioresources Development Group, Washington University in St. Louis. He is primarily interested in new crops and appropriate technology for the Third World.

LESLIE MARMON SILKO has taught creative writing at the University of Arizona. Her poetry and fiction about Southwestern Indians, including *Ceremony* (1977) and *Storyteller* (1981) have received critical acclaim. Silko was awarded a prestigious MacArthur award in 1983.

PAUL ELIHU STERN is a biotechnology policy advisor at the Institute of Food and Agricultural Sciences, University of Florida. He is a member of the Florida, District of Columbia, and New York Bars.

PAUL B. THOMPSON is a professor of philosophy at Texas A & M University. He has written extensively on issues in ethics, agricultural ethics, philosophy of technology, and philosophy of science. He is past president of the Society for Agriculture, Food and Human Values.

LUTHER TWEETEN is Anderson Professor of Agricultural Marketing, Policy, and Trade at The Ohio State University, Columbus. His scholarship has emphasized public policy for agricultural and rural trade and development at national and international levels. He is author or coauthor of six books and over 300 national journal articles and published works.

INGOLF VOGELER received his undergraduate training in geography at the University of Toronto and his graduate degrees at the University of Minnesota, Minneapolis. His research interests have focused on the underdevelopment of rural areas both in the U.S. and in Third World countries. He is the author and/or coauthor of 24 articles, one chapter, and four books, including *The Myth of the Family Farm*. He is currently professor of geography at the University of Wisconsin-Eau Claire.

ROBERT ZERWEKH is an assistant professor of computer science and faculty associate of the Center for Southeast Asian Studies at Northern Illinois University. He previously taught philosophy at the University of Delaware and the University of the Philippines.

Library of Congress Cataloging-in-Publication Data

Ethics and agriculture : an anthology on current issues in world
context / edited by Charles V. Blatz.
p. cm.
Includes bibliographical references.
ISBN 0-89301-133-9 (cloth). — ISBN 0-89301-134-7 (paper)
1. Agriculture—Moral and ethical aspects. I. Blatz, Charles V.
BJ52.5.E84 1991
174'.963—dc20 91-11713
CIP